Conversion Factors

Time
1 yr = 365.25 d = 8.766×10^3 h = 3.16×10^7 s

Speed
1 m/s = 3.28 ft/s = 3.6 km/h
1 km/h = 0.62 mph = 0.278 m/s
1 mph = 1.609 km/h = 1.467 ft/s

Acceleration
1 m/s^2 = 3.28 ft/s^2 = 3.6 km/h/s
   = 2.24 mph/s

Length
1 m = 1.094 yd = 3.281 ft
1 km = 10^3 m = 0.62 mi = 3.28×10^3 ft
1 ft = 12 in = 0.305 m
1 mile = 1.609 km = 1.609×10^3 m = 5.28×10^3 ft
1 nautical mile = 1.15 mi = 1.852×10^3 m
1 light year = 9.46×10^{15} m
1 astronomical unit = 1.

Area
1 mi^2 = 2.59 km^2 = 640 acre
1 acre = 4,047 m^2 = 2.79×10^7 ft^2
1 m^2 = 10.76 ft^2
1 ha = 10^4 m^2 = 0.01 km^2
1 km^2 = 100 ha = 10^6 m^2

Volume
1 gallon (US) = 3.785 L
1 gallon (Imperial) = 1.2 gallon (US)
1 m^3 = 10^3 L = 264 US gallons = 35.3 ft^3
   = 6.29 bbl
1 barrel (bbl) = 42 US gallons
   = 0.159 m^3 = 159.1 L

Mass
1 kg = 10^3 g = 2.21 lb
1 lb = 0.453 kg = 4.536×10^{-4} ton (metric)
1 ton (metric) = 1,000 kg = 2.24×10^3 lbs
1 ton (short) = 2×10^3 lb = 907 kg

Force
1 N = 0.2248 lbf
1 lbf = 4.448 N

Pressure
1 Pa = 1 N/m^2
1 atm = 101 kPa = 760 mm Hg = 14.7 lb/in^2

Energy
1 quad = 10^{15} Btu = 1.055 EJ
1 Btu = 1.055×10^3 J = 2.93×10^{-4} kWh
1 kWh = 3.6 MJ = 3.412×10^3 Btu
1 Calorie (food calorie) = 4.184 kJ
1 therm = 10^5 Btu = 1.055×10^5 kJ
1 gram of TNT = 1 kcal
1 ton of TNT = 4.18×10^9 J
1 electron-volt (eV) = 1.602×10^{-19} J

Power
1 W = 1 J/s
1 kW = 1.34 hp = 3,413 Btu/h
1 TW = 30 quads/yr
1 hp = 0.746 kW
1 ton refrigeration = 1.2×10^4 Btu/hr
   = 3.517 kW

Radiation
Activity: 1 becquerel (Bq) = 1 decay/s
   1 curie (Ci) = 3.7×10^{10} Bq

Exposure: 1 gray (Gy) = 100 rad
   1 roentgen = 2.58×10^{-4} C/g

Dose: 1 sievert (Sv) = 100 rem

Fuel Equivalents

1 billion barrel of oil equivalent (bboe)
   = 269 million metric tons coal
   = 290 million short tons coal
   = 5.64 trillion cubic feet natural gas
1 barrel of oil equivalent (boe) = 5.8 GJ
1 gallon of fuel oil = 146 MJ
1 metric ton of coal = 25 GJ
1 cubic meter of natural gas = 37 MJ
1 kilogram of TNT = 4.18 MJ
1 metric ton of dry wood = 18 GJ
1 kWh of electricity = 3.6 MJ
1 kg of natural uranium (U-238) = 500,000 MJ
1 g of uranium (U-235) = 74,000 MJ

Powers of 10

Symbol	Prefix	Power
pico	p	10^{-12}
nano	n	10^{-9}
micro	μ	10^{-6}
milli	m	10^{-3}
kilo	k	10^{+3}
Mega	M	10^{+6}
Giga	G	10^{+9}
Tera	T	10^{+12}
Peta	P	10^{+15}
Exa	E	10^{+18}

Fuel Efficiency and Carbon Footprints

MPG	L/100 km	Pounds of CO_2 per mile	Grams of CO_2 per km	MPG	L/100 km	Pounds of CO_2 per mile	Grams of CO_2 per km
10	23.52	1.94	548	60	3.92	0.32	90
20	11.76	0.97	274	70	3.36	0.28	79
30	7.84	0.65	184	80	2.94	0.24	68
40	5.88	0.49	138	90	2.61	0.22	62
50	4.70	0.39	110	100	2.35	0.19	54

Energy and the Environment

Choices and Challenges in a Changing World

Fifth Edition

September 2021

Reza Toossi, Ph.D., P.E.

Mechanical and Aerospace Engineering Department
California State University, Long Beach

Global Digital Press
PO Box 257
Columbia, MO 65201
Email: Administrator@globaldigitalpress.org

To order:

Bookstores and Libraries: Send P.O. by
    email: sales@vervepublishers.com
    fax: 877.350.6642
Single Copy: Order online by visiting
    http://shop.vervepublishers.com/

ISBN 978-163732630-5
Library of Congress Control Number: 2006926865

Printing number: 9 8 7 6 5 4 3 2 1

Printed in the United States of America
on 100% recycled paper.

Hope has two beautiful daughters: anger and courage;
anger at the way things are, and courage to change them.
~ St. Augustine (354-430 CE)

This book is dedicated to the people closest to my heart who inspired
me, gave me the *energy* and provided me with *the environment* to
complete this work.

My late parents Hossein and Safa Toossi,
and my beautiful daughter Tara Safa

About the Author...

Reza Toossi is a professor of mechanical and aerospace engineering at California State University, Long Beach. He received his B.S. degree from the Sharif University of Technology in Iran and his M.S. and Ph.D. degrees from the University of California, Berkeley, all in Mechanical Engineering. He continued his Post-Doctoral research studies at the Lawrence Berkeley Laboratory and joined the CSULB faculty in 1981.

Dr. Toossi has worked both as a research scientist and consultant on numerous projects related to aqueous aerosols and droplets in the atmosphere, nuclear safety, sensor design, air pollution dispersion modeling, flame propagation, fluid mechanics, and fiber optics. His current interests include conducting research and teaching courses in heat transfer, combustion, hybrid-electric vehicles, hydrogen storage, environmental engineering, and concentrated photovoltaics.

Dr. Toossi is a member of ASME, ASEE, SAE, SPIE, AAPT, and TBP and a recipient of the CSULB Distinguished Faculty Scholarly and Creative Achievement, the CSULB Distinguished Faculty Teaching, and the TRW Excellence in Teaching Awards, and serves as the co-chair of CSULB Sustainability Task Force.

TABLE OF CONTENTS

Destiny is not a matter of chance, but of choice. Not something to wish for, but to attain.
~ William Jennings Bryan (1860-1925)

Energy is, inarguably, the most fundamental concept in all of the science and beyond. Chemical and biological reactions are driven, to a large extent, by energy considerations. So are bowling balls and roller-coasters. Politicians worry about energy shortages and cosmologists suspect that an excess of energy is driving the expansion of the universe. The concept of energy is found everywhere.

Energy comes in many forms and, depending on whether or not it can replenish itself in a relatively short time, can be classified as renewable or non-renewable. Today's world, however, is powered mainly by non-renewable fossil fuels—coal, oil, and natural gas. Oil is particularly important because it is liquid and, thus, conveniently transported. It is also a key component of numerous clothing, pharmaceutical, and construction products. Coal and natural gas are also important, as they generate electricity and heat our homes and offices. Only 1% of all energy consumption is fulfilled by renewable sources: solar, wind, waves, and geothermal; 88% comes from fossil fuels, while nuclear and hydroelectric account roughly equally for the remaining 11%. Fossil fuels are, however, of limited supply, and unless huge new deposits are discovered, they soon will be depleted. It is estimated that, at the current rate of consumption, we will run out of conventional oil in 40 years, natural gas in 60 and coal in 180 years. If the growth in demand is considered, especially in many developing countries, these numbers will be even lower.

The United States, the largest economy in the world, is particularly dependent on oil. Oil consumption in this country accounts for roughly a quarter of the world's utilization. Today, about 60% of U.S. conventional oil comes from abroad, as compared to about 30% in the early 1970s. The ratio is expected to increase as consumption increases, while reserves become depleted. Consumption in China and India, in particular, are expected to grow by two-thirds in the next quarter-century.

As the world is waking up to the realities of energy scarcity, there are works in progress to develop new and alternative sources of energy. Progress in generating electricity from waves, solar sources, and the wind is being reported. Hybrid vehicles are slowly gaining traction, although fuel cell cars still remain a distant goal. New findings show that, contrary to original beliefs, biofuels do not reduce greenhouse emissions and may, in fact, divert vast resources away from food production. The recent shortages in food supplies around the world are partly due to the fact that the subsidies many farmers receive to plant corn and other crops to make biofuels are more than what they would earn from cultivating food crops. The situation is expected to get worse in the near future.

A new UN report on the effects of global warming on climate patterns, land resources, and vegetation is sobering. The trends point to a complicated blend of changes, including violent shifts in weather patterns, disruption in patterns of food production, and restrictions on the availability of fresh water resources. As of today, many international treaties aimed at reducing the impacts of the burning of fossil fuels on the environment have been negotiated. There have been failures and successes, but the final verdict on their effectiveness is still out.

Although this textbook is written at a level suitable for an introductory course in energy and environment for undergraduate students with very little mathematics or science background, it can be read by anyone interested in the technical, political, environmental, and economic issues related to energy. The earlier editions of the text were mostly well-received by faculty, who used this text in their classrooms. The energy world is, however, constantly in transition. New resources are being found and old reserves are being consumed. Technological innovations are also abundant as newer, more efficient, methods of producing power are discovered in the laboratories, and brought to market. The dynamic nature of the energy field, as well as new and continuous efforts to develop sustainable methodologies that deal with the rapid rise in population, and accelerated rate of consumption -- in particular, by Chinese, Indian, and other developing nations -- require regular assessments of the energy landscape. Textbooks on energy often become obsolete, shortly after publication, which in our case, necessitated not only a major reorganization of the book but also adding new materials, technology innovations, and data updates. In the course of writing the text, great care was taken to avoid excessive detail, while emphasizing the fundamentals of energy and important environmental and technological concepts.

This manuscript is divided into 15 chapters. In Chapter 1, we introduce general concepts related to energy and its sources, reserves, production, and patterns of use. Chapter 2 deals with mechanical forms of energy and the concepts of work, power, and simple machines. The history, formation and many uses of conventional forms of fossil fuels -- coal, petroleum, and natural gas are discussed in Chapter 3 and mostly rewritten to reflect the change in energy reserves as a result of new discoveries of unconventional sources -- tar sands, shale oil, and gas shale.

In Chapter 4, we introduce the reader to the concepts of temperature, heat, and the principles of thermodynamics. Furthermore, we show how these concepts can be used to design practical machines ranging from internal combustion engines and electricity-generating power plants to refrigerators, air conditioners, and heat pumps. In Chapter 5, we cover the basics of electricity generation, storage, transportation, and distribution. The applications of smart grids and distributed generation and their impact on providing clean renewable energy to urban and rural areas are explained.

A short review of different transportation systems is given in Chapter 6, and the contribution of new automotive technologies (fuel cells, electric, and hybrid vehicles), as well as autonomous driving on future transportation systems, are evaluated. The environmental consequences of fossil fuel use on indoor and outdoor air pollution and their long term effects on climate change are discussed in Chapter 7. The atomic structure of matter and the methodology to extract power from nuclear resources are discussed in Chapter 8 in some details.

Geothermal energy is one source that provides thermal energy directly, without the need to burn biomass or fossil fuel (Chapter 9). The next few chapters give a summary of renewable sources of energy -- solar (Chapter 10), biomass (Chapter 11), wind (Chapter 12), and hydro (Chapter 13). A brief overview of modern economic theories is given in Chapter 14 and is used to evaluate the economic merits of deploying different energy technologies. The economics of the environment and the costs associated with environmental damage and issues associated with globalization are also discussed. In the final chapter (Chapter 15), we define sustainability from economic and environmental perspectives, and how different abatement technologies may impact climate change. A possible road map for a sustainable future is proposed.

To assure that the text appeals to the widest audience -- science and engineering, as well as liberal arts students, the text is organized in a highly modular form. Each chapter stands alone and can be taught in any order that the instructor deems suitable. Widely different curricula can be designed and tailored to any audience simply by selecting to focus on sections relevant to the discipline. For example, the syllabi for an environmental engineering course may include a summary of various energy technologies, with emphasis on climate change, air pollution, radiation, and environmental economics; a science curriculum may emphasize physics, technologies and incorporate some engineering designs. Each chapter is concluded with a list of additional exercises that include problem-solving, essay questions, multiple-choice and true/false questions, and one or more mini-projects. In addition, certain sections are designated as "advanced," and are identified by special icons. Many chapters, also have addendums labeled as "Digging Deeper," which involve a more thorough and quantitative analysis of the subject matter. These sections can be excluded for GE courses and students with limited mathematical skills, without loss of generality. For easy reference, all essential data, formulas, and tables of unit conversions are compiled in four appendices and a glossary of terms at the end of the book.

Writing a textbook is no easy task and is rarely if ever, accomplished without help from others. I wish to take the opportunity to thank my many colleagues and friends who made valuable suggestions and provided valuable insights, edited the manuscript, or assisted in design and layout. Dr. Igor Glozman, professor of physics and astronomy at Highline College, offered invaluable input on the organization and presentation style. Special thanks to Dr. Darwin Church, professor of physics at the University of Cincinnati Clermont College, who copy edited the manuscript and contributed greatly, not only to content but also to assure clarity of concepts and accuracy of information. The same goes for Dr. Nasser Farahbakhsh of the CSULB Electrical Engineering Department, who took a special interest in the subject and made editorial suggestions that helped improve the structure, the flow, and the lucidity of the content. Finally, this book would not have been possible if it were not for the valuable input of numerous students who took a GE course with the same title, in recent years, at California State University, Long Beach.

The author wishes to acknowledge many constructive criticisms and suggestions by a number of colleagues who took their valuable time to evaluate the previous editions. In particular, I would like to thank the following individuals who pointed out errors and inconsistencies, and made specific recommendations:

Professor Steven Arnold (University of Denver)
Professor Amir Faghri (University of Connecticut)
Professor Kyle Forinash (Indiana University)
Professor Jonathan Frye (McPherson College)
Professors Jack Hamilton and Ola Opara (University of Utah)
Professor Thomas Huber (Gustavus Adolphus College)
Professor Anthony S. Kondoleon (Lake Sumter Community College)
Professor Orest Symko (University of Utah)
Professor Kambiz Vafai (University of California, Riverside)
Professor Ling Jun Wang (The University of Tennessee, at Chattanooga)

As a final note, any manuscript is prone to having a certain number of typographical errors, at least in the first edition. In the case of this publication, the typographical errors actually have been planted on purpose, and that purpose is suggested by the famous American cartoonist Randy Milholland: "Typos are very important to all written form. It gives the reader something to look for so they aren't distracted by the total lack of content in your writing."

Reza Toossi
September 2021
Long Beach, California

CHAPTER 1

Energy: Past, Present, and Future

Oil Derrick at Sunrise (Creative Commons) ~Burningman, 2007

Energy is liberated matter, matter is energy waiting to happen. ~ Bill Bryson, A
Short History of Nearly Everything

Energy has been in continuous demand from the dawn of human existence, first in the form of food for survival and the powering of muscles for hunting and gathering and, later, in the form of wood for heating and cooking. Homo sapiens learned to exploit the provisions of nature, water, and the wind to design practical devices that simplified their tasks and made life more comfortable. Wood eventually was replaced by coal as the fuel of choice when James Watt designed the steam engine that ignited the Industrial Revolution. A few decades ago, the power of the atom was harnessed in the form of nuclear fission. Today, work continues to explore nuclear fusion that potentially will provide us with a clean, unlimited source of energy.

Leslie White, the noted American anthropologist sees the technological progress, measured by how humans utilize energy as the primary factor driving the development of human civilization. For much of history, the energy consumed by humans was limited to about 2,000 Calories per day (97 watts) in the form of food that was foraged or hunted. It was just barely enough to keep our ancestors alive. At around 250,000 years ago, they learned to control fire to cook food, to keep warm, for lighting, and to provide protection from animals and insects. As a result, human activities could extend into hours of the night. Cooking the food allowed humans to digest complex hydrocarbons and starches, giving more energy per unit of food consumed, which along with eating various nuts and berries, may explain the increase in human brain size. The amount of food available, however, was enough to support just one person per square kilometer.

The First Energy Transition occurred at about 7000-4000 BCE when humans substituted manual power with an animal's muscle. Now humans could begin to farm and domesticate sheep, goats, and pigs that provided almost all his basic needs -- their dung for fertilizing the crops, their milk for food, their wool and hides (skins) for garments, their horn and bone as sharp arrows, and their fat for candles. Cattle, oxen, and buffaloes were domesticated around 4000 BCE. Horses and camels were domesticated next, which were a source of meat but also worked the farm and hauled carts and wagons. The use of animals freed man from his inherently low capacity to deliver sustained power of around 50- 90 W. Depending on their sizes, oxen were able to offer powers up to 500 W, which is equal to the labor of 6-8 adults men. Draft animals allowed faster transportation and various crop processing tasks and boosted agricultural productivity. The combined labor of many humans and draft animals could deploy short-term pulses of power of up to 100 kW, enough to move large masses of stone structures needed to build the ancient civilizations of Egypt, Mesopotamia, Greece, and Rome. They also learned to use collar harnesses to increase power and iron hooves to support animal weight and improve traction. This allowed food to be brought from farther distances, facilitated trade which allowed larger communities to flourish, and population density rose to 20-30 person/km^2 of cultivated land. It is estimated that roughly 5-20 million people inhabited the earth.

Humans have known the use of firewood as fuel for many thousands of years, as evident from soot and smoke residues in caves and early dwellings. Wood was turned into charcoal by heating it in the absence of oxygen, removing water and other volatile constituents that increased its carbon content, produced little smoke, and could be burned indoors. Charcoal had one additional advantage over wood – it burned at a hotter temperature that allowed smelting of tin, copper, and bronze. Smelting iron, however, turned out to be more difficult; iron is rarely found in its pure form and requires a higher temperature than could be achieved in primitive ovens that used charcoal. Furthermore, charcoal contained impurities that contaminated iron making it difficult to forge and produced iron that was too brittle. For the next few millennia, humans mastered the art of metallurgy by smelting tin, copper, and bronze, and eventually iron.

The Second Energy Transition occurred when animal labor was supplemented with non-organic sources of energy, wind, and water. The invention of the wheel in Mesopotamia around 3500 BCE, working of metals, pottery, and deployment of windmills, watermills, and sails in larger and larger boats were among major factors that marked the agrarian transition. Power increased rapidly as more work could be carried out in shorter and shorter amounts of time. During the same period, better agricultural techniques allowed food to be prepared with less effort, which further aided the growth of cities. From its birthplace of agriculture in the Near East, agriculture progressed westward, and by 1750 BCE, it had reached Northern Europe; the world population increased to about 300 million by 1 CE.

The Chinese invention of gunpowder during the eleventh century and the introduction of cannons in the thirteenth century increased demand for the iron that in turn increased demand for wood. The availability of cheap and abundant energy and ease of transport to faraway distances also played an important role in how Europe developed. Holland, in particular, benefited, as it possessed large quantities of peat (decayed organic matter) and long stretches of canals that crisscrossed the country. A large number of windmills operated newly invented sawmills and facilitated the construction of a massive fleet of ships that gave the Dutch a great advantage for worldwide trading and for new military conquests that made Holland the world's strongest economy during the 17th century. Unfortunately, this accompanied destruction of virtually all major forests of Europe. Holland's Golden Age did not last very long, as its industrial progress was limited by the use of peat and by the low efficacy of wind power. Peat had a low ignition temperature, not sufficient for the smelting of iron.

Coal was ultimately proved to be a superior fuel after a process was discovered that removed the sulfur contaminant and turned coal into coke. Coke is the purest form of carbon when all the volatile matter is driven off; it burns at higher temperatures suitable for the production of a large volume of pig iron and for building manufactured products. Furthermore, the energy density of coal was much higher than peat and much easier to store. This discovery provided, Britain with its large deposits of coal, a unique capability for large-scale production of iron that ignited the Industrial Revolution.

The Industrial Revolution represented a watershed not only in energy use but also in economic and population growth. Before the industrial revolution, heat and motion were two entirely different forms of energy. The motion was mainly from humans (mostly slaves) and animal muscles; wind and water were also used in a limited way for such tasks to sail and pull water from a well. The heat came directly from burning wood, peat, charcoal, and later coal. Converting motion to heat was easily done through friction, although it hardly resulted in any useful form of energy. Converting heat to motion was not, however, that simple. The only example known was the conversion of chemical energy from food to muscle work by humans and animals through metabolism. With the invention of the steam engine in 1712 by Thomas Newcomen and later improvement by James Watt in 1769, the heat generated from burning wood and coal could be converted into kinetic energy by rotating a shaft that operated machinery. Now heat and motion were simply two forms of energy that could be converted to each other. The combination of steam power and iron gave England the necessary components to build the rail system that offered a faster and more flexible transportation system to far distances without having the problem of fuel supply. By the early nineteenth century, windmills were gradually being replaced with the steam engine.

The Industrial Revolution also brought about a major shift in how we view material resources. Before the Industrial Revolution, economic output was mostly constrained by the limited supply of land. This was certainly true for animals, but also food and raw materials -- wool, cotton, and timber. Mineral productions depended on smelting ore, which also was limited by the amount of wood and, therefore the available forestlands. Coal was fundamentally different, however; it was a concentrated form of energy that could be dug up in large quantities from a limited parcel of land, which meant access to energy was no longer tied to the availability of the land. Power delivered by machines multiplied in ways unimaginable only decades earlier. At around 1900, a steam engine could attain 8,000-10,000 hp, compare to that delivered by a windmill (8-10 hp) or a watermill (3-5 hp), a horse or a donkey (0.5-1 hp), and a man (0.1 hp). The result was exponential economic growth, doubling the industrial output every few decades. This, in turn, radically transformed living standards, and along with that, it led to a rapid rise in population. *The Third Energy Transition* was fully underway -- the substitution of mills by engines and biomass by coal.

*The Fourth Energy Transition o*ccurred in the late nineteenth and early twentieth century when kerosene substituted whale oil for illumination, alcohol was replaced by petroleum to drive combustion engines, and coal was used to generate electricity. Our ability to generate electricity got another boost when by the mid-twentieth century we employed the power of the atom and added nuclear energy to our basket of energy resources. As a result, the technological man of 1970 in the US consumed approximately 230,000 kcal of energy per day (~115 times that of primitive man) with about 26% of that amount being electrical energy. Figure 1-1demonstrates the gradual yet steady increase in energy resource utilization throughout the history of mankind and a much more rapid rise following the Industrial Revolution. It is also a common understanding that the increase in energy utilization is accompanied by a parallel and steady increase in human scientific and technological prowess, as well as wealth frequently measured by total Gross Domestic Products (GDP) per capita.

The Fifth Energy Transition must necessarily involve abandoning our current addiction to fossil fuels in favor of low-carbon and renewable energy sources: biomass, solar, wind, hydro, and geothermal energies. For the past couple of decades, wind energy has been the fastest-growing source of renewable energy, increasing by an average of 22% per year. Solar energy has not kept pace and grew by only 3% a year. The new innovative technologies offered more efficient photovoltaic cells at lower costs and the promise of the solar renaissance in the near future. Other renewable sources are expected to follow similar growths.

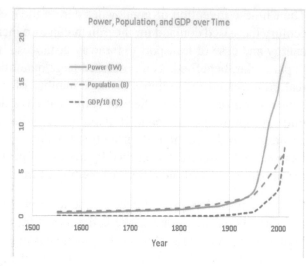

Figure 1-1

Total global energy consumption rate, population, and GDP over time (1500 –Present)
Ref: Adapted from P R. Ehrlich et al. Nature 486, 68-73 (2012) doi:10.1038/nature11157

Energy in the 21st Century

Human progress has largely been achieved by using vast amounts of energy. The future expansion of our economy will surely demand even a larger amount. Twenty century saw a rapid rise in the production and consumption of fossil fuels, which brought about economic, social, technological, and environmental changes unparalleled anytime throughout history, but also resulted in environmental degradation manifested by a change in the climate, acidification of rivers, and polluting the atmosphere. Oil and electricity have transformed every aspect of our lives by changing the way we farm, drive, and cloth. Oil like coal is a concentrated form of energy, but it has the advantage of being a liquid that can be easily transported. It can also be used in a great number of products such as cosmetics, pharmaceuticals, lubricants, and synthetic fabrics. Electricity is not a resource that can be harvested, but it is a clean and convenient form to store and deliver energy.

As our conventional fossil resources dwindle, we are finding new non-conventional resources such as tar sands, oil shale, and shale gas, that will surely carry us for additional decades, although environmental factors may limit their use. Other resources at our disposal are nuclear and renewables. How much energy we will need and how we are meeting the energy challenge is debated. Numbers can vary quite significantly, so ultimately, it is a matter of

Table 1-1 Daily Per Capita Consumption of Energy (x 1000 kcal)*						
	Primitive man 1,000,000 years ago	*Hunting man 100,000 years ago*	*Early agricultural man 5,000 years ago*	*Advanced agricultural man 1,000 years ago*	*Industrial man 100 years ago*	*Modern technological man today*
Transportation				1	14	63
Machinery**			4	7	24	91
Heating		1	4	12	32	66
Food***	2	2	4	6	7	10
Total	**2**	**3**	**12**	**26**	**77**	**230**
* To convert to GJ/yr multiply the table entries by 1.527. ** Agricultural and industrial *** Including animal feeds Source: Cook, E., "The Flow of Energy in an Industrial Society," *Scientific American*, 1971, pp.135.						

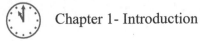

personal opinion which scenario ultimately prevails.

How our energy situation will look in 20, 50, or 100 years is not clear and depends on several factors such as world population, the state of technology, economic health, environmental factors, and even political climate. One thing is clear, however. To ensure a sustainable environment, our consumption of fossil fuels must decline. This can take place by reducing the overall consumption of energy, either by the incremental increase in energy efficiency or by adopting sound conservation strategies using energy intelligently, efficiently and in a responsible way. The other option is to substitute fossil fuels with clean, renewable sources of energy. Cutting on energy consumption cannot be expected from large sectors of the population, especially

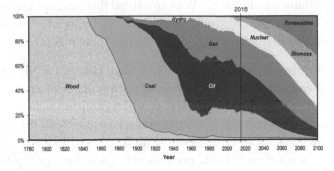

Figure 1-2
US share of primary energy.
Source: Citi Research. Bloomberg New Energy Finance.

in developing countries with limited access to energy, so much of the burden will fall on wealthier industrialized countries who must finance and develop technologies that assure continued economic expansion while minimizing the impact on the environment.

This author is optimistic that the most likely scenario is a path of sustainable development, and by 2050, we are satisfying most of our energy needs from renewable resources (Figure 1-2). According to this scenario, fossil fuels and nuclear will continue to play important roles in bridging the gap until the mid-century when the population has stabilized, and technological advances have made renewable energy widely available, and the cost is commensurate with nonrenewable resources. The next few decades may prove to be one of the most interesting eras for energy enthusiasts. In fact, some economists proclaim that energy and the environment (as well as for biotechnology and information technology) will become the most dominant sectors affecting the economy in this century.

The Big Picture

Energy is what runs our lives, our planet, and our world. The concern is whether we can responsively use our energy resources to save our terrestrial civilization. The visionary Russian astrophysicist Nikolai Kardashev has contemplated energy in more advanced civilizations. In 1964, he theorized that depending on the total amount of power that is available to them, three types of civilizations could be envisioned. Type I civilization is a planetary civilization like ours that uses available energy on its home planet. Type II civilization uses the energy of a planet's parent star (our solar system), and Type III civilization uses the energy available anywhere in its entire galaxy. Whether there are alien civilizations that already have mastered harvesting such a huge amount of energy is, of course, anybody's guess. We haven't harnessed, yet, all the energy available in our home planet, and therefore are still in Type 0 civilization.

What Is Energy?

Energy is generally regarded as the single most important concept in all of the science. Energy is the intangible form of matter; matter can be touched, whereas energy cannot. The word "energy" is bandied about so often that we normally take its meaning for granted. We hear about people described as being "full of energy," the world as having "an energy crisis," and the need to "conserve energy." In other instances, we have used energy when we meant to imply "power" or even "force."

Despite the immense impact of energy on our lives, the term "energy" does not lend itself to a simple definition. The difficulty in producing a precise definition for energy is derived from the fact that energy is a concept, an abstract idea, and not a material object, such as an apple or a tree. As ecological journalist Richard Heinberg points out in his book *The Party's Over,* "few understand exactly what energy is and yet we know that it exists. Indeed, without it, nothing would exist." We can extend this description to define energy as what is required to make anything happen. Given that, energy must be defined indirectly in terms of what it does or is capable of doing. In fact, the presence of energy is revealed only when changes take place.

We can perceive energy only through changes in the structure of matter, or its motion and position in space. Every interaction in our universe involves a transfer of energy between two points or a transformation of energy from one form to another. In physics, energy is defined as *the ability or potential to perform work or cause change*. As this definition implies, in a strict sense, a system with energy need not do any work or cause a change, it only has to have the capacity to do so, even if no force is displaced through a distance. A piece of wood sitting at rest, someplace, does not do any work, even though it has the capacity to do so (for example, by burning it in a furnace to boil water to steam, which then turns a turbine). The piece of wood, therefore, contains energy. In fact, all objects have energy by virtue of their own mass.

As we shall see in Chapter 4, energy is conserved—we cannot create energy from nothing, and we cannot destroy it, either. We can only change it from one form to another. For example, we can turn electricity into heat through an electric heater, or use it to lift an elevator. No matter what, the ultimate fate of all forms of energy is the same -- energy will turn into heat; a frightening concept, since it implies that the world will eventually turn into a chaotic soup of uniform temperature where no further work can be done. This is what scientists refer to as the "Heat Death."

Source of Energy

It is said that the creation of the universe was based on a huge explosion, The Big Bang Theory, which took place 13.7 billion years ago. The explosion resulted in the birth of a cosmic nuclei "egg" consisting of a very condensed mass of elementary particles. This nucleus led to the formation of our stars, galaxies, and planets. These processes were of a type, which today, we call thermonuclear, i.e., energy converted into matter. Hydrogen was the first (and simplest) element that was formed and is still the most common element in the universe. It also makes up the core of our sun, which is estimated to be at a temperature in excess of 15 million degrees, with a pressure of many billions of atmospheres. The cores of heavier and bigger stars are at even higher temperatures and pressures. Every hour, approximately 16 billion tons of our solar mass is converted into energy through the fusion of hydrogen to heavier atoms such as carbon, oxygen, silicon, and eventually iron.

Most of the energy known to us has its source in the Sun, i.e., solar energy. The Sun radiates energy in all directions in the form of electromagnetic waves. A tiny fraction of this energy is beamed toward the earth, of which one-third is reflected back to the sky before ever reaching the ground. Of the remaining two-thirds, some are absorbed by the atmosphere, causing it to heat. The rest is intercepted by the earth in the form of light and heat, of which a mere 0.03% is transformed into biomass through photosynthesis. Biomass can be used as food and consumed by animals and humans, directly burned, or used to produce secondary fuels, such as methanol and ethanol. If biomass is shielded from air, it decays and, under suitable conditions, eventually can turn into fossil fuels -- coal, oil, and natural gas.

Because of different vegetation and rock formations, solar radiation does not heat the land and the ocean uniformly. Differential heating of land and water surfaces results in wind patterns and ocean waves, two major sources of renewable energy. The earth also is being affected by the gravitational forces of its neighboring celestial bodies, most notably the moon, which is the cause of tides and much of the wave patterns in open channels.

Both nuclear fuel and geothermal energy have roots in the earth's early stages of development. Uranium fuel is the remains of the radioactive decay of the heavy materials and isotopes formed during the period when the cosmic nuclei cooled. Uranium can be extracted from the earth and processed for use as fuel in a nuclear reactor. What remains inside the earth continues to produce heat and form magma that can find its way to the earth's surface. Along the way, it heats rocks, minerals, and water reservoirs, which together constitute our geothermal resources.

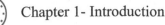

Forms of Energy

There are many different ways that we can classify energy. For example, we can classify different forms of energy as microscopic or macroscopic, primary or secondary, renewable or non-renewable, or in terms of its application as mechanical, electrical, chemical, and so on.

Macroscopic energy is energy relative to an external effect, such as the potential, kinetic, or elasticity of a system. A car in motion or climbing a hill has both kinetic and potential energy relative to a fixed point. **Microscopic** refers to those energy forms related to the atomic structure of a system and the degree of molecular activity. The sum of all the microscopic forms of energy -- i.e., the energy locked within the internal structure of atoms and molecules -- is called *internal energy*. Examples are mass, chemical, thermal, light, and nuclear energy. *Mass* is the energy of matter by virtue of its own existence. Until 1905, when Einstein formulated the General Theory of Relativity, mass was not considered a form of energy. Einstein's famous formula $E = mc^2$ (where m is the mass and c is the speed of light in a vacuum) provides a relationship between mass and the energy associated with it. It expresses the amount of energy that is given off if the matter is completely annihilated. *Chemical energy* is the energy locked in the molecules of various substances. The energy stored in a molecule of carbon dioxide is that energy, which holds two atoms of oxygen with one atom of carbon together. Biomass and fossil fuel store their energy as chemical energy. *Thermal energy*, or heat, is the energy associated with the random motion of individual molecules of matter. It can be considered as kinetic energy at the microscopic level. Geothermal and a large portion of solar energy are in the form of thermal energy. *Light energy* (also called radiant or electromagnetic energy) is the energy associated with a quantum of energy called a "photon," as it travels through space. The Sun is the source of light energy. *Nuclear energy* is the energy trapped in the nucleus of an atom. This energy can be liberated by splitting apart the nucleus of a large atom to form two or more lighter atoms (fission) or by combining two light atoms to form a heavier atom (fusion).

Depending on its source, energy also can be divided into primary or secondary. **Primary** energy sources are those sources that can be converted directly to heat or mechanical work. Human intervention is limited only to extraction, cleaning, and separation, without changing the physical or chemical characteristics of the sources. There are five main sources of primary energy that we use today; these include fossil fuel, nuclear, geothermal, solar, and tidal. **Secondary** energy comes from the transformation (processing) of primary energy. The secondary energy forms are not directly available in nature and, therefore, are referred to as **energy carriers**. For example, hydrogen is not present naturally in the atmosphere but can be manufactured through the electrolysis of water or steam reforming of methane. Ethanol, town gas, and electricity are also secondary sources of energy that can be produced from any of the primary sources mentioned above (Table 1-2).

Depending on their long-term availability, energy resources also can be classified as either renewable or non-renewable. **Renewable** resources are those that will replenish themselves naturally in a relatively short period. Solar and wind are clearly renewable; biomass is largely renewable as long as it is not exploited so fast that leads to large-scale deforestation. Geothermal hot water, steam reservoirs, and some material such as peat and wood can be considered renewable if the rate of usage is small enough so as to allow their natural replenishment over time. Geothermal dry rocks are considered renewable since they are constantly being

Table 1-2 Primary and Secondary Energy Forms	
Primary	*Secondary*
Fossil fuel	Town gas (from coal); Gasoline, heating oil, diesel, and jet fuel (from crude);
Solar (Wind, Hydro, Biomass)	Alcohol, synfuel, and charcoal (from coal, oil shale, biomass);
Tides	Hydrogen (from fossil, nuclear, solar);
Geothermal	Electricity (from anything)
Nuclear	

recharged by the heat from the earth's interior. **Non-renewable** resources are fossil fuels and uranium. Even if they never get thoroughly exhausted, the cost both in terms of money and environmental damage will make, eventually, these latter resources unattractive to exploit.

Measuring Energy

Depending on the application, energy is expressed in different units. Electric utilities charge customers per amount of kilowatt-hours (kWh) they use. Gas companies' charges are per thousand cubic feet, cubic meters, or therms. The energy in food is given in food calories (kilocalories or Calories). Physicists use joules or any of its derivatives -- kilojoules, megajoules -- when dealing with everyday objects, or electron-volts when they talk about energy at atomic scales. The oil industry has its own units, too; barrels of oil, gallons of gasoline, or million Btu of energy are the most common. Military personnel and demolition workers are mostly interested in kilotons of TNT (trinitrotoluene). The exact definition and unit conversion tables are given in the glossary of terms and appendices at the end of the book.

Below are the meanings of some of the most common energy units that will help you in understanding the material presented in this text:

The standard unit of energy and what scientists prefer to use is the **joule**, which can be thought of as the energy needed to lift a medium-size apple by one meter.

A **calorie** is the amount of energy that is needed to raise the temperature of one gram of water by one degree centigrade. A food calorie (Calorie) is equal to 1,000 calories. A gram of lettuce has 0.2, a gram of hamburger meat has 2.5, and a gram of butter has 5 Calories. A serving of chocolate chip cookies (28.3 g) has 138 Calories, or 4.9 kcal per gram, almost as much as butter or oil. The amount of energy released from the explosion of **one kilogram of TNT** explosive is 4.18 MJ or 1,000 food calories.[*]

A **kilowatt-hour** (kWh) is associated with electricity use. It is the amount of electrical energy that ten 100-W light bulbs use in one hour. A typical American household uses about 10,000 kWh per year, spending roughly about $1,500 per year on electricity bills.

A **British thermal unit** (Btu) is the amount of energy that is needed to raise the temperature of one pound of water by one degree Fahrenheit; it is commonly used to express the heating value (energy content) of various fuels. A barrel (42 US gallons) of crude is equivalent to 5.8 million Btu, a cubic foot of natural gas is 1,000 Btu, and a ton of coal releases between 15 million and 25 million Btu. Hydrogen – whether in liquid or compressed gas form -- has 50,000 Btu per pound.[†]

A **therm** is equal to 100,000 Btu, approximately the energy equivalent of burning 100 cubic feet of natural gas. Although originally a British Unit, it is no longer used in Britain, but still widely used in the US, when billing for natural gas.

Quad is short for quadrillion (10^{15}) Btu, roughly equal to 1 EJ (10^{18} J) of energy. It is used when we quote a huge amount of energy. The world annual total energy consumption is around 400 quads, 100 quads in the United States.

> **Energy Units**
>
> 1 kWh = 3.6 MJ = 860 kcal = 3,413 Btu
> 1 Therm = 100,000 Btu
> 1 quad = 1,000,000,000,000,000 Btu ~ 1 EJ
> 1 gram of TNT = 1 kcal
> 1 Calorie = 1 kcal = 4.184 kJ
> 1 Btu = 1,055 J ~ 1 kJ
> 1 eV = 1.6x10^{-19} J

> **Example 1-1:** Joule is an inconveniently big unit when we deal with individual atoms. Consider the binding energy of a molecule of hydrogen. It is found, experimentally, that the energy required to break the molecules of a gram of hydrogen into its atomic constituents (this is called dissociation energy) is 217,000 joules. What is bond energy for one molecule of hydrogen? Express this energy in terms of another commonly used energy unit, electron-volts (eV), commonly used by physicists and nuclear scientists.
>
> **Solution:** One mole of hydrogen contains an Avogadro number (6.02×10^{23}) of molecules and weighs two grams. That is, the energy that binds two atoms of hydrogen is

---

[*] A gram of TNT releases 980–1,100 calories upon explosion. It was arbitrarily standardized to one kilocalorie.

[†] Some consider waste also as a primary source, as it is a surplus from any other process that has no further use for that particular process.

$$\frac{\dfrac{217{,}000\ \text{J}}{\text{g}} \times \dfrac{2\ \text{g}}{\text{mole}}}{6.02\text{x}10^{23}\ \dfrac{\text{molecules}}{\text{mole}}} = 7.21\text{x}10^{-19}\ \text{J}$$

This is a very small amount of energy. Expressed differently, the bond energy for hydrogen is 4.5 eV.

Example 1-2: The combined populations of India, Pakistan, and Bangladesh, estimated at 1.7 billion in 2013, used a total of 736.6 mtoe (million-ton oil equivalent). What is the per capita energy consumption (kcal/d) for these countries? Compare this to the energy consumption to that of the modern industrial man (Table 1-1). **Solution:** Dividing total energy consumption to the total population gives an average of $736.6\text{x}10^{6}\ /\ 1.7\text{x}10^{9} =$ 0.43 toe per person per year, compared to the global average of 1.78 toe, and the American average of 8.0. Daily energy consumption is calculated as:

$$0.43\ \frac{\text{toe}}{\text{person.yr}} \times \frac{1\ \text{yr}}{365\ \text{d}} \times \frac{10^{7}\ \text{kcal}}{\text{toe}} = 11{,}780\ \frac{\text{kcal}}{\text{person.d}}$$

Comparable to that of early agricultural men.

Energy Resources and Energy Reserves

It is very difficult to predict the total amount of energy resources available in the world. What is certain is that almost all conventional resources have been identified and we will, sooner or later, run out of cheap non-renewable fossil fuels and uranium resources. The time it takes to use up remaining fossil resources is closely related to the accuracy for which the size of proven energy reserves is known, and the rate at which new resources are found and extracted.

The size of the reserve is not constant and varies, depending on the price and the available technology. For example, as prices go up or better drilling techniques become available, it makes more sense to drill deeper or to extract unconventional resources. That means the size of our reserve increases. Similarly, the size of uranium reserves depends on the type of reactor and on whether the public accepts the nuclear option. This is why there are so many different estimates of the size of available reserves, and so much disagreement on the time it takes before they are exhausted.

It is worth noting that the United States, with its vast coal deposits, is the richest country in terms of total energy reserves; Middle Eastern countries, cumulatively, have the largest reserves of petroleum and natural gas, but no coal, so their total conventional fossil reserves are only second to that of the United States. China and India, the countries with the highest growth in the rate of consumption, have very little reserves of oil and natural gas and must use coal, primarily if they are to rely solely on their own natural resources.

The reign of conventional fossil fuel is not expected, however, to last much longer. It is believed that world conventional oil already has peaked or is soon to peak in its production, and will be, mostly, depleted by the end of this century. Tar sands, shale oil, and shale gas may provide temporary relief, but will certainly become economically too expensive to extract, or environmentally too costly to ignore. The use of nuclear fission is closely following the trend of fossil fuel; as uranium reserves deplete, nuclear waste piles up, and problems associated with reactor safety make nuclear technology increasingly less attractive.

Energy Use in the United States

The main sources of energy are petroleum (37%), natural gas (32%), and coal (11%) in 2019. Besides, the US uses nuclear energy to satisfy about 8% of its energy needs. The remainder comes from burning wood, hydroelectric and other forms of renewable energy, mainly biomass, wind, and solar.[‡] Practically all nuclear, coal and hydroelectric capacity are used for generating electricity, while the use of petroleum is mostly limited to transportation and certain industrial processes -- primarily petrochemical. The percent contribution of energy to various sectors of the economy is shown in Figure 1-3.

In recent years, several factors, the slow-down in the economy, taking effective conservation measures, adopting more energy-efficient technologies, and policies that promote energy conservation have resulted in a small decline in consumption. At the same time, advances in horizontal drilling techniques, hydraulic fracturing technologies have enhanced production, as result, the gap between import and export of energy has been diminished (See Figure 3-10).

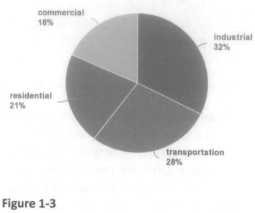

Figure 1-3
US total energy use by sector in 2019.
Source: US EIA Monthly Energy Review April 2020 (Preliminary Results), Table 2.1.

Energy Use in the Rest of the World

The rapid rise in energy consumption is not limited only to the US but is a global phenomenon. Currently, only four countries -- China, the United States, India, and Russia, together consume more than half of all the world's energy. European countries reduced their energy use by 8% in the decade between 2008-2018. North America's energy consumption remained flat. Energy use in many developing countries increased significantly -- 15% in South and Central America, 28% in Africa. Energy consumption in China and India increased by 45% and 58%, respectively. Even consumption in the oil-rich Middle Eastern countries jumped by 37%; this is particularly significant since these data indicate that a higher percentage of Middle Eastern oil was consumed at home, limited the total available for export.

It is interesting to note that, even with the seemingly rapid change in patterns of energy use, at the current rate of consumption, every North American consumes energy at about twice the rate of the Japanese or Europeans, and 3.5 times the rate of the Chinese; and compared to Indians, per capita consumption is 11 times greater. Bangladesh and Afghanistan use the least amount of energy per capita in the world -- each only about 3% that of an average American. The large discrepancy is not only because of the large economies of the United States (and Canada), but also is a reflection of their appetite for large cars, luxury items, and personal comfort.

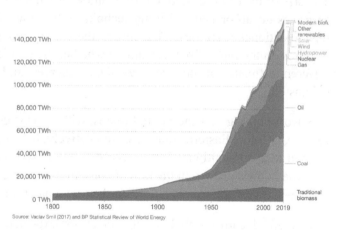

Figure 1-4
US energy consumption by source, 1800-2019.
Source: BP Statistical Review of World Energy, 2019.

Figure 1-4 shows global primary energy consumption since 1800. As can be seen from these data, fossil fuel has overtaken all other primary sources of energy, and by the beginning of this century constituted 87% of all energy consumed. Of the remaining resources, nuclear, hydroelectric, and biomass had the widest appeal. Nuclear energy is heavily favored by the industrial nations, whereas wood and dung are still widely used in some developing countries, providing an amount of energy equivalent to one billion tons of oil each year. As of 2017, hydro, wind, wave, and other renewable resources accounted for about 5.3% of the total (see Table 1-3).

[‡] If we consider the additional 2,500 billion barrels of oil equivalent (bboe) of oil shale that the US has, its shares of total fossil energy would be even greater..

Table 1-3 Primary Energy Consumption By Region*														
	Fossil Fuels		Nuclear		Hydro		Solar		Wind		Geothermal, Biomass		Total	
	TWH	%	TWH	%	TWH	%	TWH	%	TWH	%	TWH	%	TWH	%
US	16,152	17.8	839	33.1	261	6.7	19	10	184	26	85	16.8	17,540	17.8
Russia	4,893	5.4	181	7.1	173	4.5	0	0	2	0.3	0.5	0.1	5,250	5.3
China	21,566	23.7	126	5	1,064	27.4	29	15.7	168	22.4	47	9.3	23,000	23.3
India	4.779	5.3	35	1.4	131	3.4	4	2.4	38	5.9	19	3.7	5,006	5.1
Middle East	6,692	7.4	4	0.2	23	0.6	1	0.6	0.3	0	neg.	neg.	6,720	6.8
Rest	41,537	40.4	1,452	53.2	2,233	57.4	133	71.3	314	45.4	357	70.1	41,251	41.7
Total	90,845	100	2,637	100	3,885	100	186	100	706	100	508	100	98,767	100
* Ref: BP Statistical Review of World Energy, 2015. (Data for fossil fuels are converted from Mtoe to TWh.)														

Energy-Water Nexus

Energy and water use are intimately intertwined -- we need the energy to produce fresh water, and we need water to produce energy. Hydroelectric plants use water directly. Thermal power plants work by boiling water to produce steam that runs the turbines to generate electricity. To close the cycle, the used steam must be cooled in a condenser. A massive amount of water is normally required to cool that steam. Most of this water is returned to the source (a river, a stream, an aquifer, or a lake) at a somewhat elevated temperature and lower quality, while the remaining water is lost by evaporation. When fossil fuels are used to heat water, additional water is needed for cleaning and processing.

About 40% of US freshwater is used to run thermoelectric power plants, roughly equivalent to the water withdrawals for irrigated agriculture. In contrast, only 13% of fresh water is consumed for drinking. What remains is for industrial and other uses.

Depending on fuel and type of cooling technology, different plants use different amounts of freshwater. According to a report published by the Union of Concerned Scientists, nuclear plants are by far the most fresh-water-hungry, nearly eight times more than natural gas plants, and about 11 percent more than coal plants for the same amount of electricity generated. Biomass dependence on the water varies vastly depending on which plant is used. Some such as switchgrass require little water, but ethanol from irrigated corn or soy is hugely water-intensive. Table 1-4 gives water usage when energy is used directly for heating, and for the production of electricity. Water requirements for solar and wind power plants are negligible.

Table 1-4 Water Use for Various Fuels			
Source	Water Use gal/MBtu	Source	Water Use gal/MBtu
Heating		Electricity	
Coal	41 - 164	Nuclear	2,400 - 5,800
Petroleum	1,200 - 2,420*	Fossil Fuel	1,100 - 2,200
Natural Gas	3-?	Geothermal	130-?
Tar Sands	15 - 38	Hydroelectric	20-?
Shale Oil	20 - 50	Solar Thermal	230 - 270
Corn Ethanol	2,510 - 29,100**	Hydrogen	143 - 243
* Includes water extracted with oil.			
** Includes water for irrigation.			
Source: Younos, T., Hill, R., and Poole. H., "Water Dependency of Energy Production and Power Generation Systems, Virginia Water Resources Research Center, July 2009.			

Renewable Energy: The Ultimate Resource

The abundance of cheap, non-renewable sources of energy, principally fossil fuel and nuclear, have fueled our civilization and provided us much of the conveniences we have been enjoying up to the present. The pattern of energy use is expected to continue, and by 2050, according to some estimates, the global demand for primary energy will reach 500-600 EJ. Even though there are plenty of unconventional fossil fuels still available to use, the environmental and safety costs associated with these resources are making these fuels less and less attractive. Any realistic energy scenario must, therefore, include a mix of fossil fuels, nuclear, and renewable energy, with an eye toward 100% carbon-free technologies by the mid-century.

Nuclear energy seems to be an obvious choice to provide baseload electricity with little environmental costs. They do not produce any greenhouse gases, and nuclear fuel is available to last a few more decades. The accidents at Chernobyl and Fukushima and lack of proper disposal sites, however, have lowered public confidence and may not offer the long-term solution to our energy needs. Even under the best circumstances the International Atomic Energy Agency (IAEA) does not envisage nuclear energy increasing its share much beyond its present 5.8%.

Renewable resources of energy have been, so far, sidetracked to a large extent, since, until recently, prices were not competitive, conversion efficiencies were rather low, and availability was limited to certain geographical locations, or only during certain periods. Compared to traditional non-renewable resources such as fossil fuels and nuclear, for the same amount of power, renewable resources require more land and the cost is somewhat higher.

Table 1-5 Power Capacity by Renewable Energy	
Source	Power
POWER (GW$_e$)	
Hydropower	1,132
Wind	591
Solar PV	505
Biomass	130
Geothermal	13.3
Concentrating solar thermal	5.5
Ocean	0.5
HEAT (GW$_{th}$)	
Solar hot water	480

Source: REN21, Renewable 2019: Global Status Report, Paris: REN21 Secretariat.

To be able to effectively substitute for non-renewable energy resources, the alternatives must:

1. Be sufficiently abundant to satisfy the demand for a significant percentage of the market.
2. Be cost-competitive with existing non-renewable energy resources.
3. Be safe, aesthetically pleasing, and convenient to use.
4. Have the ability to replenish in a relatively short time.
5. Have environmental impacts that are substantially lower than that of current technologies.

What constitutes a renewable energy source is rather vague. Solar, wind, and ocean waves are clearly renewable. Biomass is not necessarily renewable, as fuelwood has been the main reason behind much of the deforestation; it is renewable if cropped from well-managed lots and the rate of cutting is balanced by planting new fast-growing trees and bushes. Geothermal may be considered renewable or non-renewable depending on which resources are used, how deep we go, and how fast heat is being extracted. Even nuclear has been termed renewable if breeder reactors replace all of the conventional fission reactors used today. Fusion is a renewable source of energy.

Technology Options

There are two ways to reduce energy shortages: increase supply or reduce demand. **Supply-side management** requires finding new resources and processes that increase the chance of discovery, facilitate extraction, and allow more efficient processing (higher yields). Any form of fiscal policy that emphasizes supply or production (such as subsidies and tax cuts for businesses) are also examples of supply-side management. **Demand-side management** means a reduction in consumption. It often implies strategies to reduce demand or shift load during the peak period. This can be done by the action of the government through taxes and regulations, by storing energy, by raising prices, and by promoting conservation and technologies that increase efficiency. Such technologies include better insulation, fluorescent, and light-emitting diode (LED), energy-efficient appliances, hybrid and electric vehicles, dimming lights when appropriate, and using waste energy to produce heat and power (cogeneration).

It is widely accepted that the only sensible approach to meeting future energy demand, while reducing environmental footprint is a shift from carbon-based fuels to renewable forms of energy. However, barriers such as competition with mature industries, price distortion due to existing subsidies to non-renewable resources, and lack of access to capital have prevented renewable energy to constitute a substantial portion of our energy portfolio. Fortunately, new materials and manufacturing techniques are being found to produce cheaper photovoltaic and fuel cells. Also, technologies are being developed to harness the wind, biomass, tidal energy, and ocean currents, as well as thermal and salinity gradients in the oceans, and with costs approaching those of conventional energy sources. Nuclear breeder technology is extending the lifetime of our nuclear supply by orders of magnitude. Among the changes occurring in various energy sectors include the following:

Hydropower is going through major changes. Traditional methods of hydropower generation were waterwheels and run-of-the-river plants. Research efforts also are underway, and some demonstration facilities have been built to show the potential to harness the rise and fall of tides, underwater currents, and the motion of ocean waves. The extent to which hydropower can be exploited depends largely on geographical considerations. Most industrial countries have already exploited much of their hydro capacity. African and Asian countries still have a huge amount of untapped resources mainly from the running rivers.

Wind is one of the fastest-growing sources of energy in the world. New advances in manufacturing processes have allowed the manufacture of lighter and stronger blades. Power electronics have developed to a stage where variable-speed turbines with sophisticated control strategies have resulted in better designs, a wider range of operation, and higher efficiencies. Wind is a concentrated form of solar energy, so it has a higher energy density per unit area than solar energy -- may be as much as an order of magnitude. In recent years, the cost of wind technologies has been falling significantly and therefore can effectively compete with fossil electricity without much of their environmental costs.

Solar is another potentially huge, clean, and renewable source of energy capable of producing both heat and electricity. Flat-panel solar collectors are becoming increasingly more efficient and economical. For electrical power generation, solar energy can be concentrated through a large array of mirrors and dishes (called heliostats) that can heat the water in a receiver to produce steam, or be used to run a Stirling engine. Alternatively, electricity can be generated directly by photovoltaic cells, which are becoming more and more efficient and at only a fraction of the cost that they were just a few years ago. Thin films and organic plastics have been found that could substitute for silicon semiconductors -- the material used to manufacture most photovoltaic chips. Spherical solar cells are being introduced to the market, which collects light from all directions, and therefore, has significantly higher collection efficiency.

Biomass is not only the source of all our food but also can be used as a transportation fuel or to generate electricity. Although biomass is a renewable resource, it is not clean and, if burned, produces the same type of pollutants as fossil fuels. However, unlike fossil fuels, biomass does not produce greenhouse gasses, and the overall emission is lower. Genetically modified crops are being produced that are tailored to yield higher heating values and burn with considerably less pollution.

Geothermal resources include hot water, steam, magma, and dry rock. With today's technology, only hot water and steam reservoirs can be economically exploited, but works are underway to use the earth's natural thermal gradients. Geothermal heat pumps are now available that use the relatively uniform temperature in a shallow ground to provide winter heating and summer cooling with a payback time of only a few years. As drilling technology advances, we can dig deeper and access hotter rocks and more geothermal reservoirs. In comparison to other renewables, geothermal energy is not affected by daily and seasonal variations in weather, and therefore, is a convenient source for baseload electrical generation, and applications requiring heat and steam.

Hydrogen is considered by many to be the "fuel" of the 21st century[§], as much as wood was in the 18th, coal was in

---

§ Strictly speaking, hydrogen is not a fuel, but a convenient way of storing excess energy from other sources such as nuclear, solar, etc.

the 19th, and oil was in the 20th century. Hydrogen is the cleanest of all fuels, whether it is burned or used to power fuel cells. The only by-products are heat and water vapor. Hydrogen technology is still in its infancy and may still face unanticipated problems.

Nuclear Fission is the most controversial source of energy. Although the power generated is clean and the cost is comparable to electricity by fossil fuels and hydroelectric plants, the unresolved issues of nuclear waste disposal and safety associated with these plants are daunting. In light of the terrorist attacks of September 11, 2001, these safety issues have taken an even higher priority. Work is being done to design safer advanced small modular reactors that can be buried underground. In, one design, called the *Pebble Bed Reactor*, small grains of uranium, 0.5 mm in diameter, are placed in microspheres covered by layers of porous carbon and silicon graphite coating. Thousands of these microspheres are packed into pebbles, and then the pebbles are arranged in modular forms. The design is considered inherently safe because fuel can never reach the melting temperature. Thus, the danger of meltdown scenarios similar to those at Three-Mile-Island, Chernobyl, and Fukushima is considered highly unlikely. Furthermore, the graphite will act as a casket to contain the radioactive material, even after the fuel is burned, eliminating the possibility of any radiation leak.

Nuclear Fusion is still considered the ultimate source of energy. About 40 years ago, many had predicted that, by the year 2000, fusion reactors would be operational, producing cheap, clean, inexhaustible energy. Today, we are still coping with many of the same problems we were facing in the 1960s. The current prediction is that fusion may become practical only in the second half of this century. Time will tell whether we have to revise our predictions again.

Summary

Energy is the most important catalyst for all the advances of humanity. The unprecedented economic growth of the past century was made possible only by the availability of vast resources of cheap petroleum. Conventional petroleum reserves are rapidly depleting, however, and must be replaced by dirtier unconventional resources or by clean sources of energy. The new approaches must take one or more of these three forms: 1) to stop, or even reverse, population growth; 2) to conserve energy and reduce consumption; and 3) to find new energy supplies, mainly in the form of clean and renewable resources. One thing is clear; the industrial world is continuing to demand moderately higher energy, but the major rise has been with newly emerging markets in China, India, and other developing countries. How the future will look largely depends on how we act to achieve those goals today.

ⓐ *Digging Deeper - Linear and Exponential Growth*

Many phenomena such as population growth, savings in a bank, the spread of an epidemic, and the increase in consumption of a resource behave in such a way that changes exponentially with time. Exponential growth differs from linear growth in that instead of a given quantity that grows by a fixed amount in a given time, the growth is proportional to its value at any instance of time. This might not seem to be much at the beginning, but its cumulative growth over time can become quite staggering. Let's consider a person who starts a saving account with an initial balance of $100 that deposits in a piggy bank. He continues to save by depositing an additional $10 at the end of each year. The total deposit at the end of each year will grow linearly as follows.

Year 1	Year 2	Year 3	Year 4	Year 5	Year 6	Year 7	Year 8	Year 9	Year 10
110.00	120.00	130.00	140.00	150.00	160.00	170.00	180.00	190.00	200.00

Now consider the alternative when he makes a one-time deposit of $100 to a saving account which pays 10% in interest at the end of each year. The growth is exponential, i.e., the total principal and interest grow to $110 by the end of the first year, to $121 by the end of the second year, and to $259.37 by the end of the tenth year.

Year 1	Year 2	Year 3	Year 4	Year 5	Year 6	Year 7	Year 8	Year 9	Year 10
110.00	121.00	133.10	146.41	161.05	177.16	194.87	214.36	235.79	259.37

The saving would nearly double in seven years, instead of ten years, in the previous example.

As another example of the power of exponential growth, let's consider Intel's co-founder Gordon Moore who, in a 1965 paper, predicted that the processing speed of computers, the memory capacity, and even the number of transistors that could be placed on an integrated circuit, would double every two years (Figure 1-5). That prediction, which came to be known as Moore's law, turned out to be true. The number of CPU transistors in 1971 was only 2,000. It increased to 4,000 in 1973, 8,000 in 1975, to over 50 billion today. Compare this to the number of transistors if growth was linear, that is, 2,000 transistors every two years

Figure 1-5
The number of transistors on integrated circuits (1971-2018)

(1,000 each year). Under that scenario, the number of transistors that we would have been able to fit onto a memory chip would be only 3,000 in 1972, 4,000 in 1973, 5,000 in 1974, and 50,000 today. In an attempt to keep squeezing more components onto a silicon chip, Intel has recently introduced 3-D transistors, giving new life to Moore's prediction. Not only the number of transistors has increased, but the electrical efficiency of computing (the number of computations per kilowatt-hour of electricity used) has also increased correspondingly. As more and more energy is harvested from background lighting, motion, or heat, the possibility that mobile sensors operating indefinitely with no external power source have become a possibility. What a blessing that Moore's law turned out to be true![¶]

Exponential growth, however, does not always work in our favor -- other quantities, such as the number of viruses when we catch a cold, world population, energy use, and the interest we have to pay on our mortgage back to the bank, all grow in a similar fashion.

Another example suggested by ecologist G. Tyler Miller gives an interesting perspective. "Fold a piece of paper in half to double its thickness. If you could continue doubling the thickness of the paper 42 times, the stack would reach from the earth to the moon, 240,000 miles away. If you could double it 50 times, then folded paper would almost reach the Sun, 93 million miles away!"

Example 1-3: A couple is planning to save money to pay for their newborn college tuition by putting aside $1,000 per year. How much would the child have when he enters college at 18 years of age if his/her parents decided to deposit the money in a) a safe deposit box; or b) a savings account that paid 7% interest, annually?
Solution: If the money is put in a deposit box, the growth is linear -- the annual increase is always the same. The savings is $1,000 after the first year, $2,000 after the second year, etc. At age 18, the child will have $18,000 in savings. If the money is invested in a savings account, the percentage rate of increase is the same each year, but the total increase is exponential. Let's say the parents deposit $1,000 on the child's first birthday. The bank pays 7% ($70) in interest for the first year. With the additional $1,000 deposit at the end of the first year, the total money saved after the second birthday is $1,000 \times 1.07 + 1,000 = \$2,070$, and $2,070 \times 1.07 + 1,000 = \$3,215$, after

---

[¶] The capacity to store more transistor on a chip is the main reason your mobile phones continue to become thinner and thinner. We are fast approaching limits as the size of transistors approach the size of individual atoms. See https://www.cnet.com/news/moores-law-is-dead-nvidias-ceo-jensen-huang-says-at-ces-2019/

the third. By his eighteenth birthday, the total deposit has grown to nearly $34,000, instead of the $18,000 he/she would have had if no interests were paid. The difference between linear and exponential growths becomes substantial by the time the child is ready for college.

Doubling Time

It is constructive to give a convenient method to express the growth of quantities that vary exponentially, in terms of their doubling time.[**] Doubling time is defined as the time it takes a quantity to double and can be reasonably approximated by dividing 70 by the percentage growth rate: [††]

$$Doubling\,Time = \frac{70}{Percentage\,Rate\,of\,Growth}$$

This is commonly referred to as the "Rule of 70."

Example 1-4: A bacterial colony fills up a jar at noon. If the bacteria double in population every minute when was the jar 1/16 full?

Solution: The jar is half full one minute before noon at 11:59, 1/4 full at 11:58, 1/8 full at 11:57, and 1/16 full at 11:56.

Question: What is the rate of population increase in a community in which there are only two children per family? [‡‡]

Answer: The community has a zero rate of population increase. Essentially, both parents replace themselves with their children.

Question: A popular brand of antibacterial cleaner advertises that it kills 99.9% of all kitchen bacteria. Assuming that bacteria can double their population every 24 hours, how often must the disinfectant be applied to keep kitchen bacteria in check?

Answer: Assuming that the company's claim is accurate, after the antibacterial application, 0.1% (or 1 in every 1,000) bacteria remain. For the population to reach its original level, it must increase 1,000 fold or about 10

[**] For example, it took 300 years (from 1500-1800) for the population to double from 500 M to 1B but only 125 years to double again to 2B, and an additional 49 years to reach 4B in 1974. In reality, Some coin the term "explosive growth" rather than exponential growth when it comes to population. Because of the direct link between population and consumption, the same can be told about energy and other resources.

[††] It should be noted, however, that this equation assumes that growth is taking place continuously. This is definitely true in the case of population growth (and also energy consumption). In fact, the population has grown even faster than predicted by the exponential growth..

In other instances, such as interest paid by a bank, growth comes in steps. For example, a bank that pays 3% interest per annum, compounded monthly, pays 3/12 = 0.25% each month, which results in a slightly different growth rate. This makes growth a bit slower. As we shall see in Chapter 14, banks and other financial institutions often apply the "Rule of 72" -- divide 72 (instead of 70) by the interest rate to find the time in which a saving deposit doubles in value.

[‡‡] In reality replacement fertility is higher, around 2.1 for most developed countries, and reaches as high as 3 for less-developed ones. The reason is that some of the women die before they reach their reproductive age. Also, there are slightly more boys than girls at birth.

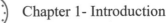

doubling times. The disinfectant must be applied at least once every 10 days!

Half-Life

A similar equation can be used to calculate the time it takes a sample, which decays in a population (i.e., has a negative growth rate), to reduce by half. This is known as the **half-life**, an example of which is the activity of radioactive material or any other sample which decreases in a given period (seconds, days, or millions of years) by a fixed percentage (See Chapter 8).

> **Worth Remembering** – When growth is exponential, it takes about 10 doubling times for a quantity to multiply by 1,000 times; 20 doubling times to multiply by 1,000,000 times, and 30 doubling times to multiply by 1,000,000,000 times.

ⓐ Digging Deeper - The Art of Approximation

As a student, and later in life, you must be able to make reasonable approximations, sometimes within a few percentage points, sometimes within a factor of two, and often within so-called "orders-of-magnitude" or "ballpark" estimates. Because the size of things in the real world varies over an enormous range, from the atom to the Milky Way and beyond, an estimate to the nearest power of 10 is usually good enough for most occasions. These are all questions of the type which do not require exact answers. Rather, they call for rough, but reasonable, estimates. When we know the value of a quantity within a factor of 10, we often refer to the estimate as to its order of magnitude. Two quantities differing by a factor of five or so, are of the same order of magnitude.

Question: Estimate the number of barrels of petroleum used by all American family cars each day.

Answer: Let us assume the US population is about 320 million, and that, on average, each family consists of five people and two cars. This means that there are about $(320,000,000/5) \times 2 = 128$ million family cars in the US Let us further assume that each car travels about 50 miles each day, with gas mileage of about 20 miles per gallon. This means that each car uses up $50/20 = 2.5$ gallons of fuel each day. Since there are 128 million cars, Americans consume about $(128,000,000) \times 2.5 = 320$ million gallons of fuel. Each barrel of oil is about 42 gallons; i.e., daily total petroleum consumption for all passenger cars is roughly $320/42 = 7.6$ million barrels of oil.

Question: Estimate the thickness of one sheet of ordinary paper.

Answer: Most people probably have limited experience in measuring the thickness of one sheet of paper. However, a relatively thick stack of such papers would probably be much easier to deal with. Always refer to something familiar! A reasonable estimate for a stack of 500 sheets, for instance, is 5 cm. Of course, 4 or 6 cm would be just as reasonable. The thickness of one sheet of paper should, therefore, be 500 times thinner or $5/500 = 0.01$ cm or 100 microns.

Many of the topics discussed in this book deal with statistics involving the number of people and cars, and the production and consumption of energy – none is known to very high accuracy, and which often change from one year to the next. You will often see data reported from various government and non-government organizations that are in contradiction or, at best, vary by a few percentage points. It is, therefore, reasonable to quote data to their closest 10th, 100th, or even millionth. It is, thus, quite acceptable to round off the numbers when we are performing calculations dealing with such numbers.

Example 1-5: What is the per capita power consumed by an American? an Indian? Compare these results with the world averages. Assume, the world population of 7.3 billion, US population of 320 million, and Indian population of 1.28 billion.

Solution: Referring to the data given in Table 1-3, we have:

World: $\dfrac{(98,767\,\dfrac{TWh}{yr}) \times (\dfrac{10^9\,kWh}{TWh})}{(\dfrac{8,760\,h}{yr}) \times (7.3x10^9\,person)} = 1.5\,kW\,/\,person$

Similar calculations show power consumption by average American as 6.3 kW and a mere 0.45 kW by average Indians.

Rules for Rounding Off

Engineers and physicists carry out experiments, often with instruments that are not precise, so there is always some uncertainty with any measurements we make. Calculations made based on these measurements are, therefore, bound to have some errors. Just because your calculators display results of your calculations to 20 decimal points does not guarantee that your results are accurate to 20 significant figures. In these instances, we truncate the results to a few digits believed to be accurate. The following rules summarize how to determine the number of significant digits:

- Non-zero digits are always significant.
- All final zeros after the decimal points are significant.
- Zeros between two other significant digits are significant.
- Zeros used as placeholders are not significant.

Applying these rules, it is easy to conclude that all the following measurements have three significant digits: 0.220 m, 2350 g, 90.0 N, 101 kPa, and 0.00527 MJ.

To round off a number to a certain number of significant figures, let's say three, we need to look at one extra significant digit. If this number was smaller than 5, we can simply drop it. If it was bigger than 5, we add one unit to the previous digit. When this digit is 5, then we must look at the number to the left of 5, round the number so that it will be even. Applying these rules:

32.047 rounded off to three significant figures becomes 32.0.
32.067 rounded off to three significant figures becomes 32.1.
32.057 rounded off to three significant figures becomes 32.0.
32.157 rounded off to three significant figures becomes 32.2.

Math With Significant Figures

Significant figures are the digits of a number that are meaningful in terms of accuracy or precision. They include:

Any non-zero digit
Zeros between non-zero digits as in 0.6005
Trailing zeros only when there is a decimal point as in 6500., or 6.500

When performing calculations using numbers with different significant digits, the final result can be no more accurate than the least accurate measurement. i.e., the least number of significant figures in any computation determines the number of significant figures in the answer. In these instances, perform the arithmetic operation, and round off the results to the least precise value.

Example 1-6: Calculate the cross-sectional area and volume of a pipe to the nearest tenth; measurements are made of the radius of the pipe, and its length, as R = 1.3 m and L = 21.465 m.

Solution: The pipe's cross-section is A= πR^2 = 3.14159×1.3^2 = 5.30929 m^2 ≅ 5.3 m^2. Its volume is V = A × L = 5.3 × 21.465 = 113.746 m^3 ≅ 110 m^3 (accurate to two significant figures).

Example 1-7: What is the area of a table cloth, 1.4 m long, and 0.920 m wide?

Solution: 1.4 has two significant figures, while 0.920 has three. Two significant figures are less precise than three, so the answer has two significant figures. The answer to this problem would be 1.3 (which was rounded from the calculator reading of 1.2880). ⓐ

Endnotes

1   Knight, E. and Smith, K. (1986). *American Materialism*, The University of Alabama - Department of Anthropology

2   Stone, L. (2007). *Genes, Culture, And Human Evolution: A Synthesis*, Blackwell Publishing.

3   Leonard, W. (2002). Food for Thought, *Scientific American, 287*(6), 106-115. doi: 10.1038/scientificamerican1202-106

4   Smil, V. (2014). World History and Energy. in Encyclopedia of Energy, Vol. 6. Elsevier Inc.

5   Historyworld (2020). History of the Domestication of Animals. [online] Available at: http://www.historyworld.net

6   Smil, V. (2004). World History and Energy, *Encyclopedia of Energy*, vol. 6, Elsevier Inc.

7   Cook, E. (1971). The Flow of Energy in an Industrial Society, *Scientific American, 225*(3), 134-144.

8   Paolo, M. (2014). Chapcter 1: Energy in History, in *The Basic Environmental History*, 4, 1-29, Springer U.K.

9   Boxer, C. R. (1977). *The Dutch Seaborne Empire, 1600-1800*, Taylor & Francis.

10 Low-Tech Magazine. Medieval Smokestacks: Fossil fuels in preindustrial times, *Low-Tech Magazine.* http://www.lowtechmagazine.com/2011/09/peat-and-coal-fossil-fuels-in-pre-industrial-times.html

11 Wrigley, T. (2011). Opening Pandora's box: A new look at the industrial revolution, 22 July 2011, http://voxeu.org/article/industrial-revolution-energy-revolution

12 Global Wind Energy Council, Retrieved from http://www.gwec.net/global-figures/wind-energy-global-status

13 Kardashev, N. (1964). Transmission of Information by Extraterrestrial Civilizations, *Soviet Astronomy, 8* (217).

14 Heinberg, R. (2003). *The Party's Over: Oil, War and the Fate of Industrial Societies*, New Society Publishers, Gabriola Island, BC, Canada.

15 Kutrovátz, G. (2001). Heat Death in Ancient and Modern Thermodynamics, *Open Systems & Information Dynamics, 8*(4), 349-359. doi: 10.1023/a:101390192099968

16 BP Statistical Review of World Energy (2020). Retrieved from https://www.bp.com/en/global/corporate/energy-economics/statistical-review-of-world-energy.html

17 Our World in Data (2020). Retrieved from https://ourworldindata.org/energy

18 DoE Energy Statistics Manual (2005). OECD/IEA/Eurostat, http://www.iea.org/textbase/nppdf/free/2005/statistics_manual.pdf

19 Energy Demands on Water Resources (2006). Report to Congress on the Interdependency of Energy and Water, US Department of Energy, December 2006. Retrieved from http://www.sandia.gov/energy-water/docs/121-RptToCongress-EWwEIA-comments-FINAL.pdf

20 Averyt, K. et al. (2011). Freshwater Use by US Power Plants: Electricity's Thirst for a Precious Resource, A report of the Energy and Water in a Warming World Initiative. November. Cambridge, MA: *Union of Concerned Scientists.*

21 Mortarty, P. K. and Honnery, D. (2012). What is the global potential for renewable energy? *Renewable and Sustainable Energy Reviews, 16*, 244-252.

22 International Atomic Energy Agency, Energy, electricity and nuclear power estimates for the period up to 2030, IAEA-RDS-1/29. Vienna: IAEA; 2009.

23 Moore, G. (2006). Cramming more components onto integrated circuits, Reprinted from Electronics, 38(8), April 19, 1965, pp.114 ff. *IEEE Solid-State Circuits Society Newsletter, 11*(3), 33-35. doi: 10.1109/n-ssc.2006.4785860

24 Freedman, D. H. (2012). 3-D Transistors, *MIT Technology Review*, May/June 2012.

25 Koomey, J., B, Sanchez, S., & Wong, H. (2011). Implications of Historical Trends in the Electrical Efficiency of Computing. *IEEE Annals Of The History Of Computing, 33*(3) 46-54. doi: 10.1109/mahc.2010.28

26 Miller, G. T. and Spoolman, S. (2009). *Living in the Environment: Principles, Connections, and Solutions*, Brooks/Cole Publishing.

Exercises

I. Discussion Questions

1. What are four energy transitions? When did they happen, and what caused it?
2. Can ethanol be considered a renewable resource? How about geothermal hot water? nuclear fission and fusion? Comment!
3. Some argue that, if external costs associated with different fuels were included in the total cost, renewable energy sources would not be necessarily more expensive than fossil fuels. Explain and give examples.
4. What are the sources of nuclear, wind, wave, and geothermal energy?
5. What is the difference between internal and external forms of energy? Give examples of each.
6. Describe the supply-side and demand-side management of energy and give examples of each. Do you favor any one approach over the others? Why?
7. Consult the 2019 US energy flow chart on the backside of the text's front cover to answer the following questions:
   a. What percentage of petroleum consumed in the United States was for transportation?
   b. What percentage of transportation fuel was in the form of petroleum?
   c. What was the most prevalent use of energy in the US?
   d. Which fraction of total US electricity generation used coal?
   e. How many quads of energy were being supplied from geothermal resources?
   f. What fraction of total US electricity was being imported?
   g. What is the largest source of energy in the United States? By how much?
   h. What percentage of the US's electrical capacity came from renewable energy?
   i. What fraction of total energy was lost as waste heat?
   j. Which sector of the economy used the largest fraction of the total primary energy?

II. Consulting the Internet

1. Find the latest data on the total energy consumption, production, and reserves for your country of birth. Where are the sources of energy, and how are they being used?
2. Update the information in Tables 1-2 and 1-4. Be careful about what the sources of information are. Usually (but not always), government, research organizations, and educational institution data are more accurate.
3. Search for world patterns of energy reserves, production, and consumption, and answer the following questions:
   a. Which country has the highest reserves of coal? petroleum? natural gas?
   b. Which country is the biggest per capita consumer of primary energy?
   c. Which country uses the highest percentage of renewable energy as part of its overall energy mix?
   d. Which country utilizes the most wind energy? hydro energy? solar energy?
   e. Which country produces the most greenhouse gases? the most per capita greenhouse gases?

III. Problems:

Exponential Growth

1. According to the data, there are 22 births and nine deaths annually for every 1,000 persons living in the world. What is the annual rate of growth in the world's population?
2. The US population marked its 300,000,000th birth sometime during October 2006. The figure was derived from the 2000 population census and assumed that there is one live birth every seven seconds, one death every 13 seconds, and one net increase in immigration every 30 seconds. Assuming that this trend continues for the foreseeable future, calculate:
   a. The annual rate of growth.
   b. The doubling time.
   c. The year when the population will reach 600 million.
3. According to the historical records, a Dutch explorer by the name of Peter Minuit purchased the island of Manhattan from Native Americans on May 24, 1626, for 60 Dutch guilders, which is estimated to be the equivalent of $24. If Peter was depositing this money in a bank which paid annual interest of 4%, how much would his investment be today?

   Hint: Trying to find the investment by calculating it year after year is cumbersome and not practical. It is much easier to calculate the doubling time first and estimate the value by counting the number of doubling times.

Arithmetics

4. What is the next number in series a) 2, 4, and 6? and b) 2, 4, and 8?
5. Express the following numbers in scientific notation: a) 523000; b) 365.243533; c) 0.0000343; d) 2.1; and e) 53,100,000,000,000,000.
6. State the number of significant digits in each measurement: a) 2565 m; b) 0.003025 km; c) 4.03×10^5 N; d) 70.00 lb; e) 3×10^{10} m/s
7. Carry out the following calculations with the correct number of significant digits: a) 3.32×2.0 b) $34.01/1.2 \times 10^{-2}$; c) $2.75 - 1.7999$; d) $12.120 + 1.452 + 3.001 + 1.6$
8. What is the cost of the copper used to make a penny? The penny has a mass of 2.500 g, and on the last check, copper was trading at $3.35 a pound. Note that a penny today is only 2.5% copper. 1 lb = 453.6 g
9. Round off the following numbers to three significant figures: 1.6508, 32.002, 5.535×10^{-2}, and 0.007545.
10. Determine the number of significant figures for the following numbers: a) 3102, b) 31.02, c) 32.0, and d) 320000.

The Art of Approximation

11. Estimate the total number of vehicles in the United States? The number of miles driven and the number of gallons of gasoline consumed each year?
12. What is the total surface area of a gram of soot from diesel exhaust? Assume soot has a density of 2 g/cm^3. Experimental results show that the most of the soot emissions from diesel engines are smaller than 200 microns in diameter.
13. By the end of 2020, the US national debt was estimated at 25 trillion dollars. Assuming the debt was going to be paid by $1 bills, what would be the size of the stack of money that is needed? Compare this to the distance between the Earth and the moon.

    Hint: A dollar bill has a thickness of 0.0109 cm.

IV. Multiple Choice Questions

1. What is considered to mark the first energy transition?
   a. Substitution of manual labor with animal power
   b. Transformation to agrarian economics
   c. Smelting of metals
   d. Use of mechanical devices such as watermills and windmills
   e. Use of coal

2. What stage of energy transition corresponds to the wide-scale use of fossil fuels for heating and electrification?
   a. The first energy transition
   b. The second energy transition
   c. The third energy transition
   d. The fourth energy transition
   e. The fifth energy transition

3. How much has the total daily energy per capita of a modern technological man increased in the past 1000 years?
   a. About 100 times
   b. About 77 times
   c. About 9 times
   d. About 3 times
   e. Not enough information is provided in the text.

4. Energy is needed to
   a. Exert a force through a distance.
   b. Lift a mass to a higher elevation.
   c. Move an electric charge through a wire.
   d. Accelerate a mass from rest to a higher velocity.
   e. All of the above.

5. Examples of secondary energy are
   a. Gravity, electricity, and magnetism.
   b. Mass, light, and food.
   c. Solar, wind, and tide.
   d. Electricity, hydrogen, and synfuel.
   e. Nuclear, fossil fuel, and geothermal.

6. Which of the following is not considered to be a primary form of energy?
   a. Ethanol
   b. Tides
   c. Food
   d. Geothermal
   e. Nuclear

7. Chemical energy is
   a. The energy locked in nuclei.
   b. The energy locked in molecules.
   c. The energy by the virtue of an object's mass.
   d. The energy associated with the motion of molecules.
   e. The energy associated with the position of molecules.

8. The source of nuclear fuel used to power today's

nuclear power plants can be traced back to

a. The thermonuclear reaction in the sun.
b. The reaction between atomic particles in interstellar space.
c. The early stages of the Earth's formation.
d. Photosynthesis.
e. All of the above.

9. Geothermal energy has its root at

a. Sun's energy stored at the upper layers of the earth's crust.
b. Chemical reactions occurring in hot water and steam reservoirs.
c. Chemical reactions occurring in volcanoes
d. Nuclear decay of various isotopes still in the Earth's inner and outer cores.
e. All of the above.

10. Per capita energy use and per capita gross national product are

a. Not related in anyways.
b. Related but poorly correlated.
c. Strongly correlated.
d. The same for all countries.
e. Inversely correlated.

11. Two convenient units for expressing a very large amount of energy are

a. Btu and Calorie
b. Therms and Calorie
c. Quad and EJ
d. Tons of TNT and barrels of oil
e. All of the above

12. What is the conversion factor between kWh and kW?

a. 3,600
b. 60
c. 1/3,600
d. 1/60
e. Cannot be converted because they represent two different quantities

13. In a modern conventional nuclear power plant, energy is produced by

a. Combining uranium atoms.
b. Burning uranium atoms.
c. Splitting uranium atoms.
d. The reaction between plutonium and uranium atoms.
e. Stripping electrons from uranium atoms.

14. Electricity is the movement of

a. Photons.
b. Atoms.
c. Molecules.
d. Electric charges.
e. Protons.

15. According to the DoE published data (consult graphical data on the backside of text's front cover) solar energy

a. Constituted slightly more than 3% of the US total energy.
b. Was used entirely to produce electricity.
c. Provided roughly 10% of the electricity from renewable sources.
d. Contributed virtually no amount of GHG.
e. All of the above.

16. The sun gets most of its energy from

a. Burning hydrogen.
b. Burning biomass.
c. Splitting atoms of hydrogen.
d. Fusing atoms of hydrogen.
e. All of the above.

17. Which fuel is currently most used for the production of electricity in the United States?

a. Coal
b. Natural gas
c. Nuclear
d. Hydro
e. Wood

18. Nuclear energy

a. Is ideal for providing base-load electricity.
b. Is best in case of emergencies during peak power.
c. Is responsible for much of our greenhouse emissions.
d. Is not attainable until the mid- 21st century.
e. All of the above.

19. Estimating the time that we will run out of our conventional fossil energy resources depend largely on:

a. The rate of consumption of energy
b. The rate at which new reserves are found
c. The price of energy
d. The state of the economy
e. All of the above

20. A civilizationusing energy available in our solar system is a

a. Type 0 civilization
b. Type I civilzation
c. Type II civilizarion
d. Type III civilization
e. Type IV civilization

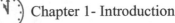

21. Installing fuel cells to shift peak demand to non-eak hours is an example of
    a. Supply-side management
    b. Supply chain enhancement
    c. Energy conservation
    d. Demand-side management
    e. Could be either a supply-side or a demand-side management.

22. Examples of supply-side management of energy include:
    a. Setting thermostat down during winter
    b. Replacing the incandescent lights with fluorescent ones
    c. Cogeneration
    d. Better drilling technologies to extract deeper oil
    e. All of the above.

23. Which of the following sets of numbers represents a linear growth?
    a. 5, 8, 11, 14, 17
    b. 4, 8, 12, 24, 48
    c. 4, 8, 16, 32, 64
    d. All of the above
    e. None of the above

24. Which of the following sets of numbers represents an exponential growth?
    a. 5, 8, 11, 14, 17
    b. 5, 8, 12, 17, 23
    c. 5, 8, 12.8, 20.48, 32.77
    d. All of the above
    e. None of the above

25. Which of the following is the unit of mass in the SI?
    a. Pound
    b. Kilogram
    c. Gram
    d. Newton
    e. Slug

26. The measurement 0.0000054 grams, expressed correctly using scientific notation, is
    a. 5.4×10^{-7} g
    b. 5.4×10^{-6} g
    c. 0.54×10^{-5} g
    d. 54 µg
    e. 54 mg

27. Which of the following numers has three significant figures?
    a. 0.002
    b. 210
    c. 0.210
    d. 0.021

28. A calculator gives the result of an operation as 542.6012. The result must be rounded off to three significant figures. Which answer should be reported?
    e. 1.021
    a. 540
    b. 542
    c. 543
    d. 542.6
    e. 542.0

29. Calculate the surface area and volume of a sphere with a diameter of 5.10 cm, to the nearest tenth measurement.
    a. 81. and 69.
    b. 82, and 69.
    c. 81.7 and 69.4
    d. 81.7 and 69.5
    e. 81.71 and 69.46

30. The correct answer for the addition of 7.5 m + 2.26 m + 1.311 m + 2 m is
    a. 13.071 m.
    b. 13 m.
    c. 13.0 m.
    d. 10 m.
    e. 13.1 m.

V. True or False?

1. Per-capita energy consumption in a modern technological society is roughly 100 times that in a primitive society.
2. More than 80% of all the energy used in the world is from fossil fuels.
3. "Heat Death" is a term scientists use to warn the public as to the dangers of global warming.
4. Coal is the fuel used for most electricity production in the world.
5. Hydrogen is a primary source of energy.
6. The law of conservation of energy was valid until Einstein showed that mass could be converted to energy.
7. Cutting subsidies to farmers to produce corn for ethanol is an example of supply-side management.
8. The main cause of global warming is the burning of fossil fuels.
9. Electron volt is the unit of energy commonly used in atomic and nuclear physics.
10. The size of a quantity that grows by 10% per year will be doubled in 10 years.

VI. Fill in the Blanks

1. Energy is the _____ to do _____.
2. The _____ is still commonly used in the petroleum industry. It is equal to 42 gallons.
3. A _____ is used to express large quantities of energy. It is equal to 10^{15} Btu.
4. _____ will likely replace fossil fuels as the main source of energy within the next two centuries.
5. $120 invested at 7% compound interest will grow to $240 in about _____ years.
6. _____ and _____ are the two countries with the highest rate of energy consumption in the world.
7. A power plant has a generating capacity of one gigawatt. This power plant can produce _____ kWh of electricity in one hour.
8. The next most logical number in the series 3, 9, 15, 21 is _____.
9. The next most logical number in the series 2, 6, 18, 54 is _____.
10. A person with a mass of 60 kilograms, weighs _____ newtons.

PROJECT I - Status of Energy Resources

In this project, you are asked to investigate the status of energy resources, reserves, and use in the United States and compare it with those of the world. The main source of data is the Energy Information Administration of the US Department of Energy (http://eia.doe.gov), but other sources may also need to be considered.

1. What is the total annual energy consumption in quads and billions of barrels of "oil equivalent" for oil, gas, coal, renewable, and nuclear? For various energy sectors: transportation, industrialized, residential, and commercial?
2. What fraction of primary energy consumption is used to generate electricity? Give the percentage from each source.
3. What are the ultimate sizes of the US and the world reserves?
4. What is the energy consumption per capita? What is the energy consumption per each $1,000 of income? Compare US data with China, India, and the European Union.

PROJECT II - Voyage Beyond the Solar System

According to an article by *Popular Science,*[*] on interstellar travel, we have to wait at least another 200 years before we can embark on this expedition. Comment on the merit of this article. The first question asked is what source of energy serves best for this application. Others envision possible strategies that include hydrogen, solar, nuclear, gravity, beam-powered propulsion, ion engine, or any other exotic fuel. Describe how each technology works, and what are the advantages and disadvantages of each approach? Explain.

Reference: Mills, M. G. "Energy, Incessant Obsolescence And The First Interstellar Missions," Presented at the 61st International Astronautical Congress, Prague, CZ January 2011, (arxiv.org/abs/1101.1066).

PROJECT III - Energy Alternatives (Group project)

There is a ballot initiative on whether a nuclear, a fossil fuel, or solar power plant should be built near the city you are living in. You are asked to assume one of these roles and act either as a proponent (pro) or opponent (con) in the following list and address the issues from that point of view.

Pro as the	Con as the
parent	child
oil company person	conservationist
electric utility	stockholder
scientist	economist
economist	scientist
business person	consumer
consumer	electric utility
regulatory agency	electric utilit

Pro as the	Con as the
parent	child
oil company person	conservationist
electric utility	stockholder
scientist	economist
economist	scientist
business person	consumer
consumer	electric utility
regulatory agency	electric utility

CHAPTER 2

Mechanical Energy

Astronomical Clock, Prague, Czech Republic, Flickr ~ Grufnik

Give me but one firm spot on which to stand, and I will move the Earth. ~ Archimedes (287-212 BCE)

Mechanical energy, in the form of muscle power, was the first energy source that humans utilized to chase and wrestle animals or escape them when in danger. Muscles were energized by chemical energy in the food that had to be foraged or hunted. Then some 11,000 years ago, as the ice age neared its end and climate became more moderate, foragers and hunters turned to agriculture. Simple tools such as wedges, ramps, and pulleys helped hunters and farmers and opened a new era in human development. The bow and arrow were used in hunting and warfare; sickle, hoe, and the plow helped increase farming productivity. The task got even simpler as humans learned to domesticate animals and relegate much of the manual labor to working animals such as oxen, horses, and mules. The great civilizations of China, Egypt, Persia, Greece, and Rome relied on forced labor and animals to plow their farms; at the same time, their soldiers fought to acquire more land and slaves. As empires crumbled and slaves became scarce, the work of humans and animals was increasingly supplemented by power from watermills and windmills.

Although the invention of windmills and watermills can be traced back to many thousands of years, their use was limited, primarily to grinding grains and navigating sailboats along rivers and on seas. They became widespread only at the end of the first millennium when Europeans used mills to operate such tools as saws and looms, and to pump water from wells. The work from muscles, the work performed by windmills and watermills, and the work done by simple tools are all examples of mechanical energy. In this chapter, we will define work, its relationship to mechanical energy, and how simple machines are used to make it easier. Wind and hydro energies will be discussed in Chapters 12 and 13, respectively.

Newton's Laws of Motion

Before we start our discussion on work, and energy, it is instructive to review Newton's Laws of Motion and the concepts intrinsically related to energy -- force and mass. Today, many aspects of Newton's laws appear to be common sense. If the object does not move, we need to apply a force. If it moves, then force is needed to stop it. If you want it to continue to move then remove the force. If you push with your hands on an object that does not move, like a solid wall, then the wall offers a resistance as if it pushes your hands away. These observations are summarized in three famous laws, namely:

Newton's First Law of Motion: *In the absence of an external force, a body at rest remains at rest and a body in motion continues to move with the same speed and direction.*

You can easily see this when you are sitting in a car that suddenly stops. You tend to go through the windshield unless you are held back by a seat belt. Why? Simply because -- braking causes to stop the car, but not you. You continue to move as if the car were still moving. Newton's First Law of Motion also is called *the Law of Inertia*.

Newton's First Law:
**All objects with mass have a common property called inertia
that keeps objects doing "what they have been doing."**

Newton's description of inertia was a radical departure from Aristotle's view which saw that the natural tendency of all objects was rest, and that everything in motion would eventually come to rest, and that some influence or "force" was needed to keep a body moving at a constant velocity. Newton (and also Galileo) showed that objects in motion would remain in uniform linear motion unless they are acted upon by some force.

Question: A helium balloon is tethered to a ribbon and hung loosely from the ceiling of a train cabin. In which direction would the balloon move if the train were to suddenly stop? What if the balloon were filled with argon gas instead?

Answer: Although the train stops, passengers, the air filling the interior of the cabin, and the balloon continue to move. Passengers and air, however, move more because they are heavier and thus have higher inertia. Relative

to the train and the passengers, the balloon is left behind and drifts toward the rear of the cabin. Since argon is heavier than air, filling the balloon with argon will have the opposite effect. The balloon now has more inertia than the air surrounding it, so it moves ahead of the air and is tilting toward the front.

Newton's Second Law of Motion: *Applying a force on a mass causes it to accelerate in the direction of the force; the object decelerates if the force is opposite to the direction of motion.*

If the object is stationary, the force tends to cause the object to move. In other words, applying a force to an object -- either by pulling or pushing -- changes the object's motion; i.e., a force is what it takes to accelerate a mass. In mathematical terms, it takes the form

> *Newton's Second Law:*
> **force = mass × acceleration**

If the mass is given in kilograms (kg), and acceleration in meters per second squared (m/s^2), then force will be in newtons (N). Weight is the downward force exerted by a mass due to gravity. i.e., W = mg.

Question: Should astronauts worry about putting on "weight" in space?
Answer: In space, astronauts can eat as much as they want without worrying about their weight. When they return to earth, however, the weight will show because of the increase in their masses.

As it appears from this explanation, gravity is a force -- a force that causes objects to be pulled (fall) toward the Earth. To be exact, we also can say that this force causes the Earth to be pulled toward the apple, although by only a minute amount. Unlike the force of pull or push by your hands (contact force), gravity acts at a distance. As we can see in later chapters, there are two other forces that act at a distance -- electricity and magnetism. We can experience the electric force by noticing the static clinging of a piece of paper to a comb. The magnetic force is what makes a magnet pick up small nails and paper clips. It should be noted here that, unlike gravitational forces that are always attractive and act on all bodies, electrical forces only act when particles are electrically charged and are attractive only when charges are of opposite signs. Electromagnetic forces are covered in Chapter 5.

Although forces are often associated with motion, there are circumstances in which forces do not result in motion. For example, a substantial amount of force is needed to push a heavy crate before it can slide on a plain surface. In other words, force is the intensity with which an object can be pulled or pushed, whether it starts to move or not.

Question: Do forces always result in acceleration?
Answer: No. If a force is not accelerating the object, it deforms it.

Newton's Third Law of Motion: *If you push on an object, the object pushes back or, as commonly stated, for every action, there is a reaction.*

This is easy to test. Pushing against a wall is opposed by the wall resistance -- as the wall is pushing back on your hands. Using the names "action" and "reaction," which Newton himself assigned to these forces, we can express Newton's Third Law as:[*]

> *Newton's Third Law:*
> **For every force (or action), there is an equal and opposite force (or reaction).**

---

[*] The term action/reaction is not entirely correct, as it implies precedence. Both forces occur simultaneously; the reaction does not happen after an action has taken place.

Question: Gravity pulls down on an apple hanging from a tree. Why doesn't the apple fall?

Answer: The force of gravity pulls down on the apple, but this force is counterbalanced by the upward force of the tree branch on the apple. Although this force is equal and opposite to the force of gravity, this cannot be considered an action/reaction pair. Remember, action/reaction pairs must exist between two different objects. Both the force of gravity and the upward pull of the tree act on the apple and not on two different objects.

Question: Can you lift yourself up by your shoelaces?

Answer: No. You cannot lift yourself by your shoelaces because the upward force on your feet is equal and opposite to the downward force of the shoelaces on your hands. Thus, you will experience zero net force and, consequently, not move.

Question: The cartoon below depicts a horse that citing Newton's Third Law, refuses to pull a cart? Is he justified?

Answer: No! Newton's third law states that whenever action-reaction forces are internal to a system, they cancel each other out. They do not cancel each other when either one is external to the system being considered.

Newton's Law of Universal Gravitation

This law states that any two masses pull on each other with a force that is proportional to the product of the two masses and, inversely, to the square of the distance between the two. In the language of mathematics:

$$F = G \frac{m_1 m_2}{r^2}$$

(2-1)

Where m_1 and m_2 are masses of the two objects, separated by a distance r. $G = 6.67 \times 10^{-11}$ N.m^2/kg^2 is the Universal Gravitational Constant.[†]

Question: Why do celestial bodies tend to be round?

---

† Actually, when Newton proposed this law, he did not know the value of the constant G, which was discovered by Cavendish about 71 years after Newton's death.

Answer: Gravity pulls all the mass toward the center.

> *Newton's Law of Universal Gravitation*:
> **Any two masses attract with a force proportional to the product of their masses and, inversely, to the square of the distance between the two.**

Example 2-1: What is the force of attraction between Lisa and her ex-boyfriend Paul, when they are standing one meter apart? What is the attractive force between Lisa and the Earth? Lisa has a mass of 55 kg; Paul has a mass of 80 kg.

Solution: Substituting in Equation 2-1, the force of attraction between Lisa and Paul is indeed very small

$$F = G\frac{m_{Lisa}m_{Paul}}{r^2_{Lisa-Paul}} = 6.67\text{x}10^{-11} \times \frac{55\times80}{1^2} = 2.9\text{x}10^{-7}\text{N}$$

The attraction force between Lisa and the Earth is equal to her weight W = mg = (55 kg) x (9.81 m/s^2) = 540 N.

Example 2-2: What is the force by which an average-sized apple is pulled toward the Earth?

Solution: The separation distance between the apple and the center of the Earth is equal to the Earth's radius (6,400 km). Substituting for the Earth's mass of 6x10^{24} kg, and the apple's mass of about 0.1 kg, in equation 2-1 results in the force of

$$F = W = \left(6.67\times10^{-11}\right)\times\frac{(0.100)\times(6x10^{24})}{(6.4x10^6)^2} \sim 1\text{ N}$$

This is the weight of the apple. Of course, the apple pulls the Earth by the same force, but at much much smaller acceleration.

Worth Remembering -- Whenever you think of Newton, think of the apple!

Work, Energy, and Power

In Chapter 1, we defined energy as the capacity to do work. This definition implies that work and energy are interrelated -- one cannot be defined without the other. Let us first introduce the more tangible concept -- work -- and then define energy in terms of it.

Work

Intuitively, **work,** often called mechanical energy, is the change in an object's state of motion that results from the application of a force. No work is performed unless the object is displaced in the same direction as the applied force. Sideway displacements do not contribute, so no work can be done by a force that is perpendicular to the displacement. To move an object twice the displacement, with the same amount of force, twice the work must be done. Likewise, if it requires twice the effort to move a twice-heavier object the same displacement, the work performed will still be two times as much. It is, therefore, understandable to define work as the product of the force times the displacement. The unit for work is newton-meter (N.m) or joule (J).

work = force × displacement

If an object does not move (in the direction of the force), then no work is performed. When the force is at an angle, only the component of the force in the direction of motion must be considered.

How much work do we need to carry a heavy suitcase along a flat air terminal? Although it appears that we consume a lot of energy (getting tired), in reality, we are not performing any work! Recall from our earlier definition, work is the product of force through the displacement the force is exerted. The force we apply is the reaction force to the force of gravity and is equal to the weight of the suitcase. Except for the small displacement (lift-off from the ground), the force is not acting through any large distance. The displacement of the suitcase is in a horizontal plane, perpendicular to the direction of the force and, therefore, **no work** is performed.

Here, it may be constructive to differentiate between the work and the effort required to carry a task. According to the classical definition, we need to do work to move an object some distance -- no displacement, no work! Going up the stairs and coming back down the same stairs requires no net work (work needed to pull your weight up is equal and opposite the work of gravity as you are coming back down). **The total effort is not zero, as force must be exerted in going both the up and down directions.**

Question: If there is no work done, why is carrying the suitcase not as easy a task as it appears?
Answer: Although little or no mechanical work is involved in carrying the suitcase, energy expended in flexing various muscles in the body to simply hold the weight above the ground is not! Similarly, pushing a car stuck in the mud or pressing on a wall does not involve any mechanical work, although it puts a strain on your muscles, which must contract and relax.

Figure 2-1
Torque.

Just as a force is a push or a pull, a **torque** can be interpreted as "force with a twist," since it results in rotation of the object upon which the force is applied. To tighten a screw or to pedal a bicycle, we must apply torque (Figure 2-1). Torque can be calculated by multiplying the force and perpendicular distance between the axis of rotation (or pivot) and the "line of action" of the force. This distance is called the "lever arm" or the "arm of the force."

$$\textbf{torque} \ = \ \textbf{force} \times \textbf{arm of force}$$

Torque has the same unit as work, joule (J) or newton-meter (N.m) in the International System of Units (SI). In the United States Customary System (USCS) the unit for torque is pound-foot (lb-ft).

$$1 \ \text{lb-ft} = 1.356 \ \text{J}$$

Question: Which of the following represents the performance of work?
a. An apple falls off an apple tree.
b. A horse pulls a carriage.
c. A balloon ruptures and air rushes out.
d. A car crashes into another car damaging both.
e. A woman carries a basket of fruit over her head.
f. A boy pushes against a wall until exhausted.

Answer: In each of the first four instances, a force has <u>caused</u> a movement in the direction of the force. In case (a), the force of gravity causes the apple to fall. In case (b), the horse applies a force in the direction of motion. In case (c), the higher pressure in the balloon forces air out. In case (d), the work exerted by the crash force results in local displacement (deformation). Instances (e) and (f), however, do not constitute work. The force that the woman applies to the basket is upward and perpendicular to the direction of her motion. Similarly, when the boy pushes on a wall, there is no displacement and he performs no work. This might be quite confusing, as in both instances, the person can become very tired. In fact, the body does continuous work to pump blood to various organs, to expand and contract various muscles in hands and feet, and to force air in and out of our lungs; all of these actions serve to maintain normal body functions. Although no mechanical work was performed in cases (e) and (f), both the woman and boy use up a lot of chemical energy via metabolism.

Question: A boy is moving a heavy box along a hallway. If the boy wants to move the box with the smallest amount of effort (putting in the least amount of work), which approach should he choose?
a. Pull the box with a rope parallel to the floor.
b. Push the box parallel to the floor.
c. Pull the box with a rope at an angle.
d. All of the above require the same amount of effort.

Answer: The answer is (d). Although the boy might be a bit more comfortable in one situation over another, the work done is exactly the same in all cases. Work is needed because of friction between the two surfaces; the amount of work is equal to the magnitude of the friction force, multiplied by the distance traveled. The component of force perpendicular to the ground is not doing any work. The smart thing to do, probably, is to put the box on a wheeled cart or a dolly to reduce the friction!

Energy

Having defined work in terms of forces and displacements, we now can turn to define **mechanical energy** as the energy acquired by an object upon which work is performed. Alternatively, it can be said that an object that possesses mechanical energy is capable of doing work. Mechanical energy can be described as either kinetic energy or potential energy.

Kinetic Energy

Kinetic energy is the energy of motion. Since any displacement can be viewed as a combination of a linear motion and a rotation, there are two forms of kinetic energy -- linear (the energy of motion of the center of mass[‡] from one location to another) and rotational (the energy due to rotational motion about the center of mass[§]). The energy from the wind and rotating flywheels are two examples of kinetic energy. The kinetic energy of a body is proportional to its mass and the square of the velocity. Thus, for instance -- at the same speed -- a van weighing twice the weight of a sedan has twice its kinetic energy. A car moving twice as fast as an identical car has four times the kinetic energy and, thus, requires four times as much work to stop,

---

[‡] The center of mass is defined as the point in a body or a system of bodies at which the entire mass may be considered as concentrated.
[§] The kinetic energy of a body in rotation is $KE = 1/2\, I\omega^2$ where I is moment of inertia and ω is the angular velcity. The topic will not be discussed further in this book..

$$KE = \frac{1}{2}mV^2 \qquad\qquad\qquad (2\text{-}2)$$

Where:

  KE = kinetic energy [J]
  m = mass [kg]
  V = velocity [m/s]

It is a matter of a simple exercise to show that, *the kinetic energy of an object can be interpreted as the work required for accelerating that object from rest*.

Example 2-3: What is the kinetic energy of a 20-g bullet leaving a rifle's muzzle at 340 m/s?

Solution: The kinetic energy is calculated as $KE = 1/2\ mV^2 = 0.5 \times 0.020 \times (340)^2 = 1,156$ J or ~ 1.2 kJ. This is not a lot of energy, roughly equivalent to the energy contained in 60 milligrams of sugar. In other words, sugar yields 320 times more energy than the equivalent mass of a bullet at high speeds (See Table 2-1 below). Why firing a bullet can be so much deadlier than throwing a sugar cube?

Potential Energy

As its name implies, potential energy is energy at rest that is waiting, capable of changing the shape or position of an object in a force field. Energy from a hydroelectric dam, from tides, and from a slingshot are all examples of potential energy. There are two types of potential energy: *potential energy of form* is the result of twisting, compressing, stretching, or bending matter out of its natural shape; and *potential energy of position* (also called gravitational energy) is the energy of a mass caused by its higher elevation, relative to its surroundings. In other words, *the potential energy of an object is equal to the work needed to lift or deform the object*. The gravitational potential energy is equal to that required to move an object a vertical distance against the force of gravity.

$$PE = mgH \qquad\qquad\qquad (2\text{-}3)$$

Where:

  PE = potential energy [J]
  m = mass [kg]
  g = gravitational acceleration [m/s^2]
  H = elevation [m]

Potential energy is measured relative to a reference height or datum. A piece of rock on a little mound on a beach has relatively small potential energy when measured against the sea level but has negative potential energy when dropped in a well; it has a very high potential energy relative to the Earth's center, however.

Example 2-4: What is the upward force needed to prevent a 6.0 kg object from falling to the ground? How much energy is needed to carry this object to the top of a three-story building with a height of 11 m?

Solution: The force to counteract gravity is $F = mg = 6.0$ kg $\times 9.81$ m/s^2 = 58.86 N. The potential energy work is $PE = 58.86$ N $\times 11$ m = 647 J.

Question: Which one requires more work in carrying a weight to the second floor -- using a ramp, stairs, or an elevator?

Answer: As long as frictional forces are neglected, all three require the same amount of work, equal to the change in potential energies of the weight between the first and second floors. When riding an elevator, the work is being done by the electric motor, but when walking upstairs, the same work must be provided by our muscles.

Potential energy is that form of energy that can be "stored," in the sense that it could later be retrieved and converted into useful work or kinetic energy. The water at the top of Niagara Falls is said to have gravitational potential energy because it can be converted to kinetic energy at the bottom of the waterfall and be used to turn a turbine. Similarly, a pole-vaulter is said to store elastic potential energy in the pole when he bends it. When the pole straightens, it does work on the athlete and sends him soaring. It is the magnetic potential energy stored in magnets, ready to be converted to kinetic energy when a piece of iron is placed close to the magnet. The same is true when jumpers take advantage of recoil energy in their feet before high jumps.

Question: You inflate a balloon by blowing into it. Do you perform work? By how much?
Answer: Yes, you do work because you are applying a force to move your diaphragm and push the air out through a distance (expanding the balloon outward). The amount of work is equal to the stored elastic potential energy; that is, the amount of energy needed to stretch (deform) the balloon.

Conservation of Energy

The principle of conservation of energy implies that the amount of energy in a system does not change; only its form does. When we throw a ball up, or when we lift a stone, we transform the stored energy of food into the motion or the position of the ball or stone. When we turn on a light switch, we convert electrical energy into light energy and some heat.

Conservation of energy is usually stated as the **First Law of Thermodynamics**, which we will visit again when we discuss thermal energy in Chapter 4. For now, let's concentrate on a special case in which there is no outside force applied to a mechanical system -- total kinetic and potential energies remain constant. This is called the *conservation of mechanical energy*, i.e., PE + KE = constant

Strictly speaking, there is no such law, since there is always some energy dissipated, and this equation should be modified to include frictional losses as:

$$PE + KE + heat\ losses = constant$$

Question: As you walk, it is the static frictional force between your shoes and the ground that propels you. How much work is done by this force on your shoes?
Answer: None. At the point of contact, your shoes do not move. The ground does work on you as a whole, and you do work on your shoes.

Example 2-5: A 500-g ball is thrown up with a velocity of 6.0 m/s. What maximum height does the ball reach before it starts its descent toward the ground?
Solution: Energy is continuously being converted between kinetic and potential energy, as the ball bounces on the floor. During each rebound, a fraction of energy is lost to the floor. Eventually, all the energy is converted to heat, and the ball stops. Applying the principle of conservation of mechanical energy to the ball, we have:
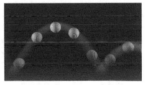
$1/2\ mV^2 = mgh$; or $h_{max} = V^2/2g = (6.0\ m/s)^2/(2 \times 9.81\ m/s^2) = 1.83\ m$
Note that this result is independent of the ball's mass.

Closely associated with energy are two other concepts commonly referred to in this text -- energy intensity, and power.

Energy Intensity

Energy density or energy intensity is the energy stored per unit length, mass, volume, or area, depending on the context. Solar energy is highly dispersed, so it has a low energy density per area, but can be focused through lenses and concentrators. On average, solar intensity is about 30 W/m² of land area over the continent of the United States.

Wind energy and the energy from biomass also are measured in terms of their energy densities per unit area. Wave energy per unit area does not, however, mean much, and is therefore reported per length of coastline (Chapter 13). When dealing with petroleum and other liquid fuels, energy per unit volume is more appropriate. For solids like coal, energy per unit mass (commonly called the **specific energy**) is of primary interest.

Table 2-1 gives energy intensities for some common substances. TNT has a much lower energy per gram than butter, sugar, and yes -- even a gram of hamburger meat. Only 60% of TNT energy is released during an explosion, so the ratio is even smaller, about 1/15 that of the energy of an equal weight of gasoline -- a fact that was not overlooked by the 9/11 terrorists[¶] who used jet fuel to bring down the World Trade Center towers in 2001.[**] As it is shown below, what makes TNT attractive for demolition is that energy can be delivered at a much faster rate (i.e. power) than gasoline.

Table 2-1 Energy Intensity of Selected Materials			
	kcal/g	*MJ/kg*	*Compared to TNT*
Bullet @ speed of sound (kinetic energy)	0.014	0.06	0.01
Lead-acid battery	0.034	0.14	0.03
Lithium-ion battery	0.17	0.7	0.17
TNT*	1	4.2	1
Sugar (carbohydrate)	4.5	19	4.5
Butter (fat)	9	38	9
Gasoline	10	42	10
Hydrogen	34	143	34
Uranium-235	2×10^7	8.4×10^7	20,000,000
* The explosive power of TNT is only 60% of this value.			

Hydrogen has 3.5 times the energy of gasoline of equivalent mass. Even in liquid form, hydrogen has a density one-tenth that of gasoline, so you can only recover one-quarter of energy from a tank filled with liquid hydrogen, instead of gasoline. If hydrogen is in gaseous form, it takes even more room and at 10,000 psi (the best available pressure tanks), only 1/6 as much energy as gasoline can be obtained. This is one of the main problems associated with hydrogen as a fuel. There are other concerns with the hydrogen economy that will be addressed in the chapter on transportation.

Power

Power is the rate at which we use energy. When the energy is in the form of work, power is defined as the work done divided by the time it takes to do that work. i.e.

$$\textbf{power} = \frac{\textbf{work}}{\textbf{time}}$$

Since work is the product of force and displacement, and displacement per unit time is velocity, then power can be calculated as:

$$\textbf{power} = \textbf{force} \times \textbf{velocity}$$

[¶] Early on the morning of September 11, 2001, Al Qaeda terrorists hijacked four commercial jets and crashed three of them into the World Trade Center in New York and the Pentagon in Washington D.C. The fourth aircraft was heading toward the White House but crashed in Pennsylvania. Over 3,000 innocent lives were lost, 265 aboard the airplanes and the rest in the buildings that collapsed as a result of the tragic incident.

[**] Note that kinetic energy released by the airplane impact with the building. Each tower was hit by a Boeing 767-200ER, which along with the fuel had a mass of 128,600 kilograms and kinetic energy of $E = 0.5 \times 128,600 \times (222.2)^2 = 3.16 \times 10^9$ J or 3,160 MJ, which was less than a quarter-percent of the energy released by burning the jet fuel. It is, therefore, highly unlikely that the WTC towers would have collapsed under the effects of aircraft impact alone.

The Power from a Rainstorm

How much energy is contained in a rainstorm that drops 10 mm of rain on one square km land area in one hour? Raindrops are 2-mm in size and formed in a cloud 250 m up. Assuming that air is saturated with moisture so that none of the droplets are evaporated as they fall. Right before a droplet hits the surface, all its potential energy is converted to the kinetic energy. i.e.,

$$1/2 \ mV^2 = mgH$$

Substituting for H = 250 m, and g = 9.81 m/s^2, it follows the droplets will gain speeds of 70 m/s (252 km/h). This is, however, unrealistic as frictional losses will dissipate much of the energy, and droplets slow down to reach their terminal velocities (when the pull of gravity cancels out the drag) within a few meters of the drop. For droplets of 2-mm in diameter, this is around 7 m/s, ten times smaller than the speed they would reach if they were traveling in a vacuum, and have only 1/100 as much energy as they started; that is, 99% of all energy has been dissipated as heat on their way down.

What is the available power remaining in the rain drops? The volume of water collected during one hour of rain fall is V = 1 km^2 x 10 mm = 10,000 m^3. Substituting for the water density, potential energy is P.E. = mgH = rVgH = 1,000 kg/m^3 x 10,000 m^3 x 10 m/s^2 x 250 m = 2.50x10^{10} J. Assuming 1% of this energy converts ultimately to the kinetic energy, the power available in one square kilometer of raindrops is

$$P = 0.01 \ x \ 2.50x10^{10} \ / \ 3,600 = 6.94x10^4 \ W = 69.4 \ kW$$

Example 2-6: How much work do you do in climbing to the roof of a building, 30 meters tall? Does it matter if you walk up the stairs slowly or fast -- even skipping every other step? What is the power you need to walk up the stairs if the vertical speed on the stairs is 0.5 m/s?

Solution: Assuming you weigh 600 N (mass of 61 kg), the total amount of work (or energy) is $600 \times 30 = 18,000$ N.m = 18 kJ. The amount of work is the same, whether you move fast or slowly. What is different is the power output, i.e., the rate at which you produce energy. You cannot carry a heavy load quickly because your power output is too low. Power is the product of force and speed: $P = 600 \times 0.5 = 300$ watts. A healthy athlete can maintain this level of power output for half an hour or so, but not much longer.

Question: It is commonly understood that we should switch to lower gears when our car descends a slippery slope or is stuck in the mud. What is the rationale for this?

Answer: Power is force multiplied by velocity. For a given engine power is relatively constant (at least over a range of operation) regardless of the gear. So when people say there is "more power" in a lower gear, it's the common misconception that "more powerful" is "more forceful." The correct statement is that the engine puts out a higher torque (or a larger force) but at a slower speed. For example, if you are towing a trailer or trying to climb a very steep grade, you need the force to be large which is why you put it in a low gear. If you are on something slippery like snow or ice, a high gear will keep the force at the wheels low so the tires don't exert enough friction (traction) with the road and spin.

Measuring Power

Depending on usage, power is often expressed in quads per year, million barrels of oil per day, and Btu per hour. The SI unit of power is joules per second, commonly called a watt (W) in honor of James Watt, the inventor of the steam engine. In the U.S., power is customarily expressed in horsepower, which is equivalent to 746 watts (1 hp = 746 W). Smaller units of power are measured in milliwatts (one-thousandth of a watt), microwatts (one-millionth of a watt), and nanowatts (one-billionth of a watt). Larger powers are expressed in kilowatts (thousand watts), megawatts (million watts), gigawatts (billion watts), and terawatts (trillion watts).

In humans and other biological systems power output is equal to the rate of chemical energy production within the body or the rate[††] of energy dissipation into an external load corrected for the mechanical efficiency (about 20-25%).[††] A horse can continuously deliver about one horsepower; a man can produce about 100 W of power (1/7 horsepower),

---

[††] The mechanical efficiency of the body is not constant, however, and depends on variables such as type, duration, and environmental parameters such as ambient temperature, humidity, and human factors such as sex, and body composition.

performing light activities such as reading, eating, and office work (Table 2-2). He temporarily can increase his power output by engaging in extraneous exercises to about 500 W (400 kcal/hour, or 0.75 h.p.) for jogging, playing tennis, or bicycling, and about one horsepower for a short period during fast runs, sparring, and sprints. The power can be as high as 5,000 W during the very short interval of a vertical high jump. [2]

Table 2-2 Power Outputs	
Flashlight (LED)	1 W
Laptop Computer	10 W
Man (continuous)	100 W
Horse	746 W (1 horsepower)
Man (sprint)	1 kW
Energy Consumption in Average Household	10 kW
Automobile (economy)	100 kW
Aircraft Fighter	1 MW
Steam Turbine	100 MW
Large Power Plant	1 GW
Space Shuttle	10 GW
World Total Energy Consumption Rate	10 TW
Hurricane	100 TW

Example 2-7: A 15-gallon fuel tank of a sedan is filled in about two minutes. Each gallon of gasoline has an energy content equal to 115,000 Btu. Estimate the rate of energy pumped (i.e., power) into your gas tank during refueling.

Solution: The total energy stored in a 15-gallon tank is 15 gal x 115,000 Btu/gal x 1,055 J/Btu = 1.82×10^9 J and the power delivered is 1.82×10^9 J/120 s = 15.2×10^6 W = 15.2 MW, comparable to the power that can be extracted from over 20,000 horses.

Question: The Itaipu Dam Power Generating Station (the second-largest power plant in the world after Three Gorges in China) has an electricity generating capacity of about 95 TWh/year (See Table 13-2). What is the average power produced?

Answer: Power is calculated by dividing the total energy by the hours of operation. Under continuous operation it would generate (95,000,000 MWh)/(365×24 h) = 11,000 MW of power. The peak power is 12,600 MW, about 15 percent higher

*Note that kW is the unit of power -- that is, the energy used in kJ, every second. **Since energy is the product of power and time, a kilowatt-hour is the measure of energy and not power.** A 1-kW device requires one kWh of energy to operate continuously for one hour. Never talk of kilowatts per hour, since it makes no sense! Occasionally one may speak of kWh/day or TWh/year to indicate the average power used in a household during any 24-hour period, or produced by a power plant in one year.*

Relationship Between Energy and Power

Proper usage of power and energy, often, is confusing to students. A rock climber and a trail hiker of similar mass moving to the top of a cliff using the same amount of work. They each have to lift their own weight the entire height of the cliff. The hiker, however, can reach the top of the cliff much faster than the rock climber. The rock climber performs the same task at a slower rate, using less power. For the same reason, you cannot carry a heavy load as quickly as a light load -- your power output is too low.

The nuclear bomb dropped on Hiroshima had explosive energy of 13 kilotons of TNT, but the energy was released in only a few microseconds; it provided a tremendous amount of power for a very short time. A starter motor works by supplying a lot of power for a short period -- long enough for the gasoline or diesel engine to reach speeds that can provide continuous power. As one swings a golf club toward a ball, he stores the kinetic energy of the motion of his hands throughout the travel but releases it over the very short time that the club comes into contact with the ball, so the actual power is quite large. For the same amount of energy, rockets deliver a lot more power than internal combustion engines, because rockets burn up their energy at a much faster rate.

Question: Two identical cars are leaving Los Angeles at the same time. The first car arrives in San Francisco in five hours, while it takes ten hours for the second car to reach the same destination. Which car consumes more energy? Which car puts out more power?

Answer: Assuming that the cars' efficiencies are equal at all speeds, both cars use the same amount of fuel (energy), i.e., work the same amount.[‡‡] The faster car, however, uses up fuel twice as fast, therefore putting out twice the power of the slower car.

Question: Suppose a small passenger sedan with a power rating of 80 hp can accelerate from 0-60 mph in 12 seconds. How long would it take a sports car with a power rating of 240 hp to accelerate by the same amount? Which car performs more work?

Answer: Both cars accelerate to the same speed (and gain the same amount of kinetic energy); therefore, they perform the same amount of work. The second car uses three times the power—which means it does the same work in one-third of the time or four seconds.

> ***Worth Remembering*** – Work is what needed to move an object through a certain distance; power is what is needed to move it at a certain speed.

ⓐ The Golden Rule of Mechanics

The "Golden Rule" of mechanics essentially states that **whatever you lose in power, you gain in displacement**. We commonly use pulleys and ramps to lift things which, otherwise, would be too heavy for muscles alone. In both cases, a smaller force achieves the necessary work, but over a greater distance. A transmission gearbox, for example, transmits power from the engine to the axle through a number of interlocking gears. To get more power, we must reduce speed (less displacement) and switch into a lower gear. A machine can increase the magnitude of the effort (input) force, or increase the velocity of the object to be moved, but not both. This is exactly what a machine is supposed to do -- ***transform work into a form most convenient to perform a task with less force.***

Question: Consider a bottle opener. In lifting the handle, you do work on the opener which, in turn, does work on the cap it is lifting. Which one is greater, your work or the work of the bottle opener?

Answer: Because the opener cannot be a source of energy, the output work (work of the opener) can never exceed the input work (your work). The opener simply aids in the transfer of energy from you to the bottle cap. In fact, nearly all of your work will go into deforming, rather than into lifting, the bottle cap.

Simple Machines

Machines are an important part of our daily existence; they vary in complexity from simple tools like screwdrivers and scissors, to more complex machines, such as cranes and automobiles. Whether powered by engines or by people, machines make our tasks easier. **A machine eases the load by changing either the magnitude or the direction of a force, or by speeding up a task.** Pliers are designed to increase the force we apply; car jacks and ropes change the direction of the force we put in; the main objective of the bicycle is to increase the speed of the force.

It should be noted that according to the law of conservation of energy in the absence of friction, machines do not reduce the work (sorry, no free lunch!). They only reduce the input force or change the direction of the force, so we can do the same work easier. This is done by spreading the same amount of work over a larger distance. In other words, **the same amount of work can be accomplished by applying a greater force over a shorter distance or a smaller force over a longer distance.**

Simple machines are designed to perform one simple task. There are six types of simple machines represented in Figures 2-2 (a thru f). Others, such as bicycles, are considered complex (or compound) because they are made out of many simple machines (frame, chain, pedals, handle bar, wheel, etc.).

    a. **Inclined plane** (any slanted surface used to raise a load from a lower level to a higher level). Work is carried out using less effort by moving a smaller force over greater distances. Examples include ramps for

---

‡‡ In reality, cars are designed to give better gas mileage at about 80-100 km/h (50-60 mph).

Figure 2-2
Simple machines - (a) ramp, (b) wedge, (c) screw, (d) lever, (e) wheel and axle, (f) pulley.

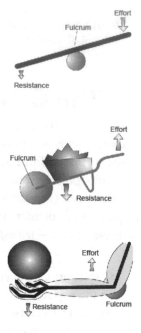

Figure 2-3
First, second, and third class levers.

wheelchairs, ramps to load luggage onto a plane, and escalators. It is believed that the Egyptian pyramids were built using similar ramps.

b. **Wedges** are double-inclined planes used mainly to distribute the force on both sides. They work by applying a smaller force over a larger area. Nearly all cutting machines (chisels, axes, scissors, and knives) are different variations of wedges.

c. **Screw** (the circular version of the inclined plane). A screw is really an inclined surface wrapped around a cylinder or a cone. Some examples are ship propellers, corkscrews, meat grinders, ordinary screws, and jar lids.

d. **Lever** (a bar or a rigid object that rests and rotates about a point called a fulcrum). Just like other simple machines levers make work easier by allowing a smaller force to be applied over a longer distance. A lever is characterized by a fulcrum or pivot, a weight (the resistance or load), and an applied force (or effort). Depending on the position where force and weight apply, relative to the pivot, there are three kinds of levers. In a **first class lever**, the fulcrum is between the effort and the resistance (pliers, seesaw, and scissors). When the weight is between the fulcrum and the force, the lever is called a **second class lever** (nutcracker and wheelbarrow). In **third class levers,** the force is located between the fulcrum and the weight (baseball bat, shovel, tong, and human arm). Figure 2-3 gives examples of various types of levers. In all these examples, the force required to carry out the tasks is reduced by making the lever arm bigger. In fact, we can show that the product of:

force in (effort) × effort arm = force out (load) × load arm

e. **Wheel and axle** is a circular lever consisting of a large wheel attached to a smaller axle with a drive force applied tangentially to the perimeter of the wheel and a load force applied to the axle. Again, a smaller force applied to the longer motion at the wheel results in a shorter, more powerful motion at the axle. Examples are windmills, gears, doorknobs, and steering wheels. A screwdriver is essentially a wheel and axle. When you use a screwdriver, you apply a relatively small force to the wheel, and the axle translates this into a much larger force.

f. **Pulley** (a chain, belt, or rope wrapped around a wheel). A pulley is often used to lift a heavy weight with less force. A pulley makes work easier because it changes the direction of force. Instead of lifting up, you will pull down on the load, using your body weight. Like other simple machines, the trade-off is the longer distance that the smaller force must travel at the end of the rope. Examples are the bicycle chain and the pulley used to move a curtain up and down.

Question: Which of the six simple machines reduce the amount of work needed to raise a load?
Answer: None of them. Machines do not change the amount of work required. They merely make the work easier.

Lifting the Earth

"Give me one lever and one firm spot on which to stand, and I will move the Earth," proclaimed the great Archimedes, the genius of antiquity who discovered the laws of leverage. He realized that a lever would allow one to lift a very heavy object while applying a very small force. In principle, his assertion about lifting the Earth, though somewhat ambitious, does seem perfectly reasonable. By using a very long lever, for instance, you could attempt to balance one object weighing as much as the Earth with an applied force on the other end. Let's suppose, for argument's sake, that Archimedes can apply a force roughly equal to his own weight. Clearly, the much lighter Archimedes would have to position himself much farther from the pivot than the heavy object. In fact, the ratio of the two lever arms would be precisely the inverse ratio of their respective weights (or masses). Since the mass of the Earth is $M_E \sim 6\times10^{24}$ kg and the mass of Archimedes was probably around 100 kg (to keep the numbers nice and round), the ratio of the arms would be roughly 6×10^{22}. A big number, but so what? Well, the difficulty arises when one considers the time involved in lifting the "earth" by any noticeable amount. For example, to lift the Earth even by 1 millimeter, Archimedes would have to move his end through a giant arc 6×10^{19} m long. Just how long do you think that would take? Working against a force equal to his weight (1,000 N), Archimedes would generate about 1.3 horsepower (1 horsepower = 746 W) if he moved his end at the respectable rate of 1 m/s. At this rate, the task would take 6×10^{19} s or about 2 trillion years. Even if Archimedes were to move his end at the speed of light — nature's fastest — the task would still take him over 6,000 years.

Question: A cart filled with bricks is to be loaded onto a truck. Three ramps of different lengths are available.

a. Which situation requires the least amount of force?
b. Which situation requires the least amount of work?
c. Which situation requires the least amount of power?

Answer: The product of force times displacement, or work, is the same in all cases. The power expenditure, on the other hand, depends on how long it takes to perform this work. If you pull faster, the time is shorter and more power is needed. Situation (a) requires the least amount of force, but the force must be applied over the longest distance. Assuming speeds are the same in all cases, it takes the longest for the cart to move up the longest ramp and the least power is consumed.

(a)

(b)

(c)

Summary

Mechanical energy is the total energy an object has, excluding the thermal and internal energies associated with the structure of its atoms and molecules. In other words, it is the sum of its potential and kinetic energies. Mechanical energy is what it takes to lift, move, turn, and twist an object. Examples of mechanical energy are energy possessed by a fastball, energy stored in the spring or a rubber band, and the energy it takes to move a heavy object up the stairs. Simple machines are devices that are at our disposal to carry out difficult tasks with less effort; they allow us to do the same amount of work by applying a smaller force (effort), but over longer distances. In performing any task there are always some frictional forces that we must overcome. For this reason, some mechanical energy always is converted to heat. In other words, in real systems, efficiencies are always smaller than "one." Any complex machine can be broken into a number of simpler machines.

ⓐ*Digging Deeper: Mechanical Efficiency and Mechanical Advantage*

To complete our discussion, it is constructive to define two factors that are important in selecting an appropriate machine for performing a given task -- mechanical efficiency and mechanical advantage:

Mechanical efficiency (ME) gives a measure of the losses that may be incurred while performing a certain job. It is the fraction of the input work that is available for carrying out the desired output work.

$$M.E. = \frac{Desired\ work\ output}{Necessary\ work\ input}$$

In an ideal machine, no energy is wasted and efficiency is 100%. In real machines, some of the input work is inevitably lost as heat. For example, to pull a bucket of water from a well, we need a pump that possibly runs on electricity. The desired outcome is to raise the potential energy of the bucket of water from the bottom of the well to the surface. The efficiency is the ratio of the rise in the potential energy of the bucket and the electrical work required to run the pump. Because some of the electricity is dissipated as heat or used to overcome frictional losses (such as that between the rope and the pulley), more work is needed, and efficiency is less than 100%

Question: Suppose you hook two machines together in series: one with an efficiency of 40% and the other with an efficiency of 60%. What is the efficiency of the two machines operating together?
Answer: If you are tempted to say 100%, try to resist. The first machine will feed only 40% of the original input energy into the second machine, which then puts out 60% of the 40%. In other words, each machine loses some energy and the net efficiency is 0.40 x 0.60 = 0.24 (or 24%).

Mechanical advantage (MA) is the factor by which the machine multiplies the force put into it. It is the ratio of the force that performs the useful work of a machine (load, or the resistance force) to the force that is applied to the machine (or the effort force). Unlike mechanical efficiency, the mechanical advantage may or may not be greater than one. Machines are designed to make a task simpler by increasing the force applied; therefore, for most machines, the mechanical advantage is greater than one. Forces are not, however, the only things that are magnified by levers. Since the longer arm of the lever has to travel a greater distance than the smaller arm of the lever, in the same amount of time, it travels faster.

$$M.A. = \frac{Force\ exerted\ by\ a\ machine}{Applied\ force}$$

You can infer from these statements that *the gain in velocity or displacement is inversely proportional to the reduction in effort* and is, therefore, inversely proportional to mechanical advantage. Hence, you may use a lever to gain either mechanical advantage or speed, but not both. For example, to reduce our effort by half, we need a machine that applies the force over twice the distance or is twice as fast. In other words, the machine must have a mechanical advantage of two.

Question: How does a car jack allow you to raise a 2,000-lb car when you can only lift a weight of 50 pounds?
Answer: The jack is a lever allowing a much smaller force applied over a longer distance. In this particular case, you must lower the jack handle by 40 cm, just to raise the car by 1 cm.

Question: What is the mechanical advantage of an inclined plane that is 6 meters long and 2 meters high?
Answer: Neglecting friction, the mechanical advantage of a ramp is equal to the ratio of the length of the slope to the height it is raised, i.e 6 /2 = 3.

Human Body as a Machine

The human body can be seen as a machine that consumes food and converts it into mechanical work and heat (See Chapter 4). Power is transmitted through the action of forces on the muscles, bones, and joints that make the body's lever system. The peak power that can be produced by a human can reach as high as 5 kW for a very short period but falls off rapidly with a longer duration (2 to 5 seconds) reaching a constant value of around 300 W after five minutes

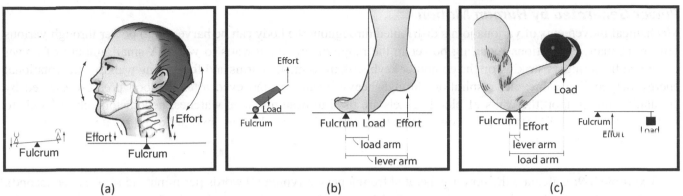

Figure 2-4
Examples of levers in human body: (a) first kind, (b) second kind, and (c) third kind.

for a trained athlete.[3]

The bones in our bodies act as **levers,** and our joints act as **fulcrums**. The force applied to the lever is called the **effort**, whereas the force that limits the motion of the lever is called the **load** or the **resistance.** Depending on the position of the fulcrum relative to arms, levers can be classified as first, second, and third kinds (Figure 2-4). Unlike machines, our bone structure is not optimal for making a particular task simpler. In fact, the human body is not designed for strength, but agility, speed, and wide ranges of motion.

As muscles contract, they pull a series of tendons and bones across joints to perform various tasks. Muscles always act as pairs, so when one contracts, its antagonist extends. Examples of first, second, and third-class levers are neck joints, the Achilles tendons, and the elbow joints. Most of the movements of the body are produced by third-class levers, where the force is between fulcrum and weight. This design lends itself to the speed of movement, rather than force. For example, when we lift a weight, the biceps and triceps work as a pair; when the biceps flex the arm (effort) or lift a weight (load or resistance), the triceps relax to extend the arm (Figure 2-5).

Question: Our muscles are much stronger than they seem. For instance, the biceps are attached to the forearm about eight times closer to the elbow (the fulcrum) than one's hand is, when lifting a weight. What is the advantage of this seemingly inefficient arrangement?
Answer: The advantage is speed (also a factor of eight), which is frequently more important in the animal world.

Question: A man is lifting a heavy weight by contracting the biceps and, at the same time, relaxing his triceps muscle. What is the force needed to lift a 10-pound weight?
Answer: The force needed is higher by the ratio of the arms (40 to 4); we need 10 times the weight of the object to support the weight. When losses are present, the mechanical advantage will be reduced by a factor equal to the mechanical efficiency.

Example 2-8: An eighty-kilogram athlete can climb 60 steps in 30 seconds. Assuming the height of each step is 0.25 m, what is the average power output during the climb? Assume $g = 10$ m/s^2.
Solution: The athlete has to pull himself up a vertical height of $h = 60 \times 0.25 = 15$ m, for the gravitational energy of PE = mgh = 80 kg $\times$ 10 m/s$^2 \times$ 15 m = 12,000 J. The power output is P = 12,000/30 = 400 W.

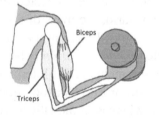

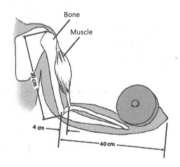

Figure 2-5
A human elbow acts as a third class lever when it lifts a weight.

Power Generated by Human Motion

Mechanical movements of various joints distributed throughout the body can be harvested to power through various sensors in manyapplications requiring power in the range of few microwatts to watts. A small amount of power generated from fingers striking on the computer keyboard, movement of arms and feet during walking, the rotational energy of pedaling a bicycle, respiration through heavy breathing, and even arterial blood pressure exerted by circulating blood upon the walls of blood vessels are used to design kinetic watches, pedometers, chest bands to monitor heartbeats, LED flashlights, computer battery and cell phone chargers, hydraulic and pneumatic systems to power bionic arms, and piezoelectric generators for various consumer electronics.[4]

Example 2-9: Calculate the power generated from a person typing 60 words per minute (5 strokes per second). A typical keyboard requires pressure from 40-50 grams of mass to depress a key the 0.5 cm necessary to register a keystroke.

Solution: The average power generated is:

$$\frac{0.045 \text{ kg}}{\text{keystroke}} \times \frac{9.81 \text{ m}}{\text{s}^2} \times 0.005 \text{ m} \times \frac{5 \text{ keystrokes}}{s} = 0.011 \text{ W}=11 \text{ mW}$$

Example 2-10: We are interested in designing shoes that use the power generated by walking for charging a cell phone. Assume a 70-kg man walking at 3.5 mph (2 steps per second), and that the heels rise and fall 5 cm during the walk.

Solution: Power is calculated in a manner similar to Example 2-9, as

$$70 \text{ kg} \times \frac{10 \text{ m}}{\text{s}^2} \times \frac{0.05 \text{ m}}{\text{step}} \times \frac{2 \text{ steps}}{\text{s}} = 70\text{W}$$

This power can be harnessed through a variety of sensors such as piezoelectric, electrostatic, and rotary generators.

ⓐ *Digging Deeper: Dimensions and Units*

Whether we are interested in measuring the volume of a soda can, the time it takes to fly between Los Angeles and Madrid, the mass of a satellite orbiting the Earth, or the power consumed in turning on a light bulb, we need *dimensions*. Different dimensions can be assigned to measure a physical quantity. Certain units of measurement are called *fundamental units* because other quantities can be expressed by using them. Two more common systems of measurement are SI (International System) or MKS (for meter, kilogram, and second), and USCS (U.S. Customary System) or FPS (for foot, pound, and second). In the SI system of units, weight (expressed in newtons) is a *derived unit*, whereas in the USCS weight (measured in pound-force) is a *primary unit*. Since weight depends on where the measurement is taking place, the U.S. system is not absolute and, therefore, not used by scientists and in international trades. An added benefit is that the SI system of units is based on the power of 10 and, therefore, simpler to use. The metric system is used everywhere except in the U.S., Liberia, and Myanmar (formerly Burma), where the USCS still prevails.

When expressing dimensions we often have to deal with very large or very small numbers. The mass of an electron is 0.00000000000000000000000000000091 kg; the average distance between the Earth and the Neptune is 4,350,000,000,000 meters. In such instances, it is best to express these dimensions in scientific (power of 10) notation, i.e., 9.1×10^{-31} kg, and 4.35×10^{12} m.

The standard unit of length is the meter. It was originally defined as one ten-millionth of the distance from the equator to the North Pole, going through Paris. The standard length has since been redefined several times and now is given in terms of the distance traveled by light in a tiny fraction of a second. The vastness of space, from the very small to the very large, requires different units of measurement. The size of an atom of hydrogen is about 10^{-10} m (1 Å); the diameter of a carbon nanotube is about a nanometer (10^{-9} m) and the length of a bacterium is about one micron (10^{-6} m). When very large distances are considered, lengths are expressed in the Astronomical Unit (or AU), defined as the average distance between the Earth and the Sun. It is roughly equal to 1.5×10^{11} m (93 million miles). To measure much greater distances, another useful unit is a light-year (ly), defined, simply, as the distance lights travel in a vacuum in a year. Since the speed of light in a vacuum is a universal constant, this length unit is also well-defined. It is equal to 9.46×10^{15} m (9.46 trillion kilometers, or 5.88 trillion miles). The size of our galaxy, the Milky Way is about 100,000 light-years.

The standard unit of time is the second. Passages of days and months and years are all natural methods of measuring time. Time also can be thought of as a continuous sequence of moments at which events occur. It has a direction and extends from the past to present to future. Because it is unidirectional, we can present it as a one-dimensional space -- a timeline. If we fix the origin at "now," then all times corresponding to a negative timeline are considered the "past" and all times corresponding to a positive timeline are considered the "future." We will return to this concept again in Chapter 4 when we discuss one of the most fundamental laws of nature -- "The Second Law of Thermodynamics."

Until 1956, standard time was defined in terms of the mean solar day, taken as 24 hours. Because the Earth's rate of rotation is gradually decreasing, the mean solar day of the year 1900 was adopted as the standard. The current definition for the second was officially adopted in 1964 as the time taken by a cesium-133 atom to make 9,192,631,770 vibrations. Many physical quantities require measuring tiny fractions of seconds -- a microsecond as 10^{-6} s, and a nanosecond as 10^{-9} s.

The standard unit of mass is the kilogram. It is defined as the mass of a platinum-iridium cylinder kept at the International Bureau of Weights and Measures, near Paris. Accurate duplicates of the standard mass have been produced and sent to standardizing laboratories throughout the world, including one that is housed in a secured vault at the U.S. National Institute of Standards and Technology (NIST) in Gaithersburg, Maryland.

Unit Conversion

In the United States, the distances between cities are usually expressed in miles, our weights are given in pounds, the energy we use to heat our homes is given in million Btu, and the money we spend on our clothing is in dollars. The same quantities are expressed in kilometers, newtons, kilojoules, and euros when we travel to Europe. It is, therefore, necessary to be able to convert these quantities from one unit to another on different occasions.

The correct way to convert units from one system of measurement to another is particularly important for scientists and engineers who consistently work on conversion factors defined as quantities that are expressed in multiples of units. The best practice to avoid getting superfluous answers as a result of errors in unit conversion is to include the units in all computations. This avoids many of the common mistakes and also allows you to quickly pinpoint any such problems. The basic concept is simple: multiply both numerator and denominator by identical quantities. In other words, multiplying any quantity by the number "1" would not

Table 2-3 Conversion Factors SI and US System of Units			
	SI	*U.S. Customary*	*Conversion*
Mass	kg	lbm (pound-mass)	1 kg = 2.2 lbm
Time	s	s	---
Length	m	ft	1 m – 3.28 ft
Area	m²	ft²	1 m² = 10.8 ft²
Volume	m³	ft³	1 m³ = 35 ft³
Weight (Force)	N = kg m/s²	lbf = 32.2 lbm ft/s²	1 N = 0.225 lbf
Pressure	Pa = N/m²	(lbf/in²) or psi	1 Pa = 1.45×10^{-4} psi
Energy	J = N m	lbf ft	1 J = 0.738 lbf ft
Power	W = J/s	hp	1 W = 1.34×10^{-3} hp
Temperature	K = 273 + °C	R = 460 + °F	1 K = 0.556 R

affect the results. All we have to make sure of is that all intermediary units cancel out, leaving only those desired in the final answer. Table 2-3 gives important conversion factors between SI and US system of units. Examples below show how the procedure works.

Example 2-11: An NFL standard-size football field width is 160 feet. Express the length in meters.
Solution: Rewrite the relationships given above in the form of conversion factors as:

$$\frac{12\ in}{1\ ft} \equiv 1; \ \frac{2.54\ cm}{in} \equiv 1; \ and \ \frac{1\ m}{100\ cm} \equiv 1$$

It can, therefore, easily be verified that

$$160\ ft = 160\ ft \times \frac{12\ in}{1\ ft} \times \frac{2.54\ cm}{in} \times \frac{1\ m}{100\ cm} = 48.77\ m$$

Speed, velocity, and acceleration: Speed is defined as the rate of change of a distance per unit time. Velocity is defined as the rate of change of a displacement per unit time. Acceleration expresses how fast speed increases. In SI units, speed and velocity are expressed in m/s and acceleration in m/s^2.

Example 2-12: A 2020 Tesla Model S has a top speed of 155 mph and can accelerate from 0-60 mph in 4.2 seconds. What are the top speed and acceleration in km/h and m/s^2?
Solution: Noting that 1 mi =1,609 m, and 1 h = 3600 s.

$$V = \frac{155\ mi}{h} \times \frac{1.609\ km}{mi} = 250\ km/h$$

Acceleration is the rate of change of velocity, or

$$a = \frac{60\ mi/h}{2.8\ s} \times \frac{1,609\ m}{mi} \times \frac{1\ h}{3,600\ s} = 9.58\ \frac{m}{s^2}$$

Mass and weight: Mass is the accumulation of matter; an apple of a certain size is made of so many atoms -- no matter how you measure it, it is always the same. In SI units, the mass is in kilograms, in USCS units, it is pound-mass (lbm). The conversion factor is 1 kg = 2.2 lbm.

The weight of an object is defined as the force that is exerted on the mass by the Earth's gravity. That force, of course, will change if we are making the measurement on top of a mountain, or at different locations around the globe.

$$W = mg \tag{2-4}$$

Where g = 9.81 m/s^2 = 32.2 ft/s^2 is the average gravitational acceleration on the surface of the Earth. *g* varies somewhat with location and decreases with altitude.

In the SI system, force is expressed in newtons. One newton is defined as the force required to accelerate one kilogram mass by one meter per second-squared; i.e.

$$\boxed{1\ N \equiv 1\ \ kg\ m/s^2}$$

In the USCS system, the force is expressed in lbf. A pound-force is defined as the weight of a one-pound mass in a gravitational force field of 32.2 feet per second-squared.

$$\boxed{1\ lbf \equiv 32.2\ \ lbm\ ft/s^2}$$

Example 2-13: Mary weighs 110 pounds. What is her weight in newtons? What is her mass in kilograms and in pounds?

A Note on Notations...

It is customary that units are represented by their first letters, in lower case, when they are spelled out -- kilograms, meters, seconds, etc. When abbreviated, they remain in lowercase, unless they are proper names -- kg, Pa, N, and m. Prefixes follow the notations shown in the table to the right.

When we are speaking of individuals, we use capital letters in accordance with English nomenclature – Sir Newton, Dr. Einstein, or Mr. Pascal. If the units are named after scientists, we use lower case again, such as pascals, joules, or newtons. As it is commonly said in physics, *the greatest honor is when your name starts to be spelled with a lower case letter.*

Question: According to *Newton*'s second law of motion, the weight of an object (in *newtons*) is measured as the product of its mass (in *kilograms*) and the gravitational acceleration constant (in *meters per second squared*). Calculate the weight of an average-sized apple with a mass of 0.1 kg at a point, with a gravitational acceleration constant of 10 m/s².

Answer: Weight = mass × acceleration = 0.1 kg × 9.81 m/s² = 9.81 N ≈ 1 N (or 1 newton). When you think of newtons, think an apple!

10^n	Prefix	Symbol
10^{-12}	pico	p
10^{-9}	nano	n
10^{-6}	micro	μ
10^{-3}	milli	m
10^3	kilo	k
10^6	mega (million)	M
10^9	giga (billion)	G
10^{12}	tera (trillion)	T
10^{15}	peta (quadrillion)	P
10^{18}	exa	E

Solution: When we talk about weight, we mean pound-force; Mary weighs 110 lbf. Mary also has a mass of 110 pounds (110 lbm). Her mass expressed in the SI units is then 110/2.2 = 50 kg; her weight, expressed in metric units is 50 × 9.81 = 490 N.

Pressure: is defined as the force per area, and expressed as pascal in the SI system of units.

$$1 \text{ Pa} \equiv 1 \text{ N/m}^2$$

In the USCS system, the pressure is expressed in lbf per square inch (psi). Other units of pressure are lbf/ft², inches of mercury, and atmospheres. The weight of our atmosphere exerts a downward force resulting in an average pressure of 100,000 pascals (100 kPa, one bar), or 14.7 psi, at the sea level.

Energy and power: The SI unit for energy is the joule, defined as the work needed to move a force of one newton by one meter. i.e. 1 joule = 1 newton-meter.[§§]

$$1 \text{ J} \equiv 1 \text{ N.m}$$

Power is the rate of consumption of energy in time. If energy is expressed in joules, and time in seconds, then power will be given in watts.

$$1 \text{ W} \equiv 1 \text{ J/s}$$

Energy and power are normally expressed in lbf-ft (or Btu), and horse power in the USCS system.

$$1 \text{ hp} \equiv 746 \text{ W}$$

Example 2-14: The monthly electricity consumption of an average household is 300 kWh. Express this number in joules.

Solution:

$$300 \text{ kWh} = 300 \text{ kWh} \times \frac{1,000 \text{ W}}{1 \text{ kW}} \times \frac{3,600 \text{ s}}{1 \text{ h}} \times \frac{1 \text{ J/s}}{1 \text{ W}} = 1.08x10^9 \text{ J} = 1.08 \text{ GJ}$$

[§§] Two more units comminly used to express heat energy are Calories and Btu. A calorie is defined as the amount of heat that is required to raise the temperature of one gram of water by one degrees Celsius (1 calorie = 4.84 J). Similarly, a Btu is defined as the amount of heat that is required to raise the temperature of one pound of water by one degrees Fahrenheit (1 Btu = 778 lbf-ft).

Example 2- 15: Fuel economy is expressed in miles per gallon (mpg) in the United States, and in liters per 100 kilometers in Europe. If the average U.S. passenger car is using 18 mpg, how is the fuel economy expressed if the same car is sold in a European market? Each gallon is 3.788 liters and each mile is 1.609 kilometers.

Solution: Noting above correction factors, the fuel consumption rate is calculated as:

$$18 \frac{mi}{gal} = 18 \frac{mi}{gal} \times \frac{1\ gal}{3.788\ L} \times \frac{1.609\ km}{1\ mi} = 7.65 \frac{km}{L}$$

For 100 kilometers of travel, the car uses 100/7.65 = 13.08 liters of gasoline. i.e., the fuel economy is 13.8 liters per 100 kilometer (L/100 km).

Endnotes

1. Gibson, T. (2011). These Exercise Machines Turn Your Sweat Into Electricit, *IEEE Spectrum,* 21 June 2011. https://spectrum.ieee.org/green-tech/conservation/these-exercise-machines-turn-your-sweat-into-electricity
2. Lakomy, H. (1993). 'Laboratory measurement of human power output during maximum intensity exercise'. *Physics Education,* 28(6), 376-379. doi: 10.1088/0031-9120/28/6/007
3. Starner, T. & Paradiso, J. (2004). "Human Generated Power for Mobile Electronics," *Low-Power Electronic. CRC Press.*
4. Cavagna, G. and Kaneko, M. (1977). Mechanical work and efficiency in level walking and running, *The Journal of Physiology,* 268(2), 467-481.

 **Exercises**

I. Discussion Questions

1. How do seatbelts help prevent serious injuries in case of a car accident?

2. Which action requires more work in carrying a weight to the second floor, from the ground: using a ramp, using stairs, or using an elevator?

3. Which pulls harder, the Earth on an orbiting space shuttle or the space shuttle on the Earth?

4. Which causes more damage to a car: a) crashing into a solid concrete wall; b) colliding head-on with an identical car approaching it with a similar speed?

5. You push a car that has run out of fuel but it doesn't move. What do Newton's laws tell you about this?

6. How can levers and pulleys help in reducing the force needed to lift a heavy object?

7. What is a compound machine? Give a few examples of compound machines and how they are made of simpler machines.

8. What do a screw, a ramp, and a wedge have in common? Explain how they reduce force?

9. Draw simple diagrams of a nutcracker, a scythe, and a crowbar. Show the following: effort force, resistance force, fulcrum, effort arm, and resistance arm.

10. Give a few examples of levers in human and other animal kingdoms. How do they help in facilitating various tasks?

11. You are using a pully to pull up a bucket of water from a deep well. How does this help in make your task easier?

12. ⓐ If the weight of an object being lifted is 200 N and the number of supporting ropes the pulley system has is four, what would be the system's mechanical advantage? How much weight would you actually be lifting?

13. ⓐ What kind of simple machine (first, second, or third) is a
    a. fork?
    b. Wedge?
    c. Seasaw?
    d. Claw hammer?
    e. Hammer?
    f. Hacksaw?

14. ⓐ Indicate whether each unit represents energy (E), power (P), or neither (N).
    a. joule
    b. megawatt
    c. newton
    d. kilowatt-hour
    e. joule/day
    f. watt /day
    g. newton-meter
    h. horsepower
    i. ton of coal
    j. billion barrels of oil per year

15. ⓐ Determine whether the tools mentioned below are first class, second class, or third class levers. Draw a diagram showing the load, effort, and fulcrum for each case.
    a. Scissors
    b. Hammer
    c. Fishing rod
    d. Nutcracker
    e. Fingernail clippers
    f. Wheelbarrow
    g. Crowbar
    h. Stapler
    i. Bottle opener
    j. Wine corkscrew
    k. Elbow joint when lifting a heavy load

II. Problems

ⓐ Newton's Laws of Motion

1. How much does a person who weighs 200 pounds on earth weigh on Pluto? Gravitational acceleration on Pluto is 0.78 m/s².

2. A skydiver is parachuting from a helicopter. What is the air resistance acting on the parachute, once it has reached its terminal velocity? The skydiver mass is 85 kg. How much does the skydiver weigh as he falls?

3. What is the force required to accelerate a 1500-kg vehicle from 0 to 100 km/h in 8 seconds?

4. A 5-kg block is being pulled across a flat surface by a 20 N force. Assuming that the force is acting parallel to the surface and the block moves with constant speed, calculate the force of friction acting on the block.

ⓐ Kinetic and Potential Energy

5. An object weighing 60 N is dropped from a height of 5 m. Find the speed and kinetic energy of the object just before it hits the ground.

6. When doing a chin-up, a student lifts his 80-kg body a distance of 0.3 meters in 1.5 seconds. What is the

power delivered by the student's biceps?

7. Two contestants, John and Mary, are competing in a rock competition. John has twice the weight of Mary, yet he finishes the race in ¾ of the time. Who did the most work? Who delivered the most power and by how much? Explain your answers.

8. What is the work required to push a 25-kg cart 200 m on a flat surface, making an angle of 30° with a horizontal plane?

9. Comets are time capsules that offer clues about the formation and evolution of our solar system, some 4.5 billion years ago. To better understand how the outer solar system was formed, a team of NASA scientists designed a probe called "Deep Impact," which was to smash into a nearby comet (actually 83 million miles away!) at very high speeds and, for the first time look into the comet. The 820-lb probe collided with the comet at 23,000 mph on July 4, 2005, making a hole the size of a football field. What was the kinetic energy of the probe (in lbf-ft and J) at the time of impact?

10. The fastest record by a marathon runner belongs to Haile Gebrselassie of Ethiopia, who ran the 42.2-kilometer race in 2 h 4 min (Berlin, 2008). It is estimated that he burned 3,500 Calories during the race. How many kWh did he burn? What was his average power expenditure?

11. Assuming the same marathon runner wants to run upstairs. How fast can he climb the stairs? Assume the athlete has a mass of 55 kilograms.

12. What is the maximum torque that a 60-kg man can apply to unscrew a tight nut using a wrench 0.25 meters long?

13. A record was set for stair climbing when a man ran up the 1,600 steps of the Empire State Building in 10 minutes and 59 seconds. If the height gain of each step was 0.20 m, and the man's mass was 70 kg, what was his average power output (in watts and horsepower) during the climb? Assuming 25% efficiency, how much heat did he produce during his climb?

14. A bicyclist in a road race like the Tour de France rides at about 20 mph (9 m/s) for over 6 hours per day. About 250 watts of power goes into moving the bike against the resistance of the air, gears, and tires. Another 750 watts or so are lost as heat. How many calories must the racer ingest per day to sustain such a rigorous regimen? (Use 1 calorie = 4.18 J)

Mechanical Advantage

15. If the mass of an object being lifted is 100 kg and the number of supporting ropes the pulley system has is four, what would be the system's MA? What is the force (effort) required to lift the weight?

16. The same mass (100 kg) is pushed up a ramp which makes an angle of 10° with the horizontal plane. What is the mechanical advantage of the incline?

17. A rod is being used as a lever to raise a box of 30 kg. The fulcrum is 1.5 m from the load and 2.8 m from the applied force. Determine the force that must be applied to lift the load?

18. Mary weighs 40 kg and Jack weighs 25 kg. They are seated on opposite sides of a seesaw. If Mary is seated 3 m away from Jack, how far should each be from the fulcrum of the seesaw? If Mary sits 2 m from the fulcrum, how far away is she from Jack?

19. To move a heavy 200-kg rock, Jack places the fulcrum of a crowbar 22 cm from the rock. How much force must he use to move the rock? Assume the crowbar is 1 m long.

20. A heavy block with a mass of 500 kilograms is to be lifted 2 meters up using either a single fixed-axis pulley or frictionless inclines at 30° and 60°. Find the mechanical advantage and effort needed for each machine? Assume g = 10 m/s².

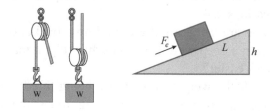

Energy and Power

21. The United States annual energy consumption is estimated to be 100 Q (Q represents one quadrillion Btu), which is roughly equal to one-quarter of the total energy consumption in the world. What is U.S. annual energy consumption in joules and kWh? Express this number in terms of billion barrel oil equivalent (bboe), and cubic kilometer oil equivalent. What is the average power output in terawatts?

22. According to the data published by the Energy Information Administration (EIA, World Energy Outlook, 2019), the world's total energy production

in 2018 was estimated at 556 quads. The same reference gives total electricity generation at 22.2 trillion kilowatt-hours. What fraction of the world's total energy was converted to electricity? Most power plants have an efficiency of around 33%, i.e., only one-third of the energy is converted to electricity while the rest is dumped into the atmosphere as waste heat.

23. The 747-400ER wide-body commercial jetliner can accommodate 416 passengers. It carries 63,500 gallons of fuel (240,370 L), covering a distance of over 8,350 miles. A Toyota Camry has a fuel efficiency of 30 mpg on freeway driving and can carry the driver and three passengers. Which of the two modes of transport is more efficient, in terms of miles per gallon, per person?

24. Compare the kinetic energy of a bullet weighing 20 grams moving at the speed of 400 m/s and the energy contained in the same mass of gunpowder. The energy density of a gram of gunpowder is 3 kJ/g. Which one is greater? What makes a bullet so deadly when it strikes a victim?

25. A hairdryer with a power rating of 1,500 watts is used for 10 minutes every morning. What is the annual electricity cost of using the hairdryer? The utility charges are, on average, $0.13 for every kilowatt-hour.

ⓐ Unit Conversion

26. What are the appropriate prefixes for powers of 10^{-9}, 10^{-6}, 10^{-3}, 10^{-2}, 10^{3}, 10^{6}, 10^{9}, 10^{12}, 10^{15}, and 10^{18}?

27. A man weighs 220 lb. What is his mass in kilograms and pounds? How much does he weigh in newtons?

28. The speed of light in a vacuum is given as 3×10^{8} m/s in the SI system of units. Express this in km/h, ft/s, and mph.

29. A candy bar has 100 Calories. What is its food energy content in joules?

30. What pressure does a 60-kg woman wearing high-heels exert on a wooden floor? Assume the woman's hills have a total surface area of 0.5 cm².

31. Gas companies charge customers for the number of therms per number of therms (100,000 Btu) they consume. Electric utilities charge customers by kWhs. Assuming the price of one therm of gas is $7.00, and one kWh of electricity is $0.15, which source of energy is more expensive? Can you justify the reason for the price differential?

32. An electric motor is rated as 30 kW. Express its power in hp?

33. The normal core body temperature of a healthy human adult is 98.6°F. Express this temperature in °C and K.

34. A car is traveling at 70 mph when it suddenly brakes until it stops 4 s later. What is the deceleration in ft/s² and m/s²?

35. Assuming an average 2,000 square-foot house in a moderate climate takes about 20,000 Btu/hr to heat, what is the daily cost of heating the house using a) natural gas, b) kerosene, c) electricity, d) coal, and e) open wood fire, given that:
    a. One therm of natural gas (100,000 Btu) costs $1.10.
    b. One gallon of heating oil costs $4.10
    c. One kWh of electricity costs $0.13
    d. One metric ton of anthracite coal costs $200.00
    e. A cord of wood (2500 lbs) costs $250.00

36. A large house is estimated to lose heat at a rate of 55,000 kJ/h. Compare the daily cost of heating this house if the heater is operating continuously and we use: a) an electric heater? a natural gas heater? Assuming natural gas costs an average of $1.50/therm, and electricity costs an average of $0.15 per kWh.

37. Start from the fundamental definitions to find the conversion factor between kWh and J.

III. Multiple Choice Questions

1. The rocket motor of a space probe is switched off when the probe reaches outer space where the gravitational field strength is negligible.
   a. The rocket decelerates until it comes to rest.
   b. The rocket will continue to accelerate forwards.
   c. The rocket will move at a constant velocity.
   d. The rocket will follow a curved path.
   e. The rocket will reverse direction.

2. The force that slows things down is
   a. Friction
   b. Centripetal force
   c. gravity
   d. Inertia
   e. Any of the above

3. How could you tell if a moving object is receiving an unbalanced force?
   a. It might deform.
   b. It might speed up.
   c. It might slow down.
   d. It might change direction.

e. It could be any of the above.

4. According to Newton's Second Law
   a. Acceleration = force / mass
   b. Acceleration = velocity / time
   c. Momentum = mass x volume
   d. Momentum = mass x acceleration
   e. Inertia = mass

5. A slope surface of 9 m in length is raised by1.5 m. This ramp acts as a simple machine with a
   a. A slope surface of 9 m in length is raised by1.5 m. This ramp acts as a simple machine with a Mechanical efficiency of 6
   b. Mechanical efficiency of 60%
   c. Mechanical Advantage of 6
   d. Mechanical Advantage of 9
   e. Mechanical Advantage of 1/6

6. If the speed of an object is doubled, then its kinetic energy is
   a. Doubled.
   b. Quadrupled.
   c. Halved.
   d. Tripled.
   e. It depends on the magnitude of the force.

7. Work is, by definition:
   a. Force multiplied by the time during which it is exerted.
   b. Force multiplied by the distance in the direction that the force is applied.
   c. Equivalent to power/time.
   d. Force times velocity.
   e. Mass times acceleration.

8. In the language of mathematics
   a. Displacement = work/force
   b. Force = work × displacement
   c. Force = displacement/work
   d. Work = force/displacement
   e. Work = displacement/force

9. If a car is going 5 miles an hour and hits an immovable concrete wall, it suffers a certain amount of damage. If, however, the car hits head on a similar car moving in the opposite direction, then that is like hitting the wall at
   a. 20 mph
   b. 10 mph.
   c. 5 mph.
   d. 0 mph.
   e. None of the above.

10. Which of the following objects possesses mechanical energy?
    a. A car traveling on a flat surface
    b. A car going downhill
    c. A drawn bow ready to be released
    d. A book sitting on the top of a bookshelf
    e. All of the above

11. Which of the following statements is true?
    a. Power is the rate of energy expenditure per unit of time.
    b. Power can be calculated as the product of force times velocity.
    c. Power can be expressed in watts or horsepower.
    d. Power refers to the work done to complete a task.
    e. (a) through (c) but not (d).

12. There are 100 steps to get from the ground floor of a building to its rooftop. Person A walks up to the roof in 100 footsteps, while person B climbs up, skipping every other step. It takes person A two minutes to reach the top, while person B does it in half the time. From the information provided, one can deduce that
    a. Both A and B perform the same amount of work, but A delivers more power than B.
    b. Both A and B perform the same amount of work, but B delivers more power than A.
    c. A performed more work because he has to walk twice as many steps.
    d. B performed less work because it takes him a shorter time to make the climb.
    e. B performed less work because he only has to work half the time.

13. Which of the following statements is true?
    a. Pulleys and ramps allow for the lifting of heavy objects with less work.
    b. Pulleys and ramps allow for the lifting of heavy objects because the same work can be performed over larger distances.
    c. Pulleys and ramps allow for the lifting of heavy objects because the same work can be performed at a slower rate.
    d. Pulleys and ramps allow for the lifting of heavy objects because they perform the same task with less force.
    e. Both b and d.

14. The "Golden Rule" of mechanics implies that
    a. Whatever you lose in power, you gain in displacement.
    b. Whatever you lose in energy, you gain in power.
    c. Whatever you lose in power, you gain in time.
    d. Whatever you lose in energy, you gain in

displacement.

e. None of the above.

15. Which of the following involves the conversion of kinetic energy?
    a. An automobile lifted by a hydraulic jack
    b. Water sitting on a reservoir on top of a mountain
    c. A rubber ball being squeezed
    d. A turbine being turned by a falling waterfall
    e. None of the above

16. Mechanical advantage is
    a. The same as mechanical efficiency.
    b. The ratio of applied force to force exerted by a machine.
    c. The factor by which a machine multiple the force.
    d. Always smaller than one.
    e. Always greater than mechanical efficiency.

17. The main function of simple machines is to multiply
    a. The force.
    b. The work.
    c. Power.
    d. Energy.
    e. All of the above.

18. What type of simple machine is the bottle opener?
    a. Lever
    b. Wheel and axle
    c. Pulley
    d. Inclined plane
    e. Wedge

19. A roller skate is an example of a
    a. Lever.
    b. Ramp.
    c. Wedge.
    d. Wheel and axle.
    e. None of the above.

20. A seesaw is an example of a
    a. Lever.
    b. Ramp.
    c. Wedge.
    d. Wheel and axle.
    e. None of the above.

21. When a claw hammer is used to pull a nail out of a piece of wood, it acts as a
    a. Wedge.
    b. Lever.
    c. Ramp.
    d. Pulley.
    e. None of the above.

22. A saw is an example of a

a. Ramp.
b. Lever.
c. Wedge.
d. Screw.
e. None of the above.

23. A wheelbarrow is
    a. A simple machine of the first kind.
    b. A simple machine of the second kind.
    c. A simple machine of the third kind.
    d. Is not a simple machine.
    e. Is not a lever.

24. A few examples of first kind levers are:
    a. Shovel, tong, and human arm
    b. Sea-saw, crowbar, and a pair of scissors
    c. Wheelbarrow and nutcrackers
    d. Shovel, sea-saw, and nutcrackers
    e. None is a first kind lever

25. Which of the following can be represented by the same units?
    a. Work, torque, and acceleration
    b. Work, torque, and kinetic energy
    c. Force, torque, and energy
    d. Force, power, and torque
    e. None of the above

26. The relationship of energy to power is like
    a. Miles to miles per hour.
    b. Force to velocity.
    c. Distance to time.
    d. Kilowatt to kilowatt-hour.
    e. Oil to electricity.

27. The SI system of units is preferable to the USCS system because
    a. The SI system is easier to use.
    b. SI units are independent of the location of the measurement.
    c. The SI system has been universally accepted by the scientific community.
    d. The SI system is finally adopted by the United States.
    e. a through c, but not d.

28. 1 Pa =
    a. 1 N.m
    b. 1 N/m
    c. 1 N/m^2
    d. J/s
    e. 1 J.s

29. What is the force required to accelerate a mass of 1 kg by 1 m/s^2?
    a. 1 W

b. 1 J
c. 1 J
d. 1 N
e. W.s

30. The weight of a bag of apples with a mass of 1 kg measured on earth is
    a. 1 J.
    b. 1 kg.
    c. 1 N.
    d. 9.81 kg.
    e. 9.81 N.

31. A bag of apples weighs one pound. Its mass is
    a. 1/32.2 lbm.
    b. 32.2 lbm.
    c. 1 lbm.
    d. 1 lbf.
    e. 1 slug.

32. A million people each have one million dollars. Their total assets are
    a. $ 2 M.
    b. $ 1 B.
    c. $ 1 G.
    d. $ 1 T.
    e. $ 1 P.

33. One-thousandth of one microsecond is
    a. 1 ms.
    b. 1 μs.
    c. 1,000 μs.
    d. 1 ns.
    e. 1 ps.

34. The energy needed to run a one-watt LED light for one hour is
    a. One watt per hour.
    b. One watt-hour.
    c. One watt.
    d. One joule.
    e. None is correct.

35. A light-year is a measure of
    a. Time
    b. Distance
    c. Sun's solar activity
    d. Annual electrical consumption
    e. None of the above.

36. How do your mass and weight change if you travel to Mars? Gravity on Mars is 38% of that on Earth.
    a. Your mass increases, but your weight remains the same.
    b. Your weight increases, but your mass remains the same.
    c. Neither your mass nor your weight change.
    d. Your mass remains the same but your weight decreases.
    e. Both your mass and weight increase.

IV. **True or False?**

1. Whenever a force undergoes a displacement, work is performed.
2. A golf ball drops faster than a Ping-Pong ball because it is heavier and experiences a stronger force of gravity.
3. An object has a zero weight only if it is placed in an environment where gravitational acceleration is zero.
4. If a dumbbell weighs 5 pounds on earth, then the Earth also weighs 5 pounds in the gravitational field of the dumbbell.
5. Mechanical efficiency is the percentage of input work that can be converted to output work.
6. Unlike mechanical efficiency, the mechanical advantage may or may not be greater than one.
7. Torque is a measure of the amount of force that is required to rotate an object.
8. When there is no friction, the sum of potential and kinetic energies remains constant.
9. In the metric system of units, torque measurements are usually given in newton-meters.
10. Torque is calculated by multiplying the force by the lever arm it is acting upon.
11. A wedge can be seen as a two-sided ramp with surfaces to distribute the load.
12. Machines are designed to reduce work.
13. The human body can be viewed as a machine that consumes food and converts it into mechanical work and heat.
14. Mechanical efficiency is defined as the ratio of input to output work.
15. In an ideal machine, the output work and the input work are equal.
16. Pulleys always multiply the force.
17. The more energy we consume, the more power we produce.
18. In a pendulum, potential and kinetic energies continuously convert back and forth.
19. To apply a higher torque, we must always use more force.
20. Any machine, no matter how complex, can always be reduced to a series of simple machines.

PROJECT I -- The Mountain of Pharaoh

The pyramids of Egypt were built to enshrine the pharaohs after their deaths. The ancient Egyptians believed that the pharaohs held the key to the afterlife for everyone, and the pyramids symbolize this strong belief. The most impressive of the Egyptian pyramids and one of the Seven Wonders of the World is the Great Pyramid of Giza. Its construction was commissioned around 2550 BCE by King Khufu of the Fourth Dynasty. The pyramid was constructed using around two million blocks of stone, each weighing an average of 2.5 tons. The heaviest blocks weighed 40 to 60 tons and were used in constructing the ceiling of the burial chamber. It has been estimated that it took 20,000 to 25,000 slaves to build the pyramid.

Possibly the oldest structure in existence, the Great Pyramid took about 20 years to build. Its base covers 13.6 acres (55,000 meters squared); at 145 m tall, it was the tallest structure in the world until the Eiffel Tower was built in 1889.

You are asked to research the probable methods that Egyptians used to build the pyramids. Carry out a simple calculation to determine the amount of energy that was expended to build the Great Pyramid of Giza. Assuming that an average man could put out 100 watts of power continuously, estimate the number of slaves it took to work 12 hours per day, over the entire year, to finish the job in 20 years.

Explain any discrepancies with data you may find in other literature. Discuss different theories on achieving this task, and comment on their feasibility.

Hint: Energy can be estimated as the amount of mass that had to be lifted from the ground to its center of mass -- the weight of the pyramid times the height of the centroid above the base. The volume and the height of the center of mass of the pyramid are $V = a^2h/3$; and $z = h/4$.

PROJECT II -- Energy Expenditure During a Climb

In this project, you are asked to calculate the amount of work done and energy consumed during a climb to the top of a six-story building. To perform this assignment, you are asked to climb up from the first floor to the roof of a six-story building twice, once at a slow rate and the second time at a faster rate.

Note the following data:
1. Your mass in kilograms.
2. The number of stairs and the average height of each stair (in meters).
3. The time it took you to climb the stairs. Take the average of the two runs
4. The time it took you to descend to the first floor. Take the average of the two runs

Now, answer the following questions:
    a. What was the total height that you climbed?
    b. What was your average speed?
    c. What was the force used to perform the climb?
    d. What is the work needed to overcome the gravitational potential energy?
    e. How much energy did you burn during the climb? Note that the actual work is a lot more (by about a factor of four) than the work of gravity. Additional energy is necessary to power your muscles, nourish and repair cells, and maintain your body temperature.
    f. Calculate the average power consumption during each run by dividing work performed by the time it took you to climb (or descend) the stairs.
    g. Calculate the average power consumption during each run by multiplying your weight by your average velocity.
    h. In which instance did you perform more work -- climbing up slowly or quickly?
    i. Assuming the work performed in climbing up the stairs is used to generate electricity to turn on a 100-W fluorescent light, how long would the light stay on?

Source	Power (typical)	Power (actual)	Hours per day	Energy per day
Cooking Microwave Electric oven	 1,500 W 5,000 W			
Cleaning Dishwasher Washing machine Dryer Vacuum cleaner	 3,000 W 2,000 W 2,000 W 2,000 W			
Cooling Refrigerator Freezer Air conditioner Others	 _____ W _____ W 1,000 W -------			
Lighting Incandescent lights Fluorescent lights Low energy LEDs	 _____ × 2-10 W _____ × 5-20 W _____ × 30-100 W			
Various Computer Display Laptop Stereo amplifier Others Others	 50 W 30 W 16 W _____ _____			
Total				

CHAPTER 3

Fossil Fuels

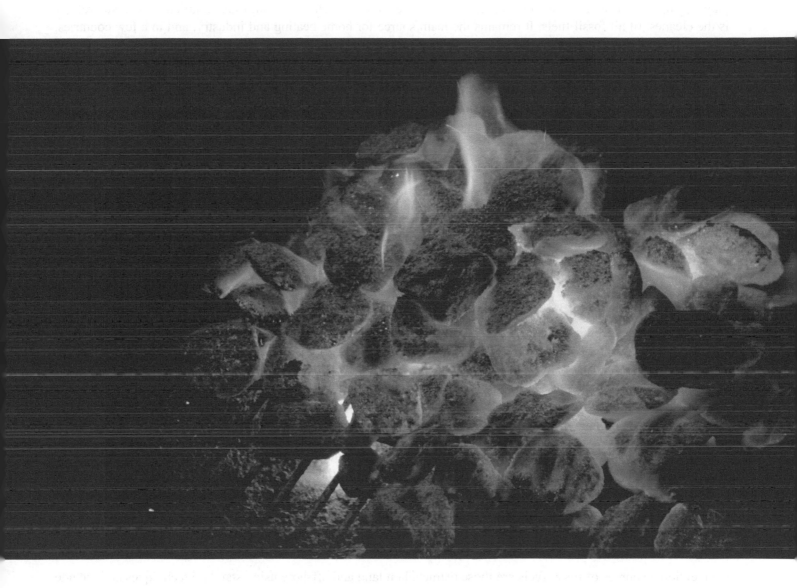

The Stone Age did not end because people ran out of stones -- it ended because they found something better.

~ *Zaki Yamani, Former Saudi Arabia's Oil Minister*

F ossil fuels are the most widely used form of energy in the world. They power practically every device we use and are used in every manufacturing application that we can imagine. Nearly 15 billion metric tons or 84% of all energy consumed every year comes from fossil fuels. The three largest consumers of energy, China, the United States, and India cumulatively consume over 54% of the fossil fuels in the world. Globally, crude oil supplies roughly 37% of the total primary consumption, coal accounts for 11%, and natural gas for 32%. The remaining 19% is from nuclear, hydro, and other forms of renewable energy.[1]

Coal is the most abundant and has been the fuel that powers nearly half the electricity produced. Oil will continue to play an important role in the world economy and will be the fuel of choice for all transportation needs. Natural gas is the cleanest of all fossil fuels. It remains the main source for home heating and industry, and in a few countries, a major source of transportation fuel. Natural gas is expected to substitute dirtier coal in many power generation facilities.

As current supplies of conventional fossil fuels are exhausted, they are substituted with unconventional forms of fossil fuels, such as oil shale, tar sands, shale gas, and synthetic oil. Unfortunately, these resources are also responsible for much of the air pollution and a great contributor to global warming.

What Is a Fossil Fuel?

Fossil fuel refers to the remains of animals, plants, or other life forms (biotic or biogenic) that have been protected from decomposition and oxidation for a very long time and that can be burned as a source of energy.[*] Imprints of leaves and marine species on fossils, branches in coal, and ambers containing remains of flies and other organic matter have often been cited as evidence (Figure 3-1). Since the source of these materials is living matter, they have the same composition as living organisms -- fats, oils, paraffin, carbohydrates, and proteins. Fats and oils are organic compounds that, like carbohydrates, are composed mainly of the elements carbon and hydrogen, with a H/C ratio increasing from solid to liquid to gaseous fuels: coal (~0.75), tar sand (1.5), oil shale (1.6), crude oil (~1.7), and methane (4.0).[2] Sulfur, phosphorus, and metals are not considered fossils because they do not originate from organic matter.

Figure 3-1
Fossil fuels are formed from remains of live plants and animals.

Contrary to popular belief, fossil fuels are not the remains of dinosaurs; in fact, most fossil fuels were formed millions of years before the first dinosaurs lived, mainly in areas that were once lush and housed many forms of plants and animals. The most likely sources are ancient trees, animals, fish, and tiny organisms that flourished in the oceans, died, and sank to the bottom. Marshlands, bogs, subtropical and tropical swamps, lakes, lagoons, and river deltas are ideal sites. The intense pressure and heat from deep inside the earth caused the decomposition of matter and gradually converted into what we call fossil fuels.

Conventional sources of fossil fuels are those extracted on land and offshore using standard techniques and include coal, oil, and natural gas. The United States is blessed with the largest amount of coal in the world, Russia has the most natural gas, but it is the Middle East, however, that is endowed with the largest volume of oil, the most desirable form of all fossil fuels.

In addition to conventional reserves, other forms of hydrocarbon -- tar sands, oil shale, and shale gas -- also are in large supply, but because of their high costs of production and adverse environmental impacts, their use, has been

* Although most scientists suggest the origin of petroleum in organic matters, some Russian scientists suggest an abiogenic with inorganic origin dating back to the early formation of the Earth. To support their argument, they point to the finding of petroleum in wells drilled down to 30,000 feet and more, but that deepest fossil ever found has been at depth of only 16,000 feet [See, for example, Kudryavstev, (1951). Against the organic hypothesis of petroleum origins, *Petroleum Economy, 9*, Moscow, pp.17] A relatively recent article seems to support this view. [Proskurowski et al., (2008). Abiogenic Hydrocarbon Production at Lost City Hydrothermal Field, *Science, 319* (5863), pp. 604-607.].

Fossil Fuels: The Facts (2016)

- At the current rates of production, world coal deposits are to last 114 years, oil for 51 and conventional gas for another 53 years.
- Over 95% of all U.S. fossil fuels are still intact in the form of coal.
- Contrary to popular belief, the major supplier of crude oil to the United States is not Saudi Arabia. It is Canada!
- Russia, Saudi Arabia and the U. S. are the largest producer of natural gas, petroleum, and coal in the world.
- Canada's tar sand reserves can yield more oil than Saudi Arabia.

Source: BP Statistical Review of World Energy, 2016

limited. As conventional resources deplete, we may need to tap into these resources to satisfy demand in the 21st century.

Carbon Cycle

Carbon is present in the form of carbon dioxide in the atmosphere or dissolved in ocean water, and trapped in sedimentary rocks. Through the process of photosynthesis, carbon dioxide, and water vapor, in the presence of sunlight of appropriate frequency, combine to produce carbohydrates, the building block of all living organisms (See Chapter 11). Depending on conditions that dead animals and plants are exposed to, carbon may return to the atmosphere as carbon dioxide or turn into fossil fuel (Figure 3-2). That is, if the environment dries up, organic matter will become exposed to air and react with it to produce carbon dioxide, thus completing the carbon cycle; if the environment is flooded with mud, stagnant water, silt, or sand, and oxygen is cut off, over millions of years, it compacts into organic-rich sedimentary rocks called **kerogen**[†] or breaks down in high-temperature pyrolysis into a black, tar-like, highly-viscous substance called **bitumen**, two precursors to the formation of different forms of fossil fuels.

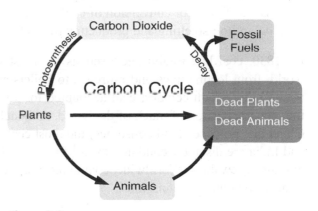

Figure 3-2
Carbon cycle in the atmosphere.
Adapted from Energy and Fuel in Society, by Radovic and Schobert, McGraw-Hill 1992.

Whether a fossil ultimately ends up as coal, oil, or gas depends on the original constituents of the kerogen, the length of time, and the geological conditions where it is buried. If the origin of kerogen is from giant terrestrial woody plants and stronger parts (trunks, roots, and branches) of trees, then carbon forms into very complicated cellulosic structures and rings that eventually bond into a graphitic structure called coal. If the kerogen is formed from marine organisms, algae, or prehistoric plankton (microscopic animals and plants lived in oceans), it breaks into shorter chains that, depending on their lengths, become a mixture of liquids and gases. The deeper in the earth (higher pressure and temperature) and more aged the kerogen, the greater the probability that the chains will break into lighter materials, and a higher fraction of the kerogen will be in the form of oil and natural gas. In addition to coal, oil, and natural gas, kerogen and bitumen can find their way into, and mix with, sand, water, and clay to form tar sands, oil shale, and gas shale.

Question: How can we make hydrocarbons renewable?
Answer: By accelerating the rate of conversion of carbon dioxide to carbohydrate to match the rate of its release into the atmosphere. Scientists are, therefore, hooked on finding plants that can grow as fast as they are being used. One possibility is algae -- burn the algae at the power plant, capture that carbon dioxide and pump it back into the greenhouse, and grow more algae.

---

† *Keros* is the Greek word for wax, and *gen* means more.

Coal

Coal has been used longer than any other form of fossil fuel. Even early cavemen used coal (nicknamed **black rock**) for heating purposes. Because of its abundance and its cheap price, wood was, however, the dominant energy source for much of the world until the sixteenth century. In the early seventeenth century, after many forests had been cleared and wood became scarce, coal substituted for wood as the main source of fuel. The coal extracted from shallow seams was high in sulfur and burned with an irritating smell but at higher temperatures than wood, which made it more desirable, not only for home heating but also for the smelting of iron and other metals. The Industrial Revolution brought rapid growth in agriculture, textiles, metal manufacturing, and transportation. As the economy grew, so did the need for raw materials and new goods that accelerated the cutting of wood; coal's prominence as the dominant form of energy became clear.

By the late eighteenth century, the steam engine had become the primary method of producing power throughout Europe. Manufacturing these engines required smelting of iron, possible only by utilizing large quantities of charcoal's intense heat. Charcoal was produced by burning wood, which fast was becoming scarce throughout Europe. A new process was found for conversion of coal to *coke* which burned cleaner and at higher temperatures, and substituted charcoal in iron-smelting and production of steel.[3]

By 1830, coal had established itself as the most valuable commodity that fueled every aspect of the industrial world, from locomotives and railroads to boilers and heavy machinery. Coal's glorious march continued, and by the early twentieth century, coal accounted for 90% of all energy supplies in the world and the key ingredient in the industrialization of much of the world. Although the U.S. has the greatest amount of reserves in the world, it is China that produces (and consumes) the most coal, more than all the other countries combined. The United States and India are distant second and third.[4] Europe and Japan are reducing their use of coal in favor of cleaner natural gas and renewables. Worldwide, coal plants are responsible for 40 percent of electricity generation and one-quarter of all carbon dioxide emissions.

Formation

Coal is a sedimentary rock found underground in layers that range in thickness from a few centimeters to several meters. The first stage of coal formation involves the accumulation of dead vegetable and organic matter in a swamp where the stagnant water prevents oxidation of the organic matter and decomposes anaerobically. Under the heavy weights of water and ground, the carbonaceous material gradually turns into a dark-brown, compact material known as *peat*. Peat is a class of kerogen with a high C/H ratio. Over time, peat is compressed and heated to form *lignite (brown coal)*. Lignite is soft, brownish-black coal, containing about 30% carbon. It is also of the lowest quality and the most abundant type of coal in the world. Traces of the texture of the original wood may even be found in pieces of lignite. At greater depths, lignite is transformed into *bituminous (soft coal)* and, ultimately, *anthracite (hard coal)*. Therefore, one expects to find anthracite in very old deposits in deep layers and lignite in the younger deposits, and in those closer to the surface.

Quality of Coal

The quality of coal is typically categorized by its rank. The **rank** of the coal represents its morphological development from peat to lignite, sub-bituminous, bituminous, and ultimately, anthracite. The higher the coal is ranked, the greater is its carbon content, resulting in more energy being liberated when it is burned (Table 3-1). In addition to its rank, coal can be classified by its grade. Better

Table 3-1 Coal Ranks and Their Properties			
Rank	*Age (million years)*	*Carbon Content*	*Heating Value * (kJ/kg)*
Anthracite	350	85-95%	35,000 and up
Bituminous	300	45-85%	25,000-35,000
Sub-bituminous	100	35-45%	20,000-25,000
Lignite	60	25-35%	10,000-20,000
Higher heating values.			

grades have less sulfur and burn with fewer emissions and less ash. The grade of the coal can be improved by removing the impurities through the cleaning or other chemical processes.

Anthracite has the highest carbon content and produces more heat for the same mass. It also contains less sulfur and moisture. Bituminous and sub-bituminous coals are of medium quality, and lignite is of the lowest quality, has the highest moisture content, and has relatively low energy content.

Reserves

Only five countries, the U.S., Russia, China, Australia, and India, own three-quarters of all world coal reserves – estimated at 1,055 billion metric tons (Table 3-2). Despite what one might expect, there are no coal mines in the Middle East. The U.S.'s reserves are estimated at 250 billion metric tons, with more than half of them in only three states: Wyoming, West Virginia, and Kentucky. Anthracite is most commonly found in Pennsylvania and accounts for only 1% of U.S. coal reserves. About 90% of coal is bituminous and sub-bituminous, and the rest is essentially lignite. Eastern and mid-continent coalfields contain mostly bituminous coal, while sub-bituminous coal is predominantly found in the Western states. Most lignite is mined in Texas, Montana, and North Dakota. Figure 3-3 shows a map of major coalfields in the United States. At the current rate of consumption, U.S. coal reserves will last another 150 to 300 years.

Table 3-2 Major Prven Coal Reserves (2018)		
Country	Total Recoverable Reserves (Billion metric tons)	Percentage of the total
U. S.	250	23.7
Russia	160	15.2
Australia	147	14.0
China	139	13.2
India	101	9.6
Rest of the World	215	35.5
Total	1055	100

Source: BP Statistical Review of world Energy, June 2019.

Extraction

Depending on how deep it is buried, and the local geology, coal can be extracted by surface (open-cast) or underground (deep) mining. **Surface mining** involves the removal of soil to access buried coal seams (Figure 3-4). *Area mining* applies to shallow mines where the surface is relatively flat. *Contour mining* refers to surface mines on steep hills or mountainous regions.

Underground mining is done by one of two methods: room-and-pillar and longwall mining. In *room-and-pillar mining*, coal is mined by cutting a network of "rooms" into the seam. Up to half of the coal is extracted in this manner, leaving the other half (pillars) to support the weight of the roof. As drills retreat, the standing pillars are removed, allowing the roof to collapse. In *longwall mining*, essentially all the coal contained in a large rectangular block or "panel" of coal is excavated.[5] As coal cutting machines run back

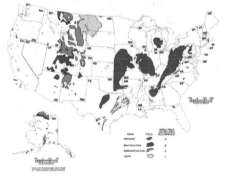

Figure 3-3
American Coal Fields.
Source: EIA/DoE

and forth along the face, they cut coal of about one meter thick during each pass. According to the World Coal Association, surface mining accounts for roughly two-thirds of U.S. coal production but only 40 percent of global coal production. The remainder is from underground mining.

Processing

Once it was extracted, coal is loaded on a chain conveyor and transported out of mine and onto large trucks or railroad cars for cleaning and processing (Figure 3-5). Since coal is formed primarily underneath swamp beds, it contains a large amount of sulfur. Coal preparation consists of a pretreatment process to wash, crush and grind coal, and then to separate undesirable mineral-rich parts.[6] Different methods are used for desulfurization that includes physical, chemical, and biological processes.[7] *Physical cleaning* techniques exploit either difference in specific gravity or surface properties between the organic matter and the associated minerals. Since sulfur is heavier than coal, most of it sinks to the bottom and is removed. *Chemical cleaning* techniques involve leaching with oxidizing or alkaline solutions at high temperatures. *Biological cleaning* relies on microorganisms that "eat up" sulfur without affecting carbon content.

Figure 3-4
Strip mining.

Although most sulfur is removed during preparation processes, the coal still contains considerable amounts of sulfur which, when burned, produces sulfur dioxide. Modern power plants use wet or dry scrubbers to remove the remaining sulfur in their smokestacks before it is released into the atmosphere. In wet scrubbers, limestone slurry is sprayed onto the flue gases where it combines with sulfur to form a paste that is left behind. Dry scrubbers consist of a fixed sorbent bed of activated carbon, char, and alumina impregnated with copper. Large bag houses remove larger particles, while electrostatic precipitators filter smaller particulates.

Figure 3-5
Coal trains can be as much as one and a half miles long, and are made up of 125-150 cars each weighing about 100 tons.

Petroleum

The term petroleum (nicknamed **black gold**) comes from the Latin roots *petra*, "rock," and *oleum*, "oil"; it literally means rock oil and refers to gaseous, liquid, or solid hydrocarbons found beneath the Earth's surface, under very high pressures and temperatures. The solid and semi-solid forms of petroleum are called asphalt and tar; the liquid form is usually referred to as crude, although many use the words petroleum to mean crude oil. **Liquids** encompass petroleum and petroleum products substitutes such as crude oil, condensates, biofuels, natural gas liquids, and products of liquefaction of coal (See below).

Crude oil is composed of a multitude of hydrocarbons consisting of paraffin, aromatics, and more complex molecules containing carbon, hydrogen, and oxygen, in addition to traces of metals. It is not only a convenient source of energy for generating electricity and powering our cars but also the main ingredient in much of the plastics, waxes, medicines, cosmetics, solvents, lubricants, feedstock, and a host of other petrochemical products we use in our daily lives. In fact, because of its limited availability, many consider petroleum to be too valuable to be used in transportation, heating, or generating electricity.

Petroleum Geology

Geologists' search for petroleum involves a detailed understanding of the types and structure of rocks, their depths, pressures and temperature distributions underground. For petroleum to form, several conditions must be met. Various elements necessary for the accumulation of large quantities of petroleum include a source rock, a porous reservoir rock, and a trap. The main purpose of **traps** is to prevent oil and gas from leaking away. Layers of rocks folded to create a dome and rocks next to fault lines are ideal. Unlike coal, oil and gas can diffuse through porous rocks and escape to the surface.

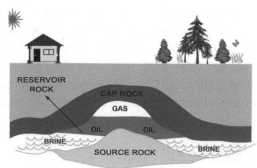

Figure 3-6
Underground reservoir.

To form petroleum, organic-rich matter, kerogen or other plant and animal remains must be deposited, over a long period of time -- many millions of years -- in what is called a **source rock**. A good petroleum source rock is sedimentary rock such as shale or limestone with sufficient porosity buried deep enough underground to provide intense heat and pressure for chemical reactions to occur. Once the petroleum is formed, it must be able to migrate to the reservoir rock. **Reservoir rocks** are rocks with sufficient *porosity* (large pore sizes to hold petroleum), and *permeability* (pores are interconnected, to allow gas and oil to flow through them). Reservoir rocks are predominantly sedimentary (sandstones and carbonates). Limestone, dolomites, and salt with smaller pore sizes can also work, but often require fracturing to increase permeability. Large reservoirs are formed only if the migration is stopped and oil and gas are trapped by the impermeable **cap rocks**. Common types of caprock are sandstone. Faults often cause movements of the rock layers blocking gas and oil passing through the fault boundary. Since there is always some water and salt present, the oil is usually found above a pool of brine. Natural gas is the lightest and accumulates above the oil (See Figure 3-6).

History of Oil Exploration in the United States

Although oil has found its proper place in the world for only the last century, it has been known to man as a useful product for a very long time. As early as 3000 BCE, oil was used in Mesopotamia (current Iraq) as caulking to seal the cracks of buildings and joints in boats. The Egyptians used oil as a lubricant for their chariots, and the Romans used it to light their arrows before launching them at enemies.[8] The Greek historian, Herodotus, reported that by 600 BCE, oil in Persia was routinely extracted from wells that were only a few meters deep and brought to the surface by buckets and pulleys, and used for heating, lighting, making asphalt, and as weapons to set fire to enemy houses and garrisons.[9]

In 1852, the Canadian geologist, Abraham Gesner, succeeded in distilling kerosene from crude. Crude quickly replaced whale oil, which was more expensive, burned dirtier, smelled bad, and was less luminous. Gesner's kerosene was cheap, did not have the bad smell, and could be burned in existing lamps, and slowed the massive killing of whales that were nearing extinction.[10] The first commercial oil well in the United States was built by Colonel Edwin L. Drake (who was not a Colonel, but faked the title to get legitimacy in the eyes of investors) in 1859 in Pennsylvania (Figure 3-7); it produced about 1,000 gallons per day. Within one year, 2,000 new oil wells were dug and a new industry was born. The oil boom in Pennsylvania did not last very long as wells dried up within a few years; Drake went bankrupt and died a few years later.

Figure 3-7
"Colonel" Edwin Drake first commercial oil well in Pennsylvania.

In 1864, a young entrepreneur, John David Rockefeller, purchased his first oil refinery in Cleveland, Ohio. As the Civil War ended and the country was becoming industrialized, Rockefeller saw the opportunity and bought more and more refineries. He eventually acquired control over every stage of oil production, from extraction to retail, including transportation, research, marketing, and even the manufacturing of barrels. In 1870, he combined his smaller companies into the Standard Oil Company and offered shares to the public. Being the largest customer of the railway industry, he managed to negotiate a favorable rate for transporting his crude, and manipulated the price of kerosene, forcing many competitors to close their shops, file for bankruptcy, or sell assets to Rockefeller's Company. By 1879, Rockefeller controlled 90% of all refinery operations and a quarter of all petroleum in the U.S. Threatened by his absolute control over the industry, several oil companies sued Rockefeller, claiming that Federal Law prevented Rockefeller from operating refineries outside of Ohio. Fearing the loss of control, Rockefeller established the Standard Oil Trust.[11]

On November 1, 1879, Thomas Edison was awarded a patent for his most famous invention, the "electric lamp." The switch to electricity (which was generated primarily by burning coal) could adversely impact oil demand and the price of crude. The concerns did not last very long, however, when Henry Ford introduced his automobile (the

A Brief History of the Contemporary Middle East: Oil and Blood

He who owns the oil, will own the world... ~ Henri Berenger, French Oil Minister in 1919.

European interest in the Middle East dates back to the 16th century when the Portuguese Navy seized the island of Hormuz in the Persian Gulf to control trade routes to India, China, and the African coast. In 1798, Napoleon crossed the Mediterranean Sea and overtook Egypt. The opening of the Suez Canal in 1869 provided Europeans with a shorter shipping route that expanded their trade and, with it, flaming the rivalry between two major European powers, France and Britain, for control of Egypt and later the rest of the Middle East. In 1872, Persia granted the British Baron Julius Reuter, the founder of the Reuters News Agency, a 70-year contract to operate the railway and exploit its minerals, including oil. This was followed by a second major concession in 1901, to another British financier, William Knox D'Arcy, which in exchange for a mere £20,000 and 16% of the profit, he was granted the exclusive right to explore oil and construct pipelines from anywhere in Persia to the Persian Gulf. In 1909, the Anglo-Persian Oil Company (later to be renamed British Petroleum) was established to oversee exploration and production. Because of strong Russian opposition, five northern provinces bordering Russia were excluded.[i] In 1908, major reservoirs of oil was discovered in Persia; shortly after that, the British fleet converted from coal to oil.

By the start of the 20th century, the British and French had seized much of the Ottoman Empire's Arab territory, including Egypt, Sudan, Algeria, Morocco, and Tunisia. Kuwait, Qatar, Oman, and other Gulf states had become British protectorates. The Ottomans, however, had a firm grip on the main Arabian (mainly Mesopotamia and Arabian Peninsula) oil fields. At the same time, internal combustion engines had been invented and oil had become a major source of contention in international affairs and as a major energy source driving the economy of the modern industrial world.

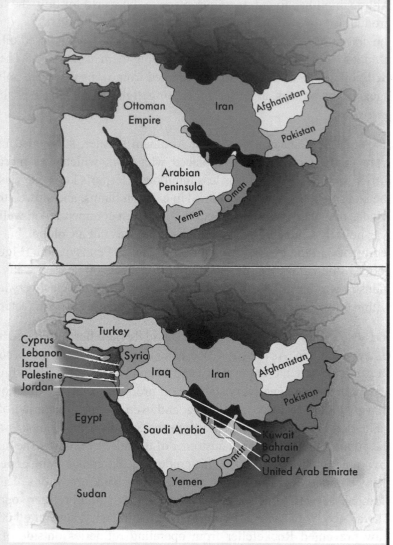

When World War I (WWI) began in 1914, the Ottoman Empire sided with the Austrians and Germans against the Allies, principally Britain and France. The Arab masses were left to decide between 500 years of Ottoman domination and European hegemony. As the Ottoman Empire weakened, the British sought the support of local Arab leaders, notably Hussein, the Sharif of Mecca, and his two sons, Faisel and Abdullah (later to become rulers of Saudi Arabia, Iraq, and Jordan), who fought alongside the British against the Ottomans.

In 1916, Britain and France secretly drafted the Sykes-Picot Agreement, in which the Arab world was divided into two spheres of influence; the Mediterranean coast was to be run by France, while Britain was to control Mesopotamia (current Iraq) and Greater Syria. Palestine would be under international administration. WWI ended in 1918, only after Allied bombings of Romanian oil fields, which effectively cut much of the petroleum supply route to Germany. Ottomans had lost control of the Middle East and the empire was reduced only to what is today's Turkey. The British had established bases in oil-rich Iraq and Kuwait Harbor.

The Paris Peace Conference (Conference of Versailles) in 1919 officially put an end to the war. A new map for the Middle East was drawn where Britain was to control the Arab Peninsula and a mandate to run Iraq, Palestine, and Egypt, while Syria and Lebanon became French protectorates. Except for the Russian oil, three companies -- Standard Oil, British Petroleum, and Royal Dutch Shell -- controlled almost all the petroleum production in the world.

After WWI, a bitter struggle for control of world oil reserves ensued. The British, French, and Dutch excluded U.S. companies' access to territories under their control. In 1920, Congress retaliated and passed the Mineral Leasing Act that punished those countries by denying them the right to produce oil in the United States. A settlement eventually was reached after all restrictions were removed by various parties to the conflict. To assure a secure and continuous supply of oil for the foreseeable future, the U.S. sought to establish ties with Middle Eastern oil exporters. In 1933, Standard Oil of California began exploration work in Saudi Arabia; it eventually merged with Esso (Exxon), Texaco, and Mobil and formed the California-Arabian Oil Company, later to be renamed the Arabian-American Oil Company (Aramco).

By 1939, Germany had to import more than 75% of its fuel from abroad. Only 8% of its consumption was from domestic oil fields, and the remainder was produced by syntheses of petroleum products from coal. Using the Fischer-Tropsch process, coal was compressed into gas, which then was mixed with hydrogen. Further treatment of this primary substance generated fuel, chiefly diesel oil. The fuel had an octane rating of only 40, not sufficiently high enough to be used as aviation fuel. Americans had, however, formulated tetraethyl lead, which raised the octane to a maximum of 87. Another invention in 1935 made it possible to produce isooctane with a rating of 100. This gave the crucial advantage to the U.S. and Britain in the form of air superiority -- one of the factors that helped them in reversing the outcome of the impending war.

The Second World War (WWII) of 1939-1945 was the German attempt to reverse the defeat it had suffered in WWI and fulfill its imperial ambition over Europe, Russia, and the Middle East. Its huge dependence on foreign oil supplies, the lack of hard foreign exchange for the purchase of oil,[ii] along with rampant rumors that the world proven reserves of petroleum were about to run out, Germany was set on securing its petroleum needs through military action and invaded the neighboring countries. Learning from its mistakes during WWI, Germany had to cut off the oil supply routes of the enemy. In 1941, Italian forces stationed in Libya invaded Egypt; the Germans followed suit and attacked the Suez Canal. Both attempts failed, however. In May 1941, the British took control of Iraq; Iranian oil fields were seized later that year. As the war dragged on and supplies diminished, Germany launched its ill-fated attack against Russia, at least in part, for the capture of oil fields in Grozny, Baku, and the Caucasus. As the Russian Army retreated, they destroyed all fuel supplies, denying Germans their much-needed fuel. Germany was eventually defeated and WWII ended in 1945. Ironically, the war had ended, once again, when Allied forces destroyed, sabotaged, or blockaded the Romanian oil fields and refineries in Ploesti.

At the time WWII ended, the Middle East produced slightly less than 5% of the world's oil supply; over 60% came from the U.S., which was providing virtually all oil for the Allied armies in World War II.[iii] In the years that followed, the U.S., Japan, and other Western Powers underwent a rapid economic expansion and, with it, their need for more Middle Eastern oil grew. The disillusionment of many Middle Eastern countries with the West and anger over what many considered the exploitation of their national resources mandated reform. Iran's nationalist Prime Minister nationalized its oil industry in 1951, a move that resulted in the Shah's departure from Iran, and instigated the subsequent 1953 coup that brought him back to power. In 1956, Egyptian president Gamal Nasser nationalized the Suez Canal. In 1958, a military coup overthrew the monarchy in Iraq. Ben Bella led Algerian independence in 1962. In 1979, the Iranian Revolution overthrew the monarchy. In September 1980, taking advantage of the turmoil in post-revolutionary Iran, Iraq invaded Iran, in part to seize control of the massive oil field on the Iran-Iraq border. The war lasted eight years and left an estimated one million dead before the war was finally over.

Having accumulated a debt of over $17 billion, Kuwait demanded unrestricted access to the Ramallah oil fields, 95% of which were in Iraq. New and superior technology in slanted oil drilling allowed Kuwait to extract oil and sell it below OPEC's official prices. In an effort to keep Kuwait from what he claimed were Iraqi oil reserves, Iraq invaded Kuwait in 1990, which subsequently led to the First and Second Gulf wars in 1991 and 2003.

To reduce dependence on Middle Eastern oil, ever since the Gulf Wars ended, the U.S. has made a special effort to tap into its unconventional oil and gas reserves. New technological advances in hydraulic fracturing and directional drilling—developed for natural gas production from shale formations enabled natural gas to be economically produced from shale and other unconventional formations and contributed to the United States becoming the world's largest natural gas producer in 2009. In the past, the oil and natural gas industry considered resources locked in tight, impermeable formations such as shale uneconomical to produce. The use of these technologies has also contributed to the rise in U.S. oil production over the last few years. In 2009, U.S. annual oil production increased over 2008, the first annual rise since 1991, and has continued to increase each year since. Between January 2008 and May 2014, U.S. monthly crude oil production rose by 3.2 million barrels per day, with about 85% of the increase coming from shale and related tight oil formations in Texas and North Dakota.[IV]

The rapid expansion of tight oil and shale gas extraction using high-volume hydraulic fracturing has raised, however, concerns about its potential environmental and health impacts. Concerns include potential adverse impacts to ground and surface water supplies, and to air quality. In addition, some have raised concerns about potential long-term and indirect impacts from reliance on fossil fuels and resulting greenhouse gas emissions and influence on broader energy economics. The environmental impact of conventional and unconventional oil and gas resources is discussed in some detail in Chapter 7.

i Shwadran, B. (1973) *The Middle East: Oil and the Great Powers*, 3rd ed., New York.

ii Becker, P. W. (1981).The Role of Synthetic Fuel in WWII Germany: Implication for Today?, Air & Space Power Journal. Jul-Aug.

iii Karam, P. A. (2020) Oil Discovered in the Middle East, Gales Science and Its Time.

Science Encyclopedias almanacs transcripts and maps.

iv Ratner, M. and Tiemann M., (2015) *An Overview of Unconventional Oil and Natural Gas: Resources and Federal Actions*, Congressional Research Service. <https://fas.org/sgp/crs/misc/R43148.pdf>.

horseless carriage), which was running on gasoline, a byproduct of the distillation of crude. Between 1900 and 1910, nearly half a million automobiles were sold and, with that, petroleum found its prominent place in the American economy, solidifying Rockefeller's control over the price of oil.

The new oil discovery in Texas in 1901 attracted thousands of wildcatters and entrepreneurs, which led to the formation of new, powerful oil companies, such as Gulf and Texaco.[12] Those companies challenged Standard Oil's monopolistic power and forced the government to file a lawsuit, accusing Standard Oil of artificially manipulating prices. In 1911, the Supreme Court ordered Standard Oil to break into several smaller companies.[‡] Soon thereafter, World War I was in full swing, concluding only when the Allies successfully blockaded Germany's oil supply routes and caused much of the German industry, trains, and military machines to come to a halt. WWI ended in 1918 only to reemerge 20 years later as WWII -- partly as a result of conflict over the control of major oil fields in Grozny, Baku, and Caucus Mountains (See Box "A Brief History of the Middle East: Oil and Blood").

As the process of rebuilding and industrialization accelerated after WWII, so did the U.S. appetite for new sources of fossil energy, and soon thereafter domestic resources were unable to meet the increasing demand, and our dependence on foreign oil grew. The nationalization of oil industries by several major oil-producing countries in the 1950s and 1960s and the emergence of the **Organization of Petroleum Exporting Countries** (OPEC) in 1960 established by five countries of Iran, Iraq, Kuwait, Saudi Arabia, and Venezuela as a major player in controlling world market raised new concerns over the long-term availability of oil reserves (Figure 3-8).[§]

In 1970, the Club of Rome, an international think-tank of scientists, economists, businessmen, and political leaders, commissioned a study and published *The Limits to Growth*,[13,14] and concluded that unless major steps were taken to limit population and slow industrialization, within a time span of fewer than 100 years much of the natural resources would be depleted, resulting in global economic crises, famine, and irreversible environmental damage.[¶]

The doomsday scenarios predicted by earlier forecasts seemed to become even more authentic in 1973, following the Arab-Israeli War and the oil embargo by OPEC, and again in 1979, as a result of the Iranian Revolution, and within a decade the price of oil increased sharply. Upon discovery of a vast amount of nonconventional oil, the price of oil dropped to an all-time low of $10.70 a barrel in 1998 again, but it started to soar again.[15] Higher oil prices brought windfall profits for oil companies, but also a major recession throughout the world. As the oil scare spread so did calls for the development of alternative sources of energy and higher efficiency. It also accelerated the search for new petroleum

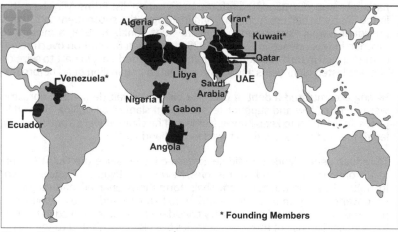

Figure 3-8
OPEC members.

resources which eventually, led to the discovery of new oil fields in the Caspian Sea, Africa, the North Sea, and Mexico; this caused oil prices to drop once again (Figure 3-9).[**]

---

‡   Standard Oil of New Jersey, Standard Oil of New York, Standard Oil of California, Standard Oil of Ohio (later taken over by BP), Standard Oil of Indiana (which became Amoco), Continental Oil (which became Conoco), and Atlantic Oil (which became Arco).

§   Since then, nine other nations (Algeria, Angola, Ecuador, Gabon, Indonesia, Libya, Nigeria, Qatar, and the United Arab Emirates) have joined the group .

¶   Models such as this are widely referred to as "pessimist," or "neo-Malthusian" models, after 1798's Thomas Rohr Malthus "Essay on the Principle of Population," who assumed population grows exponentially, but resources only linearly

** It should be noted that this point of view had its own critics. For example, Hermann Kahn, in his 1976 book, The Next 200 years: A Scenario for America and the World, 1976. argues that human ingenuity will, at the critical moments, intervene to devise technologies that can assure continuous development and better use of resources. Therefore, according to these technological optimists, resources are not finite but grow as needs arise. As we will argue throughout the book, we believe even with technological innovation and, at this time, additional unknown resources, the resources can eventually run out and we will, sooner or later, have to face the unwanted consequences of our resource mismanagement.

Figure 3-9
Crude oil real prices 1861 until 2018 .
Source: Natural Resources, T. Row Price.

To prevent prices from falling, OPEC cut production, putting an even greater burden on its member countries that heavily depended on oil revenues for their economic livelihoods. To boost their revenues, some countries actually sold their oil below-market prices and at volumes above the limit set by the organization. The problem became so widespread that OPEC lifted the quotas by the mid-1980s. Since then, OPEC has tried several times to manipulate prices by limiting production. Their attempts failed every time, however, because they could not agree on a unified pricing policy and because developed countries made the transition to other resources such as coal, gas, and nuclear power. A six-fold increase in population during the past century and higher energy demands by developing countries, along with the rapid depletion of fossil resources, resulted in new tensions that began with the 1991 invasion of Kuwait by Iraq, leading to the First Gulf War and continued with the U.S. invasion of Iraq in 2003.[††]

Recent technological advances in areas of horizontal drilling and seismic imaging technology (fracking), making unconventional energy sources accessible, and a cost, in line with conventional petroleum and gas production, lessening U.S. reliance on imported foreign oil. The rising demand for alternative and renewable energy sources has also helped reduce the hegemonic control of OPEC in fixing the oil prices, making it less relevant in dictating the global energy policies. Besides, oil exports account for a big chunk of these countries' GDP, and so these countries must sell up to the limit of their production capacity. This pushes prices down until a point that extracting unconventional resources are no longer competitive. Figure 3-10 shows the gap between import and export of petroleum since 1990. The difference between these two indicates the amount of petroleum the U.S. imports to make up for shortages in the domestic

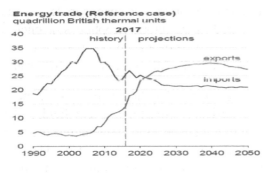

Figure 3-10
U.S. net import of petroleum.
Source: US Energy Information Agency, 2017.

supply. The gap was the largest in 2006, but has been decreasing ever since, and is on its way to becoming a net energy exporter by 2022. Several factors are contributing to this decline: more aggressive drilling, the switch to unconventional resources, such as oil sands and shale gas, a slow-down in the economy, and higher fuel efficiency for cars and trucks.

---

†† OPEC members collectively control 75% of the world's proven conventional oil reserves and produce 40% of the world's oil, but consume only 7% of the oil, themselves. Contrary to the public belief, Venezuela and not the Saudi Arabia, has the highest reserves of oil (conventional and nonconventional). The technology to pump the ultra-heavy crude is much more complicated, and as a result, it produces less oil than Saudi Arabia.

From Oil Well to the Gas Pump

Finding Oil

In the early days of oil exploration, few technologies could locate oil reservoirs precisely; they were mainly limited to the random drilling of exploratory oil wells (wildcats). Today, advances in geological science and the availability of new sensors make this process considerably more accurate. Although no one technology can be used to accurately verify the presence of oil or pinpoint its exact location, combinations of various technologies improve the probability of success. Petroleum discovery techniques have consistently become more precise, which increases the chance of finding new oil, while at the same time reduces drilling costs. In the 1970s, one in 25 exploration wells struck oil; today the odds of hitting petroleum or gas has increased to one in ten in high-risk "wildcat" wells, and typically to better than in one in three in other exploration activities.

Two technologies frequently used in geological mapping are the gravimetric and seismic methods.

The gravimetric surveying uses variations in the local earth's density as an indication of the presence of local deposits of coal, petroleum, or other ores. If the Earth were a sphere of uniform density, the gravitational forces would be the same everywhere. The force of gravity is not uniform, however, which indicates variation in density at different locations -- the stronger the gravity, the higher the density. Petroleum often is found in porous rocks, so the lower bulk density of a region relative to its neighboring strata can be an indication of existing porous structures and, thus, one indication of the presence of petroleum reserves. Today, it is possible to measure small variations of gravitational constant "g" with a gravity meter, which may prove to indicate the presence of oil deposits. A gravity meter is, essentially, a mass-spring system in which the frequency of the oscillation is a measure of the gravitational constant.

The seismic mapping exploits changes in the velocity of sound as it travels from one medium to another. Waves can propagate through a uniform medium indefinitely until they encounter a boundary or discontinuity and are reflected back. In the seismic exploration (depth sounding) technique, vibroseis vehicles (thumper trucks) initiate seismic signals by dropping heavy weights from a height of 2-3 meters on plates coupled to the ground and generate low-frequency signals. Alternatively, shock waves can be initiated by surface explosions in shot holes that propagate through the ground. The change in density (such as when it encounters oil or a coal deposit), is telegraphed back and measured by detectors (geophones or microphones) that are distributed at various locations around the detonation point. The time of arrival (velocity) and intensity (strength) of the reflected shocks are used to construct the 3-D geological map of the region and to determine the potential for the presence of oil and coal deposits.

In addition to gravitational and seismic methods, other techniques have been developed that monitor differences in the electrical resistance, magnetic field, and other properties of the surrounding rocks and porous media; liquids rich in petroleum have a much higher electrical resistance than brine and its surrounding rock. Data collected on density, conductivity, and other physical properties then can be used to construct 4-D geological maps (time is the fourth dimension) to track the motion of the fluid and improve chances of oil discovery and recovery.

Occasionally, oil wells are discovered below ocean surfaces and drilling must be carried out offshore. The process is similar to onshore drilling except that derricks must be mounted on platforms some distance away from the shorelines. Platforms can be built permanently and fixed, to the ocean floor or may float – anchored with wire rope and chains to the sea bottom. Offshore drilling is considerably more expensive, and in the case of spillage, poses a great potential danger to the marine environment and local ecosystem.

Recovery

Once geologists pinpoint the location of a potential oil reserve, drilling begins. To facilitate drilling oil derricks or drilling rigs are constructed and positioned directly above the wellbore. With luck, the well will reach the oil directly. If not, the well may have to be capped and another one drilled nearby. Tapping into brine and gas reservoirs won't help since any removal of these constituents from the well causes a reduction in reservoir pressure, making oil extraction more difficult. Earlier oil wells needed only a few meters of drilling. Today, we might have to dig many thousands of meters to find any oil, if at all. Advanced technologies are developed that make drilling tasks simpler, however.

New drill bits made with diamonds, have become harder and can cut through rocks and angles previously not feasible. Drill holes are also getting slimmer, which requires less dirt removal and disposal. *Directional drilling* has allowed searching for oil in depths of up to six kilometers and exploring areas previously inaccessible to geologists.

Initially, oil is under sufficiently high pressure, which causes it to gush out naturally and, therefore, no pumps are needed (flush production), but as more and more oil is extracted, a pumping facility may be needed to help maintain the flow of oil. The operation stops once the pressure has dropped below the settled production point. This is the **conventional method of production** and is called the *primary recovery* method. Roughly 10-20% of the oil can be extracted using this method. Beyond this point, additional oil can be recovered only by **enhanced oil recovery** techniques.[16] *Secondary recovery* involves injecting water, natural gas, or carbon dioxide[‡‡] into dead wells to displace the oil and raise the pressure or push the remaining oil into neighboring production wells, where it can be extracted (Figure 3-11). An additional 25-30% of the available oil can be recovered using the secondary technique; unfortunately, it raises the cost of oil production by 50-100%.

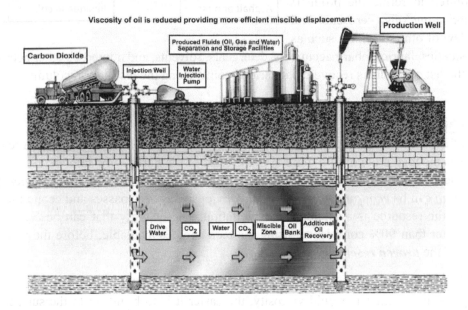

Figure 3-11
Enhanced oil recovery.
Image courtesy of NREL, Department of Energy.

The *tertiary recovery* technique relies on reducing oil viscosity. Viscosity is a measure of the ease with which a fluid flows; water has a very low viscosity, but honey's viscosity is high. Oil viscosity varies widely depending on its source. For example, heavy oil can be 100s to 1,000s of times more viscous than conventional oil. Viscosity can be reduced by raising the temperature, either by injecting superheated steam or by combustion. The common method is the cyclic steam injection (often referred to as the "huff and puff" process) to heat the oil that can flow underground. In the latter, a small underground detonation results in a shock wave that propagates across the oil deposit. The shock wave heats the oil and breaks it into smaller molecules, making it flow easier. Another 20-30% of the oil can be recovered using the tertiary method. The combined primary, secondary, and tertiary methods can recover about 50-60% of the oil deposit. Once these techniques are exhausted, the well is no longer usable and must be capped.

‡‡ This method called CO2 sequestration has been suggested as a plausible approach to remove greenhouse gases and combat global warming. We will come back to this in Chapter 7.

Refining

When extracted from the ground, crude oil is not pure but contains sand, water, and a number of minerals. The basic refining processes take place in the crude distillation unit; crude oil is heated to temperatures as high as 600°C and becomes a vapor. The vapor enters the bottom of a long atmospheric distillation tower and rises through the column and cools. When the temperature reaches the boiling temperature of one of the constituents, it will condense and be removed from the column and stored. The process called fractional distillation is continued until the crude is separated into its components. The lightest compounds condense at the top of the tower and are taken off as LPG (liquefied petroleum gas). Heavier hydrocarbons are removed at intermediate steps. Sand settles to the bottom of storage tanks and is easiest to remove. Other contaminants are removed by electric or chemical means. Further chemical processing is required to refine the products into gasoline, lubricating oils, kerosene, and chemicals for a slew of other products such as plastics, paint, cosmetics, fabrics, pharmaceuticals, detergents, solvents, and numerous other petrochemical products. Table 3-3 shows the list of products recovered at various points along the distillation column.

Table 3-3 Product of Petroleum Distillation			
Product	Molecular Structure	Boiling Point	Use
Gaseous fuels	C1-C4	-164 to 30	Gas stoves, RVs
Ether	C5-C7	30 to 90	Solvent
Gasoline	C5-C12	30 to 200	Motor fuel
Kerosene	C12-C16	175 to 275	Diesel and jet fuel
Fuel oil	C15-C18	Up to 375	Furnace
Greases	C18 and up	Semisolid	Lubricant
Paraffins (waxes)	C20 and up	Solid	Candles
Asphalt and tar	---	Residue in column	Roofing and paving

Resources and Reserves

Before delving further, we must distinguish between the reserves and resources that a certain region or country has. *Ultimate resource* is the total amount of a mineral in the crust of the Earth -- the known and predicted deposits that may or may not conceivably be discovered and recovered. Of this, only a portion is *technologically recoverable*, and even a smaller portion can be *economically recovered*. Obviously, as time passes and economic conditions change, a bigger portion of the resource is available for exploitation. The quantity that can be *economically* and *legally* exploited with a better than 90% confidence, using the technologies available, before the wells are abandoned is commonly known as the *proven reserve* (Figure 3-12).

To estimate the size of the reserve both the rock permeability and fluid viscosity must be known -- the higher the rock permeability and the smaller the fluid viscosity, the easier it is to bring oil to the surface. The ratio of rock permeability to fluid viscosity is called *mobility*. Reserves with the highest mobility are the easiest to access. As can be deduced from above, resources continuously decline, whereas depending on price and technology, reserves may or may not increase.

Peak Oil

The most famous model pertaining to finite natural resources is that of geologist **King Hubbert**, who argued that rate of discovery of any major oil reservoir starts from zero, reaches a maximum and then drops until no more oil is found.[§§] Hubbert assumed a symmetrical bell-shape (Gaussian) curve which implied that, at its peak, half of all reserves have been discovered.[17] The pattern seems to happen both for individual oil fields and for the aggregates of fields such as all that belong to a specific country. In individual oil fields this phenomena is caused by geological factors inherent to the structure of the oil reservoir. At the national or global level it is caused by logistical factors. When we start producing oil from a region, we usually find and develop the biggest, most accessible oil fields first.

[§§] It is worth noting that the Hubbert model does not apply only to oil, but to other non-renewable resources such as coal, natural gas, uranium, and minerals, as well, although for the sake of clarity, we are using oil as an example.

As output declines, we must tap into new fields that tend to be smaller with lower production rates that don't compensate for the decline of the large fields they are replacing.[18]

Hubbert made the assertion that oil discovery, like shooting a target, is a statistical event. There is a certain chance that a sharp shooter will hit the bull's eye, but there is also a chance that he misses and strikes some distance away. The probability drops as the shooter aims less and less accurately. Oil discovery is similar in the sense that the chance of drilling success is highly unpredictable. At the early stages, when a natural resource is discovered, the exploitation is slow and the chance of success in finding oil is small. Production is likely to rise exponentially as technology becomes more mature, and as additional uses for the resource are found. As reserves are used up and resources become scarcer, the probability of finding new resources declines; oil companies must dig deeper and production costs increase. Eventually, a point is reached where the rate of discovery reverses its course and starts to slow down. The rate continues to decrease until all resources are found and depleted (Figure 3-13).

The significance of Hubbert's model lies with the accuracy in which he was able to predict U.S. conventional oil production. For example, in 1956, when many saw U.S. oil reserves as effectively unlimited, he predicted that its production would peak in about 1970 at 9.6 million barrels per day. He also estimated that the world's oil production would peak around the year 2000 and that even finding an additional 50% in new petroleum resources would not extend petroleum life more than a few years.[19]

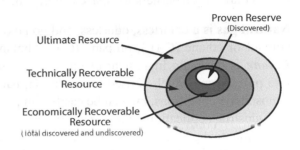

Figure 3-12
Resources and Reserves.

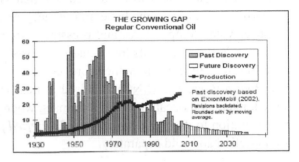

Figure 3-13
Conventional oil discoveries by decade.
Source: Hirsch, R. (2005) "The Inevitable Peaking of World Oil Production." The Atlantic Council of the United States, Bulletin Vol. XVI, No. 3, October 2005

Although the prediction was made some decades ago, they proved to be remarkably accurate until recently, when advances in the hydraulic fracturing along with improvements in exploration and production technologies have made available a huge pool of unconventional reserves at prices that compete with conventional oil. Including these resources as part of oil reserves changes the overall picture, possibly shifting the peak oil by several decades in the future. The ramification of these technologies on water resources, geological hazards, and environmental health are not known, however, and may ultimately determine the extent in which unconventional resources can fill the gap between demands for fossil resources and production. According to the International Energy Agency (IEA), the oil shale boom has put the United States as the top oil and natural gas producer in the world, overtaking both Saudi Arabia and Russia, and expected soon to become self-sufficient in energy.

Natural Gas

The earliest reference to natural gas goes back to 400 BCE when the Chinese seeped natural gas through bamboo pipes to light their cities and boil seawater to desalinate it for drinking.[20] The Zoroastrians kept fires alive in their places of worship by flaring natural gas as a symbol of light, warmth, and energy. But it was not until the late eighteenth century when coal gas (mainly composed of natural gas) was sold commercially and used in British street lamps. Up to only a few decades ago, most natural gas discovered was flared off or re-injected into the ground, since petroleum was cheap and abundant and the transport of gas through pipelines was difficult and expensive. Its use increased during the latter half of the twentieth century when it proved to be a convenient and relatively clean

Figure 3-14
Natural gas.

fuel to burn in gas burners for space heating and cooking (Figure 3-14).

Natural gas is a colorless, odorless, and nontoxic mixture of hydrocarbons, primarily methane (CH_4), but a certain amount of ethane (C_2H_6), propane (C_3H_8), butane (C_4H_{10}), pentane (C_5H_{12}), and hexane (C_6H_{14}) are also present. *Ethane* is the main ingredient of ethylene, used widely in the manufacturing of plastics; it may also be turned into polystyrene which is used in insulation, packaging material, and antifreeze. Like ethane, *propane* is a gas at atmospheric conditions, but can be easily compressed and turned into liquid and used as a fuel in homes, farms, and for industrial applications. *Butane* is a liquid, used directly as the fuel for cigarette lighters, or mixed with propane to make liquefied petroleum gas and used for space heating, outdoor gas-powered grills, and camping stoves. Butane is not a suitable fuel for transportation as it is a highly flammable gas, and has an offensive odor. *Pentane* and heavier hydrocarbons are liquid; they have industrial applications but not as liquid fuels.

Dry natural gas refers to a purified gas that is entirely methane. Commercial natural gas *(wet natural gas)* is primarily a mixture of methane and ethane. At normal temperature and pressure, pentane and hexane are liquid, but at elevated temperatures and pressures typical of underground reservoirs, they become gas and flow out with other gases. Because of its low density, it costs about four times as much to transport natural gas through pipelines as it does for crude oil; it is, therefore, common to liquefy natural gas by cooling it to -162°C (-259°F). Once cooled *liquefied natural gas* (LNG) is stored at near atmospheric pressures and shipped in cryogenic containers aboard large tankers and ocean liners to terminals, where it is warmed back to gaseous form, and sent through pipelines for redistribution to its final destinations. *Liquefied petroleum gas* (LPG) or "bottled" gas is when propane and butane are liquefied and sold separately.

Natural gas liquids (not to be confused with *liquefied natural gas*) are hydrocarbons other than methane that are separated from natural gas and liquefied through some processing. These include ethane, propane, butane, and longer chain hydrocarbons. Today, natural gas is finding its prominent place as a relatively clean source of energy and for the production of hydrogen and other useful products and accounts for 23% of the global energy portfolio. Natural gas can be burned directly to produce electricity when demand is high. When not burned, natural gas is pumped back to abandoned wells or reinjected to raise well pressure and enhance the oil recovery.

When burned, natural gas does not produce a visible flame, therefore, additives (usually mercaptan, a nontoxic substance containing sulfur that smells like rotten eggs) are added to warn people of the danger of gas leakage. It burns in a relatively narrow range of air/fuel mixture, but it can violently explode in the presence of an ignition source, such as a spark or a flame. Methane is a potent greenhouse gas, but because it has a much lower percentage of carbon to hydrogen, it produces 40% less carbon dioxide, compared to the amount of coal that would deliver an equal amount of energy. If leaked, however, the damage it causes is serious and outweighs its advantages over coal and other unconventional fossil fuels.

Formation

The same factors that promote the formation of petroleum also help in the formation of natural gas. It is, therefore, expected that natural gas is found at locations near oil fields, often in association with petroleum -- thus its name -- *associated (dissolved) gas*. It is liberated when oil is brought to the surface in the same manner that carbon dioxide gas is liberated when someone opens a carbonated drink (See Box "The Deadly Lake"). Two mechanisms are mainly responsible: decomposition of organic matter by bacteria, and thermal decomposition of kerogen. The latter depends strongly on the depth of burial, temperatures, and pressure. Deeper deposits and higher temperature and pressure favor the formation of lighter and purer hydrocarbons. Like petroleum, natural gas does not exist in large pools or lakes but resides within small pores that exist within rocks. Sandstone and limestone have a favorable *porosity* (i.e., have pores large enough for gas to diffuse) and a high degree of *permeability (i.e.,* pores are connected to provide channels through which gas can travel to the surface). If the gas diffuses through the pores of sedimentary rocks and accumulates in an impermeable reservoir separate from the oil reservoir, the gas is called *non-associated (dry) gas.*

The Deadly Lake

Lake Kivu on the border between Congo and Rwanda is unique in the world in one crucial way: it conceals an enormous quantity of dissolved methane gas -- 65 cubic kilometers -- lying dormant at the bottom of the cold lake.[i] The source of this gas is believed to be tiny single-celled microorganisms called archaea that consume dissolved carbon dioxide (from two nearby active volcanoes) to produce methane. Some methane also is formed through bacterial fermentation of acetate in the lake bed sediments. Deeper waters can trap methane to higher concentrations. Commonly referred to as limnic eruption, overturn can occur if the water is saturated and the buildup of methane gas is allowed. If the pressure of gases exceeds the pressure of the water at a given depth, it can trigger a sudden eruption forming a cloud of explosive gas suffocating humans and other living animals.[ii] In a deadly episode at Lake Nyos in neighboring Cameroon in 1986, more than 1,700 people and 3,500 livestock were asphyxiated when over 80 million cubic meters of carbon dioxide was released. [iii]

Lake Nyos after the limnic eruption.

If, on the other hand, the water is brought to the surface, either by a pump or naturally through mixing or siphoning, it will lose its ability to hold the methane, releasing it in the form of gas bubbles that can be collected and piped away with potential to produce around one gigawatt of electricity.[iv] Methane, being 25 times less soluble in water than carbon dioxide, is bubbled first, leaving carbon dioxide dissolved in the water.

i Halbwachs, M., et al. "Investigation in Lake Kivu after the Nyiragongo Eruption of January 2002," European Community Humanitarian Office, Communauté européenne – ECHO 1 rue de Genève B- 1049 Bruxelles.
ii A few petroleum geologists have gone so far as to blame the loss of ships and airplanes in the Bermuda Triangle on sudden pulses of methane gas released from a hydrate layer below the Atlantic Ocean. As the ocean boils with a sudden squirt of methane bubbles, ships can be swallowed before having time to make distress calls, and plane engines might be choked by the rising plume of methane gas.
iii Bavier, J., "Deadly Mix of Gases Lurks in Congo's Lake Kivu; Explosive Methane Could Be Tapped To Generate Power," The Washington Post, June 17, 2007.
iv Rosen, J., "Lake Kivu's Great Gas Gamble," MIT Technology Review, Vol 118, No. 3.

Methane also can be produced by bacteria and is referred to as ***biogenic methane***. These microorganisms can live in the digestive systems and intestines of animals, and constitute a major release from decomposing landfills.

Reserves and Resources

Nearly half of all conventional natural gas reserves lie in three countries, Russia, Iran, and Qatar. The United States has a little more than 5% of the world's conventional natural gas reserves. When accounted for unconventional gas, U.S. ranks number one as the top producing natural gas. Because it is relatively clean, natural gas consumption has been increasing steadily by an average of 2.8% annually, faster than other sources of fossil fuels. If consumption continues to grow at this rate, natural gas reserves will remain available for another 200 years. However, this number is believed to be optimistic – because of the effort to reduce the effect of greenhouse gases, it is expected that by 2040, natural gas will replace coal as the fuel of choice for generating electricity, depleting resources at a much faster rate than initially estimated.[21]

Unconventional Resources

The sharp increase in demand for cheap energy, the rapid decline in conventional fossil resources, along with the successful application of hydraulic fracturing technology, allowed profitable exploitation of unconventional and tight oil reservoirs, and a sharp rebound in US oil production, and a rapid departure from Hubbert's original prediction. The extent to which these resources are technically and economically recoverable is not fully known, but experts believe that ultimate reserves of unconventional oil are approximately equal to the identified reserves of conventional crude oil in the Middle East.[22]

Oil shale and Tar Sands

Two potentially rich sources of fossil fuel are oil shale and tar sands. **Oil shale** is actually a misnomer. It is not a shale but a sedimentary rock tightly packed in clay, mud, and silt beneath the earth's surface, and it doesn't contain oil, but rather a solid, waxy organic compound *kerogen* that has not yet been transformed into crude oil (Figure 3-15).¶¶ Steam is needed to hydrogenate kerogen into hydrocarbons, which then may be refined into gasoline and other petroleum products. The organic content of oil shale is small -- about half that of coal. The U.S. is endowed with huge deposits of oil shale, estimated at one trillion barrels of oil equivalent, in the banks of the Green River flowing through Colorado, Utah, and Wyoming. Russia and Brazil are also rich in oil shale.

Figure 3-15
Oil shale

Tar sands are grains of sand containing the thick, viscous, asphalt-like, soluble organic liquid called *bitumen*, the same material that contains in bituminous coal. About 10-15% is bitumen, with the rest consisting of sands and other inorganic material, and is considered as waste. Worldwide resources of tar sands are estimated at around two trillion barrels of heavy crude, with the largest reserves in Athabasca, Canada.[23] Orinoco Belt in Venezuela is second.

Both tar sands and oil shale are solid; they cannot be extracted like crudes and so must be either mined and brought to the surface or heated in-situ***, with electric heaters and in the absence of oxygen, to high temperatures until the oil flows through the porous rock and is pumped through the boreholes. Oil shale must be heated, however, to a much higher temperature around $500°C$, compared to only $80°C$ for tar sands, before it releases any oil. The oil that is produced from the refining of oil shale and tar sand is typically referred to as synthetic crude or **syncrude**.

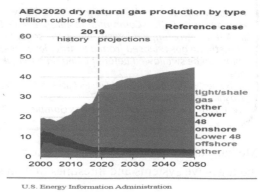

Figure 3-16
Shale and tight gases have added significantly to U.S. gas reserves.
Source: Annual Energy Outlook, Information Agency 2013 U.S, EIA, (http://www.eia.gov/ forecasts/aeo/ Annual Report.). Accessed July 14, 2013.

When in-situ retorting is used, the yield is smaller. The main advantage is that no dirt is lifted and so there is no tailing and no disposal problem. The major challenge is heating the oil shale without contaminating the aquifers. At present, most of the mining is at the surface, so strip-mining is the most common. The majority of tar sand is buried deep underground, so it cannot be mined easily, and requires underground mining.

Much of the heavy oil in place around the world is either technically or economically unrecoverable because the energy required to mine, refine, and convert to marketable products exceeds the energy yield when they are burned. Compared to conventional petroleum, tar sands and oil shale productions are much dirtier, demand much more water for extraction and processing, and generate two to four times greenhouse gases. Their yield is also low, taking as much as two tons of sands to create one barrel of oil.

Shale Gas

Shale gas is natural gas locked in tiny bubble-like pockets within layered sedimentary rock such as shale. While shale gas is trapped in rock, *tight gas* is dispersed and flows within low-porosity silt or sand. It has been known for some time that the United States is endowed with vast deposits of shale gas that stretch under New York, Pennsylvania,

---

¶¶ Oil shale is not the same as shale oil. *Oil shale* is an inorganic rock that contains a solid organic compound known as kerogen, from which liquid hydrocarbons called *shale oil* can be produced.
*** This method is called *in-situ* (Latin for in-place) retorting.

and Ohio. The largest is Marcellus shale, stretching 1,000 miles from New York to Virginia, soaked with natural gas, which can be released only when shale is fractured allowing the gas to migrate toward the surface under pressure. Because of its high cost of production, shale gas as a viable energy source was largely ignored. High prices of petroleum and natural gas, along with the maturing of horizontal drilling technology in the last decade, have brought new attention to this resource.

How big the reserves are, is not clear at this time, but estimates vary considerably depending on cost and allocated uncertainty (See Gigging Deeper: Natural Resources -- How Long Do They Last?". According to the EIA, natural gas from shale resources, considered uneconomical just a few years ago, accounts for 827 trillion cubic feet (Tcf) of proven reserves, and by 2040, is expected to provide 45 percent of the world's liquid supply.[24] If all this is true, then shale gas resources make the U.S. the largest repository of natural gas in the world (Figure 3-16).

These newfound sources of energy have dramatically changed the U.S. energy landscape, and although considered to be a blessing by some, may prove to be environmentally dangerous, and a major impediment to the development of renewable energy technologies, and reducing carbon emissions.

Hydraulic fracturing

Two new technologies have significantly improved the yield while reducing costs. **Horizontal drilling** has enabled mine owners to reduce the need for extensive drilling and reach faraway reserves with relative ease, and with less energy spent. **Hydraulic fracturing** *(or fracking)* is the process in which a crack is created that extends a few hundred feet from the well. A mixture of water, sand, and other chemicals (lubricants, scale inhibitors, and biocides), called *proppant,* is injected into the well. If the pressure of the fluid exceeds the weight of the rock above, the rock fractures, allowing gas to diffuse through the pores and brought to the surface before escaping.

The hydraulic fracturing practice has been highly controversial and of major public concern. Many see the technology as essential in tapping vast resources of fossil fuels and a necessary step to reduce U.S. dependence on foreign oil. Others point to a large amount of water needed in the operation, and the dangers associated with injecting fluids containing harmful chemicals deep underground -- dangers that include potential damage to aquifers and groundwater contamination. There also is mounting evidence that this approach leads to small earth tremors and create underground pockets that result in soil instability and cave-ins.[25, 26] Most of these earthquakes are in the magnitude 3–4 range, large enough to be felt by people, yet small enough to not cause damage.

The Energy Policy Act of 2005 specifically exempted hydraulic fracturing from regulation under the Safe Drinking Water Act passed by Congress in 1974, to ensure clean drinking water free from both natural and man-made contaminates. It also exempts companies from disclosing the chemicals used during hydraulic fracturing. The components of fracking fluid are considered to be proprietary information. What *is* clear is that many of the chemicals used in the operation, and some gaseous emissions are highly poisonous and may cause serious bodily damage and other physical impairment. Recent attempts to accelerate the extraction of nonconventional resources have put the United States as the top producer of petroleum and natural gas in the world (See Tables 3-4 and 3-5).

Table 3-4 World Top Producers of Petroleum (2018)		
Country	Production (Mbbl/day)	Percentage of the total
United States	15.0	18.6%
Saudi Arabia	12.0	14.9%
Russia	10.8	13.4%
Iraq	4.5	5.6%
Iran	4.0	5.0%
China	4.0	5.0%
Canada	3.7	4.6%
UAE	3.1	3.8%
Rest of the world	**23.5**	**29.2%**
Total	**80.6**	**100%**

Source: U.S. Energy Information Administration, 2019.

Table 3-5 World Top Producers of Natural Gas (2018)		
Country	Production (Billion m³/ day)	Percentage of the total
United States	766	19.6%
Russia	635	16.3%
Qatar	188	4.8%
Iran	185	4.7%
Canada	150	3.8%
China	138	3.5%
European Union	118	3.0%
Norway	117	3.0%
Rest of the world	1603	41.1%
Total	**3,900**	**100%**

Source: International Energy Agency, 2019.

Other unconventional sources of fossil fuel include methane hydrate, coal bed methane, and synthetic gas:

Methane hydrates (also called *fire ice* or *methane hydrate*) are icy deposits of crystallized natural gas and water, buried under the extreme pressures and cold temperatures of the deep oceans and Arctic permafrost that have been formed by the disintegration of certain bacteria. As the methane hydrate is dug and brought to the surface it warms up, releasing methane that then can be collected and transported through the pipelines. Because most resources are buried underneath the ocean floors, offshore production is often needed. It is estimated that hydrate fields contain twice the energy of all other forms of fossil fuels combined. These reserves are virtually untapped, as the cost of extraction is prohibitively high; even after natural gas is extracted, it has to be transported thousands of miles from Arctic regions before it can be used. One option is to convert it to liquid synthetic fuel, such as methanol before it is sent through pipelines.

Coal bed methane is natural gas produced from coal seams by microbial action or from thermal processes in the absence of air or oxygen. Some of this trapped gas may be released during coal mining, which has led to several accidental explosions.

Coal gas (also known as *town gas, illumination gas, synthetic gas, producer gas, manufactured gas,* or *wood gas*) is produced by gasification of coal, or from natural gas by steam reforming. Pulverized coal is heated in the absence of oxygen to form volatile products (carbon monoxide, carbon dioxide, methane, and unburned hydrocarbon), which then are collected at various points along a distillation column.

During the nineteenth century, coal gas was used primarily for cooking and heating, and later in gas lanterns that illuminated most major European cities. It was replaced first by petroleum, and later by natural gas as these resources became available. Coal gas can be burned directly in power plants, or converted to methane, gasoline, or turned into hydrogen, and other useful products. Also, through a process called Fischer-Tropsch, coal gas can be turned into liquid and used as a transportation fuel. The process was developed by the Germans during WWII to produce much-needed petroleum to run their military machines. The process was, however, quite costly and the yield was rather low, around three barrels of petroleum per ton of coal. The same process can be used today using coal or even biomass as the primary source, on a much larger scale, and with better efficiency. The cost of conversion is still high and, at this time, may not be able to compete with the price of petroleum directly bought on the open market.

Summary

No doubt fossil fuels have been and will remain, the most important source of energy for the foreseeable future. Much of today's technology has come about because of the availability of cheap and abundant fossil reserves. Unfortunately, in a relatively short time, we have managed to consume nearly half of our estimated conventional oil and much of our coal and natural gas resources. The unconventional resources have expanded the size of the reserves, but only if we are willing to pay higher prices, and accept their many adverse environmental consequences. Tar sands and oil and gas shales can extend the life of petroleum for some time. Methane hydrate is another huge potential source of natural gas. Unlike what the proponents of "peak oil" believe, it is not the production capacity, but a decline in demand along with the environmental cost of the oil consumption will be the main bottleneck to the petroleum production.

The environmental concerns associated with fossil fuel extraction, processing, and combustion are many. Fossil fuel is not clean and leaves a trail of environmental destruction that includes changes to the landscape, flora and fauna, the release of toxins to aquifers and landscape, and eventually the release of various air pollutants that affect health and result in global warming. In recent years, there has been much research on clean coal technologies. The emphasis has been on removing sulfur and other contaminants from coal before it is burned. Although these technologies help to improve air quality near power plants and industrial facilities that use coal as the primary source of energy, many of the problems associated with coal extraction and processing remain unresolved.

Fortunately, there is hope that renewable sources of energy will become available soon and at reasonable prices. Nuclear energy can offset rising demand for a short period. The new resources provide a cheaper and cleaner alternative to coal and can act as a bridge to the wide acceptance of renewable alternative sources of energy.

Digging Deeper: Hazards Associated with Fossil Fuel Use

Pre-Combustion

Before fossil fuel is burned in engines to power our automobiles, used in power plants to generate electricity, or processed to manufacture consumer products, it must be mined, refined, and transported. Each step of the way, there are safety hazards to be considered and precautions to be taken. Thousands of miners lose their lives as a result of mining accidents. Vast areas of land undergo irreversible damage, are contaminated with toxic substances that affect human and animal health, and degrade property. The environmental impact of oil and gas production and use includes natural seepage through rocks, spills from pipelines, gas stations, tank barges, motor vehicles, and onshore and offshore oil platforms and blowouts.

Coal

Coal has several advantages that make it popular for use in power plants: it is relatively cheap and plentiful; it can be transported by truck, ship, and rail; it is easy to store and burn, and can be liquefied to produce synthetic oil. On the other hand, there are many problems associated with coal extraction, cleanup, and combustion that make coal relatively less desired.

Hazards associated with tunnel operation include cave-ins, explosions from dust buildup, carbon monoxide poisoning, and lack of sufficient ventilation. Coal miners are exposed to ubiquitous noise from such operations as drilling, milling, blasting, and material handling which at a minimum is a nuisance, but may also result in permanent hearing losses. Heat and humidity affect workers in tropical regions and in deep mines with large dry rock temperature gradients and insufficient ventilation. In addition to physical hazards, mine workers may be exposed to chemicals present naturally in mines or used to facilitate operation. Exposure to radon gases is known to cause lung cancer. Worldwide, coal accidents kill thousands of miners each year. Compared to some other countries, the number of deaths in the U.S. is relatively low, however.[27]

Although tunneling operations harm miners the most, strip-mining has the greatest environmental impacts. These include the destruction of fertile surface soil, permanent changes in the landscape, and the possibility of acidic or alkaline drainage to the surface. Those working on surface mines are less exposed to radon but are at increased risk of solar UV radiation and melanoma. In many industrial countries, public and environmentalist pressure has forced local governments to require coal mining companies to reclaim the land and restore it to its original form after strip-mining is concluded.

Tar Sands and Oil Shale

The most serious concern is probably the extent to which land is disturbed and possibly becomes unstable and useless for agricultural and pastoral use. The flora and fauna may undergo permanent changes. The extraction requires massive amounts of water; also it produces lots of residues (called tailing), which occupy many times the volume of crude they produce. The production of petroleum products derived from these resources entails substantially more carbon dioxide and other greenhouse gases.

Petroleum and Gas

Environmental concerns associated with crude and natural gas include seepage, well blow-outs, transport, and spillage.

Natural Seepage

Depending on the type of geologic formation, some crude and gases always diffuse through the soil and naturally discharge into the atmosphere. Traditionally, these leaks were considered to be a great asset in locating the reservoirs that were later drilled and extracted. Worldwide, it is estimated that each year, up to 14 million barrels of crude seep naturally into the atmosphere or the oceans. Of these, about 1.5 million barrels are in the United States, and over 90% of that is in the Gulf of Mexico.[28]

Subsidence

Ground subsidence is a major hazard in many human activities involving the extraction of large volumes of fluid from underground reservoirs. The two most common fluids that may cause subsidence beneath the surface are water and petroleum. Subsidence occurs also as a result of oil extraction. So long as the pressure of the fluid is enough to support the weight of the overlying rock, no subsidence occurs. However, as fluid is withdrawn, reservoir pressure decreases, causing the roof to eventually collapse. One method to lower the danger of subsidence is waterflooding common in primary oil extraction. The fluid replaces the oil extracted, and pressure is maintained. Subsidence can occur also as a result of a sudden collapse of land over an underground cavity such as an abandoned coal mine, although this is a relatively rare event. Among the major cities that have experienced major subsidence as a result of the gradual withdrawal of water are San Joaquin Valley in California, Venice in Italy, and Houston in Texas. Parts of the city and port of Long Beach in California suffered major problems due to rapid land subsidence related to the extraction of oil from the underlying Wilmington oil field.[29]

Well Blowouts

The biggest blowout, and the worst environmental disaster in U.S. history, happened on April 20th, 2010, when a BP (formerly British Petroleum) floating oil platform, 40 miles off the coast of the Gulf of Mexico, caught fire, wounding 28 and killing 11.[30] The rig eventually sank, and oil started gushing out from a deep-water oil well 5,000 feet (1500 m) below the ocean surface. According to some estimates, as much as five million barrels of oil were spilled into the Gulf, before the well was capped three months later. The resulting oil slick covered an area of 2,500 square miles (6,500 km²).

Prior to this disaster, the most famous oil spillage in the United States was in Santa Barbara, California, in 1969. The Union Oil Company Well Number 21, located 5.5 miles off the Santa Barbara coast, experienced a blowout during drilling. A massive mixture of oil, gas, and drilling mud spewed out onto the platform. The well was capped a few days later, but not before 100,000 barrels of oil were released into the Pacific Ocean.[†††] The incident was a major impetus for the environmental movement in the United States.[‡‡‡] Besides the Santa Barbara blowout, there have been16 other accidents in the U.S. since 1964, and an additional 150,000 barrels have been spilled.

Transport

With the exception of the pipelines, trucks and tankers are the two most effective ways of moving oil today. Some two billion barrels of oil are transported every year along various routes around the globe. It is, therefore, imperative that some oil releases result from occasional accidents involving vehicles. The container vessel M/V Cosco Busan spilled 53,000 gallons (~1260 barrels) of heavy fuel oil (bunker fuel) into the San Francisco Bay after a collision with a bridge in 2007. More than 50 public beaches had to be closed for up to one month. About 20 years earlier, another oil tanker, named the *Exxon Valdez*, collided with the Bligh reef and emptied its cargo (260,000 barrels or 11 million gallons) of oil – 200 times greater than that of the San Francisco incident -- into Prince William Sound in

---

††† For details of accident see Incident News, https://incidentnews.noaa.gov/incident/6206

‡‡‡ In 1981, Congress adopted the Outer Continental Shelf (OCS) Moratorium, which prevents the leasing of coastal waters off the Atlantic and Pacific coasts for fossil fuel development. In 1989, following the Exxon Valdez oil spill, Alaska's fishery-rich Bristol Bay was added to the nearly nationwide moratorium on offshore oil and gas development. The ban was lifted in 2008 by President George W. Bush, allowing drilling to resume within 100 miles offshore, or 50 miles offshore, if a state opts in to allow leasing off its coastline.

Alaska, before it ran aground in 1989.[31] Although no human life was lost in the accident, the oil covered 2,000 km of coastline and 28,000 km^2 of ocean, at a cost of billions of dollars to the local economy and enormous damage to the environment.[32] The largest oil spill in history was during the 1991 Gulf War when Iraq attacked Kuwaiti oil terminals, wells, and tankers; according to some estimates 5-10 million barrels of oil were spilled into the Persian Gulf.

In addition to spillage from tankers and trucks, there are spills from offshore oil platforms, land drainage, waste disposal, pipelines, as well as offshore supply vessels. Compared to other spills rampant in the oil and gas industry, the volume of these spills is relatively small.

Effects of Oil Spills on the Environment: The effects of oil spills on the environment are many.[33] Oil does not mix with water and, because it is lighter than water, spreads over the surface of the water very rapidly, forming a thin slick. Depending on their composition and size, oil droplets can vaporize, or congeal into sticky tarballs. Heavier oil and oil contaminated with other residues will sink to the bottom and contaminate the deep underwater environment. Lighter oil will float to the surface, eventually wash ashore, contaminating beaches and reefs along the coastlines.

In addition to short-term effects, oil spill consequences may last for months and years -- even after beaches are cleaned and oil slicks are removed. Over time, oil disintegrates by *photolysis* (decomposition by sunlight) and *biodegradation* (decomposition due to microorganisms), turning into compounds that may take more than a hundred years to break up. To make matters worse, these chemicals are highly carcinogenic, even at low concentrations. As oil evaporates, they form clouds and when it rains, enter sewers, flow into rivers and bays, and water supplies.

The economic impact of oil spills could be devastating to local populations that depend on fishing and tourism. The indirect consequences of spills are depreciation of property values, reduced business activities, and curtailed future investments. Oil spills harm mammals, turtles, fish, and birds through oxygen deprivation, poisoning, loss of their thermal insulation, and the ability to control their body temperatures, leading to hyperthermia and death.

> ***Did You Know That...*** It is estimated that there are over 7,000 sunken vessel wrecks in U.S. coastal waters, some submerged for decades, which may contain as much as 4.3 million barrels of oil. (Based on ERC's Worldwide Shipwreck Database as presented in Michel, et al. 2005).

Combustion of Fossil Fuels

Fossil fuels, whether in the form of coal, oil or natural gas are substantially hydrocarbons, with varying carbon-to-hydrogen ratios. It reacts with oxygen in the air when burned, forming a number of products mainly carbon dioxide and water vapor. In its simplest form, this chemical reaction can be written as:

Fuel + Oxidizer $\rightarrow$ Product + heat

This reaction is *exothermic, i.e.,* produces heat. In addition to carbon and hydrogen, fossil fuels may contain oxygen and traces of other elements, such as sulfur and metals, which complicate the combustion. In the present analysis, we assume that all impurities have been removed and the reactions are such that all the fuels are burned to produce carbon dioxide and water vapor. For example, methane, gasoline, and coal burn in oxygen as:

Methane: $CH_4 + 2O_2 \rightarrow CO_2 + 2H_2O + heat$

Gasoline: $C_8H_{18} + 12.5O_2 \rightarrow 8 CO_2 + 9H_2O + heat$

Coal: $C + O_2 \rightarrow CO_2 + heat$

Such reactions, in which the oxidizer is just enough to convert all fuels to carbon dioxide and water vapor, are called **stoichiometric**. When the reactant mixture has fuel or oxygen in excess of what is required for a stoichiometric ratio, the mixture is fuel rich (oxygen lean) or oxygen rich (fuel lean), respectively. If air were used instead of oxygen (air is a mixture of 1 part oxygen and 3.76 parts nitrogen), the reaction would remain the same except that the nitrogen in the air would appear unburned in the product.

Example 3-1: Calculate the stoichiometric air-to-fuel ratio necessary for burning natural gas in the air. Natural gas consists mainly of methane.

Solution: The stoichiometric reaction of methane is

$$CH_4 + 2 (O_2 + 3.76 N_2) \rightarrow CO_2 + 2 H_2O + 7.52 N_2$$

16 kg methane + 275 kg air → 44 kg carbon dioxide + 36 kg water vapor + 211 kg nitrogen; or
1 kg methane + 17.2 kg air → 2.75 kg carbon dioxide + 2.25 kg water vapor + 13.2 kg nitrogen

Similar analyses give 15.1 kg of air and 3.08 kg of carbon dioxide per kg of petroleum. Note that although methane and gasoline have very different structures, they have a similar air/fuel ratio and produce roughly the same amount of carbon dioxide per mass of fuel burned.

According to the EIA, the United States consumed 82.8 quadrillions Btu (Quads) of fossil energy in 2014 (See Table 3-6). Using various conversion factors given in this book, we can estimate the total amount of carbon dioxide emission from fossil resources at 5,446 million metric tons, or roughly 17 tons per capita.

Table 3-6 U.S. Carbon Emission from Fossil Fuels (2014)					
		Emission Factors		Total Emission	
	Heating Value	kg carbon per kg fuel	kg CO_2 per kg fuel	Carbon Emission (million metric tons)	Total CO_2 Emission (million metric tons)
Natural Gas	37 MJ/m³	0.75	2.75	514	1,414
Petroleum	34.5 MJ/L	0.84	3.08	459	2,279
Coal	30 MJ/kg	1	3.67	478	1,753
Total Fossil	--	--	--	**1,450**	**5,446**
[1] Energy Information Administration, Short-term Energy Outlook, October 2015. (*http://www.eia.gov/forecasts/steo/pdf/steo_full.pdf*).					

Incomplete Combustion

If chemical reactions proceed fully to completion, there would be little pollution, and hydrocarbons would be relatively clean. Unfortunately, these reactions do not reach equilibrium, and other gases such as nitric oxides (NO and NO2) and carbon monoxide (CO) are always present. Reactions take longer to reach completion than the time available in the combustion chamber, and some hydrocarbons might remain unburned in the product. Therefore, products will be exhausted before reaching equilibrium. The degree to which the reaction completes depends on such variables as the combustion temperature and pressure, residence time, and mixture ratios. Details of the processes are outside the scope of this book and will not be discussed further. Those interested should consult more advanced texts on the subject.[34]

Coal is probably the dirtiest of all fossil resources; it produces more carbon per unit energy content, has the highest percentage of sulfur, and produces more nitric oxides. The relative impact on global warming and overall air quality is considered to be the greatest, producing twice the carbon dioxide as oil for the same amount of energy. Many studies have been conducted on the possibility of sequestering carbon dioxide in abandoned coal beds. Others suggest storage in deep oceans and underground saline aquifers. Carbon sequestration strategies are discussed in Chapter 15.

Coal-fired power plants are also the single largest source of mercury, accounting for half of all man-made mercury pollution in the United States. Mercury exposure can attack the nervous system, affecting everything from brain development to muscle coordination. Once released into the atmosphere, it settles into rivers, lakes, and oceans, where it is absorbed and ingested by fish and eventually shows up in our foods. In addition to mercury, coal plants have been emitting arsenic, cadmium, lead, and particulates. In the last couple of decades, new technologies have been developed to cope with some of the problems associated with coal combustion. Generally dubbed "Clean Coal Combustion," they include:

Pulverized Coal Combustion with Supercritical Boilers -- uses a high-temperature, high-pressure boiler to achieve higher efficiency -- 1.2% for every 20°C rise in temperature. Flue gas desulfurization uses limestone (calcium carbonate) to absorb SO_2 emission. NO_x emission is controlled by deploying selective catalytic reduction (SCR) that uses ammonia and a catalyst at 300-400°C to convert NO_x to N_2. Larger particulate (ash) is removed by gravitational means. Smaller particles are collected by electrostatic precipitators, scrubbers, and baghouses.

Integrated Gasification Combined Cycle (IGCC) -- uses the hot exhaust from a gas turbine to generate steam that drives a steam turbine. Traditional IGCC used coal gas, but more modern systems use natural gas to operate gas turbines. The combined gas and steam turbines has the advantage to provide both heat and power when needed. The **Combined Heat and Power (CHP)** scheme is especially attractive in regions with long, cold winters, where a large fraction of energy need is for heating.

"Clean Coal" Combustion

Clean coal is a misnomer, as we can never burn coal without the environmental pollution associated with it. There are attempts, however, to clean coal before burning, and remove carbon, as much as possible, from entering the atmosphere:

In the *pre-combustion method,* used mainly in IGCC (integrated gasification combined cycle) power plants. Coal, under extreme heat and pressure, and in the presence of steam, is converted into syngas, a gaseous mixture of carbon monoxide, hydrogen, and minute amounts of other gases (See Decarbonization above). A water-gas-shift reactor then converts the CO to CO_2, which is subsequently removed through physical or chemical absorption processes. An ionic liquid membrane selectively permeates hydrogen before it is mixed with air and burns inside a gas turbine, or is used in a fuel cell to generate electricity. The solvent cost is high, however, which increases the cost of electricity by about 30% above conventional pulverized coal plants.

The *post-combustion method* is used in pulverized coal plants -- coal burns in air to heat water to steam, which runs a turbine to generate electricity. CO_2 is exhausted in the flue gas at atmospheric pressure, which is then removed by various absorbents. CO_2 capture is more difficult than the pre-combustion method, as it is diluted with burned air. The most efficient approach is amine-based wet scrubbing, where the exhaust gas stream is bubbled through an amine solution that serves as an absorbent. The liquid stream is then sent to a desorption tower, where the liquid is heated to free the CO_2. The process is, however, energy-intensive, substantially adding to both the energy and water use, erasing much of the advantages carbon capture provides.

The *air-capture method* aims at removing carbon that is already released into the atmospheric air. The process involves pumping air through corrugated sheets of material soaked with solutions that absorb carbon dioxide to form carbonate. As the carbonate settles down through the stack, it is collected and sequestered, or combined with hydrogen to produce hydrocarbon fuel.

In the *oxy-combustion method*, coal is burned in pure oxygen. Because nitrogen does not have to be heated, the flame temperature is higher, combustion efficiency is improved, and practically all carbon is burned to carbon dioxide. The exhaust is then cooled until water is condensed out. What remains is pure CO_2, which then can be compressed or liquefied and stored. The oxy-combustion method can be used in existing combustors; the boilers can be made more compact as the volumes of flue gases that must be treated are smaller.

Heating Values

Heating value (also called calorific value or heat of combustion) refers to the amount of thermal energy that is released by burning a unit amount of fuel.[§§§] For gaseous and liquid fuels, such as methane and gasoline, the heat of combustion is usually given per unit volume, while for solids such as coal, it is expressed per unit mass. Roughly speaking, we can show the following relations between the energy releases of various forms of fossil fuels.[¶¶¶]

1 kg coal ~ 1 liter of petroleum ~ 1 cubic meter of natural gas

It is interesting to note that, per unit mass, different fossil fuels have relatively similar calorific values (See Table 3-6). This is logical because all fossil fuels are hydrocarbons. Except for a slight variation in energy trapped between different bonds that form their molecules, these hydrocarbons are expected to release similar amounts of heat. As for coal, depending on the shares of carbon, volatile matter, moisture, ash, and sulfur, coal energy content can vary by a factor of three. Ash refers to all incombustible materials present in the coal and may constitute up to 40% of its dry mass.

Water-Fossil Fuel Nexus

There is a strong link connecting the consumption of fossil fuels to water use. Although water is a renewable resource, clean freshwater is not. To be used sustainably, water cannot be withdrawn from reservoirs and other sources faster than it is replenished through the natural hydrological cycle. Desalination and other filtering methods may suggest that freshwater is readily accessible, but it must be noted that all these technologies are heavily dependent on the use of fossil fuel that is non-renewable, dirty, and requires a lot of water to harvest and use.

Conventional crude oil undergoes a series of water-intensive processes from extraction and processing until combustion and disposal of residuals.[35] The demand for water is considerably greater when enhanced oil recovery techniques are employed.[36] Unconventional petroleum resources -- tar sand, shale oil, and tight oil -- require water for mining operations such as digging, crushing, and heating the rock. The leftover tailing contains nitrate, arsenic, boron, barium, and other heavy metals, that if leached into surface and groundwater supplies, could potentially contaminate drinking reservoirs and lands that are allocated to growing foods and other agricultural products.

Natural and shale gas involve similar operations with a similar dependence on water resources. In addition, there are indications that fracking may have instigated leakage of natural gas to groundwater, to such extent that the increase in methane concentrations caused tap water to be ignited.[37]

Like petroleum and natural gas, water is used throughout coal production from extraction and processing to disposal of ash and other byproducts of combustion. Water also plays an important role when slurries are used to transport coal via pipeline to a power plant.

Fossil fuels have major impacts on climate change, which in turn affect the global distribution of water. It is projected that climate change will result in disruption of weather patterns with an increase in storm frequency and intensity amplifying runoff of contaminated surfaces, acidifying lakes and rivers, which in turn reduces access to clean drinking water, increases fish mortality, impacts migration of birds and other wildlife, and results in loss of animal habitats. ⓐ

[§§§] Heating values are expressed either as higher (gross) or lower (net) heating values, depending on whether the products of combustion are cooled back to their initial reactant temperature, and whether water in the combustion product is condensed out. If water in the exhaust is in the form of vapor, the heating value is called net or lower heating value (LHV). If the water vapor is cooled so all the water is condensed out, then additional heat is available and the heating value is called gross or higher heating value (HHV). For most reactions the exhaust is relatively hot, therefore little condensation takes place and LHV is a more realistic number to use. The HHV is most appropriate in certain devices such as natural gas furnaces used in resident ial units and air conditioners that use condensers.

[¶¶¶] In U.S. Customary units: [1 gal of petroleum ~ 14 pounds of coal ~ 150 ft³ of natural gas]

ⓐ *Digging Deeper: Natural Resources -- How Long Do They Last?*

One of the most intriguing questions of our time is the remaining quantity of our natural resources (fossils, minerals, precious metals, etc.) and the length of time they will last. Many have tried to answer this question, often with greatly different outcomes. The estimate is difficult to make and depends on the future prices consumers are willing to pay, the future technologies that are available, the true size of reserves, and the rate that these reserves are consumed.

Whether there is an upper boundary to a natural resource or not, that is, whether or not a resource is truly exhaustible, depends on whom we ask this question. The **optimists** argue that no natural resource is truly exhaustible and there is nothing to fear. They point out that, over the years, the reserves seem to be increasing. As we consume more oil and our known reserves deplete, other reservoirs are found that offset the increase in consumption. In addition, technology helps to increases productivity and reduce the cost, both improve the reserves. For example, only 10-20% of oil could be recovered when the only method of extraction was by the natural gushing of oil or by pumping the oil from wells (primary method). When secondary and tertiary methods of extraction became possible, the efficiency climbed to 50%. Today we can use horizontal drilling to navigate to the oil reservoir taking the lowest-cost route, and recover around 70% of the oil. In the future, technological advances can increase the extraction efficiency to approach 80% to 90%.[38]

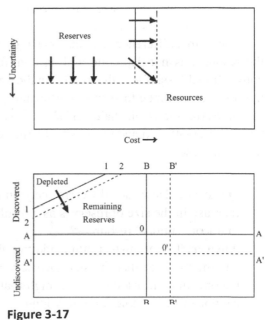

Figure 3-17
McKelvey's box.
As resources deplete and prices rise, recovery of additional resources makes more economic sense and line B-B shifts to B'-B' to the right. At the same time, expected discovery of more resources adds to the reserves and line A-A moves down to A'-A'. As the total reserves expand, so does the amount consumed, and the diagonal line 1-1 moves to 2-2.

The **pessimists** refute this argument by pointing out that better technologies can increase the amount of oil that is extracted, but not the total size of reserves. In addition, while new technologies have enabled the discovery of new resources, the additional energy required may not justify further exploration. A large portion of the oil extracted from the Middle East today gushes out naturally, with relatively little need to use enhanced oil recovery techniques. We have to dig deeper and deeper to access oil as more and more is being extracted. That means, as the energy used per gallon of oil increases, we would eventually reach a point where the cost of drilling and the energy needed to recover the oil would outpace the economic benefits (the break-even point) and exploration would necessarily stop.

A model proposed by the U.S. Geological Survey called "McKelvey's Box," often is used to address the relationship between reserves and resources****.[39] The size of this box represents the total amount of resources available. To the *optimist*, the box is not of a finite size but varies with the cost of production and the probability that a resource can be found (Figure 3-17). If the resource is scarce, as the argument goes, its price continues to rise over time, the cost of production goes up, and there would be more effort in conservation and developing new technologies that can point to new discoveries and more efficient recovery methods. The *pessimists* see the size of this box as finite, stressing that future discoveries and technological innovations cannot catch up with the demand, and that, eventually, the size of the reserves -- for all practical purposes -- will shrink to zero. For example, data shows that U.S. conventional oil discoveries have decreased every decade, since the 1950s and that, since 1962 (except in 1970 when Alaskan oil was discovered), the new oil reserves never have been enough to meet the rise in demand.

No matter which point of view is considered, as time passes, technological innovation and better production

**** It is worth noting that this model does not apply only to oil, but to other nonrenewable resources such as coal, natural gas, uranium, and minerals, as well; for the sake of clarity we are using oil as an example.

techniques allow a larger portion of resources to become economically extractable. Putting it all together, we can see that the quantity of the remaining reserves can change as a result of two factors:

1. It increases due to the discovery of additional resources, higher prices, newer technologies, and more efficient extraction and processing techniques.
2. It decreases because of additional consumption.

Legislation can act either to increase or decrease production costs and indirectly impact the size of the reserve. The remaining reserve is the difference between the total and amount already exploited. As long as this difference remains unchanged or increases in size, the resource is not depleting and is, therefore, sustainable. For conventional fossil fuels, the trend is in the opposite direction, and the reserves continue to shrink. Fortunately, new unconventional resources (tar sands, oil shale, and shale gas) are being discovered that have greatly expanded the size of the resource and thus the life of the reserves.

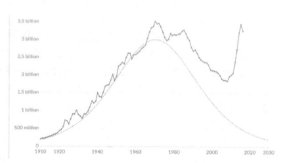

Figure 3-18
Forecast of global oil production growth trend.
Source: BP statistical review of world energy.

Question: How do different economists view the vast increase in the size of reserves as a result of new discoveries in unconventional resources?

Answer: To optimists, finding additional resources supports their arguments that no resource is truly finite. The pessimists agree that the size of reserves has been expanding in the short term, but the environmental cost of unconventional resources is so high that, if included in the total cost of extraction, will eventually prove they cannot be sustainable for a very long time.

So what are the real numbers? Although there is no way to predict the exact amount of undiscovered oil, there are indications that we have reached, or soon will reach, peak discovery—i.e., the point where half of all conventional reserves have been used up. First, contrary to some claims, there cannot be huge amounts of undiscovered oil laying underneath the earth's surface. There are now technologies available that can accurately pinpoint exact locations of oil thousands of feet underground. The entire globe has been carefully scanned and most major oil reservoirs have been identified. North Sea oil production already has passed its peak. The Caspian Sea oil fields have been identified and it has been determined that no more than 50 billion barrels of oil can be ultimately extracted -- enough to meet, at the current production level, world demand for an additional 1.5 years.[40] There has been much speculation about the Alaskan Arctic National Wildlife Refuge (ANWR). Latest U.S. Geological Survey (USGS) studies have determined that, ultimately, these reserves hold between 5.7 and 16 billion barrels of technically recoverable oil.[41] That is enough to meet only two to six months of the world's oil demand. This is against the backdrop of the enormous cost of damage to the environment and natural wildlife.

The easiest and crudest way to determine the number of years that petroleum reserves last is to divide the total reserve (R) by the rate of annual production (P). This, of course, assumes that consumption remains flat for a foreseeable future. As new sources of energy are found, and depending on how the reserves are estimated and what the economic and geopolitical conditions are, the ratio R/P has regularly changed over the years. Today it stands at 70. Not only are data manipulated to fit a particular interest, but we also cannot accurately estimate what resources will be discovered in the future, either. The best we can do is predict the probability of finding them. The uncertainty increases as we make our predictions farther into the future. Geologists often do this by assigning a probability to their reserves estimate. For example, the oil industry gives proved reserves a 90% certainty of being produced (1P). They give probable reserves a 50% certainty (2P), and possible reserves a 10% certainty (3P) of actually being produced. It is, therefore, quite natural to see wide discrepancies, depending on which source reports the reserve data. The median estimate 2P, is probably the best estimate, as errors and biases tend to cancel each other out. As of July 2016, the estimated petroleum proven reserves (1P) in the world were 381 bbo (billion barrels of oil); Saudi Arabia at the top with 70 billion barrels, followed by Russia with 51 billion, and Iran with 32 billion. The U.S. share was estimated at 29 bbo or 7.6% of the world total.[42]

When nonconventional resources are included, estimates are harder to predict, as multiple factors such as our ability to transition to renewable energy resources, and environmental costs of extraction and production must be considered. Based on the current best available days, it is expected that the peak production for oil and natural gas production will be sometime around the mid 21st century (See Figure 3-18).

Exponential Growth (revisited)

In Chapter 1, we introduced the concept of exponential growth. Here, we give a more formal analysis and show how it is used to calculate the accumulative growth over a time period, and ultimate resource lifetime.

Let's assume the rate of consumption of a resource is growing at a fixed percentage rate, r.

$$\frac{dN}{dt} = rN \tag{3-1}$$

Integrating over time yields

$$\frac{N}{N_0} = e^{rt} \tag{3-2}$$

Where:
    N_0 = Current rate of consumption ($t = 0$),
    N = Rate of consumption at a later time (t), and
    r = Growth rate

Exponential growth is often characterized by its doubling time, T_2, defined as the period in which the quantity N (in this case, the consumption of a resource) grows to twice its initial value ($N/N_0 = 2$). We have

$$T_2 = \frac{\ln 2}{r} = \frac{0.693}{r} = \frac{69.3}{R} \cong \frac{70}{R} \tag{3-3}$$

Where R is the percentage growth per year $(R = 100 \times r)$. This formula was discussed in Chapter 1, but no proof was given.

> **Example 3-2:** A father deposits \$1,000 for his newborn baby in a bank that gives him 10% in interest. Assuming no other deposits are made for this child, how long would it take his money to grow to a million dollars?
> **Solution:** Substituting for N_0 = 1,000, N = 1,000,000, and r = 0.10 into Equation (3-2), we have:
>
> $$t = \frac{\ln(N/N_0)}{r} = \frac{\ln(1000)}{0.1} = \frac{6.91}{0.1} = 69.1 \text{ years}$$
>
> Approximately 70 years or 10 doubling times.

To project future oil production, we need to know three vital statistics: the total produced up to the present, and the size of the known and future reserves to be discovered and exploited. The time it takes for the oil to be exhausted requires also the knowledge of the pattern of consumption and the state of technology that oil companies can pump out of known oil fields before abandoning them.

Question: Some energy experts believe we have passed peak oil production, or about to reach peak conventional oil very soon. Assuming that we are now at the peak oil, and the oil production continues to increase at the current level of 2.3 percent a year, for how long would our oil reserves be expected to last?

Answer: An amazing feature of the exponential growth is that the consumption during any doubling time period exceeds the total of all the previous consumption, i.e. the remaining half will last for only 30.4 years (70/2.3). Even if we have underestimated our total reserves by 50%, we have bought ourselves just a bit of time.

Cumulative Consumption

The cumulative consumption of the resource between the present time, $t = 0$, and time, $t = T$, in the future is found by integrating N over time, giving

$$Q = \int_0^T N dt = \frac{N_0}{r}\left(\exp(rT)-1\right)$$

(3-4)

Example 3-3: U.S. energy consumption increased from 76.8 quads in 1984 to 100.4 quads in 2004. Assuming that the consumption followed an exponential growth pattern, find:

a. The annual growth rate.
b. The doubling time.
c. Total cumulative U.S. energy consumption during this period.

Solution: Substituting into Equation 3-2 through 3-4, we have

a. $\dfrac{100.4}{76.8} = e^{20\lambda};\quad \lambda = 0.013 = 1.3\%$

b. $T_2 = 70/1.3 = 53.8$ years
c. $Q = 76.8/0.013\ (e^{0.013 \times 20} - 1) = 1{,}754$ quads

r (% / year)	EET (years)
1	58.3
2	47.4
3	40.5
4	35.7
5	32.0

Resource Lifetime

As a resource is discovered, it will be extracted, and eventually consumed. The rate of production, therefore, will follow the rate of discovery. In the beginning, the rate of discovery exceeds the rate of production, and surplus production will help to build up reserves. Eventually, we reach a point when the rate of discovery just balances the rate of production and our reserves are at their maximum. After this time, the rate of production (and consumption) exceeds the rate of discovery and we necessarily have to dig into reserves. The process continues until all reserves are exhausted. The total area under the production curve is, thus, equal to the ultimate recovery.[43]

The simplest (but less accurate) way to estimate resource life is by assuming that the rate of consumption will stay the same until the reserves are exhausted. The so-called *static exhaustion time* (SET) [44] is calculated by dividing the total reserve Q_∞ by the production (consumption) rate.

$$SET = \frac{R}{P} = \frac{Q_\infty}{N_0}$$

(3-5)

When the production rate is not constant and grows exponentially with time, we have depleted our resources, when total accumulated consumption approaches the total reserves Q_∞. This time is called the *resource life* or *the exponential (dynamic) expiration time* (EET) and is found by rearranging Eqn. (3-4) as:

$$EET = \frac{1}{r}\ln\left(\frac{r\,Q_\infty}{N_0}+1\right)$$

(3-6)

In this equation, Q_∞ represents the ultimate size of the resource (given in barrels of oil, tons of coal, etc.), N_0 is the rate of consumption (given in barrels of oil per year, tons of coal per day, etc.) at time $t = 0$ when we started to tap the reserves.

Example 3-4: The total world petroleum endowment (that is already produced and that will remain to be exploited) is estimated at 3,563 billion barrels. The same data indicate the cumulative production of 708 billion barrels and proven (remaining) reserves of 2,855 billion barrels. Assuming that oil consumption was at 98.9 million barrels a day in 2000, calculate the remaining life expectancy (exponential expiration time) of the world's petroleum reserves.

Solution: Substituting for the total size of remaining reserves ($Q_\infty = 2,855$ bbo), the annual consumption rate of $N_0 = (98.9 \times 10^6) \times 365 = 36.1 \times 10^9$ barrels/year (36.1 bbo/y) at the turn of the century, the exponential expiration time is calculated for different rates of consumption growth; results are tabulated in the table to the right.[a]

Endnotes

1   BP Statistical Review of World Energy (2015). Retrieved from http://www.bp.com/en/global/corporate/energy-economics/statistical-review-of-world-energy.html

2   Thorndike, E. (1976). *Energy and environment*, Reading:Addison-Wesley.

3   Mountjoy, E. (2020). History of Coke, https://iup.edu/archives/coal/mining-history/history-of-coke

4   World Coal Statistics, Retrieved by https://www.worldometers.info/coal

5   Longwall Mining, (1955). U.S. Energy Information Administration. Office of Coal, Nuclear, Electric and Alternate Fuels, DOE/EIA-TR-0588.

6   Gao, J. (2004). *Coal, Oil Shale, Natural Bitumen, Heavy Oil, and Peat*, in Encyclopedia of Life Support Systems (EOLSS), Developed under the Auspices of the UNESCO, Eolss Publishers, Oxford, UK, http://www.eolss.net

7   Ohtsuka, Y. (2004) *Desulfurization of Coal, in Coal, Oil Shale, Natural Bitumen, Heavy Oil and Peat*, [Ed. Gao Jinsheng], in Encyclopedia of Life Support Systems (EOLSS), Developed under the Auspices of the UNESCO, Eolss Publishers, Oxford, UK. http://www.eolss.ne

8   Malanima, P. (2010). *Energy in History*, in World Environmental History, [Eds Mauro Agnoletti, Elizabeth Johann, Simone Neri Serneri], in Encyclopedia of Life Support System (EOLSS), Developed under the Auspices of the UNESCO, Eolss Publishers, Oxford, UK. http://www.eolss.net.

9   Arabian traveler Baladzori (Al-Belazuri Ahmed) describes in "The Conquest of the Countries" that political and economic life on Absheron had been long connected with oil. (Published in English "The Origins of the Islamic State," by P.K. Hitti and F.C. Murgotten, v.1-2, N.Y., 1916-1924)

10 Macini, P. (2009). *History of Petroleum Engineering-Upstream*, in Encyclopedia of Life Support Systems (EOLSS), Developed under the Auspices of the UNESCO, EOLSS Publish,ers, Oxford, UK. http://www.eolss.net.

11 Laughlin, R. (2004). *John D. Rockefeller: Oil Baron and Philanthropist*. Greensboro, North Carolina: Morgan Reynolds Publishing.

12 Oilen, R. and Hinton, D. (2007). *Wildcatters: Texas Independent Oilmen*, Texas A&M University Press.

13 Meadows, D. (1972). *The Limits to Growth: A Report for the Club of Rome's Project on the Predicament of Mankind*, Universe Books, 2nd ed.

14 Meadow, D. (2002) *Limits to Growth: 30-Year Update*, Chelsea Green Publishing Company, pp. 94.

15 Cobb, K. (2021). Why Oil Prices are 10 Times More than in 1998, Retrieved from https://oilprice.com/Energy/Oil-Prices/Why-Oil-Prices-are-10-Times-More-than-in-1998.html

16 Enhanced Oil Recovery (2021). U.S. Department of Energy, Office of Fossil Energy, Retrieved from http://energy.gov/fe/science-innovation/oil-gas/enhanced-oil-recovery

17 Hubbert, M. (1949). Energy from Fossil Fuels, *Science, 109*(2823), 103-109.

18 Chefurka, P. (2019). World Energy And Population: Trends To 2100. Countercurrents.org, https://www.countercurrents.org/chefurka201109.htm

19 A similar argument is proposed by C. J. Campbell in The End of Cheap Oil, *Scientific American*, March 1998. The reserves at the time were 1,020 Gbo, and the annual production was 23.6, giving the world 43 years of supply.

20 Hopkins, P. (2007). *Oil and gas pipelines: yesterday and today*. American Society of Mechanical Engineers (ASME), [online]

Pipeline Systems Division (PSD), International Petroleum Technology Institute. http://www. engr. mun. ca/~ spkenny/ Courses/Undergraduate/ENGI8673/Reading_List/2007_Hopkins. pdf .

21 CAPP (2005). Canadian Association of Petroleum Producers. Annual Report, 2005, http://www.capp.ca

22 For an informative discussion of unconventional oil reserves, and a scathing critique of Peak Oil see [Bill Kovarik, The Oil Reserve Fallacy: Proven reserves are not a measure of future supply].

23 Bartis, J., et al. (2005). *Oil Shale Development in the United States: Prospects and Policy Issues.* report prepared by, for the National Energy Technology Laboratory of the U.S. Department of Energy. [online] RAND Infrastructure, Safety, and Environment division of RAND Corporation, http://www.rand.org/pubs/monographs/2005/RAND_MG414.pdf

24 Exxon Mobil (2016). *The Outlook for Energy: A View to 2040*, http://cdn.exxonmobil.com/~/media/global/files/outlook-for-energy/2016/2016-outlook-for-energy.pdf

25 FAQs - Earthquakes, Faults, Plate Tectonics, Earth Structure: *Can We Cause Earthquakes? Is There Any Way to Prevent Earthquakes?* (2009), USGS. October 27.

26 Induced Earthquakes (2015). [online] U.S. Geological Survey, http://earthquake.usgs.gov/research/induced.

27 Donoghue, A. (2004) Occupational health hazards in mining: an overview. *Occupational Medicine,* 54(5) 283-289.

28 U.S. Department of Interior (2002). *OCS Oil Spill Facts*, Minerals Management Services.

29 Mayuga, M. N., and Allen, D. R. (1970). Subsidence in the Wilmington Oil Field, Long Beach, California, U.S.A., in Land Subsidence, edited by L.J. Tison, International Association of Hydrological Sciences, pp. 66-79.

30 Deep Water Horizon, BP News letter (2020). Retrieved from http://www.bp.com/en_us/bp-us/commitment-to-the-gulf-of-mexico/deepwater-horizon-accident.html

31 Graham, S. (2003). Environmental Effects of Exxon Valdez Spill Still Being Felt, *Scientific American*, September 2003.

32 U.S. Environmental Protection Agency (1993). Understanding Oil Spills and Oil Spill Response, Publication Number 9200.5–105, Washington, D.C.

33 The Biggest Oil Spills in History (2010). *Foreign Policy Magazine*, April 30, 2010.

34 See for example, Seinfeld, J. (1975). *Air Pollution: Physical and Chemical Fundamentals*, McGraw-Hill, Inc.

35 Allen, L., et al. (2011). Fossil Fuels and Water Quality, *The World's Water*, Volume 7, Chapter 4., Editor Peter H. Gleik.

36 Kuwayama, Y. (2016). Exploring the Water-Energy Nexus: Water Use for Fossil Fuel Extraction and Processing. *Resource Magazine*, Jan 7, 2016.

37 Lustgaten, A. and Kusnetz, N., (2011). Feds Link Water Contamination to Fracking for the First Time, *Propublica,* December 8, 2011, https://www.propublica.org/article/feds-link-water-contamination-to-fracking-for-first-time

38 J Laherrere, J. (2003). Will the natural gas supply meet the demand in North America? *International Journal of Global Energy Issues, 19*(1), 1.

39 McKelvey, V. and Duncan, D. (1963). United States and world resources of energy, Presented at 3rd symposium on development of petroleum resources of Asia and the Far East (ECAFE), Tokyo, Japan.

40 Analysis of Crude oil Production in the arctic National Wildlife Refuge. (2008) Washington D.C.; GPO: U.S. DoE, EIA, SR/OIAF/2008-03.

41 Hubbert, M. (1956). Nuclear energy and the fossil fuels in Drilling and production practice, *American Petroleum Institute*, pp. 7-25.

42 The American Oil and Gas Reporter (2020). Retrieved from https://www.aogr.com/web-exclusives/exclusive-story/u.s.-holds-most-recoverable-oil-reserves

43 Deffeyes, K. (2001). *The Hubbert Peak: The Impending World Oil Shortage.* Princeton University Press.

44 BP Statistical Review of the World Energy (2020). Retrieved from https://www.bp.com/content/dam/bp/business-sites/en/global/corporate/pdfs/energy-economics/statistical-review/bp-stats-review-2020-full-report.pdf

Exercises

I. Discussion Questions

1. What is the difference between ultimate, recoverable, and proven reserves?
2. Why is it impractical to completely extract all the petroleum in a reservoir?
3. How does the size of a reserve change with the discovery of a new source? With finding a more efficient drilling technology?
4. Describe each of these terms and how they are different from each other:
   a. Charcoal
   b. Coke
   c. Fire ice
   d. Coal bed methane
   e. Coal gas
5. Define each term and their differences:
   a. Dry and wet natural gas
   b. Liquefied natural and petroleum gas
   c. Liquid natural gas and Natural gas liquid
   d. Shale oil, and oil shale

II. Problems

1. What is the upper limit to the quantity of oil that the earth could contain?
2. Assume an oil-exporting country producing one million barrels of oil a day today, of which 500,000 barrels are used for its local consumption every day. If the production decreases by 3% a year, while its local consumption increases by the same amount, how long does it take for the country to run out of its oil? What is the percentage drop in total oil export?
3. The yield on a savings account is given as 10%, calculated annually. How much will savings of $1,000, deposited today, grow in five years? How long does it take for our investment to grow to $2,000?
4. A Certificate of Deposit account accrues interest at the rate of 5% a year, compounded at the end of every quarter. How much interest does $10,000 accumulate if the account is locked for five years?
5. The U.S. population grew by 13% over the period from 1990 to 2000. Assuming U.S. population was estimated at 304 million in 2009 and that the rate of growth remains constant for the foreseeable future, estimate:
   a. The U.S. population in 2020.
   b. The latest data released by the Department of Commerce gives US population as 331 million. Compare this with data calculated from exponential growth assumption and comment on the accuracy of the model.
6. Use data of Table 3-2 to estimate the exponential expiration time for coal in the United States. U.S. coal consumption was one billion metric tons in 2009 and is expected to increase at a rate of 2% per year.
7. How long does it take for the population of bacteria which grows by 10% a day to triple (T_3)?

III. Multiple Choice Questions

1. Fossil fuels are
   a. Formed by the collision of a large meteorite with the Earth that resulted in the extinction of the dinosaurs.
   b. Formed by oxidizing carbon naturally present in organic matters.
   c. Formed from the remains of ancient trees, marine species, and microorganisms in oceans.
   d. Formed from the decay of dead dinosaurs
   e. All of the above.
2. The largest resources of conventional fossil fuel are:
   a. Coal in Russia, oil in the Middle East, and natural gas in the U.S.
   b. Coal in the U.S., oil in the Middle East, and natural gas in Russia.
   c. Coal in China, oil in the Middle East, and natural gas in the U.S.
   d. All in the U.S.
   e. All in the Middle East.
3. If the source of organic matter of the fossil fuel is from roots and trunks of trees, the most likely outcome is
   a. Coal.
   b. Petroleum.
   c. Natural gas.
   d. Peat.
   e. Any of the above.
4. The fossil fuel with the lowest ratio of carbon to hydrogen is
   a. Coal.
   b. Petroleum.
   c. Natural gas.
   d. Peat.
   e. Hydrogen

5. Lignite is typically characterized by its
   a. Old age, high heating value, and low sulfur content.
   b. Old age, low heating value, and low sulfur content.
   c. Young age, high heating value, and low sulfur content.
   d. Young age, low heating value, and high sulfur content.
   e. Young age, low heating value, and low sulfur content.

6. U.S. anthracite deposits lie mostly in
   a. Virginia.
   b. Kentucky.
   c. Pennsylvania.
   d. Texas.
   e. Montana.

7. Area mining is a term commonly referring to
   a. Mining to flatten land to prepare it for large-scale construction projects.
   b. Cutting a network of underground tunnels to extract coal.
   c. Mining a large rectangular block or "panel" of coal.
   d. Extracting coal from shallow mines when the surface is relatively flat.
   e. A technique used to survey large areas of land in search of coal mines.

8. The best method for removing sulfur from coal is:
   a. To apply biological cleaning that relies on microorganisms that eat up sulfur.
   b. To apply physical cleaning techniques, such as washing and gravity.
   c. To apply chemical cleaning techniques that cause sulfur to bond with other materials instead of carbon.
   d. To burn coal in a furnace at high temperatures.
   e. a-c, but not d.

9. Which countries were original members of OPEC?
   a. Iran, Iraq, Saudi Arabia, Libya, and the United Arab Emirates
   b. Iran, Iraq, Saudi Arabia, Algeria, and Tunisia
   c. Iran, Iraq, Saudi Arabia, Kuwait, and Venezuela
   d. China, the U.S., and Russia
   e. Angola, Algeria, Qatar, United Arab Emirates, and Ecuador

10. Which of the following statements is not correct?
    a. The greater the porosity of the reservoir rock, the easier is to extract oil.
    b. The greater the permeability of the reservoir rock, the easier is to extract oil.
    c. Reserves with the highest mobility are the easiest to access.
    d. The lower the density, the fastest fluid flows through the rock.
    e. The higher the permeability and the smaller is the viscosity of the fluid, the higher is its mobility.

11. Among the OPEC members that border the Persian Gulf are
    a. Iran, Libya, Kuwait, and Saudi Arabia.
    b. Iran, Iraq, Algeria, and United Arab Emirates.
    c. Iran, Iraq, Kuwait, and Saudi Arabia.
    d. Iraq, Venezuela, Qatar, and Saudi Arabia.
    e. Pakistan, Iran, Iraq, and Kuwait.

12. The largest reserves of conventional natural gas are in
    a. Saudi Arabia.
    b. Iraq.
    c. The United States.
    d. Russia
    e. China.

13. The largest reserves of coal reside in
    a. Saudi Arabia.
    b. Iraq.
    c. The United States.
    d. The Russian Federation.
    e. China.

14. In the deep underground pockets containing petroleum,
    a. Oil is on top, water is in the middle, and gas is at the bottom.
    b. Oil is on top, gas is in the middle, and water is at the bottom.
    c. Water is on top, oil is in the middle, and gas is at the bottom.
    d. Gas is on top, water is in the middle, and oil is at the bottom.
    e. Gas is on top, oil is in the middle, and water is at the bottom.

15. Peat
    a. Is the highest quality form of fossil fuel.
    b. Is the first stage in the formation of coal.
    c. Is embedded in tar sands.
    d. Is made by compressing animal dung.
    e. Is the nickname for Peter.

16. The U.S. refers to its proven reserve as the _____ percent probability of finding new reserves

a. 10%
   b. 50%
   c. 90%
   d. 99%
   e. 100%

17. Gasoline is a product of refining
   a. Propane.
   b. Ethanol.
   c. Coal.
   d. Petroleum crude.
   e. Natural gas.

18. What is the name of the fluid used to facilitate oil flow by keeping fractures in the rock open?
   a. Fractant
   b. Proppant
   c. Flowant
   d. Crackant
   e. None of the above

19. To increase their revenues, OPEC members have, on occasion, engaged in practices that involved
   a. Raising prices.
   b. Cutting production.
   c. Setting quotas.
   d. Selling oil beyond their designated allocations.
   e. All of the above.

20. Most U.S. electric generation comes from
   a. Crude oil
   b. Natural gas
   c. Nuclear
   d. Coal
   e. Wind

21. Petroleum is primarily used in the United States for
   a. Transportation.
   b. Generating electricity.
   c. Heating and cooling buildings.
   d. The petrochemical industry.
   e. The pharmaceutical industry.

22. Oil shale consists primarily of
   a. Sea shales containing remains of dead marine organisms.
   b. Kerogen.
   c. Kerosene.
   d. Bitumen.
   e. All of the above.

23. Which of the following statements is true about tar sand?
   a. Tar sand is expected to play a significant role in energy production in the twenty-first century.
   b. Almost 90% of all tar sand deposits in the world

reside in the U.S.
   c. Tar sand is a clean source of energy; unfortunately, it is expensive to produce.
   d. Per mass basis, tar sand yields a relatively large amount of energy.
   e. All of the above.

24. Natural gas combined-cycle combustion turbines
   a. Have greater combined efficiency.
   b. Have lower rates of pollutant emissions.
   c. Can be used as central or distributed.
   d. Reject heat at lower temperatures.
   e. All of the above.

25. Natural gas liquid is
   a. The same is liquefied natural gas.
   b. Shale gas turned into liquid.
   c. Liquid hydrocarbon after methane is removed.
   d. Natural gas cooled to very low temperatures.
   e. None of the above.

26. Propane is the fuel of choice in farms and in rural areas, mainly because it is
   a. Safer to use than methane.
   b. Can be easily compressed and turned into a liquid from methane.
   c. Cleaner than methane.
   d. Cheaper than methane.
   e. More plentiful than methane.

27. Which fossil fuel creates the lowest amount of carbon dioxide per kilogram of fuel burned?
   a. Butane
   b. Methane
   c. Coal
   d. Liquefied petroleum gas
   e. All four produce roughly the same amount.

28. Fire ice is another name for
   a. Methane hydrate
   b. Coal bed methane
   c. Syngas
   d. Natural gas stored under polar ice caps
   e. Coal gas

29. Natural gas liquid
   a. Is another name for liquefied natural gas (LNG).
   b. Is another name for liquefied petroleum gas (LPG)
   c. Consists of hydrocarbons other than methane that is separated from natural gas and liquefied.
   d. Is the natural flow of liquid petroleum during the primary phase of oil recovery.
   e. Is the product of petroleum distillation having C5-C7 molecular structure.

30. For each kilogram of gasoline, we burn in our cars, we pollute about _____ kilogram of air.
    a. 1
    b. 15
    c. 100
    d. Over 1,000
    e. Cannot tell

IV. True or False?

1. The higher the H/C ratio in the fuel, the dirtier the combustion will be.
2. It is possible to find natural gas even if no petroleum is found.
3. The largest resources of natural gas reside in Saudi Arabia.
4. Methane hydrate is crystalized methane and water.
5. A great portion of coal reserves resides in the Middle East.
6. The secondary recovery technique relies on reducing oil viscosity.
7. At the point at which oil production reaches its peak, half of all oil has been already consumed.
8. During the next doubling time for coal production, we will use as much coal as we have used up to this point.
9. Oil shale is an oily substance usually found in seashells.
10. Shale gas is the gaseous residue from decomposing shellfish and other marine animals.

V. Fill in the Blanks

1. Coal reserves are typically categorized by their_____ .
2. Although _____ has the most coal reserves in the world, it is _____ which produces the most coal.
3. Tar sands are grains of sand containing a viscous carbonaceous substance called _____.
4. The combustible fuel in oil shale is a waxy solid called _____.
5. As coal is heated at high temperatures, a mixture of carbon monoxide and hydrogen, called _____, is produced.
6. The propane and butane removed from natural gas are usually liquefied under pressure and sold as _____.
7. The other name for liquefied petroleum gas is _____ gas.
8. The total amount of a resource produced as of today is called _____ production.
9. The quality of coal called its rank, is a measure of the amount of _____ in the coal.
10. The lower sulfur content of coal is an indication of its higher _____.

PROJECT I -- Hubbert's Curve

Describe the major assumptions implicit in King Hubbert's prediction concerning oil production. Use his estimates on world petroleum production (Figure 3-13) to calculate the growth rate during the decades spanning from 1900 to the present.

1. Plot the cumulative total production as a function of time. What does this graph look like? Why?
2. What is the size of the total endowment?
3. What is the doubling time, assuming that peak production occurs at or near the turn of the century?
4. Based on his prediction, and assuming that the pattern of production follows his estimates, how much longer will our petroleum resources last?

PROJECT II -- Peak Uranium and Coal

Hubbert's analysis is not limited to oil production but can be applied to any non-renewable resources such as coal, natural gas, and even uranium. Search the EIA website to find the latest data on the ultimate size of these resources in the United States and the world, the rate of production and the pattern of consumption. For these resources, find:

a. The current rate of production
b. The time and amount of the peak production
c. The exponential expiration time

PROJECT III -- Non-Fossil Petroleum

There are two theories about how petroleum was formed. Although most scientists believe the origin of petroleum is biogenic, resulting from the decay of organic matter that is stored in sedimentary rocks (biogenic theory), a group of Ukrainian/Russian scientists proposes an abiogenic theory; i.e., hydrocarbon was trapped inside the Earth as it was formed, and gradually migrated to the surface. Discuss the evidence presented by both schools of thought. Which theory is more believable and why? What are the ramifications of each theory, if proven correct, on the world supply of petroleum?

Note: For a good summary and detailed list of literature, see, for example, Ragheb, M., "Nuclear, Plasma and Radiation Science: Inventing the Future." Chapter 4-Biogenic and Abiogenic Petroleum, available online at https://netfiles.uiuc.edu/mragheb/www.

Endnotes

1   Thorndike, E. (1976) *Energy and environment*. Reading:Addison-Wesley.

2   BP Statistical Review of World Energy (2015) http://www.bp.com/en/global/corporate/energy-economics/statistical-review-of-world-energy.html.

3   Mountjoy, E. (2020). History of Coke, Retrieved from https://iup.edu/archives/coal/mining-history/history-of-coke

4   World Coal Statistics, https://www.worldometers.info/coalMountjoy, E. (2020) History of Coke. https://iup.edu/archives/coal/mining-history/history-of-coke

5   Longwall Mining, (1955) U.S. Energy Information Administration. Office of Coal, Nuclear, Electric and Alternate Fuels, DOE/EIA-TR-0588.

6   Gao, J. (2004) 'Coal, Oil Shale, Natural Bitumen, Heavy Oil, and Peat;, in Encyclopedia of Life Support Systems (EOLSS), Developed under the Auspices of the UNESCO, Eolss Publishers, Oxford, UK, http://www.eolss.net

7   Ohtsuka, Y. (2004) *Desulfurization of Coal, in Coal, Oil Shale, Natural Bitumen, Heavy Oil and Peat*, [Ed. Gao Jinsheng], in *Encyclopedia of Life Support Systems* (EOLSS), Developed under the Auspices of the UNESCO, Eolss Publishers, Oxford, UK. http://www.eolss.ne

8   Malanima, P. (2010) 'Energy in History', in World Environmental History, [Eds Mauro Agnoletti, Elizabeth Johann, Simone Neri Serneri], in *Encyclopedia of Life Support System* (EOLSS), Developed under the Auspices of the UNESCO, Eolss Publishers, Oxford, UK. http://www.eolss.net.

9   Arabian traveler Baladzori (Al-Belazuri Ahmed) describes in "The Conquest of the Countries" that political and economic life on Absheron had been long connected with oil. (Published in English "The Origins of the Islamic State," by P.K. Hitti and F.C. Murgotten, v.1-2, N.Y., 1916-1924)

10 Macini, P. (2009) 'History of Petroleum Engineering-Upstream', in *Encyclopedia of Life Support Systems* (EOLSS), Developed under the Auspices of the UNESCO, EOLSS Publishers, Oxford, UK. http://www.eolss.net.

11 Laughlin, R. (2004) *John D. Rockefeller: Oil Baron and Philanthropist*. Greensboro, North Carolina: Morgan Reynolds Publishing.

12 Oilen, R. and Hinton, D. (2007) *Wildcatters: Texas Independent Oilmen*, Texas A&M University Press.

13 Meadows, D. (1972) *The Limits to Growth: A Report for the Club of Rome's Project on the Predicament of Mankind*, Universe Books, 2nd ed.

14 Meadow, D. (2002) *Limits to Growth: 30-Year Update*, Chelsea Green Publishing Company, pp. 94.

15 Cobb, K. Why Oil Prices are 10 Times More than in 1998. https://oilprice.com/Energy/Oil-Prices/Why-Oil-Prices-are-10-Times-More-than-in-1998.html.

16 Enhanced Oil Recovery, U.S. Department of Energy, Office of Fossil Energy, http://energy.gov/fe/science-innovation/oil-gas/enhanced-oil-recovery.

17 Hubbert, M. (1949) 'Energy from Fossil Fuels'. *Science,* vol. 109, no. 2823, pp. 103-109.

18 Chefurka, P. (2019) World Energy And Population: Trends To 2100. Countercurrents.org. Available at: https://www.countercurrents.org/chefurka201109.htm.

19 A similar argument is proposed by C. J. Campbell in 'The End of Cheap Oil', *Scientific American*, March 1998. The reserves at the time were 1,020 Gbo, and the annual production was 23.6, giving the world 43 years of supply.

20 Hopkins, P. (2007) *Oil and gas pipelines: yesterday and today*. American Society of Mechanical Engineers (ASME), [online] Pipeline Systems Division (PSD), International Petroleum Technology Institute. http://www. engr. mun. ca/~ spkenny/ Courses/Undergraduate/ENGI8673/Reading_List/2007_Hopkins. pdf .

21 CAPP (2005) Canadian Association of Petroleum Producers) Annual Report, 2005, http://www.capp.ca.

22 For an informative discussion of unconventional oil reserves, and a scathing critique of Peak Oil see [Bill Kovarik, The Oil Reserve Fallacy: Proven reserves are not a measure of future supply].

23 Bartis, J., et al. (2005) Oil Shale Development in the United States: Prospects and Policy Issues. report prepared by, for the National Energy Technology Laboratory of the U.S. Department of Energy. [online] RAND Infrastructure, Safety, and Environment division of RAND Corporation. http://www.rand.org/pubs/monographs/2005/RAND_MG414.pdf .

24 The Outlook for Energy: A View to 2040 (2016) Exxon Mobil, http://cdn.exxonmobil.com/~/media/global/files/outlook-for-energy/2016/2016-outlook-for-energy.pdf

25 FAQs - Earthquakes, Faults, Plate Tectonics, Earth Structure: Can We Cause Earthquakes? Is There Any Way to Prevent Earthquakes? (2009), USGS. October 27.

26 Induced Earthquakes (2015) [online] U.S. Geological Survey, http://earthquake.usgs.gov/research/induced.

27 Donoghue, A. (2004) Occupational health hazards in mining: an overview. *Occupational Medicine,* vol. 54, no. 5, pp.283-289.

28 OCS Oil Spill Facts. (2002) U.S. Department of Interior, Minerals Management Services.

29 Mayuga, M. N., and Allen, D. R. (1970) Subsidence in the Wilmington Oil Field, Long Beach, California, U.S.A., in Land Subsidence, edited by L.J. Tison, International Association of Hydrological Sciences, pp. 66-79.

30 Deep Water Horizon, BP News letter, http://www.bp.com/en_us/bp-us/commitment-to-the-gulf-of-mexico/deepwater-horizon-accident.html.

31 Graham, S. (2003) Environmental Effects of Exxon Valdez Spill Still Being Felt, *Scientific American*. September 2003.

32 U.S. Environmental Protection Agency (1993) Understanding Oil Spills and Oil Spill Response, Publication Number 9200.5–105, Washington, D.C.

33 The Biggest Oil Spills in History (2010) *Foreign Policy Magazine*, April 30, 2010.

34 See for example, Seinfeld, J. (1975) *Air Pollution: Physical and Chemical Fundamentals*, McGraw-Hill, Inc.

35 Allen, L., et al. (2011) Fossil Fuels and Water Quality, The World's Water, Volume 7, Chapter 4., Editor Peter H. Gleik.

36 Kuwayama, Y. (2016) Exploring the Water-Energy Nexus: Water Use for Fossil Fuel Extraction and Processing. Resource Magazine, Jan 7, 2016.

37 Lustgaten, A. and Kusnetz, N., (2011) Feds Link Water Contamination to Fracking for the First Time, *Propublica*, December 8, 2011. https://www.propublica.org/article/feds-link-water-contamination-to-fracking-for-first-time.

38 J Laherrere, J. (2003) Will the natural gas supply meet the demand in North America? *International Journal of Global Energy Issues, vol.* 19, no. 1, p.1.

39 McKelvey, V. and Duncan, D. (1963) United States and world resources of energy, Presented at 3rd symposium on development of petroleum resources of Asia and the Far East (ECAFE), Tokyo, Japan.

40 Analysis of Crude oil Production in the arctic National Wildlife Refuge. (2008) Washington D.C.; GPO: U.S. DoE, EIA, SR/OIAF/2008-03.

41 Hubbert, M. (1956) 'Nuclear energy and the fossil fuels in Drilling and production practice', *American Petroleum Institute*, pp. 7-25.

42 The American Oil and Gas Reporter (2020) https://www.aogr.com/web-exclusives/exclusive-story/u.s.-holds-most-recoverable-oil-reserves

43 Deffeyes, K. (2001) *The Hubbert Peak: The Impending World Oil Shortage*. Princeton University Press.

44 BP Statistical Review of the World Energy (2020). Retrieved from https://www.bp.com/content/dam/bp/business-sites/en/global/corporate/pdfs/energy-economics/statistical-review/bp-stats-review-2020-full-report.pdf

CHAPTER 4

Thermal Energy

Hot air Balloons (Creative Commons) ~ Image by Logga Wiggler

When you can't make them see the light, make them feel the heat. ~ Ronald Reagan (1911-2004)

The laws of thermodynamics control, in the last resort, the rise and fall of political systems, the freedom or bondage of nations, the movements of commerce and industry, the origins of wealth and poverty, and the general physical welfare of the race
~ Frederick Soddy (1877-1956)

Thermal energy is the energy associated with heat. Although the concept of heat is not new, its formal understanding only became clear during the nineteenth century, when it was shown that heat is the result of the motion of molecules—a concept that laid the foundation for the laws of thermodynamics.

In this chapter, we will give formal definitions of heat and temperature and explain how heat can be transferred as a result of a temperature difference. Then, we will discuss various modes of heat transfer and the laws of thermodynamics. Finally, we will show how these laws are used to design power plants, efficient machines, and other practical devices.

Heat and Temperature

Two of the earliest words that children learn are "hot" and "cold." They quickly learn to avoid touching hot stoves and getting too close to fires. They also learn to protect themselves with warm clothes in wintry weather and to stay in the shade on hot summer days. Despite this common perception, precise definitions of heat and temperature are no less elusive than most abstract concepts in physics. As we shall soon learn, heat is a form of energy that flows from a hot object to a cold object, as a result of a temperature difference that exists between them. It was the Scottish scientist Joseph Black (1728-1799), a founder of modern chemistry and a pioneer in the study of heat, who, for the first time, distinguished between the quantity (caloric value) and the intensity (temperature) of heat.

> **Question**: In one of the experiments conducted by Black, he noticed that when heated a block of ice, its temperature didn't rise until all the ice was melted. What conclusion can you make from this observation?
> **Answer:** That temperature and heat were two different things. Heat can be added to a substance without raising its temperature, and temperature can increase without adding any heat (for example, by compressing a gas in an insulated container).

Heat

Heat is perceived as something that produces a sensation of warmth. The sensation will, of course, be stronger in higher temperatures. There cannot be any heat transfer between two objects that are at the same temperature. The amount of heat transferred depends on the temperature difference and the conductivity of the path between the two objects; the direction of heat flow is always toward the cooler object.

Earlier philosophers considered heat as a substance that was passed from hot objects to colder ones. Heat was synonymous with hotness and remained the property of the substance for 2,000 years. During the seventeenth century, two German physicians, Johann Becher (1635-1682) and Georg Stahl (1659-1734), proposed heat as a substance that had mass and, like water that flowed from a higher to a lower elevation, heat flowed from a hotter to a colder object. This substance was called ***phlogiston*** (meaning flammable in Greek) and was given off when matter was burned, leaving true mass behind. Cold simply meant the lack of this substance. Black showed that when matter was burned, it produced carbon dioxide, which was an invisible gas that left the objects as they burned, eliminating the need for the mysterious fluid. During the same period, Joseph Priestley (1733-1804) discovered oxygen, an essential component of the air. Antoine Lavoisier (1743-1794) measured the weight of the product of combustion of substances that burned with oxygen and showed that they remained the same as the original reactants, so nothing was lost. Lavoisier's experiments proved that mass is conserved and, therefore, phlogiston could not have had mass, as originally assumed. Lavoisier failed, however, to dispel the notion of heat as a substance and replaced phlogiston with another substance called ***caloric***, which had no mass.

> *The Law of Conservation of Mass:*
>
> **Matter is neither created nor destroyed:**
> **it merely changes in form.**

It was not until the middle of the nineteenth century that Benjamin Thompson* (1735-1814) and James Prescott Joule (1818-1889) showed that this theory is also wrong; heat is not a substance, but rather a manifestation of motion at the molecular level (kinetic theory). For example, when we rub our hands against each other, both hands get warmer, even though, initially, they were at the same cooler temperatures. If heat were a fluid, then it would not have flowed between hands at the same temperatures. Instead, the hands are heated because the kinetic energy of motion (rubbing) has been converted to heat in a process called "friction."

Question. What does warming of hands resulting from rubbing them together suggest about the caloric theory of heat?
Answer: The caloric theory is again in trouble. If both hands are cold and at the same temperature, and if caloric can neither be created nor destroyed, where does the caloric fluid come from?

Question: Why was the concept of heat as a fluid so well received for so many centuries?
Answer: Because it met all the human notions of how a fluid should behave. It could pass from one body to another, similar to the flow of water in a river or a pipe. When a hot object came into contact with a colder one, the hot object cooled and the cold one got hotter as if some substance were passing from one to the other. Heat also was capable of running a steam engine in the same manner that water could turn a waterwheel.

Question: In an attempt to draw the equivalency of heat and work, Joule designed an apparatus consisting of a container of water, a paddle wheel, and a thermometer. The paddle was connected to a weight by a rope wrapped around a pulley. As the weight dropped, the paddle agitated the water and caused it to warm, raising its temperature. His careful and thorough quantitative measurements showed that work expended during the fall of the weight could be converted into heat. How does Joule's experiment show the fallacy in the calorific nature of the heat?
Answer: The concept of heat as caloric satisfactorily explains the flow of heat from hotter to colder objects. Calorific theory, however, fails to describe how work creates heat as in Joule's experiments. Production of heat required the flow of calorific, which neither could be created nor destroyed. The only conclusion that can be made is that no such fluids could exist and *heat was not a conserved quantity like mass*.

Temperature

The word "temperature" seems so familiar to most of us that we often take it for granted. While our built-in senses do provide us with a qualitative characterization of temperature, our senses often can be unreliable and misleading. On a cold winter day, for example, an iron railing seems much colder to the touch than a wooden fence post, yet both are at the same temperature. This "deception" by our senses arises because iron conducts heat away from our fingers much more readily than wood does.

Consequently, what we need is a more reliable and reproducible method for establishing the relative "hotness" or "coldness" of objects. Thermometers have been designed for just that very purpose. Thermometers come in many varieties and styles, but they all work the same way.

> SIY Put one hand in a glass filled with hot water (of course, not too hot!) and the second hand in a glass filled with cold water. If you now remove both hands, the hand from the hot water feels cold, while the one from the cold water feels warm. Aren't both hands feeling the same air temperature?

Temperature Scales

Thermometers are commonly used to measure temperatures. They are constructed by attaching a narrow capillary tube (stem) to a much larger reservoir (bulb) containing a colored liquid, such as water, alcohol, or mercury. As a thermometer heats up, the volume of the liquid in the bulb increases -- having nowhere to go, liquid climbs up

---
* Aka, Count Rumford

the tube; the higher the temperature, the more expansion of the liquid. For a given volume expansion, the smaller the cross-sectional area of the capillary tubes, the higher the height of the column of fluid -- and more accurate temperature reading is possible. Referring to the fluid analogy, temperature, as a measure of coldness or hotness of an object, could easily be interpreted as the "height" of the caloric fluid within the thermometer.

To be useful, thermometers have to be calibrated. Using two reference points (fixed points in nature that always remain the same) makes it possible to divide the distance between them into a number of equal intervals. The first thermometers were divided into 360 parts, like degrees of a circle (thus, the term "degree"). In 1708, Gabriel Fahrenheit (1686-1736) used spirits as the fluid and a mixture of ice, water, and salt to produce the lowest attainable temperature in a laboratory setting at the time, which was set as the zero mark. The second reference point he used was the temperature of the human body, which was assigned the value of 96. The choice of 96 is believed to be due to the fact that it is divisible by 2, 3, 4, 6, 8, 12, 16, 24, 32, and 48. Today, the Fahrenheit scale uses the freezing and boiling points of water as 32° and 212°. According to this scale, the normal body temperature is 98.6°F.

Swedish astronomer Anders Celsius (1701-1744), who assigned the numbers 0 and 100 to the freezing and boiling points of water, to define what is known as the centigrade scale.[†] In 1948, the International Committee on Weights and Measures adopted this scale as the temperature standard, calling it Celsius, in honor of its inventor.

In the United States, temperature is measured predominantly in degrees Fahrenheit. Most other countries use Celsius. Both temperature scales use the freezing and boiling points of water as a reference.

As we will see when we introduce the laws of thermodynamics, there is a lower limit to the temperature that can be reached. This temperature, called the Zero Absolute Temperature (-273.15° Celsius or zero kelvin), is understood to be the lowest possible internal energy that a body can have. There is no upper boundary to temperature, although the highest predicted temperature is 10^{38} K, which was the suspected temperature at the very beginning of the creation of Universe, the Big Bang.

Table 4-1 gives formulas for converting temperatures between Celsius, Fahrenheit, and Kelvin scales.

Table 4-1 Temperature Conversion Formulas
°F = 1.8 × °C + 32   (i)
°C = (°F − 32) / 1.8   (ii)
K = °C + 273   (iii)

Example 4-1: What is the body temperature (98.6°F) expressed in degrees Celsius? In Kelvin?
Solution: Applying equations in Table 4-1, we have:
°C = (98.6 - 32)/1.8 = 37
K = 273 + 37 = 310

Thermal Properties
Different substances have different abilities to retain or transport heat. For example, some materials, like Styrofoam and cork, are better insulators than aluminum, and some materials, like sand and brass, warm more quickly than water or grass. Thermal properties of materials are best understood, mainly by three quantities: density, heat capacity, and heat conductivity.

Density is mass per unit volume. It determines how closely molecules are packed, and therefore energy is transferred through the collision of one particle with another. The **heat capacity** of a substance measures its ability to retain heat. It is defined as the quantity of heat required to raise a substance's temperature by one degree. Water has a higher heat capacity than sand because it takes more heat to warm up by the same amount than sand does. In other

---
[†] To be exact, Celsius used zero as boiling point and 100 as the freezing point of water. Not long after Celsius died, the Swedish botanist, Carolus Linnaeus, suggested inverting the centigrade scale (marking 0 as the freezing point and 100 as the boiling point of water.

words, for the same amount of heat, the sand temperature rises more than water temperature. Closely related to heat capacity is *specific heat,* which is the heat capacity per gram of substance. Thus, a bigger object will have a greater heat capacity, but the same specific heat. The more loosely the components of a solid are held together, the higher the substance's specific heat. Graphite has a higher specific heat than diamond because diamond's lattice structure is more tightly bound than the graphitic structure of carbon. The quantitative relationship between heat transfer Q, and temperature rise over a material of mass m, and specific heat c is given by:

$$Q = mc (T_2 - T_1) \tag{4-1}$$

Example 4-2: How much heat is required to raise the temperature of 600.0 g of silver 65°C? The specific heat of silver is 0.24 J/g g.°C)
Solution: Q = 600 x 0.24 x 65 = 9,360 J.

Thermal conductivity is a measure of a body's ability to pass on heat. Diamond is an excellent conductor, silver is also very good, with copper not too far behind. Air appears toward the end of the list, meaning it is a very poor conductor but an effective insulator. No heat can be conducted in a total vacuum. In SI units, density (ρ) is expressed in (kg/m³), specific heat (c) is expressed in kJ/kg.K, and thermal conductivity (k) is expressed in W/m.K. Table 4-2 gives thermal properties of several materials.

Table 4-2 Thermal Properties of Selected Materials										
Good Conductors				*Average conductors*				*Poor conductors (good Insulators)*			
Material	*k* (W/m.K)	*c* (kJ/kg.K)	*ρ* (kg/m³)	*Material*	*k* (W/m.K)	*c* (kJ/kg.K)	*ρ* (kg/m³)	*Material*	*k* (W/m.K)	*c* (kJ/kg.K)	*ρ* (kg/m³)
Diamond	2,200	0.62	3,500	S. Steel	16	0.50	7,800	Wood (oak)	0.17	2.40	750
Silver	429	0.23	10,470	Ice (0°C)	2.20	2.05	800	Asbestos	0.15	0.84	2,400
Copper	400	0.38	8,900	Concrete	1.70	0.65	2,300	Fiberglass	0.040	0.84	48
Aluminum	220	0.80	2,700	Glass	0.80	0.80	2,700	Glass wool	0.040	0.66	52
Iron	80	0.45	7,840	Water	0.60	4.18	1,000	Air (dry)	0.024	1.0	1.0

k = thermal conductivity; c = specific heat; ρ = density

Question: Which has the higher specific heat, lead or water?
Answer: Lead atoms are over three times heavier than water molecules. Thus, a given quantity (by mass) of water has more molecules than the same quantity (by mass) of lead. Consequently, a given quantity of heat is distributed among fewer lead atoms than water molecules. This means that lead will experience a greater temperature increase and thus has a lower specific heat.

Question: Licking a silver spoon that's been sitting in a very hot cup of coffee probably won't burn your tongue, but a spoonful of the same hot coffee dropped on your tongue could leave a blister. Why?
Answer: The heat capacity of coffee (water) is over sixty times that of silver. That is, silver contains much less heat energy than coffee at a given temperature.

Another quantity closely related to thermal properties of material is coefficient of thermal expansion. **Thermal expansion** is the tendency of matter to change in shape, area, and volume in response to a change in temperature. Some materials such as copper expand upon heating and so have a high coefficient of thermal expansion. Other materials like rubber (at normal temperatures) and silicon (at cryogenic temperatures) contract (rather than expand) upon heating.

Question: What are applications of materials with negative thermal expansion?

Answer: There are many potential applications for materials with controlled thermal expansion properties. For example, we can mix a negative thermal expansion material (which contracts upon heating) with a "normal" material (which expands upon heating), to make a zero expansion composite material that does not shrink or expand in winter or summer. Another application is in preparing dental fillings from a composite material that has the overall expansion to that of tooth enamel, avoiding complications that may arise when drinking a hot or a cold drink.

Heat Transfer

Scientists distinguish between heat and energy, in that heat exists only when entering into or out of something. After it enters or leaves the body, it is no longer heat -- it has become energy. Heat can be transferred from one body to another if there is a temperature difference. Depending on whether two objects are in contact, whether a fluid is involved, or whether there's nothing in between, one of the following mechanisms will be dominant -- conduction, convection, or radiation. Heat transfer is an important mechanism in regulating our body temperature (Figure 4-1).

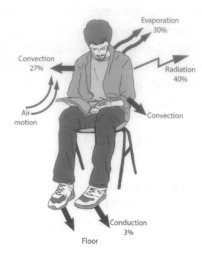

Figure 4-1
All modes of heat transfer are involved in temperature regulation of the human body.
Adapted from Thermodynamics by Cengel, Y. A. (2011).

Conduction

Conduction is the transfer of heat, from molecule to molecule, through a substance. If a steel bar is temporarily heated at one end, its molecules become agitated and move faster than neighboring molecules. When fast-moving molecules collide with slower molecules, some energy is transferred from faster to slower molecules. The chain reaction moves along the bar until its temperature is uniform. Although conduction can take place in gases and liquids, its effect is most significant when two solids come into contact. The effect also is more pronounced in objects with higher heat conductivities and larger temperature differences. The closer the molecules are packed, the easier conduction takes place. The rate of heat transfer across a solid slab increases with larger surface area, greater temperature differences across the slab, and larger thermal conductivity, and is inversely proportional to slab thickness. In the language of mathematics:

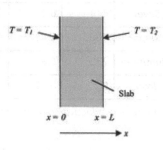

$$Q = kA\frac{T_2 - T_1}{L}$$

(4-2)

In this equation:

Q = Rate of heat transfer from the slab by conduction [W]

k = Thermal conductivity [W/m.K]

A = Area of conducting surface [m^2]

T$_1$ and T$_2$ = Temperatures across the slab [°C or K]

L = Slab thickness [m]

Question: Why do animals living in freezing climates often burrow into the snow to sleep?

Wind Chill Factor

Air circulation promotes cooling for two basic reasons. It removes the warmed layer of air, blanketing our bodies, which could potentially (in still air) act as insulation against conductive heat loss, and it promotes cooling by evaporation.

While some cooling can increase our comfort level, a strong wind, also, can create an unbearably chilling environment. On a windy day, air currents cause greater heat loss, as the warmer insulating air layer next to the body is continuously replaced by the cooler ambient atmosphere. The effect of the wind on how cold we feel is conveniently expressed in terms of the wind chill factor (WCF). Wind chill factor describes the rate of heat loss from exposed skin due to the combined effects of the wind and cold. The higher the wind speed, the higher the rate at which heat is removed from the body, and the lower the body temperature becomes. Above velocities of 40 miles per hour, any increase in wind speed has little additional effect on the body's loss of heat.

It must be emphasized that WCF expresses an actual cooling rate and not simply some illusory sensation, as anyone living in the "windy city" of Chicago, will attest to. For instance, the figure at right shows that for an air temperature of 10°F and a wind speed of 15 mph, the cooling power of the moving air is equivalent to that of still air at -7°F. The wind chill factor is a good way to determine the potential of frostbite or hypothermia.*

Wind (mph)	Temperature (°F)																	
Calm	40	35	30	25	20	15	10	5	0	-5	-10	-15	-20	-25	-30	-35	-40	-45
5	36	31	25	19	13	7	1	-5	-11	-16	-22	-28	-34	-40	-46	-52	-57	-63
10	34	27	21	15	9	3	-4	-10	-16	-22	-28	-35	-41	-47	-53	-59	-66	-72
15	32	25	19	13	6	0	-7	-13	-19	-26	-32	-39	-45	-51	-58	-64	-71	-77
20	30	24	17	11	4	-2	-9	-15	-22	-29	-35	-42	-48	-55	-61	-68	-74	-81
25	29	23	16	9	3	-4	-11	-17	-24	-31	-37	-44	-51	-58	-64	-71	-78	-84
30	28	22	15	8	1	-5	-12	-19	-26	-33	-39	-46	-53	-60	-67	-73	-80	-87
35	28	21	14	7	0	-7	-14	-21	-27	-34	-41	-48	-55	-62	-69	-76	-82	-89
40	27	20	13	6	-1	-8	-15	-22	-29	-36	-43	-50	-57	-64	-71	-78	-84	-91
45	26	19	12	5	-2	-9	-16	-23	-30	-37	-44	-51	-58	-65	-72	-79	-86	-93
50	26	19	12	4	-3	-10	-17	-24	-31	-38	-45	-52	-60	-67	-74	-81	-88	-95
55	25	18	11	4	-3	-11	-18	-25	-32	-39	-46	-54	-61	-68	-75	-82	-89	-97
60	25	17	10	3	-4	-11	-19	-26	-33	-40	-48	-55	-62	-69	-76	-84	-91	-98

Frostbite Times: ☐ 30 minutes ☐ 10 minutes ☐ 5 minutes

Surce: National Oceanic and Atmospheric Administration (NOAA)

* At wind speeds of 4 mph or lower, it is possible to have wind chill temperatures warmer than the actual temperature. This is because our body warms the layer of air next to our skin. Since air is relatively still, it acts as insulation, protecting us from colder air farther away.

Answer: In addition to fur and thick skin, air spaces in the snow help animals protect themselves in harsh weather. Snow, a poor conductor, slows the loss of body heat. In freezing weather, an igloo would provide a warmer shelter than would a wooden shack because the snow and ice are better insulators than wood.

Question: To keep a body warm in the cold of winter, would it be more beneficial to wear two layers of light clothing or one layer of clothing twice as thick?
Answer: Two layers; there is always some air trapped between the layers, providing additional insulation.

Convection

Convection is energy transfer by bulk motion. Unlike conduction, which is a microscopic phenomenon, convection involves the macroscopic interchange of energy between two mediums. Convection is most prominent in gases and liquids, where the distances between molecules are too large for conduction to be effective. Convection can be classified as natural or forced. In natural convection, fluid motion is a result of a density gradient, whereas forced convection is mainly due to a pressure gradient. Hot air balloons rise as a result of natural convection because they contain hotter, lower-density air. Helicopters are lifted by forced convection resulting from the pressure difference across their propeller blades. Dogs often pant to get rid of excess heat by forced convection.

It should be noted that heat transfer by convection and conduction are closely linked. Consider, for example, the cooling of a hot plate by blowing air over it. As the cold fluid replaces the warmer fluid (convection), the difference in temperature between the plate and the fluid right next to it increases, and more heat is conducted away from the plate; the process continues until the surface temperature approaches that of the fluid, in this case, the surrounding air. A fan placed in front of a car radiator functions in a similar manner.

In buildings, convection losses are due to air infiltration through the cracks, windows, and other openings in walls. Additional losses occur due to air movement inside and wind motion outside the exterior glass and windows. In a typical building, infiltration losses are the most significant and are comparable to losses by conduction. Common insulation materials such as fiberglass, rigid boards, cotton, and feathers work by creating tiny air pockets that slow down the convection flow of heat.

Like conduction, the rate of heat transfer by convection increases by the larger area, larger temperature differences (in this case, between the solid surface and the fluid next to it), and by the ability of the medium to carry heat away. Unlike conduction, no thickness can be assigned to the region where heat transfer is taking place. For this reason, it is a common practice to define a convective heat transfer coefficient that takes into account the fluid properties, as well as flow velocity, geometry, etc. Heat transfer by convection can be written as:

$$Q = hA(T_s - T_\infty)$$
(4-3)

Where:

Q = Rate of heat transfer by convection [W]

h = Convective heat transfer coefficient [W/m^{2}K]

A = Surface area [m2]

T_s and T_∞ = Temperatures at the surface and far away from it [°C or K]

Convection is important not only at the local level but also plays a role in large-scale movements of the atmosphere. The major winds are convection currents driven by temperature differences caused by non-uniform heating of the earth by solar radiation. The winds, in turn, drive the ocean currents.

Question: Why do water bubbles in a kettle rise during boiling?
Answer: The water in contact with the bottom plate warms by conduction, becomes lighter, expands, and rises. The water farther away from the bottom plate is colder and heavier and, thus, sinks to take the place of rising columns. The process continues until all the water boils and eventually evaporates.

The same process happens in the atmosphere. During the day, the ground warms up by absorbing solar radiation, heating the air next to it, and causing it to rise. At night, the ground loses its heat by radiating back to space, the air parcel in contact with the ground is dense and remains still, next to the ground. If it continues to cool, the moisture in the air will eventually condense, forming fog.

Question: A man exposed to a cold wind curls up to reduce the surface convection heat transfer from his clothed body. By how much is he capable of reducing the heat loss if he curls instead of standing up? Assume that the person can be represented as a cylinder 180 cm tall and 30 cm in diameter when standing and as a sphere when crouching.
Answer: Assuming that this person occupies roughly the same volume of space, whether standing or crouching. It is left to students to show that under these conditions, the sphere's surface area (crouching) is 28% smaller than the surface area of the cylinder (standing), reducing the rate of heat loss from his skin by 28%.

Question: Can stirring coffee help in lowering its temperature faster?
Answer: Yes. Stirring cools coffee in two different ways -- first by conducting heat away to the metallic spoon and through convection, by increasing its exposure to cooler ambient air.

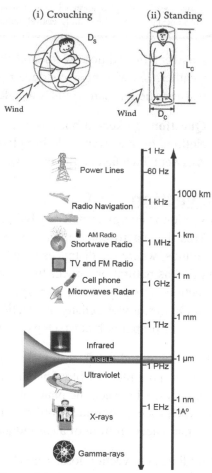

Figure 4-2
Electromagnetic wave spectrum.

Radiation

Radiation is the transport of energy of light migrating from a hotter to a colder surface. Unlike conduction and convection which require a material medium to transport heat energy, radiation transports energy via **electromagnetic** (EM) waves, even in a vacuum, with wavelengths that range in size from very long radio waves the size of a football field to very short gamma rays smaller than the size of the nucleus of an atom (Figure 4-2). Wavelength is the distance between two successive crests or troughs in a wave. No matter what the wavelength, they all travel at the speed of light, which is 300,000 kilometers per second in a vacuum.

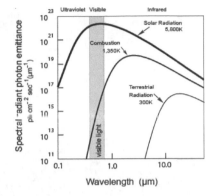

Radiation also can be expressed equally well in terms of tiny particles of energy called photons. The most energetic radiations are gamma rays and x-rays. Gamma rays come from the nuclei of certain atoms with wavelengths smaller than the size of the atom; x-rays come from the innermost orbits of electrons. The least energetic radiations are from electric transmission lines, radar, and radio waves.

Figure 4-3
Solar and terrestrial radiations as a function of wavelengths. Note the logarithmic scale and that most solar radiation is in the visible range, whereas terrestrial radiation is much lower intensity and is in the infrared.

Example 4-3: Cellular phone networks use a portion of the radio frequency spectrum designated as ultra-high frequency, or "UHF", for the transmission and reception of their signals. Frequency bands used in the United States are centered around 800 MHz (megahertz); one megahertz means one million cycles per second. What is the wavelength?
Solution: Because EM travels at the speed of light, their wavelengths and frequencies are related by
$\lambda = c / f = 3 \times 10^8 / 800 \times 10^6 = 0.375$ m

Whether a body emits energy at one wavelength or another depends on its temperature and surface properties. The higher the frequency, the shorter the wavelength and the more energetic the photon particles are. In fact, it can be demonstrated that the wavelength of the most energetic photons is inversely proportional to its temperature. In other words,

$$\lambda_{max}(\mu m) \times T(K) = 2{,}898 \; \mu m.K \qquad (4\text{-}4)$$

Different colors emit radiation differently; black objects emit the most, white objects the least. **Blackbody radiation** is the maximum amount of radiation of all objects maintained at a particular temperature.[‡] The fraction of blackbody radiation emitted by real surfaces is called emissivity. The emission is spread over all wavelengths, but as Equation 4-3 dictates, the higher the temperature, the shorter will be the wavelength at which peak emission occurs. The relation between radiation emission at a given wavelength in a unit time (emittance) is a complex function of temperature and pressure. The graphical representation of the results is given in Figure 4-3 for three different temperatures. 5,800 K for solar radiation in the outer atmosphere, 300 K for terrestrial radiation, and an intermediate temperature of 1350 K representing the radiation from a flame. The area under the curve represents the total emission from a black object and is given by

$$E = \sigma T^4 \qquad (4\text{-}5)$$

Where

E = Total emissive flux [W/m^2]

[‡] Most sources of light are not perfect blackbody sources. Incandescent lights behave mostly as blackbody radiators. Non-filament light sources, such as gas discharge lamps emit at discrete frequencies characteristic of that gas. Laser-emitting diodes (LEDs) emit at combination of several spectral lines.

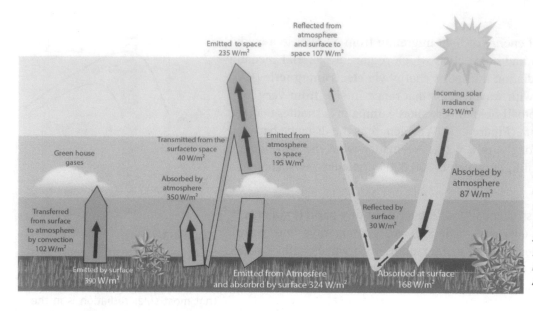

Figure 4-4
Schematic of the global annual average energy budget of the earth's atmosphere. The width of arrows indicates the magnitude of the flux (W/m²).

Source: Kiehl and Trenberth, 1997: Earth's Annual Global Mean Energy Budget, Bull. Am. Met. Soc. 78, 197-208.

σ = Stefan-Boltzmann constant ($\sigma = 5.67 \times 10^{-8}$ W/m².K⁴)

T = Surface temperature of the radiation source (K)

Solar and Terrestrial Radiations

Our primary source of energy is the radiation emitted by the sun, reaching us in the form of electromagnetic radiation, of different frequencies. Fortunately, much of the very-high-intensity radiation, such as gamma-ray, x-ray, and high-frequency ultraviolet radiation is attenuated by the atmosphere, and little of that reaches the surface of the earth. Most radiation penetrating the atmosphere is in the visible range that provides light. It also has a large component of infrared radiation that provides warmth. The combined visible and infrared radiation is what we normally call, "**thermal radiation**." As radiation hits the earth, a part of it is absorbed and raises the surface temperature. To maintain the equilibrium, this energy must be discarded in the form of infrared emissions. Figure 4-4 shows schematics of the average energy budget of the earth. Of the incoming solar radiation, nearly half is absorbed by the surface. That heat is returned to the atmosphere as sensible heat, by transpiration (latent heat), and as thermal infrared radiation.

Radiation at wavelengths shorter than 0.3 microns (high-intensity ultraviolet) is dangerous to humans; photons are sufficiently energetic to break bonds in molecules of living matter, causing damages ranging from simple sunburn to cancer and death. Fortunately, most are filtered out by the earth's atmosphere -- mainly the ozone layer. Wavelengths between 0.3 and 0.4 microns (near-ultraviolet) are weakly absorbed by clouds and dust in the atmosphere, while the rest reach the earth's surface. The atmosphere is largely transparent to the visible light covering wavelengths from 0.4 microns for deep violet to 0.7 microns for bright red. It is, however, virtually opaque to infrared radiation with wavelengths longer than 0.7 microns.

Microwaves have frequencies close to the resonance frequency of water molecules, and therefore, are readily absorbed by water molecules, a feature exploited in microwave ovens for the rapid heating of food. Microwaves are reflected by

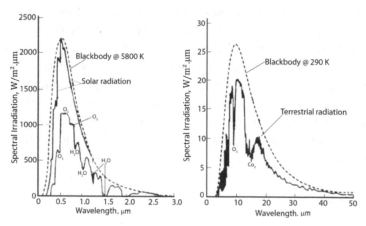

Figure 4-5
Solar and terrestrial radiations.
Adapted from Fundamentals of Heat Transfer by Bergman, et al. (2011). Wiley & Sons.

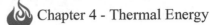

metals but are transparent to gases and plastics. Radar, TV, and radio waves have very long wavelengths from many meters to kilometers and, thus, are of very low energy; they are mainly of interest in communications.

Not all the radiation emitted by the sun reaches the earth, nor all the radiation leaving the earth ends up in the deep sky. The effect of absorption and scattering by atmospheric gases, ozone, water vapor, oxygen, and carbon dioxides is shown in Figure 4-5. Ozone absorbs strongly both in the ultraviolet and infrared; carbon dioxide and water vapor are strong absorbers in the infrared region around 2-3 microns, and again in 12-15 micron ranges. As we will see later, this is the main property responsible for the atmosphere's behavior as a greenhouse; letting solar radiation in, while trapping terrestrial infrared radiation, results in the global warming phenomenon.

An object at room temperature, say 20°C, emits nearly all its energy in infrared. The human body, at ordinary temperatures (37°C), also emits in the infrared region. In fact, 98% of the radiation from a bare human body ranges from 5-75 μm in wavelength. Using a special infrared camera, it is possible to "see" a human body or a passing gasoline car in total darkness. The image will not look like what we see with our single-lens cameras but will be a contour map of constant temperature regions. An infrared (thermal) image of a man wearing a tee-shirt is shown in Figure 4-6.

Question: What is the peak emission and total emissive power for radiation emitted by Sun, and by Earth?
Answer: From Figure 4-5, it is easy to infer that peak solar radiation lies around 0.5 μm corresponding to the color yellow of the visible light, and peak terrestrial radiation lies at around 9.7 μm, which falls in the infrared region of the radiation spectrum. These results also indicate why Sun appears yellowish to us, but we cannot see a person in the dark. Total emissive powers for solar and terrestrial radiations are calculated from Equation 4-4, as 6.42×10^7 W/m^2, and 460 W/m^2 of emitting surface, respectively. Most radiation is lost to space or absorbed and reflected by gas particles, thus, only a very small fraction of the solar radiation, from a high of 350 W/m^2 at the equator to a low of 100 W/m^2 at the poles, reaches the earth surface. Terrestrial radiation also is modified by the surface emissivity, and by particle absorption in the atmosphere.

Question: If human beings emit infrared, why do we see them in "visible" light?
Answer: What we see is not emitted light, but the reflection of light from other sources (sunlight, fluorescent light, etc.). This is why, in the absence of a light source (total darkness), there is no light reflected back to the eye and a person cannot see or be seen.

Radiative Exchange

Unlike conduction and convection losses that increase with temperature differences between cold and hot objects, radiation losses increase as the differences of the temperatures to the fourth power. The radiative heat transfer between two surfaces can be expressed as:

$$Q = \varepsilon \sigma A (T_{hot}^4 - T_{cold}^4) \qquad\qquad (4\text{-}6)$$

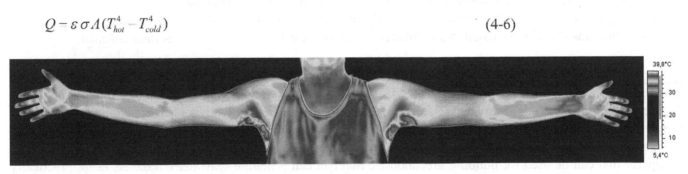

Figure 4-6
Thermal image of a man. The hotter regions (bare skin) are lighter in color, and cooler spots (tee-shirt, arm pits) are darker grey. The choice of shades of grey is arbitrary and does not imply a physical significance.
Image courtesy of Thermotronics Inc., Brazil.

In this equation,

Q = Net radiative energy exchange [W]

A = Area of radiative surface [m²]

ε = Surface emissivity [-]

T_{hot} and T_{cold} = Temperatures of the hot and cold surfaces [K]

In buildings, radiative losses are most significant when the surrounding terrain is either much colder or warmer than inside. Roofs can radiate a substantial amount of energy to the cooler night sky. They also provide a low-resistance path to solar heat during the summer months. Window glass is much colder than adjacent walls during the winter, causing internal heat, such as heat released by the occupants or heaters, to migrate toward windows. This results in a larger temperature difference across the glass layer and causes more heat to escape through windows. Double-glazing the windows, closing the curtains, and adding additional insulation in the walls and attic can significantly reduce these losses.

Question: In most of the Greek Cycladic islands, houses are painted white.[§] Why?

Answer: The white color reflects the harsh summer sun, keeping the inside cool. Indeed, it is recommended today, to paint roofs white. Also, called cool roofs, they can reflect 60% of the sunlight, reducing inside temperature by as much as 40°F in hot summers. Besides, the demand for air conditioning is reduced, which in turn reduces carbon dioxide emission and its impact on global warming.

Question: You can easily feel the heat from the sun through a glass window, but behind a sheet of glass you do not feel much heat from a fireplace. Why?

Answer: Common window glass is transparent to the wavelengths of radiation between 0.3-2.5 μm. A large portion of solar radiation falls in this range, allowing both sunlight and solar heat to pass through. Flames, however, emit at wavelengths in excess of 2.5 μm, the same region where window glass is practically opaque.

Question: Assuming that coffee is most desirable when it is hot, is it best to add creamer to coffee immediately after the coffee is poured or to add it right before drinking the coffee?

Answer: Creamer should be added as soon as the coffee is poured. Two effects are of importance: First, creamer makes coffee lighter in color, reducing its emissivity and heat loss from radiation. Secondly, adding creamer sooner decreases the temperature difference between coffee and the environment, reducing the rate of conductive and convective losses.

Question: Winter nights are normally cooler under a clear sky. Why?

Answer: On a clear night, terrestrial radiation escapes the atmosphere lowering the temperature. On the other hand, on a cloudy night, much of the terrestrial radiation is absorbed by the cloud and reradiated back to the earth.

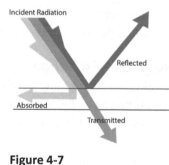

Figure 4-7
Surface radiation

Absorption, Reflection, and Transmission of Radiation

When radiation hits a surface, some is absorbed, some are reflected, and some is transmitted through a surface (Figure 4-7). Some materials absorb and reflect little radiation, so practically all the incident radiation passes through. They are called *transparent*. Other materials do not allow any radiation to pass through. These materials are called *opaque*. Glasses and some clear plastics are nearly transparent to visible radiation but opaque to infrared radiation, a property that can be used for building greenhouses. Sunlight can penetrate seawater ten meters deep. Practically all colors except the color blue are absorbed, making the water appear bluish. The surface gets warmer, forming a stable temperature gradient between the warm surface and cold deep water. As we will show later, we can exploit this temperature difference to design heat engines to produce power.

---

§ Originally was painted white by the order of Metaxas, the ruler of Greece in 1938 in an effort to stop the spread of cholera.

When solar radiation hits a landmass, it warms the air next to the ground, lowering its density. The situation is unstable, as warm air tends to rise, leaving a vacuum behind that must be filled by air rushing toward it. We will revisit this when we discuss local wind patterns in Chapter 12.

Thermodynamics

Thermodynamics is made up of two Greek words: *therme* (heat) and *dynamis* (power); it is the science that describes the dynamics of heat and how it can be converted to power. Thermodynamics is a phenomenological theory derived from four very simple observations: 1) heat cannot flow between bodies of the same temperature; 2) heat and work are just two different forms of energy; 3) heat always flows from a hot body to a cold body; and 4) there is a temperature (called zero absolute temperature) that can never be reached. These observations have been refined and reformulated as the zeroth, first, second, and third laws of thermodynamics. These laws are important because they provide the basis for designing many practical machines and modern devices that change heat into work (such as an automobile engine or a power plant) or turn work into heat or cold (such as an electric heater, a refrigerator, or a heat pump).

Equilibrium (The Zeroth Law of Thermodynamics)

Two objects at the same temperature are at equilibrium and remain at equilibrium until the temperature of one of the objects changes. On the other hand, if we put two objects of different temperatures next to each other, one object heats and the other cools until both bodies reach the same temperature. Saying it differently, if object A is in thermal equilibrium with both objects B and C, then objects B and C also must be in thermal equilibrium.

Although it seems that the zeroth law is obvious and deserves no special formulation, it is, indeed, a very important one. Not only, it allows us to measure temperatures of objects but, in fact, is the basis of all measurements. When a mercury thermometer measures the air temperature as 0°C, in reality, it invokes the zeroth law by assuming that the thermometer was in thermal equilibrium with the air, but also with a mixture of ice and water in the factory where it was calibrated. In other words, the mercury had expanded precisely as much as it did when it was placed in the ice-water mixture. When a thermometer is brought into contact with a patient's body, it compares its reading to an arbitrary scale in which one thermometer was calibrated by placing it in thermal equilibrium with two reservoirs, such as an ice bath and boiling water.

As stated above, the zeroth law can be extended to apply to other measurements such as wind speed, current in a wire, or fallout from a nuclear blast.

> **The Zeroth Law of Thermodynamics:**
>
> **Objects at equilibrium must have the same temperatures.**

Conservation of Energy (The First Law of Thermodynamics)

Up to the late nineteenth century, it was believed that potential energy and kinetic energy interchanged without a loss -- the principle commonly known as the "conservation of mechanical energy" (See Chapter 2). In reality, the conservation was not perfect. Some energy was lost through air resistance and friction. However, if we assume that all losses eventually turn to heat and that heat is a form of energy, then the suspicion arises that total energy is conserved. This is the law of conservation of energy, or the First Law of Thermodynamics, which states that:

> **The First Law of Thermodynamics:**
>
> **Energy can be neither created out of nothing nor destroyed into nothing, but it only can be changed from one form to another.**

Although we often talk about the transformation of energy, we should note that the nature of energy has not changed. We are only talking about its manifestation from one form to another. For example, a glass resting on the edge of a table has a certain potential energy. If the glass is knocked off the edge, its potential energy is converted to kinetic energy as it accelerates toward the ground. When the glass hits the ground, the kinetic energy is converted to light energy (sparks), sound energy (a bang), thermal energy (heat), and chemical energy (the glass breaks). The amount of work performed by an engine never equals the full amount of chemical energy released by the burning fuel. The portion of energy not converted to the useful work of turning the wheels goes to exhaust heat, radiator heat, and heat radiated into the environment -- collectively called the waste heat.

Question: If energy can be neither created nor destroyed, how can people claim that there is an "energy shortage?"
Answer: Terms such as "energy shortage" and "energy waste" are misnomers. According to the first law, energy can never be wasted; it may only be converted to a form not readily usable to us. While total energy must remain constant, useful energy -- that which can be used as fuel or to perform work -- may be in short supply.

The First Law of Thermodynamics is the basis of all energy conversions. Numerous practical devices have been designed that accomplish useful tasks through the conversion of energy from one form to another. Table 4-3 gives examples of different kinds of energy conversions.

> **First Law and Nuclear Reactions**
>
> In the century and a half, since the first law was formulated, the law has come into question, on occasion. For example, nuclear reactions seemed to occur in violation of this law. Thanks to the pioneering work of Einstein and others, the first law continues to be upheld -- at least so far.

Table 4-3 Examples of Different Kinds of Energy Conversions					
From/To	**Mechanical**	**Thermal**	**Chemical**	**Electrical**	**Light**
Mechanical	Bicycle, Gearbox	Friction	Matches	Wind Generator, Microphone	Sparks
Thermal	Gas turbines	Heat pipe, Heat exchanger	Sintering/Catalysis	Thermocouple	Luminescence
Chemical	Rockets, ICE	Metabolism	Digestion	Battery, Fuel cell	Candle
Electrical	Electric motor, Loudspeaker	Resistor heater	Electrolysis	Transformer, Inverter	Light bulb
Light	Solar sail	Flat-Plate Solar collector	Photosynthesis	Solar Cells	Fluorescence

Chaos and Disorder (The Second Law of Thermodynamics)

Heat flows spontaneously from hot objects to cold ones. Water flows from high mountains toward rivers. Air rushes out of a punctured rubber balloon. Smells tend to diffuse outward to span greater distances. Humans grow older with each breath. A house left unattended quickly becomes disorganized. More simply put -- events happen in a certain direction -- from order to disorder, from concentrated to diffuse, from useful to useless, from available to unavailable. This is one statement of the Second Law of Thermodynamics which, generally, can be stated as:

> *The Second Law of Thermodynamics:*
>
> **All natural processes tend to go from order (concentrated) to disorder (dispersed).**

Although many people think the Second Law of Thermodynamics must only be of interest to physicists, engineers, and those who deal directly with heat and energy, the second law has far-reaching consequences, not only in

Historical Interlude

Contrary to what most believe, Lord Kelvin was not the first person to formulate the law of the conservation of energy. The first law was first proposed by a German physician by the name of Julius Robert Mayer (1814-1878), who worked aboard a ship sailing to the East Indies. While in Java, he noticed the blood of natives to be considerably redder than that of his fellow countrymen. He attributed this to the higher, intense tropical heat and a greater concentration of unused oxygen in their blood -- caused by their bodies using less oxygen and requiring less heat to maintain their body temperatures. He further proposed that food energy is the only source of energy required for growth and to power muscles. When muscles perform work, the energy that is consumed must be balanced by the oxidation of food. Although not sufficiently supported by experiments, Mayer provided the first indication for equivalency of heat and work and conservation of energy.[i]

[i]*"The Century's Progress in Physics,"* by Henry Smith Williams, *Harper's New Monthly Magazine,* Volume 95, No. 566, July, 1897, pp.258-259.

predicting the fate of the universe but also in all aspects of our daily lives (See Box "Entropy"). The second law gives us guidelines for what we can and cannot do. It tells us how to design better machines and provides us with a blueprint for using our resources more efficiently. In short, it gives us a sense of direction.

Question: What should we expect after a severe earthquake? What will happen to snow as it warms?
Answer: Accordingly, it predicts that earthquakes flatten buildings – decreasing order. Similarly, as the air gets warmer, snow is expected to melt, going from a state of high order (ice's lattice structure) into disorder (unstructured liquid).

The second law does not imply, however, that there cannot be (on a local scale) a transformation from chaos back to order. In fact, this is the main mechanism by which we can defy nature. When we build houses, we change the randomly distributed bricks, lumber, and clay into structured walls of living rooms, bedrooms, and kitchens. We bring order into our house by cleaning it. What the second law precludes us from doing is not creating order, but creating order without causing even more disorder somewhere else (usually in the neighborhood).

Entropy

Measuring the temperature of a room or the pressure of the tires on a car are, of course, easy and routine tasks. All that is needed is a thermometer or a pressure gauge. But how can we measure chaos? Is there a way to quantify how much dirtier my room is than yours? An Austrian scientist, Ludwig Boltzmann (1844-1906), attempted to do exactly that (Figure 4-8). The result of his studies is summarized in a single equation that defines *entropy*[¶] (from the Greek root meaning transformation or evolution) as a measure of randomness, or the total number of ways that a system can rearrange itself.

Figure 4-8
Ludwig Boltzmann (1844-1906). His famous entropy equation $S = k \log W$ is carved on his gravestone in Vienna.

The approach can best be illustrated by considering a system in perfect order (let's say a tray of 1,000 coins, all with heads facing up). The more the system is agitated, the more the coins flip over and turn to tails, and the more randomly the coins are distributed. The ultimate outcome is when exactly half of the coins are tails and the other half are heads. Any further attempt does not (statistically) change the outcome., i.e., we have reached a state of equilibrium. This is the state with the maximum number of configurations (number of ways that we can rearrange the coins) and therefore is the most probable.[**]

Question: It is an easy task to mix two tablespoons of salt and pepper. It takes quite a bit of work, however, to separate a mixture of salt and pepper into its constituents. Why?
Answer: Salt and pepper, by themselves, are relatively orderly, but when mixed, the disorder increases

---

[¶] Coined by Rudolf Clausius, who took *en* and *y* from *energy* and inserted *trope* which means "transformation" in Greek in the middle.
[**] There are only two configurations that constitute order (all heads, or all tails); there are many more configurations that there are randomly distributed.

considerably. Separating salt and pepper requires work because we need to create order by reducing the mixture's entropy.

Question: An electric heater dissipates electrical energy into heat (and some light). What are the implications of the first and second laws of thermodynamics?
Answer: The first law assures that electrical energy is completely converted to heat (and light). The second law implies that the energy flow is from order (flow of electrons in the electric coil) to disorder (random motion of heated air molecules in the room).

Question: When a gas balloon is heated, it expands. What happens to the entropy?
Answer: As the balloon expands, it opens more room for gas molecules to occupy. In other words, the possibility that gas molecules take new configurations. The position of the molecules will be known with less certainty and thus the balloon's entropy increases.

Question: Ice is a more structured form of molecules of H_2O than liquid water. Therefore, as water freezes during a cold wintry night, its entropy decreases. Wouldn't this be a violation of the law of entropy?
Answer: Not at all. To freeze the water, heat has to be removed. This heat goes into the atmospheric air in the vicinity of the body of water. The increase in entropy of the air would more than compensate for the reduction of entropy in the water. Remember, the entropy of a system can increase or decrease. It is the entropy of the universe that continually increases.

Question: Creationists argue that the evolutionary processes appear to prefer more orderly structures, in violation of the second law, which prefers disorder. What is wrong with this argument?
Answer: It should be pointed out that the increase in disorder suggested by the second law applies only to a *closed system*. The Earth is not a closed system, receiving a continuous supply of energy from the sun.

Question: If molecules are moving randomly, then is it possible that, in a freak instant of time, all the air is sucked into a corner of a room, depriving the rest of the people in the room of oxygen?
Answer: The second law is a probabilistic law, i.e., the system of particles can take any arrangement, so, such an occurrence is theoretically possible, although highly improbable!![††] Rest assured that the **most probable state is that of uniform distribution** of air particles throughout the room. We call such a state **equilibrium.**

Even though entropy is telling us the direction of time, it does not tell us its speed; no matter what we do in our lives, we will create some entropy, somewhere in the world, so we are continuously changing available matter and energy into waste. How we do it will affect how fast we deplete our available resources.

The second law and the ultimate fate of the Universe. According to the second law, the universe is continuously slipping into chaos, things turn from order to disorder, heat flows from warm to cold, wind flows from high pressure to low pressure, current flows from high to low electric potential, the matter becomes less concentrated, etcetera, until eventually all non-uniformities in nature disappear, and we reach what we call thermodynamics equilibrium or a "heat death." When that happens, calm becomes prevalent throughout the world, and nothing will ever happen again -- entropy of the world reaches its maximum, there is no way to tell the past from the present and the future. The arrow of time has ceased to exist.

Relationship to the First Law

A gas that is heated can expand and push a piston to perform a task, such as pushing a car forward. When its brakes are applied, a car will slow down because of friction. In the first example, heat was used to do some work, or deform a material. In the second instance, work (kinetic energy of motion) was converted to heat the road and the tires. These observations are consistent with the First Law of Thermodynamics; heat is converted to work, and work is converted to heat, implying that mechanical energy (work) and thermal energy (heat) are quantitatively the same. In

[††] Indeed we can find that the probability is on the order of $1/N_{AV}!$, where N_{AV} is Avogadro number equal to $6..02x10^{23}$.

Entropy[i]

Only entropy comes easy. ~ Anton Chekhov (1860-1904)

Just as the constant increase of entropy is the basic law of the universe, so it is the basic law of life to be ever more highly structured and to struggle against entropy. ~ Vaclav Havel (1936-2011)

The concept of entropy is not unique to physicists and engineers but also has appealed to historians, philosophers, and social scientists. In short, it is a measure of the natural decay within a system, living or nonliving, and whether it is a physical or social system.

The Greeks believed that the world was created in perfect order by the Deity, who also placed within that order, the seeds of decay. The Golden Age was a state of pure perfection, a state of perpetual bliss and innocence, in which there was no disease, no crime, and no hunger. But, it wasn't very long until Pandora's curiosity tempted her to open a gift box from Zeus – a box that, once opened, unleashed all the evils previously unknown to humankind. The Golden Age continued its downward spiral, replaced by the Ages of Silver, Bronze, Heroic, and Iron, each more tarnished than the one before. The destruction continued as chaos replaced the order, and corruption spread throughout the world until such time as the Deity intervenes and brings order back into the universe. Ever since, history has been seen as an ever-repeating cycle, moving from order to chaos. Buddhism and Hinduism espouse similar mythology, adhering to an endless cycle of existence; each death begets a form of rebirth. But, unlike the Greek notion of continuous decay, each cycle leads down the path of Enlightenment, until the absolute state of truth, or Nirvana, is reached. Christian theology rejected the cyclic notion of history, but retained the idea of a decaying world with a distinct beginning, middle, and end in the form of Creation, Redemption, and the Final Judgment.

Descartes and Newton viewed the universe as a machine that worked precisely and according to a set of laws that dictated the precise motion of heavenly objects, as well as those of subatomic particles. Knowing the state of the universe at any given time was enough to predict its motion at any time in the future -- therefore, in principle, it was possible to predict the fate of the universe a priori. In *"The Wealth of Nations"* Adam Smith extended the mechanical view to financial systems by proclaiming that, as there are sets of laws that dictate the motion of planets and stars, there also are economic laws that predict the movement of capital. As long as these laws are obeyed and in the absence of artificially induced government regulations, economic growth is sustained and progress is inevitable. In the theory of biological evolution described in his book *"On the Origin of Species,"* published in 1859, Charles Darwin seems to suggest that there is a natural selection to evolutionary progress, not in the direction of eventual decay and destruction, but toward a state of progress and order. The **survival of the fittest** meant to some, a triumph of order over disorder and of the healthy over the sick, just as Adam Smith's view promoted self-interest and accumulation of wealth.

As Rifkin elegantly points out, unlike some who view human history as steps toward progress and higher efficiency, every stage of development has been a new entropy watershed, in which humans had to work harder and exploit natural resources faster, and to a greater extent, just to maintain the minimum needed for survival. Great changes have occurred not as a result of the building of abundance, but as a result of the dissipation of existing resources. In England, coal replaced wood, only because most British forests had been cleared. Today, oil is the fuel of choice, but it is harder to drill; we must dig deeper and deeper as we use up that which is most available; splitting atoms is even more difficult. Another example is found in the way we clothe ourselves. Wool replaced leather, and cotton replaced wool out of necessity; to make leather it was necessary to kill an animal -- wool required raising sheep, which needed vast areas of grazing land formerly allocated for growing crops. Cotton replaced wool since it could be cultivated in overseas colonies and imported back to the mother countries, for the manufacture of clothing. As the access to colonial lands became more restricted, synthetic fibers replaced cotton, but at the expense of the huge amounts of energy needed to run more complex machinery.

Economic progress, often thought to be the result of an increase in productivity and ever-more complex technology, in closer inspection, follows the law of entropy. The technological achievements of recent decades have been made possible only through the expenditure of greater quantities of energy, and the production of a corresponding amount of waste. The price per Btu of energy has been rising steadily, which, in turn, has affected the price of food, housing, healthcare, and all other indicators of economic activity. Inflation, then, is ultimately a measure of the entropy rise in the environment. New technologies do not turn waste into value but extract energy at a higher and higher cost to the environment. Increased productivity, thus, is nothing more than increased energy flow-through and greater disorder at a price that, ultimately, has to be paid for by the entire society. In reality, the greater gross national product is, the bigger is the national cost of turning useful energy into useless energy.

i Adapted from Rifkin, J., "Entropy: A New World View," The Viking Press, 1980.

both instances, the total energy of the system has not changed.

It is true that work can be converted to heat rather easily, but experience tells us that the reverse -- cooling the tires and road to move the car backward -- is not possible. This shows that heat and work are qualitatively different -- work can be turned entirely to heat, while the reverse is not true. This simple observation is a direct consequence of the Second Law of Thermodynamics, which states that processes occur naturally in a preferred direction and not the other, although energy expenditure is exactly the same in both cases.

Work has a higher quality than heat (2nd law), even though they are numerically the same (1st law).

To understand the difference between heat and work, let's examine what happens as a ball falls on a table. It simply bounces up and down a few times, and each time, the ball reaches a lower height, until it eventually comes to rest. On a macroscopic scale, the ball can be visualized as a number of particles packed together in a sphere. When the ball is released, molecules have only local vibration about their equilibrium position, with no net motion downward. As the ball loses its potential energy, particles of the ball move in unison (coherently) with the same average velocity as that of the ball. The more it falls, the average velocity increases until it reaches the table. As it collides, some of the energy is transferred to the molecules of the table, causing them to move at random (incoherently). The particles at the surface of the table continue to collide with the molecules below them, distributing their energies to even more particles. The ball, on the other hand, reverses its motion forcing all the molecules to move up again in a coherent fashion, but with decreasing velocity. The repeated collisions with the table will eventually exhaust all the orderly motion of the ball into the random motion of the molecules in the table (and the ball). Both the table and the ball are heated slightly. The conversion of the disorderly motions of the molecules in the table to the orderly motion of the ball is another matter and is explained below when we discuss the operation of heat engines.

It should be noted that if it weren't for the second law, we could convert heat and work back and forth without ever running out of energy. A car would convert the work to heat, which could then be reconverted back to work to push the car further and further, without ever needing to fill the gas tank again. Recycling would return all the material used to the original form, ready to be used in another product, although some energy was expended in the process. The truth is that every time one form of energy (or material) is converted to another form, although the total remains the same (1st law), it becomes a bit less useful, or becomes less available for doing work (2nd law). In other words, nature will impose a penalty by making it lose some of its potentials. Every time we burn a lump of coal, we are reducing the availability of energy and our ability to do work. The same is true with recycling: matter degrades with every use until it becomes a total waste -- requiring more and more energy for reprocessing, and in the process, polluting the environment.

Casino Analogy

C.P. Snow (1905-1980), the famous British Physical Chemist and novelist, summarized the three laws of thermodynamics in a casino metaphor in the following ways: In his example, you, the player, are the source, the house is the sink, and the money is the unit of transaction.

First Law - You cannot win (that is, the total amount of money in your pocket and the casino's safe is constant).

Second Law – You cannot break even (that is, there is a preferred direction that money travels -- from your pocket to the casino's safe).

Third Law - You cannot get out of the game (that is, you are likely to play until all your money is exhausted).

Analogy to Cash and Gift Certificate

The difference between work and heat can be compared to that of cash and a retail store's gift certificate. Cash and gift certificates have the same nominal value in the same way that work and heat are quantitatively the same (1stLaw). Cash is of a higher quality because it has a wider application. Similarly, work is of a superior quality because it can be used in more ways (2nd Law). When purchasing an item from the retailer, its gift certificate has the same utility as cash. The same is true when work is used to perform a task that can be accomplished equally well by heat. For example, a resistance heater uses electricity (a form of pure work) to heat a house -- a task that could easily be done using a gas heater.

Question: Those who have visited casinos in Las Vegas or other gambling places, notice that they require to exchange cash for plastic chips. Comment!

Answer: Aside from the casino claim that it is more sanitary to handle chips, they are exchanging cash with something of a lower quality; chips have lower cash values outside that casino, or even in restaurants and gift shops within the casino. You have lost some value, even before you start the game!

This, however, does not mean that the gift certificate is of no value outside the retail store, since it can be traded for other services or even cash, but at a smaller amount than its face value. The same can be said for heat; we can use heat to produce work (in a heat engine), but at an efficiency of less than 100%

Question: A poor student stops at the gas station to put some gasoline into his gas tank, when he discovers all he has, is a $50 gift certificate. The attendent offers him only $30 worth of gas in exchange for the gift certificate. What is the efficiency of this transaction?

Answer: Recall the definition of efficiency as the ratio of what we desire (gasoline) to what we have to pay (gift certificate). The efficiency is $30/$50 = 60%, i.e., only 60% of its nominal value is useful. The other 40% is unavailable for further transactions.

Availability of Energy

As we discussed above, as one form of energy is converted to another form, the first law of thermodynamics guarantees that no part of the energy is lost. A flywheel spinning at high speed has a large amount of energy. As the flywheel slows down, some of the energy goes to heat up the air. The molecules of air are accelerated but move in all directions. It is now very difficult to use the random motion of air molecules to turn a shaft and produce useful work. Some of the ability to perform work is lost (all energy is not available) and we have lost some ability to restore the original state of the flywheel. As long as the flywheel spins at its original speed, all its atoms rotate in a predictive way and in complete unison -- there is no loss of availability. The same can be said of the potential energy of falling water in a dam. The entire energy can be used to turn a generator to produce electricity, to propel a car, or lift an elevator; the potential to perform work has not been diminished.

The concept of loss of availability is closely related to the production of entropy. As the orderly motion of molecules is turned into random motion (by friction), the system loses its ability to perform work, and entropy increases. The system has undergone some *irreversibility*. The system can be brought back to the original state, however, but this requires doing additional work, which itself is associated with even more losses. The availability of energy decreases even more.[‡‡]

Note, that this does not imply random motion of particles cannot be converted to orderly motion and perform work. As we shall see below, only a fraction of the heat energy can be converted to work (as in a heat engine).

Question: Why is it more advantageous to use a gas heater over an electric heater for heating a room?
Answer: Remember that most electricity is generated in power plants by burning some form of fossil fuels. In the process, 70% of the energy is lost to the atmosphere (see "Heat Engines"). Additional losses occur during

---

[‡‡] The students who take a more advanced course in thermodynamics will learn of a new term, "exergy," that distinguishes the part of energy in a system that can be converted to work (is available) from the part that cannot (is unavailable). Unlike energy, exergy is not conserved and destroyed in all real processes.

transmission before the electricity is converted back to heat -- a task that could be accomplished directly by burning gas in a gas heater. Using electricity for heating purposes is similar to using cash when you could have used the gift certificate instead!

Absolute Temperature (The Third Law of Thermodynamics)

The laws of thermodynamics do not put any limit on how high temperatures can rise. But is there a limit on how low we can go? This temperature is called absolute zero (-273.15°C) -- a temperature so low that it cannot be reached.[§§] As substances cool, their molecules move with less speed and their kinetic energy decreases. Actually, it can be shown that the kinetic energy of particles is directly proportional to temperature. To rephrase, the temperature can be seen as a measure of the kinetic energy of particles. It is, therefore, easy to understand that at temperatures of absolute zero, all molecules are motionless (have zero kinetic energy) and entropy approaches zero.

It must be noted that although molecular motion stops at zero absolute temperature, subatomic particles are not stationary, but continue to oscillate about their equilibrium position. For example, the entropy of a substance that is not pure crystalline (such as a gas, liquid, or an alloy) is not zero at absolute zero.

> *The Third Law of Thermodynamics:*
>
> **The entropy of a perfect crystal at absolute zero is exactly equal to zero.**

Thermal Devices

One of the important applications of thermodynamics is in designing devices that transform one or more forms of energy into more useful forms (for us). Of course, we wish to design these devices so they use the least amount of energy, with the highest efficiencies possible. The First Law of Thermodynamics requires a minimum amount of energy to achieve a task. The Second Law of Thermodynamics puts a limit on how efficient this device can be. From a theoretical standpoint, a device is most efficient (ideal) when it operates with no frictional losses; so in reality, most systems have lower efficiencies.

Thermal devices can be classified into those that produce (or remove) heat, or produce (or require) work. Some examples of thermal devices we use or are impacted by, in our everyday lives are engines, power plants, refrigerators, heat pumps, and air conditioners. In all these devices, some form of fuel is consumed. Whether used in automobiles or jet aircraft, heat engines convert part of this energy to shaft work that eventually runs the vehicle (Figure 4-9a). Power plants work in a similar fashion, but their work output is mainly in the form of electricity. Refrigerators, air conditioners, and heat pumps work in, essentially, the reverse direction; they use fuel energy to "pump" heat away from the space we want to cool (Figure 4-9b) or "pump" heat into the space that we want to heat (Figure 4-9c). No matter what the application, part of the energy is always discarded as waste energy into the surrounding atmosphere. In other words, it is impossible to build devices that convert 100% of the input energy into useful forms. Furthermore, because there are always some frictional losses, actual efficiency is always less than the maximum theoretical efficiency dictated by the laws of thermodynamics.

[§§] The lowest temperature ever recorded in the laboratory is one-half billionth degree above absolute zero (0.5×10^{-9}K)-- NASA News Release, September 11, 2003..

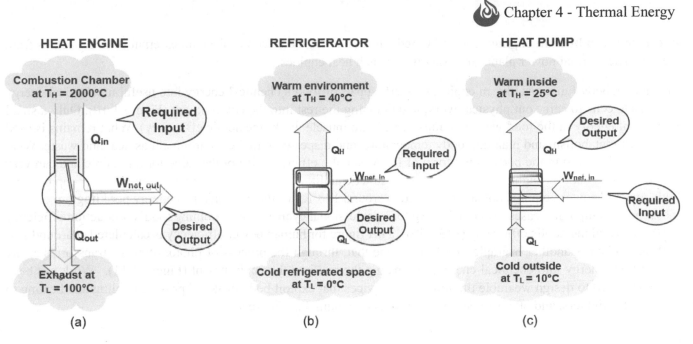

Figure 4-9
(a) Heat engines, (b) refrigerators, and (c) heat pumps

Heat Engines

Heat engines are devices that convert heat to work. The principle of operation is rather simple; heat is removed from a reservoir at high temperature (source) and partially converted to work. Some of the energy must be discarded to a low-temperature heat reservoir (sink) as waste heat in the process. The smaller the waste, the higher the efficiency at which that engine operates. Unfortunately, the second law of thermodynamics forbids the efficiency to exceed a certain limit determined by the temperatures of the source and the sink.

Internal combustion engines are one example, with widespread applications in power generation and transportation. The source of heat is typically a mixture of hydrocarbon fuels and air that is burned inside a combustion chamber to produce power. The power is transmitted through a shaft, which can run a generator to generate electricity, drive the crankshaft of an automobile, or provide thrust to propel a jet aircraft. Among the most common internal combustion engines are gasoline and diesel engines and gas turbines. These devices are discussed in detail when we cover transportation systems in Chapter 6.

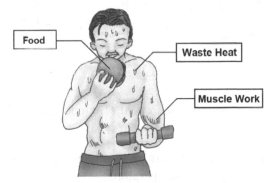

Figure 4-10
The human body is a heat engine, taking input energy in the form of food, converting a part of it into muscle work, and rejecting the waste heat as sweat and other excrement.

Figure 4-11
Energy exchange inin plants

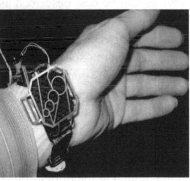

Figure 4-12
The wearable sensor for tracking the power produced by humans.

In **external combustion engines**, fuel is burned outside the engine or comes from an external source, such as from the sun. The thermal power plants are examples of such heat engines.

The human body functions like an engine, converting part of food's chemical energy into useful mechanical energy for muscle cells to carry out physical work, and dumping the rest into the environment (Figure 4-10). Only a small fraction of energy in the food we eat is transformed into muscle work (metabolic efficiency). What remains is used to support metabolism and maintain body temperature, and dispersed into the environment as heat and waste. What is not used is stored in the body in the form of fat. Metabolic efficiency is not the same for all people and can vary depending on gender, weight, condition of health, athletic abilities, and age. Although maximum power can be quite high, average power output is not and is limited to around 1 to 1.5 watts of mechanical energy per kilogram of body mass (power output increases to about 4 W/kg for a professional cyclist). By combining food's production efficiency (~10-15%) and metabolic efficiency (~13-25%), a net figure for human power efficiency is calculated at around 1.3-3.75%. A plant is another example of a heat engine that, through the process of photosynthesis, transforms a tiny part of light energy into chemical energy, dissipating the rest into the environment (Figure 4-11). Work has been also conducted to design wearable thermoelectric devices that exploit body heat and provide cooling and heating to soldiers, firefighters, and others under extreme weather conditions (Figure 4-12).

Refrigerators

The second law explains how the universe is continuously slipping into chaos. This does not mean that there cannot be (on a local scale) a transformation from disorder to order. In fact, this is the main mechanism by which we can defy nature.

Air conditioners and refrigerators are devices that move heat away from a space in defiance of the common perception that heat only moves from a higher to a lower temperature; i.e., heat is removed from the space (inside a refrigerated space or an air-conditioned room) and dumped into a reservoir (sink) at a higher temperature (Figure 4-13). In the case of the household refrigerator, the sink is the kitchen. In the case of the air-conditioner, it is the outside air. Energy input in the form of electricity or heat is needed to make the uphill transfer of heat possible. The price is, of course, the expenditure of energy and the creation of disorder outside the immediate neighborhood of these devices. The operation of these devices can be best described as heat engines operating in reverse. No matter what the application, part of the energy is always discarded as waste energy into the surrounding atmosphere. In other words, it is impossible to build devices that convert 100% of the input energy into useful forms. Furthermore, because there are

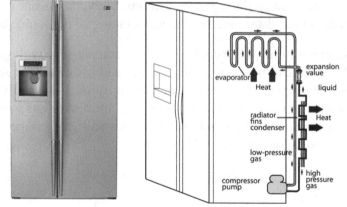

Figure 4-13
Refrigerator.

always some frictional losses, actual efficiency is always less than the maximum theoretical efficiency dictated by the laws of thermodynamics.

In household refrigerators, at the inlet to the condenser, the refrigerant has a temperature of 30-40 degrees above the ambient, and at the outlet, it has a temperature of 10-15 degrees above the ambient temperature.

Heat Pumps

As explained in the second law, the thermal energy of any substance vanishes only at absolute zero temperature. This means even cool outdoor winter air has some thermal energy. The heat pump is a device that utilizes this thermal

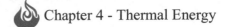
energy by bringing it into the house and heating its interior. Of course, by removing this heat, we make the outside temperature even cooler!

To move this energy inside, a heat pump circulates a fluid called refrigerant, which absorbs heat from outdoor air and releases it indoors (Figure 4-14). Heat pumps can be used for cooling, as well. This process is the reverse of the heating process; it removes the heat from the inside of an air-conditioned room and dumps it into the already warm, outdoor environment.

Figure 4-14
Heat pump.

The operation of a heat pump as a heating device is shown in Figure 4-15a. The refrigerant flows inside a closed loop. At point 1, the refrigerant vapor enters a compressor where it is compressed to a temperature warmer than the indoor air. The compressor needs some energy, usually in the form of electricity, to function. At point 2, the heated refrigerant enters an indoor heat exchanger where it gives off its thermal energy and, with the aid of a fan, uniformly heats the room. In the process, some of the vapor is condensed back to liquid (point 3) inside the heat exchanger (thus, the name "condenser"). The liquid then enters a valve or capillary tube at point 4, where it rapidly expands and cools to a temperature lower than that of outside. The mixture then enters a heat exchanger, where the heat from outside air causes it to vaporize (thus the name "evaporator"). An outside fan facilitates this heat transfer. The refrigerant vapor leaves the evaporator at point 1 and the cycle repeats.

During the summer, when cooling is desired, the unit functions by reversing the direction of flow and switching the role the two heat exchangers play (Figure 4-15b). In this mode, the outside heat exchanger is a condenser where heat is extracted, whereas the inside heat exchanger acts as an evaporator, removing heat from the space where cooling is desired.¶¶

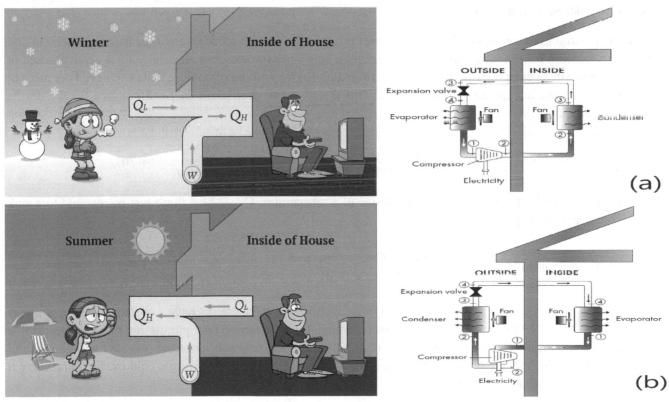

Figure 4-15
Principle of operation of a heat pump (air conditioner) in (a) heating (top) and (b) cooling (bottom) modes.

¶¶ When heat pump works in the cooling mode, it is in effect a refrigerator or an A/C unit. It is often customary to reserve the word "heat pump" to mean "pumping heat" (i.e. working in its heating mode) . In the remainder of this book, we refer to heat pump when it operates in the heating mode. When in cooling mode, use equations derived for refrigerators.

Efficiency

The term "efficiency" means different things to different people. Economists refer to efficiency in terms of the maximum profit that can be gained from a given transaction. Social scientists refer to efficiency as the cost that society, as a whole, will bear, compared to the cost, if certain actions were or were not undertaken. An efficient worker performs more work in a shorter time, and an efficient programmer writes the same program with fewer instructions. An energy-efficient refrigerator uses less electricity for the same amount of cooling as a less efficient refrigerator uses. A car that uses less fuel for the same distance traveled is more efficient than a similar car that gives lower miles per gallon. No matter what, we can all agree that efficiency is higher when the desired output is achieved with the less-required input.

$$\text{Efficiency} = \frac{Desired\ Output}{Required\ Input} = \frac{What\ we\ get}{What\ we\ have\ to\ give\ as\ a\ payment}$$

In the case of the heat engine, what we desire is the ability to turn the engine (produce mechanical work). Of course, this requires an expenditure of energy (gasoline).

$$\text{Heat Engine Efficiency} = \frac{\textbf{Amount of work delivered}}{\textbf{Heat input required}} = \frac{W_{net}}{Q_{hot}} = \frac{Q_{hot} - Q_{cold}}{Q_{hot}} \qquad (4\text{-}7a)$$

In this equation, Q_{hot} is the heat supplied from a source (gasoline in a spark-ignition engine, and coal in a coal-fired power plant); Q_{cold} is heat that is rejected to a sink (radiator, exhaust pipe, or smokestack). The practical heat engines operate at efficiencies of around 30-50%.

In the case of a refrigerator (an air conditioner, or a heat pump in the cooling mode) we will be happier when the unit produces more cooling for the same amount of electricity it consumes (or uses less electricity for a given amount of cooling). The performances of refrigerators are defined in terms of the amount of cooling that is achieved per amount of electricity that is needed to run the compressor. This is called **the coefficient of performance** (COP). In the language of mathematics:

$$\text{Coefficient of performance of refrigerator } = \frac{\text{Amount of cooling delivered}}{\text{Work required}} = \frac{Q_{cold}}{W_{in}} = \frac{Q_{cold}}{Q_{hot} - Q_{cold}} \qquad (4\text{-}7b)$$

In this case, Q_{cold} is the heat removed from the interior of a refrigerator; Q_{hot} is heat that must be rejected to a sink (kitchen or outside ambient).

$$\text{Coefficient of performance of heat pump } = \frac{\text{Amount of heating delivered}}{\text{Work required}} = \frac{Q_{hot}}{W_{in}} = \frac{Q_{hot}}{Q_{hot} - Q_{cold}} \qquad (4\text{-}7c)$$

Depending on the size and evaporator temperature, typical commercial refrigerators have a coefficient of refrigerants between 1 and 5. The COP for practical heat pumps is around 4 to 5, meaning heat pumps can provide four to five times more heating than the electricity consumed. The COP decreases markedly once the outside temperatures fall below -5° to -10°C. No laws are broken! All a refrigerator does is capture energy from a cold medium and carry it to a warm medium; it does not create it.

A good COP for heat pump units starts at about 2.0 for an air source heat pump and about 3.0 for a geothermal heat pump (to be discussed in Chapter 9). In comparison, electric heaters have efficiencies close to 100%, oil and gas heaters have efficiencies of 50% to 90%, and wood stoves' heating efficiencies range from 20% to 60%. This means that a heat pump is about 2-3 times more efficient than a resistance electric heater; something to consider when we shop for efficient home and space heaters. Of course, the purchasing cost is somewhat higher.

Gas vs. Electric (Revisited!)

At a department store, you inquire about a suitable heater for your house. The salesperson offers you two heaters, a gas heater with 70% efficiency and an electric (resistance) heater with an efficiency of 97%. Which one would you choose?

The first inclination might be to purchase the electric heater. It is more efficient, it is cleaner, and might even be cheaper. A slightly more careful analysis will reveal that the salesman is actually giving you first-law efficiencies. The electricity used to run the electric heater comes from a gas-powered generating station with 33% efficiency. The electricity is transmitted through a power line from the power station to your home. An additional 5-10% (let's say 10%) is lost through heating the wire (Joule heating). The overall efficiency (system efficiency) of the electric heater is then (0.33)(0.90)(0.97) = 28.8%. Assuming transmission losses of 5% through gas pipes, the first-law efficiency of the gas heater is (0.95)(0.70) = 66.5%.

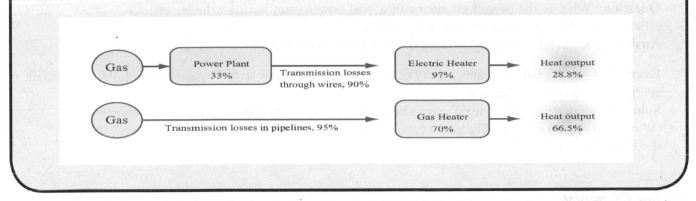

This concept easily is extended to all other devices described in Table 4-4. For example, a resistance heater is a device that converts electricity (work) into heat. So, its efficiency is defined as the ratio of the heat delivered to the electrical work put into it -- exactly the inverse of the efficiency we defined for a heat engine (try to understand the concept instead of memorizing the formulas). Similarly, the efficiency of a light bulb is the ratio of the amount of light energy output to electrical energy input.

It should be noted that energy efficiency is not the same thing as energy conservation. *Energy efficiency* means doing a given task with less energy. *Energy conservation*, on the other hand, means reducing energy use by cutting down on, or abandoning, a service. Turning off a light or lowering the room thermostat are examples of energy conservation. Examples of energy efficiency include replacing an existing single-pane window of your house with a newer, double-pane window, trading a gas water heater for a solar one, or replacing incandescent lamps with fluorescent lamps of the same rating. Unlike energy conservation measures that may require certain inconveniences, *no sacrifices are made* when we replace the older, less-efficient device with the energy-efficient ones, as both perform essentially the same functions.

Table 4-4 Typical Efficiencies of Various Conversion Devices		
Electric motors	Electrical → Mechanical	60% - 90%
Electric heaters	Electrical → Thermal	95% - 99%
Candle	Chemical → Light	0.04%
Incandescent (tungsten) lamp	Electrical → Light	3% - 5%
Fluorescent lamp	Electrical → Light	10% - 15%
Gas heaters (space)	Chemical → Thermal	90% - 95%
Gas water heaters	Chemical → Thermal	15% - 25%
Batteries (lead-acid)	Chemical → Electrical	85% - 95%
Steam locomotive	Thermal → Mechanical	5% - 10%
Automobile engine	Chemical → Mechanical	15% - 30%
Coal power plant	Chemical → Thermal	30% - 45%
Nuclear power plant	Nuclear → Thermal	30% - 35%
Photovoltaics	Light → Electrical	5% - 20%
Wind turbines	Mechanical → Electrical	30% - 40%

Overall Efficiency

Conversion of energy from one form to another does not always take place in a single step. For example, generating electricity requires the burning of fuel in a boiler (conversion of chemical to thermal energy) and expanding the burned gases in a turbine (conversion of thermal to mechanical energy) that runs an electric generator (conversion of mechanical to electrical energy). At each step of the way, some of the energy turns into waste energy that dissipates into the surroundings. The overall efficiency is calculated as:

$$\text{overall efficiency} = \text{boiler efficiency} \times \text{turbine efficiency} \times \text{generator efficiency}$$

$$\frac{\text{electrical efficiency}}{\text{chemical efficiency}} = \frac{\text{thermal efficiency}}{\text{chemical efficiency}} \times \frac{\text{mechanical efficiency}}{\text{thermal efficiency}} \times \frac{\text{electrical efficiency}}{\text{mechanical efficiency}}$$

Question: What is the overall efficiency of a coal power plant having a boiler efficiency of 88%, turbine efficiency of 40%, and generator efficiency of 98%?
Answer: The overall efficiency is 0.88 x 0.40 x 0.98 = 0.345 (34.5%).

Example 4-4: An engine extracts 2,000 J of energy from a reservoir at 900°C, and dumps 1,400 J into a sink at 100°C. What is engine efficiency?
Solution: Work delivered is the difference between the energy input and output from the engine (W = 2,000 - 1,400 = 600 J). The actual engine efficiency is the ratio of the net work to energy input, i.e., $\eta = 600/2,000 = 0.30$ (30%).

Carnot Efficiency

Wouldn't it be great if we could build a machine that puts out more work than we put into it? This machine would constantly create new energy and we would never have an energy shortage. This would be ideal, and many people have dreamt of making such machines.[***] These machines, commonly known as **"perpetual motion machines"** (PMM), once started, would not need additional expenditures of energy. Sounds too good to be true? It is. In the real world, all machines produce less work than the energy that goes into them. Useful energy is always lost as heat. That's the reality but, as shown by those who attempt to design PMMs, not everybody chooses to accept it.[†††]

Question: In 1992, Seiko introduced a watch that needs no battery, requires no winding, and never stops working. Has Seiko finally succeeded in building a perpetual motion machine?
Answer: No. Although these devices are the closest things to PMMs, they do not violate any laws of physics. A Seiko watch (commonly known as a "kinetic watch") uses the wrist's rotational movement to move a small permanent magnet in and out of a coil, creating a current that charges a capacitor and powers the watch.

Question: Our solar system has been moving around the sun for a very long time and does not seem to slow down. Can the solar system be considered a PMM?
Answer: If we look at the grand scale, the motion of the universe, indeed, conforms to the rules set out by the laws of thermodynamics. Energy is continuously poured in, externally and on a massive scale, to power the motion of all the galaxies and the motion of all that is within them. Even the solar system has to adhere to the laws put forth by nature!

Not only is the construction of such engines (PPM of the First Kind) impossible, the Second Law of Thermodynamics prevents the construction of engines that can convert "all" or "nearly all" of the heat input into useful work -- this machine (called PMM of the Second Kind) would continuously churn in heat to produce an equivalent amount of work, subsequently this work could be used to drive a heat engine and transform work back into heat that we started with, and motion continues. This can be understood by noting that heat is a less-ordered form of energy than work,

---

[***] There are two kinds of PMM. The machine that creates energy without equal expenditure of energy violates the 1st Law of Thermodynamics and is called a perpetual motion machine of the first kind. The machine that creates a net order in the universe violates the 2nd Law of Thermodynamics and is called a perpetual motion machine of the second kind.

[†††] Many processes in nature seems to operate perpetually -- electrons continually orbit nuclei, planets orbit the sun, and rivers and wind flow on year after year. While all of these are perpetual in one sense of the word, they have nothing to do with perpetual motion machines which violate the first or second law of thermodynamics.

and complete conversion of heat to work would accompany a reduction of entropy, which is impossible.

Many inventors have proposed devices that violate the First and Second Laws of Thermodynamics. Some, like Maxwell[‡‡‡], did so from a purely philosophical standpoint, but many have actually dared to propose such machines as practical devices. Many have even received patents and accumulated great wealth from their "inventions!" As you may have guessed, nobody was ever able to produce a working prototype.

Question: An inventor proposes to design an engine that uses coal to boil water and make steam. The steam is subsequently used to run an engine that converts the work output to heat and boils more water to steam. No additional coal is needed. Would you invest in this invention?

Answer: The proposed mechanism seems reasonable if the engine had to satisfy only the first law. The second law, however, requires energy to be degraded, becoming less and less available with each cycle. This engine constitutes a perpetual motion machine of the second kind and, therefore, cannot work.

Question: One of the consequences of the second law is that whenever energy is transformed from one form to another, at least some of the energy changes to a more dispersed form, such as heat. Is it possible to design devices that transform energy in the opposite direction, i.e., take it from a dispersed form to a more concentrated form?

Answer: The second law only precludes going from disorder to order for isolated systems. Many practical devices are not isolated and, thus, do not have to follow this restriction. For example, an air conditioner works by removing heat from a room and dumping it outside at a higher temperature. In this case, we are re-concentrating energy. To do so, however, we need to spend even more energy in the form of electricity.

In an attempt to improve the efficiency of the early steam engines, a young French scientist by the name of Sadi Carnot (1796-1832) provided the theoretical framework to this ceiling and proposed an ideal engine that works between two reservoirs at different temperatures. Heat is removed from a source at temperature T_{hot}, part of which is discarded to a sink at temperature T_{cold}; the difference is available as work. The best this engine can do is to achieve a loss of entropy from the source that just balances the gain in entropy by the sink. The net entropy production will then be zero. Carnot showed this would be true only when $Q_{hot}/Q_{cold} = T_{hot}/T_{cold}$. Under such ideal conditions, the efficiency of the engine is the maximum attainable and is equal to

$$\eta_{ideal, E} = \frac{T_{hot} - T_{cold}}{T_{hot}} \qquad (4\text{-}8a)$$

Because heat cannot be dumped into a sink at zero absolute temperature, building engines with 100% efficiency is an impossible task. According to this equation, the maximum theoretical efficiencies of all engines working between these two temperatures are the same, independent of which working fluid is used. Please note that T_{cold} and T_{hot} are temperatures of cold and hot reservoirs and must be expressed in kelvins. Kelvin temperatures are calculated by adding 273 to temperatures expressed in degrees Celsius. To obtain an efficiency of unity, this equation shows that the engine must operate either with a source temperature of infinity, or a sink temperature of zero kelvin -- the first one a physical impossibility and the second one ruled out by the Third Law of Thermodynamics. The maximum source temperature is limited by the material of the turbine or combustor walls (around 650°C for steam turbines, 1,400°C for gas turbines and reciprocating engines). The minimum sink temperature is limited by the exhaust gases and is normally not much lower than 150°C. Using these numbers, the maximum theoretical efficiencies are found to be 54% for steam turbines and 75% for gas turbines, gasoline, and diesel engines. In practice, friction and other thermal losses at the wall limit these efficiencies to about 30-50%.

---

‡‡‡ James Clerk Maxwell (1831-1879) was a Scottish mathematician and physicist, most known for his theoretical formulation of the laws of electromagnetism.

Example 4-5: What is the maximum efficiency of an engine that, theoretically, could be built to operate between the temperature reservoirs of Example 4-4?

Solution: The maximum efficiency is given by the Carnot limit, $\eta = 1 - (100+273)/(900+273) = 0.682$. As it appears, the engine's actual efficiency, 30%, is less than one-half of its theoretically possible efficiency of 68.2%.

Question: As it is demonstrated in Figure 4-12, we can harness waste energy from the human body to perform work. What is the maximum power that can be utilized using this energy?

Answer: Assuming an ambient temperature of -10°C to 25°C (263 to 298 K), and that body waste is at the body temperature of 37°C (310 K), Carnot efficiency is calculated at somewhere between 3.9% and 15.2%. While sitting, an average person can expend around 100 W. Assuming that 100% of the heat is captured and that an engine with Carnot efficiency can be constructed, about 4-15 W is available in the form of useful power. With today's technology, thermopiles with efficiencies of 0.2-0.8% can be built for temperature ranges of 3-20°C.

Question: An inventor claims to have designed an engine working between temperatures of boiling water (100°C) and ice-water (0°C), and in the process, converting half of the input energy to work. Would you invest in his company?

Answer: The most efficient engine that can be built is the Carnot engine, working between these reservoirs at temperatures 273 and 373 kelvins, i.e., the maximum possible efficiency is $\eta = 1 - 273/373 = 26.8\%$. Attaining an efficiency of 50% is impossible.

Question: Air pollution is considered by many to be a direct result of incomplete (inefficient) combustion. Comment!

Answer: The common assumption that air pollution results from the inefficient burning of fossil fuels, is not correct. When a hydrocarbon fuel such as natural gas is burned in the air, the product of the reaction is a mixture of water, carbon dioxide, carbon monoxide, oxides of nitrogen, and several other gases in such concentrations that maximize the overall entropy. Cleaner fuels, better burners, and more exotic catalysts, although may increase combustion efficiency and reduce pollutant emissions, cannot eliminate air pollutants, altogether. In other words, complete combustion (of hydrocarbons), defined as burning with carbon dioxide, water, and molecular nitrogen as their only end products, is not possible and is directly in violation of the Second Law of Thermodynamics.

Just as there are limits to the amount of work a heat engine can provide, there are limits to the amount of cooling that a refrigerator can deliver. In this case, the desired effect is the amount of cooling; the price we have to pay is the electrical work of the compressor. The result is that the best refrigerator that can be manufactured is a Carnot refrigerator. This refrigerator requires a minimum work (electricity) for a given cooling load or a maximum cooling effect for a given amount of electrical work. The coefficient of performance for a Carnot refrigerator is:

$$COP_{ideal, R} = \frac{T_{cold}}{T_{hot} - T_{cold}} \qquad (4\text{-}8b)$$

By a similar argument, the ideal limit set by a Carnot heat pump is:

$$COP_{ideal, HP} = \frac{T_{hot}}{T_{hot} - T_{cold}} \qquad (4\text{-}8c)$$

Example 4-6: An ideal heat pump is to keep a space at 27°C, by removing heat from the cold outdoors at 0°C. What is the heat pump's coefficient of performance? What is the minimum power required, if space is losing heat at the rate of 30,000 kJ/h?

Solution: Minimum power expenditure requires a heat pump that works under Carnot conditions.

$$COP_{Ideal,HP} = \frac{(27+273)}{(27+273)-(0+273)} = 11.1$$

To maintain the temperature, the heat pump must be able to supply enough heat to replace heat loss from the room, i.e., 30,000 kJ / 3,600 s = 8.33 kW. Power input is 8.33 kW / 11.1 = 0.75 kW.

Question: A homeowner interested in heating his house is offered two options: an electric heater with an efficiency of nearly 100%, or a heat pump with a COP of 4. Which option makes more sense?

Answer: Resistance heaters work by converting electricity to heat. Even at 100% efficiency, the amount of heat is equal to the electricity consumed. Heat pumps, on the other hand, use electricity to extract the energy from the cold ambient air, dumping both into the house. A heat pump with a heating COP of 4, supplies four times the heat as the electricity used to run it. The heat pump will make a lot more sense. The only thing the homeowner has to worry about is the initial cost of the unit, which is usually recovered in a few years.

To avoid confusion, usually, the performance of a heat pump is specified by two numbers, the COP as defined above for heating, and the Energy Efficiency Ratio (EER) for cooling. EER is expressed in Btu/Wh, defined as the ratio of the cooling capacity (in Btu/h) for each unit of required electrical power (in watts). Haven't we made a total mess of the units?

Large commercial refrigeration units are rated in kilowatts per ton. The relationship between EER and COP is given as:

$$EER = 3.413 \times COP_R$$

In the United States, the efficiency of air conditioners is often averaged over the range of outside temperatures during the cooling season and is called the "seasonal energy efficiency ratio" or SEER. SEER numbers of 20-25 are common with modern refrigeration units. Air conditioner sizes are often given as "tons" of cooling, where one ton of cooling (12,000 Btu/h) equals the amount of power that needs to be applied continuously, over a 24 hours period, to melt 1 ton of ice. A two-ton (24,000-Btu/h) refrigerator with a SEER of 20 uses 1.2 kilowatts of power during the cooling season.[§§§]

Example 4-7: What is the annual cost of a 2-ton refrigeration unit with a SEER of 18, operating for 800 hours per year? Assume the average electricity cost of $ 0.20 per kWh.

Answer: The annual cost of operation is calculated as:

$$\frac{(2 \text{ tons}) \times (12,000 \text{ Btu/h.ton}) \times (800 \text{ h}) \times (\$ 0.20 \text{ /kWh})}{(18 \text{ Btu/Wh}) \times (1,000 \text{ W/kW})} = \$ 213.33$$

Thermoelectric Power Generation

Thermoelectric (TE) power generation is the direct conversion of heat into electricity. It relies on the Seebeck effect, a phenomenon in which a temperature difference between two dissimilar materials produces a voltage difference. If the pair is connected through an electrical circuit, current flows and electricity is generated. The source of heat could be a burning gas, waste heat, or any source in the 700-1,700°C range. Specialized materials such as bismuth-telluride can operate at temperatures as low as 150-200°C. The voltages produced by the Seebeck effect are small,

[§§§] As an Energy Star product, the air conditioners sold in the United States must have a SEER of at least 14.

usually only a few microvolts (millionths of a volt) per kelvin temperature difference at the junction. Many TE devices can be connected in series to produce appreciable output voltage or in parallel to increase the maximum deliverable current. Small-scale electrical power generators can be built if a large temperature difference is maintained across the junctions. Since thermoelectric devices are heat engines, their efficiency is limited by Carnot's efficiency.

Laws of Thermodynamics Applied to Matter

Laws of thermodynamics are not unique to the transfer and conversion of energy but can also be applied to matter. In the absence of nuclear reactions, the first law implies that matter is conserved for each of the chemical elements. The second law states that matter, through processes of mixing, dispersion, and dissipation, is degraded as it transforms from high-quality raw materials (fossil fuel, copper ingot) to low-quality waste and discarded to the environment until all matter becomes *unavailable*. In other words, elements become increasingly mixed to the point that it becomes impossible to separate them from each other and be recycled.

Summary

Understanding the laws of thermodynamics is fundamental to understanding the workings of the universe. In this chapter, we covered these laws and their relevance in designing useful thermal devices. In describing the working principle of such devices (a thermal power plant, a heat engine, a refrigerator, or any other thermodynamic system, for that matter), we concluded that:

1. At least two reservoirs, at two different temperatures, are needed. This is one of the important consequences of the Second Law of Thermodynamics, which states that we cannot convert heat to work with a single heat source. In the case of a steam power plant, the steam generator and condenser are the two reservoirs. In internal combustion engines, the two heat reservoirs are hot combustion gases and relatively cold water in the radiator and gases in the exhaust. Two reservoirs in a refrigerator are the evaporator and condenser coils containing the vapor and liquid phases of a refrigerant.
2. Some form of fuel is always needed to provide heat to the high-temperature heat reservoir. For power plants, the energy needed to heat water comes from an external source which could be a fossil, nuclear, or less commonly, solar or geothermal. For refrigerators and heat pumps, it is the electricity.
3. To increase efficiency, we must either increase the temperature of the source or lower the temperature of the sink. We are limited to atmospheric temperatures for the sink, but we can increase the source temperature. In power plants, we can raise the steam temperature by increasing the boiler pressure (water boils at a higher temperature if the pressure is greater). Raising the compression ratio, minimizing heat losses, and using better fuels can similarly increase internal combustion efficiency. Refrigerators have higher efficiencies with refrigerants with lower boiling points (and higher condenser temperature).
4. Higher efficiencies not only reduce fuel consumption but also protect our environment by producing fewer pollutants. In addition, higher efficiency means a smaller fraction of energy must be disposed of as waste heat, commonly termed "thermal pollution," which is a major source of global warming.

The first and second laws of thermodynamics will give engineers the blueprint for implementing methodologies and develop technologies that can improve energy efficiency. The most important among them are:

a. Better designs -- Energy efficiency can be increased by substituting the older units with newer and more energy-efficient units. The new designs can utilize variable speed motors that can be adjusted to match a specific need. For example, variable speed air-blowers can provide building ventilation and conditioning as the cooling and heating load changes. More efficient lighting (including bulbs, reflectors, diffusers, and ballasts) can provide the same amount of illumination while consuming less electricity.
b. Smarter sensors -- Smart sensors can be used to adjust parameters to assure the most efficient operation.

For example, we can use motion and light sensors to adjust the thermostat and dim or turn the lights off depending on the time of the day, room occupancy, or the amount of light entering through the windows.

c. Energy leak and loss prevention -- Heat losses can be reduced by regular monitoring, inspection, and proper maintenance and through deploying thicker walls and better seals and insulations

d. Advanced integrated energy management concepts -- Heat normally released into the atmosphere still contains significant amounts of useful energy. Systems commonly known as cogeneration (electricity and heat) and tri-generation (electricity, heat, and steam), can utilize waste heat directly, produce process steam, or generate additional electricity.

e. Matching resources to the task -- Resources should be used that closely match the tasks at hand. For example, higher-quality forms of energy (electricity, gravitational, and kinetic energies) should be reserved for tasks that require more concentrated forms of energy and higher torques. Electrical motors, lighting, and computers are such examples. On the other hand, space heating and cooling require low-quality energy and lower-temperature heat reservoirs. In these instances, gas or solar heating might be the best options.

f. Passive strategies -- These include storage, use of shutters, better and lighter color paints, and double-glazed windows.

Digging Deeper: Living Organisms and the Laws of Thermodynamics

Despite the fact that biological systems are not in thermal equilibrium, the laws of thermodynamics can be applied locally to individual cells, the building blocks of all living organisms. The implication of the first law is simple and clear; the energy fed to the system must be balanced by the work performed and the waste energy rejected into the environment. Food is the source of this energy, which ultimately finds its roots in the sun, through the processes of photosynthesis. During digestion, food molecules are broken down into progressively simpler molecules (chemical-chemical conversion); in the process, some of the energy stored in those molecules is converted by the metabolism to thermal energy (chemical-thermal conversion) necessary to maintain our body temperatures, to restore normal body functions, and to store the remains as fat.[10]

The validity of the second law is a bit more difficult to see since living organisms seem to move in a direction opposite to the natural flow of energy. As tiny seeds develop to become strong plants, and as babies mature, they become more structured and, thus, seem to violate the second law in a big way! It should be noted, however, that the second law applies only to isolated systems such as the universe, itself. Earth is not an isolated system because it exchanges energy with the sun and the surrounding atmosphere. Living organisms scavenge both energy (heating or cooling by the environment) and mass (eating, breathing, and sweating) and therefore are not isolated systems. Living things will stay away from the equilibrium state (death) by continuously feeding off the available energy (food, air, and sun) around them -- i.e., every living being creates its own order at the expense of creating waste, thus increasing the entropy of its environment. Every step of biological evolution is associated with increasing complexity (greater stored information) while creating more and more disorder (greater scattered information) in the universe (See discussion on the food chain when we cover bioenergy in chapter 11). The sanctity of the second law is, thus, preserved!

Applications in Human Biological Systems

It takes energy to stay alive. Whether we are eating or participating in rigorous exercise, we metabolize food as a source of energy. Even when we are not doing any work or are sleeping, we consume food energy. The minimum energy needed for survival and to maintain the equilibrium of all vital functions (nervous, cardiovascular, respiratory, and digestive systems) when a body is at rest (sedentary) is called the basal metabolic rate (BMR). The brain and the liver, two organs that jointly make up only 4% of body weight, are responsible for half of all metabolic activity. As chemical energy in food converts to heat, body temperature tends to rise. To maintain a constant temperature, the body reacts by transferring the energy to the circulatory system and to the skin, where it eventually dissipates into the environment. BMR is generally higher in males and for heavier, healthier, and younger animals. BMR is about 1.45

watts for a rat, 80 watts for an average-sized person, and 266 watts for a medium-sized cow.

Over the past century, numerous scientists have studied the basal metabolic rate for a large number of mammals and concluded that it varies with the surface area through which the body must lose heat. Noting that body surface area scales with the square of the length, while its mass and volume vary as length cubed, it can be easily concluded that $BMR \sim M^{2/3}$. Further studies on a large range of animals, from mice to elephants, showed BMR and mass correlated better as $BMR \sim M^{3/4}$. Others have found correlation exponents in the range of 0.46-0.78. The BMR for human babies is proportional to mass for the first year of life but decreases to $M^{0.6}$ as he grows to full adulthood. What is clear is that specific BMR (BMR per unit mass) decreases with larger animals. Smaller animals exhibit higher mass-specific metabolic rates to overcome the larger heat losses associated with their larger surface-to-volume ratio. This is accomplished by a high rate of food intake (shrew), retreating to more protective environments (insects), dropping their body temperatures close to ambient (hummingbirds at night), or increasing their body temperatures (lizards during the day).

BMR does not account for any physical activity, so additional energy is needed to carry out daily tasks. Physical activities can be divided into aerobic and anaerobic activities. During aerobic activities, oxygen breaks down carbohydrates (glucose, sucrose, or starch), fat, and protein and converts them to energy. Examples of aerobic exercises are dancing, jogging, swimming, and biking. Anaerobic activities burn carbohydrates without oxygen, with maximum bursts of energy of short duration. Examples are weight lifting, push-ups, chin-ups, and sprinting. The amount of daily energy needed is different for different people and can vary with gender, size (mass), and levels of physical and mental activity. As a rule of thumb, it usually is assumed that an average man requires 2,500 Calories per day, whereas an average woman needs only 1,800 Calories per day in food intake.

Question: Which organism has a higher basal metabolic rate, a hummingbird or an elephant?
Answer: Hummingbirds weigh approximately 2.3-4.5 grams and have proportionately larger surfaces in relation to body mass; they can lose heat faster. Gram by gram, hummingbirds have the highest metabolic rate of any animal, roughly 12 times that of a human being and 100 times that of an elephant. Their BMR is around 29 W, which means they need to consume 600 Calories of food every day. No wonder that each day, they have to visit hundreds of flowers to gather enough nectar to survive.

Measuring Food Energy
Food energy is usually expressed in Calories. One Calorie (with the capital C) is equal to the heat energy that is required to raise the temperature of one kilogram of water by one degree centigrade. A smaller unit of thermal energy is a calorie (with a small c), which is 1/1000th of the food calorie:

1 Calorie = 1 kilocalorie = 1,000 calories = 4,184 joules

Unfortunately, calorie notation can cause some confusion. What should be remembered is that when we talk about a food calorie, we are talking about kilocalories, whether capitalized or not.

Food, Exercise, and Dieting
The energy required by our body is provided by the food we eat. The major food categories are carbohydrates (mainly sugar, bread, and rice), proteins (primarily meat, milk, and eggs), and fats. In addition, most plant-based foods contain other nutrients like vitamins, minerals, and water, which are drawn up from their roots during growth. Although they are small in quantity, these are essential ingredients in metabolizing the calories stored in food. The human body metabolizes these foods differently, roughly 93-98% for carbohydrates and fats, and 77% for proteins. While each gram of fat yields 9 kilocalories (38 MJ/kg) when burned, carbohydrates and proteins yield only 4 kcal (17 MJ/kg) and 5.3 kcal (22 MJ/kg) of energy, respectively. The energy contents (calorific values) of some common foods are given in Table 4-5.

Metabolism and the Animal Kingdom

Unlike their cold-blooded neighbors, warm-blooded animals must always maintain constant body temperature, irrespective of the temperature of the environment. In cold climates, they fight against losing too much heat; in hot climates, they try to stay cool by dissipating excess heat. The rate at which heat is generated in, and lost from, an animal's body depends very much on the size of the animal. Larger animals have more mass to "feed" and therefore generate more metabolic heat. Larger animals also have more surface area from which heat is lost. While it would seem that the larger animals have to contend with a greater heat loss, it is the specific heat loss (i.e., heat loss per unit of body mass) that is more relevant to the animal's survival. Since mass is proportional to L^3 and surface area is proportional to L^2, the specific heat loss is actually proportional to $1/L$ (or $M^{-1/3}$). In other words, as the metabolic rate is lost through the body surface, it is logical to expect that an organism will adjust its BMR to overcome heat losses through the surface (skin) proportional to $M^{2/3}$. A similar relationship also has been found in plants.

Amazingly, we can actually predict (or at least rationalize) certain patterns of behavior of different animals on the basis of simple scaling arguments. A very small animal must compensate for its lost body heat by an almost continual intake of food. A mouse eats a food equivalent of about one-quarter of its body weight, daily. The tiny shrew (smallest mammal) eats nearly its body mass in food every day and will die of starvation if forced to go without food for more than about three hours. A giant elephant, on the other hand, faces the opposite problem of getting rid of excess heat. It's no wonder that elephants take every opportunity to cool themselves off at waterholes. We can, therefore, understand why a mouse might want to be in a warm spot, while an elephant prefers a cool one. For insects, the surface-to-volume ratio is so much larger than that of any warm-blooded animal that they cannot possibly eat fast enough to maintain a constant body temperature. What to do then? Fortunately for the insects, the body temperature of a cold-blooded creature matches that of the surroundings. This provision of nature greatly reduces heat loss and, consequently, the insect's food requirements.

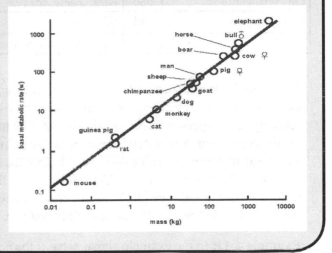

To maintain weight, obviously, the energy input (food) must be equal to that of the output (expenditure). When the balance is not maintained, a person may experience some weight gain or weight loss.[¶¶¶] Physiologists and physicians have studied but differed in opinion on the root causes of weight gain by people. Some attribute the propensity to gain weight to a special gene and hormonal imbalance. Others believe bodies develop fat cells during childhood that become active as the body ages. Still, others attribute obesity solely to overeating. No matter what the actual medical reason for weight gain, to maintain our weight, the total energy intake by food must balance the energy expenditure of normal basal metabolic rate and that expended by work and other physical activities (See Table 4-6). If the energy intake exceeds the energy expenditure, the excess energy is stored as fat. As a rule of thumb, we need to burn roughly 3,500 extra Calories to lose one pound of fat. As Muller puts it, "losing weight is easy! Just remember the First Law of Thermodynamics: conservation of energy. Oh, and you'll have not to mind being hungry."

Example 4-8: How much mass will a starving male (i.e., zero food intake) lose in one week?
Solution: Assuming the minimum body requirement of 2,500 kcal (10,460 kJ) per day, and 38 MJ/kg of body fat he can metabolize 10,460 / 38,000 = 0.27 kg of his own body fat each day. The total weight loss in one week is only 1.93 kg (4.2 pounds). Not a very good way to lose weight!

Example 4-9: According to one study, since the 1960s, the average individual living in the United States has increased caloric intake by about 250 Calories each day.[12] How much weight would one gain by staying on the new diet for one year?
Solution: The total excess intake of energy over one year is 250 × 365 = 91,250 kcal. The added weight is 91,250/3,500 = 26 lbs (11.8 kg).

[¶¶¶] It should be noted that when it comes to the topic of food and physical fitness, weight is understood to mean mass. An astronaut in space still has the same mass, even though he has lost all his weight.

Table 4-5 Food Calories (all values are averaged)				Table 4-6 Energy Expenditure for Average Adult		
Food	kcal	Food	kcal	Activity	Cal/h	W
Apple, large	100	Egg (one)	80	Sleeping	60	70
Bacon, 2 strips	100	French fries (regular)	250	Sitting, standing , office work	100	116
Banana, small	90	Ice cream (one scoop)	300	Walking downstairs	205	240
Beer, one glass	150	Steak (1/4-lb)	200	Walking upstairs	500	580
Bread and butter (one slice)	80	Mayonnaise (1 tbsp)	92	Jogging	400	465
Butter (one teaspoon)	36	Milk, one glass	166	Tennis	400	465
Cake, a slice	350	Milk shake	420	Dancing (ballroom)	300	350
Chicken, fried (1/2 breast)	230	Orange juice (one glass)	120	Skiing (downhill)	300	350
Cheeseburger	350	Pizza, cheese, one slice	180	Skiing (cross county)	600	700
Coke, one glass	110	Hamburger	275	Bicycling (20 km/hr)	450	520
Doughnut	150	Spaghetti, one serving	400	Boxing (sparring)	620	720

Example 4-10: Suppose a 70-kg person spends eight hours sleeping, one hour bicycling or similar moderate exercise, two hours reading or eating, two hours watching television, and eleven hours working at a desk or relaxing. Is this person likely to gain weight if he maintains a 2,300-Calorie daily diet? If he maintains this diet for the entire year, how much is he expected to gain or lose?

Solution: Referring to Table 4-6, we calculate the energy expenditure to be (8×70 + 1×450 + 2×100 + 2×80 + 11×100) × 3,600 = 8.9 MJ = 2,125 kcal/day. Since this person is taking in 2,300 Calories and burning only 2,125 Calories, he will gain weight. Over a period of one year, he has stored (2,300 - 2125) × 365 = 63,875 kcal, in form of 63,875 /3,500 or 18 pounds of his body fat.

Example 4-11: In the example above, what if the person weighs 80-kg, but maintains the same diet?

Solution: In this case, his rate of energy consumption has increased to 80/70 × 2,125 = 2,428 kcal/day, which is more than his daily energy intake of 2,300 Calories by 128 Calories every day. Over one year, this translates into a loss of 13 pounds of fat.

Example 4-12: How many steps does a person with a mass of 75 kg have to climb to burn out the calories in a quarter-pound burger? Table 4-5 gives the chemical energy content of a hamburger as 275 Calories.

Solution: The food he eats must satisfy many needs. It must maintain his body temperature, drive his blood to the heart and other organisms, repair or replace worn-out tissues, and perform mechanical work such as carrying daily activities and climbing the stairs. Roughly 25% of the energy contained in the food is available for mechanical work. In our example, the amount of mechanical work possible is $W = \eta.Q = 0.25 \times 275 = 68.75$ kcal = 287,650 J. The mechanical work is $W = mgh$ or $h = 287,650/(75 \times 9.81) = 391$ m, or about 1,955 steps of 0.2 m high (roughly the height of a building 100-stories tall!).

Body Mass Index

Among health care professionals, perhaps the best-known method for assessing body size is the Body Mass Index, defined by the National Institute of Health (NIH) as body mass (in kg) divided by height (in m) squared.

$$BMI = \frac{M}{h^2}$$

(4-8)

Other factors, such as the waist-to-hip ratio, may also be important in determining the ideal weight for a healthy person. According to this scale, adults with a BMI between 19 and 25 are considered to have a healthy weight, those below 19 are underweight, those between 25 and 30 are overweight, and those above 30 are considered obese.

Example 4-13: A woman is 160 cm (5'3") tall and has a mass of 75 kg (165 pounds). Calculate her BMI. How much does she have to reduce to bring her weight to a range deemed to be healthy for her height?

Solution: BMI is calculated from Eqn. (4-8) as:

$$BMI = \frac{75}{(1.60)^2} = 29.3$$

Which, according to the NIH criteria, is substantially overweight, bordering on the threshold of being obese. She needs to lower her weight by about 10-20 pounds (ideally, through more exercise and better nutrition).

ⓐ *Digging Deeper: The First-Law and the Second-Law Efficiencies*

Real engines can never achieve the ideal efficiencies given by Carnot. First, real engines always have frictional and conductive losses that cannot be completely eliminated, thereby limiting their maximum performance. Second, depending on its intended end-use, a device may not be able to utilize the full potential of the energy needed to operate it. To quantify these limitations, two types of efficiency are defined:

The **first-law efficiency** (or simply, efficiency) defined above, is based on the first law principle of conversion of one form of energy to another, without any consideration to the quality of the energy resource. The first-law efficiency is input/output efficiency, i.e., the ratio of energy delivered in the desired form and the energy that must be expended to achieve the desired effect. It does not differentiate between the qualities of the energy sources. Because only a part of the input energy is converted to work, the first-law efficiency for a heat engine is always less than one. If the object of the device is to produce heat, such as that of an electrical resistance heater, the efficiency is very high, close to one. Friction will obviously turn all the available work to heat, so it has an efficiency of one. As we will see below, refrigerators utilize some of the thermal energy from the ambient, so they will have efficiencies of greater than one. Because of our common intuition that efficiency must always be less than unity, refrigerators perform with what is commonly referred to as "the coefficient of performance."

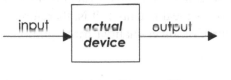

$$First\ Law\ Efficiency = \frac{Useful\ Energy\ Out}{Total\ Energy\ In}$$

Question: What is the first-law efficiency for a heat engine? For an electric heater? For an electric motor? For an electric light bulb?

Answer: A heat engine is a device that converts chemical energy (fuel) to mechanical work. Therefore, the first-law efficiency is the ratio of shaft work to heat input. Typically, first-law efficiencies of 15-30% can be achieved for automobile engines. An electric heater is a device for converting electrical energy to heat; in this case, the first-law efficiency is the ratio of heat given off to the electrical work needed to operate the heater. Aside from small radiant losses through the heating coil, electric heaters are very efficient devices for their stated purpose and efficiencies close to 100% are achievable. Electric motors lose some energy through friction and coil heating and are generally around 90% efficient. Incandescent light bulbs are designed to convert electricity to light. A major fraction of the energy is, however, lost through heating the filament. Their efficiency is rather low, at around 5%.

Unlike the first-law efficiency that ignores the qualities of the energy, the **second-law efficiency** compares the efficiency of an actual device to that of the same or a similar device operated under ideal conditions. It measures the actual energy used, as compared to the minimum amount of energy needed to accomplish the same task under ideal conditions (or the actual output as compared to the maximum output that could be achieved under ideal conditions for the same task), i.e., the second-law efficiency is the ratio of the actual efficiency to that of an ideal device. By definition, the second-law efficiency of all ideal devices is equal to one, and for all real devices is smaller than one.

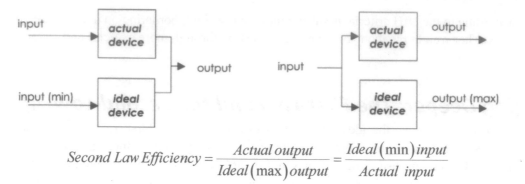

$$Second\ Law\ Efficiency = \frac{Actual\ output}{Ideal\,(max)\,output} = \frac{Ideal\,(min)\,input}{Actual\ input}$$

Example 4-14: What is the second-law efficiency of the engine of Example 4-5?
Solution: The actual and theoretical efficiencies are calculated as 30% and 68.2% (See Examples 4-3 and 4-4). The second-law efficiency is the ratio of actual to theoretical efficiencies, i.e., 0.30/0.682 = 0.44. The engine operates only at 44% of its theoretical maximum.

Example 4-15: Two inventors are looking for investors to fund development and marketing of their new engines. Both engines have efficiencies of 30%. The engine of the first inventor runs on petroleum that burns at 1,200 K. The engine of the second inventor uses waste heat at 800 K. Assuming that both claims can be verified and that both exhaust the combustion product to a sink at 400 K, in which engine do you invest?
Solution: The ideal efficiency of the first engine is 1 - 400/1200 = 0.67, whereas that of the second engine is 1 - 400/800 = 0.5. This means that the first engine runs at roughly 45% (0.30/0.67) of its ideal potential; the second engine runs at 60% (0.30/0.50) of its ideal potential. It is, therefore, clear that the second inventor achieves the same amount of work from a source of lower quality (lower ignition temperature). The second inventor offers a better opportunity!

Question: You are approaching a salesperson, who offers you an electric and a gas heater (for the same price) to heat your house. The electric heater has an efficiency of 100%; the gas heater has an efficiency of only 80%. Assuming that you are conscious of your valuable non-renewable resources, as well as, the environment (and, ideally, you are), which option do you choose? The local utility uses natural gas to produce electricity.
Answer: At first glance, it seems that the electric heater is a more efficient heater and it, therefore, is the obvious choice. But wait! Electricity is generated from a plant which is only 30-40% efficient (let's take 35%). So, for every 100 units of natural gas, only 35 units of electricity is generated. Even if all this energy goes into heating the house, it is still less than the 80 units of heat that are provided by the gas heater. Although the first-law efficiency of the electric heater is quite high, the second-law efficiency of the gas heater is much higher than that of its competitor. Indeed, if you check your utility bills, you will find that electricity costs three to five times more than gas for the same amount of energy. Note: Electric companies charge you by the kWh, gas companies charge you by cubic feet (or cubic meters) of gas or by therms (100,000 Btu), so you need to convert the units.

The discussion above shows that using the quantity of energy to indicate a system performance often leads to misleading conclusions. In the example above, we showed that a gas heater is a more efficient option than an electric heater. As you might have guessed, the best way to heat the room was by using a heat pump, and not an electric heater. ⓐ

126

Endnotes

1   Pielou, E. (2001). *The energy of nature*, Chicago: University of Chicago Press.

2   Akbari H, Menon S, Rosenfeld, A. (2009). Global Cooling: Increasing World-wide Urban Albedos to Offset CO_2. *Climatic Change, 94*(3-4), 275-286.

3   Georgescu-Rogen, N. (1971). *The Entropy Law & the Economic Process*, Cambridge, MA: Harvard University Press.

4   Leonov, V. (2009). Thermoelectric and Hybrid Generators in Wearable Devices and Clothes. Proceedings of the 2009 Int'l Workshop on Wearable and Implantable Body Sensor Networks, *IEEE Computer Society*, pp. 193-200.

5   Stevens, J. (1999). Optimized Thermal Design of Small Thermoelectric Generators, Proc. 34th Intersociety Energy Conversion Eng. Conf. Soc, of Automotive Engineers, paper 1999-01-2564.

6   Suchilin, V. A, Sumzina, L. V, and Maksimov, A. V. (2017). Method for Refrigerators Efficiency Increasing, IO P Conf. Series: Materials Science and Engineering 262 (2017), 012121, doi:10.1088/1757-899X/262/1/01212

7   Angrist, S. (1968). Perpetual Motion Machines. *Scientific American, 218*(1), 114-122. doi: 10.1038/scientificamerican0168-114

8   Curzon. F., and Ahlborn, B. (1975). Efficiency of a Carnot Engine at Maximum Power Output, *American Journal of Physics*, 43:22-24.

9   Ayres, R. (1978). Resources, Environment &Economicz: Application of the Materials/Energy Balance Principle, New York: *John Wiley & Sons*.

10 Faughn, J. (1998). Life Science Applications for Physics, *Harcourt, Saunders College Pub.*

11 Prigogine, I., Nicolis, G., & Babloyantz, A. (1972). Thermodynamics of evolution. *Physics Today, 25*(11), 23-28. doi: 10.1063/1.3071090

12 Smil, V. (2008). Energy in Nature and Society: General Energetic of Complex Systems, *The MIT Press.*

13 Muller, R. (2003). The Physics of Diet, *MIT Technology Review,* November 14, 2003.

14 Thompson, D., Edelsberg, J., Colditz, G., Bird, A., and Oster, G. (1999). Lifetime Health and Economic Consequences of Obesity. Archives Of Internal Medicine, *159*(18), 2177. doi: 10.1001/archinte.159.18.2177

 # Exercises

I. Discussion Questions

1. Caloric theory considered heat as a substance that flows from one body to another. Kinetic theory proclaims that heat as a motion. Which theory explains the heating of two blocks rubbing against each other better?

2. How can you use the results of Joule's experiment to show that heat and work are different forms of energy?

3. Name the main components of a steam power plant, a gas turbine, a heat engine, an air conditioner, and a refrigerator? What are the common working fluids used for each device?

4. The temperature of the water at the bottom of Niagara Falls is slightly warmer than the water at the top of the waterfall. To what do you attribute this temperature difference?

5. Karl Christian Planck, the German philosopher (1819-1880), suggested there is a chance that if a kettle of water is placed on a fire, the water could freeze. Comment on what he possibly might have meant.

6. Define heat capacity, specific heat, thermal conductivity, and coefficient of thermal expansion. Does a substance with high specific heat necessarily have high thermal conductivity and a high coefficient of thermal expansion? Give examples.

7. Which one is better insulation, Styrofoam, or aluminum? Why?

8. When the dealer switches your cash with casino chips, he already has given the house an advantage, even before he has dealt the cards. Comment!

9. Which of the following violates the Second Law of Thermodynamics? Explain.
   a. You visit a friend's house and find it to be tidier than you found it on your previous visit.
   b. Spraying water on the pavement cools the air.
   c. A glass is dropped on a hard surface but does not break.
   d. A glass is dropped on a hard surface and shatters into many small pieces.
   e. A coin land heads up, 10 times in a row.
   f. You run a film backward to see a scene you missed.

10. Would a biological evolution that resulted in intelligent humans, with an obvious increase of order and complexity, violate the Second Law?

II. Consulting the Internet

1. Search the Internet to learn about the Philadelphia carpenter, John Worrell Keely, and his 1837 invention, the hydro-pneumatic pulsating vacu-engine (the Keely motor), which allegedly, could push a railroad train 3,000 miles on only one liter of water. What do you think of his invention? Why haven't we implemented his invention yet? Is there a possibility that such a device could be built sometime in the future?

2. Give examples of some famous perpetual motion machines patented in the United States. Explain how they violated the laws of thermodynamics? Were these PMM devices of the first kind or second kind?

3. List some major commercial manufacturers of resistance heaters, gas water heaters, engines, refrigerators, and heat pumps. In each category, what are the criteria by which their performances can be measured (efficiency, COP, EER, SEER)? Are there any brands that offer vastly superior products to their competitors?

III. Problems

Temperature and Heat

1. The all-time highest temperature ever recorded is 134°F on July 10, 1913, at the Greenland Ranch in the Death Valley. The lowest natural temperature ever directly recorded is −128.6 °F at the Soviet Vostok Station in Antarctica on 21 July 1983. Express these temperatures in degrees Celsius?

2. At what temperature do both Celsius and Fahrenheit scales show the same numerical value?

3. Convert the temperature of a healthy body (98.6°F) to degrees Celsius and kelvin.

4. A 2-kW electric resistance heating element is immersed in 30 kg of water initially at 15°C. Calculate the time it takes for the water to boil. Specific heat of water is 4.18 kJ/kg.K.

5. To measure temperatures over a wide range, an inventor proposes to use mercury as the fluid and its melting and boiling temperatures (-38.8°C and 357°C) as the reference points, and divide the distance between them into a number of equal intervals. Write the conversion formula between this arbitrary scale, and °C and °F.

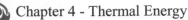

Heat Transfer

6. What is the temperature felt by a naked person exposed to the ambient air at 30°F, and the wind speed of 30 mph? What would be the effective temperature if the wind dies down to 10 mph?

7. A black object is heated until its surface temperature reaches 2,000 K. What is the wavelength at which peak emission occurs? Is the object visible to the naked eyes?

8. Redo the previous problem, but assume a surface temperature of 220 K.

9. What is the total emissive power from a black surface heated to 2,000°C?

10. What is the net radiative exchange between two black surfaces at temperatures 400 K, and 1,500 K?

Thermodynamics

11. An OTEC plant operates in a region with a water surface temperature of 22°C. The temperature of the water drops to 4°C at a depth of 1,000 m and below. What is the maximum possible efficiency?

12. A heat engine burns fuel at a rate of 3,000 kJ per min. What is the power output if it has a thermal efficiency of 25%?

13. In the example above, what is the second law efficiency if the engine operates between temperatures of 900 and 300 kelvins?

14. The energy conversion efficiencies in a three-step process are 60% for the first step, 40% for the second, and 80% for the third. What is the overall efficiency of this three-step process?

15. A 5-kW air conditioner is to maintain room temperature on a summer day. Assuming that hourly heat gains by solar radiation, cooking, and other appliances amount to 54 MJ, what is the COP of this refrigerator?

16. A 5-kW heat pump maintains a house at 22°C on a wintry night when the outside air temperature is -2°C. The house is losing heat at a rate of 3,000 kJ/min. Is this heat pump powerful enough to do the job?

17. A house requires a heat input of 3 kW to maintain its temperature at 22°C. The owner is offered two options, a resistance heater with an efficiency of 96%, and a heat pump with a COP of 3.5. Assuming an outdoor temperature of 2°C,
    a. Which is his best option and why?
    b. What are the first- and second-law efficiencies of the electric heater and the heat pump?

c. How much will the electric bill change, if the owner opts for an electric heater, instead?

18. A heat engine operates by extracting 2,000 kJ of heat from a source at 1500 K, and dumping 800 of waste heat into a sink at 300 K.
    a. Does this engine violate any known laws of thermodynamics?
    b. How much work does this engine produce?
    c. What are the first and second law efficiencies?

19. An air-conditioner produces a 3-kW cooling effect while rejecting 5 kW of heat to its surroundings. What is its coefficient of performance?

20. Could this heat engine be built? Explain.

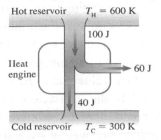

21. Could this refrigerator be built? Explain.

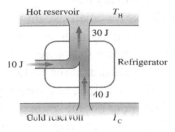

22. ⓐAn air conditioner with a coefficient of performance of 4 is capable of removing 18,000 kJ/h from a room at 295 K and rejects it to outside air at a temperature of 315 K.
    a. Does this air conditioner violate any known laws of thermodynamics?
    b. Calculate the electrical power consumption in kW.
    c. What is the minimum amount of work under ideal conditions?
    d. Determine EER and second law efficiency for this air conditioner.

23. ⓐ An air conditioning unit with a capacity of 7,500 Btu/h and SEER of 15 is used to cool a residential house over a three-month summer period. Assuming that, on average, the air conditioner is on for 10 hours per day, find the total cost of running the air conditioner if the electricity cost is 20¢/kWh.

24. ⓐ Consider two inventors, A and B, both proposing engines that have an efficiency of 30%. Inventor A uses natural gas with a flame temperature of 1000 K. Inventor B uses a geothermal heat source at a temperature of 600 K. Both engines dump their waste heat to ambient at 300 K. Which engine is superior, and why? What are the first-law and second-law efficiencies for both engines?

ⓐ **Food, Diet, and Exercise**

25. A basketball player is using an average of 400 watts of power during a basketball game. How long does he have to play to burn off a Big Mac (750 Calories)?

26. A 50-kg woman is jumping rope at a rate of 50 times per minute for 15 minutes. Each jump, on average, raises the center of mass by 0.5 m. How much energy does this woman consume?

27. What is the BMI value for a 70-kg woman who is 155 cm tall? Is she overweight or underweight, and by how much? If she is overweight, and if she intends to reduce her weight by aerobics only (no dieting) over six months, for how long does she have to exercise every day?

28. A 110-lb (50 kg) woman pedals a stationary bike for 20 minutes, at an average speed of 20 km/h (12.5 mph). Calculate the power consumption rate, total Calories burned, and the metabolic equivalent (METs). 1 MET is defined as the energy expenditure rate in kcal per hour per kilogram of body mass.

29. To maintain a constant weight, we must consume about 2,000 kilocalories of food energy per day of inactivity. How long could you live off your fat by starving (which is not a good way of losing weight)?

IV. Multiple Choice Questions

1. Heat is
   a. A substance with a mass that flows from a high temperature toward a low temperature.
   b. A massless substance that flows from a high temperature toward a low temperature.
   c. The result of the kinetic motion of particles.
   d. The same as work.
   e. A measure of temperature.

2. The reason sand gets warmer than water at sunny beaches is that
   a. Sand is denser than water.
   b. Sand can conduct heat much better than water.
   c. Sand has higher specific heat than water.
   d. Sand has a lower specific heat than water.
   e. Sand is less transparent than water to solar energy.

3. A Btu is a unit of
   a. Heat flow rate.
   b. Energy.
   c. Power.
   d. Specific energy.
   e. None of the above.

4. Heat transfer in solids is mostly by
   a. Conduction.
   b. Convection.
   c. Radiation.
   d. Ablation.
   e. All are equally important.

5. Heat transfer in liquids is mostly by
   a. Conduction.
   b. Convection.
   c. Radiation.
   d. Evaporation.
   e. All are equally important.

6. Heat transfer in flames is mostly by
   a. Conduction.
   b. Convection.
   c. Radiation.
   d. Conduction and convection.
   e. All are equally important.

7. Heat transfer by conduction increases with
   a. The temperature gradient across the object.
   b. The thermal resistance of the object.
   c. The thickness of the object.
   d. The volume of the object.
   e. All of the above.

8. Radiant energy (light) travels
   a. In a medium, but not in a vacuum.
   b. In gases, but not in liquids and solids.
   c. Faster in a vacuum than in a medium.
   d. Faster in a medium than in a vacuum.
   e. With infinite speed in a vacuum.

9. Night vision cameras operate in the
   a. UV range.
   b. X-ray range.
   c. Visible range.
   d. Infrared range.
   e. TV range.

10. Why do some apples appear red to us?
    a. Red apples absorb the red portion of visible light.
    b. Red apples transmit the red portion of visible light.

c. Red apples absorb all colors except red.

d. Red apples absorb the infrared portion of visible light.

e. Red apples reflect the ultraviolet portion of visible light.

11. A lamp which has an efficiency of 15%
    a. Converts 15% of thermal energy to light.
    b. Converts 15% of electrical energy to light.
    c. Converts 15% of electrical energy to light and heat.
    d. Converts 85% of electrical energy input to light.
    e. Converts 15% of the electrical energy to work.

12. When you stir a hot cup of coffee with a wooden spoon, the coffee
    a. Warms mainly by conduction through the spoon.
    b. Cools mainly by conduction through the spoon.
    c. Cools mainly by convection.
    d. Cools mainly by radiation to the surrounding air.
    e. Stirring does not affect its temperature.

13. A battery is a convenient device to convert
    a. Electrical energy to mechanical energy.
    b. Chemical energy to thermal energy.
    c. Thermal energy to electrical energy.
    d. Chemical energy to electrical energy.
    e. Thermal energy to chemical energy.

14. During photosynthesis
    a. Light is converted to chemical energy.
    b. Light is converted to electrical energy.
    c. Light is converted to thermal energy.
    d. Thermal energy is converted to light.
    e. Thermal energy is converted to mechanical energy.

15. According to the Zeroth Law of Thermodynamics,
    a. Temperatures lower than zero absolute temperature can never be achieved.
    b. The total energy of a substance will always remain the same.
    c. Objects at equilibrium must have the same temperatures.
    d. Heat always flows in the direction of decreasing temperature.
    e. There is no such law.

16. According to the First Law of Thermodynamics,
    a. Energy cannot be created, nor can it be destroyed.
    b. The available energy of a system in all real processes decreases.

c. Heat transfer is from a hotter to a colder object.

d. Heat cannot be converted entirely to work.

e. All of the above.

17. According to the Second Law of Thermodynamics,
    a. One day the universe will reach "heat death."
    b. One day we can invent devices to go back in time.
    c. One day we can finally attain the temperature of absolute zero.
    d. One day we can design refrigerators that do not require any work input.
    e. One day we can design thermal engines with near 100% efficiency.

18. According to the Second Law of Thermodynamics,
    a. Some energy is lost when it transforms from one form to another.
    b. Energy can be neither created nor destroyed.
    c. Energy becomes more dispersed during all real processes.
    d. Entropy remains unchanged as work is converted to heat and vice versa.
    e. All of the above.

19. Which of the following observations are consistent with the Zeroth Law of Thermodynamics?
    a. When we turn on a light bulb, some energy is lost as heat.
    b. It is the basis of all measurements.
    c. There is a temperature below which is impossible to achieve
    d. The ultimate fate of the universe is total chaos.
    e. Entropy vanishes at zero absolute temperature.

20. An electric resistance heater extracts 1 Btu of electricity and converts it into 1 Btu of heat. This resistor does not violate
    a. The Zeroth Law of Thermodynamics.
    b. The First Law of Thermodynamics.
    c. The Second Law of Thermodynamics.
    d. The Third Law of Thermodynamics.
    e. All of the above.

21. Which of the following observations are consistent with the Second Law of Thermodynamics?
    a. If you puncture a hole in an inflated helium balloon, helium will escape.
    b. The ultimate fate of the universe is heat death, where there are no temperature, electric potential, and pressure nonuniform anywhere.
    c. We can never build a thermal engine with 100% efficiency.
    d. Even the cooling of a room is associated with

the entropy increase of the entire Universe.
  e. All of the above.
22. A particular light bulb produces 8 J of thermal energy and 2 J of radiant energy. What is the efficiency of this light bulb?
  a. 400%.
  b. 80%.
  c. 25%.
  d. 20%.
  e. Depends on the type of light bulb.
23. The efficiency of car engines can be improved if
  a. We design a heat sink that operates at a lower temperature.
  b. We use better fuels.
  c. We reduce friction.
  d. We increase the combustion temperature.
  e. All of the above.
24. The entropy of a system
  a. Always increases.
  b. Always decreases.
  c. May either decrease or increase.
  d. Remains the same for all irreversible processes.
  e. Remains constant, only if energy remains constant.
25. Saving one Btu of electric energy
  a. Saves zero Btu of total energy.
  b. Saves less than one Btu of total energy.
  c. Saves one Btu of heat.
  d. Saves about 3-4 Btu of heat.
  e. Has no relationship to saving other forms of energy.
26. Refrigerators
  a. Operate in violation of the Zeroth Law of Thermodynamics.
  b. Operate in violation of the First Law of Thermodynamics.
  c. Operate in violation of the Second Law of Thermodynamics.
  d. Operate in violation of the Third Law of Thermodynamics.
  e. Do not violate any laws of thermodynamics.
27. If you left your refrigerator door open, the average temperature in the room would
  a. Be lower than what was before.
  b. Be higher than what was before.
  c. Be the same as what was before with uniform temperature throughout the room.
  d. Be the same as what was before, but some regions will be hotter, while others will be colder.
  e. Depend on its brand.
28. Roughly, what percentage of energy from burning coal can be converted to electricity in a coal-fired power plant?
  a. Less than 15%
  b. 15-30%
  c. 30-45%
  d. 45-60%
  e. More than 60%
29. Diesel engines
  a. Are a type of external combustion engines
  b. Do not need spark plugs to work.
  c. Cannot operate in space because there is little or no oxygen.
  d. Produce less soot particles than gasoline engines, because they function under leaner conditions
  e. All of the above.
30. The human body works as a heat engine, converting _____ % of food energy to the mechanical energy necessary to carry on daily physical activities while disposing of the rest as waste heat.
  a. Less than 1%
  b. Between 1 to 5%
  c. Between 15-25%
  d. About 60%
  e. More than 90%
31. A 100-hp engine can accelerate a car from 0-60 mph in 10 s. To accelerate the same car from 0-60 mph in 5 s we need an engine with a power rating of
  a. 25 h.p.
  b. 50 h.p.
  c. 200 h.p.
  d. 400 h.p.
  e. Acceleration has nothing to do with an engine's power.
32. A well-insulated box is partitioned, one side contains boiling water at 100°C, and the other side contains ice water at 0°C. The partition is removed until the temperature is uniform throughout the box.
  a. Both the energy and entropy of the box increase.
  b. Both the energy and entropy of the box remain the same.
  c. The entropy of the box increases, but its energy decreases.
  d. The entropy of the box increases, but its energy remains unchanged.
  e. The entropy of the box decreases, but its energy

remains unchanged.

33. An engine uses a fuel providing 600 J, but loses 400 J of this energy through the exhaust pipe and other losses. This engine has a thermal efficiency of
   a. 33.3%
   b. 40%
   c. 60%
   d. 66.7%
   e. Not enough information

34. Which of the following situations is allowed by the Second Law of Thermodynamics? Explain.
   a. Designing a heat engine that exploits the temperature differences at the top and bottom of the oceans.
   b. Converting 100 joules of heat energy into 100 joules of work.
   c. Converting 100 joules of work into 100 joules of heat energy.
   d. Extracting heat from the cold outside air to heat the interior of a house in the winter.
   e. Eliminating 100% of the waste heat from a power plant with super-insulating materials.

35. An inventor claims to have designed a heat engine, which extracts 2,000 kJ of waste heat at 600 K, dumping 800 kJ of waste heat into a sink at 300 K, and converting the rest to useful work.
   a. This engine operates with an efficiency of 40%.
   b. This engine operates with an efficiency of 50%.
   c. This engine operates with an efficiency of 60%.
   d. This engine violates the second law of thermodynamics.
   e. This engine violates the first law of thermodynamics.

36. An ideal air conditioning unit maintains a house at 20°C by dumping heat into the atmosphere at 40°C. This refrigerator has a coefficient of performance of
   a. 0.064.
   b. 0.50.
   c. 14.65.
   d. 15.65.
   e. No such air conditioner can be built.

37. If air resistance is negligible, the total of potential and kinetic energies of a freely falling body _____.
   a. Increases
   b. Decreases
   c. Becomes zero
   d. Remains the same
   e. Cannot tell

38. Name the physical quantity, which is equal to the product of force and velocity.
   a. Work
   b. Energy
   c. Power
   d. Acceleration
   e. Torque

39. An object that has potential energy may have this energy because of its
   a. Speed
   b. Acceleration
   c. Momentum
   d. Location
   e. All of these

40. A man has a mass of 90 kg and a height of 160 cm. According to NIH criteria this man
   a. Is anorexic
   b. Is underweight
   c. Is normal
   d. Is overweight
   e. Is obese

V. True or False?

1. Heat is a mass-less substance that resides inside an object.
2. Temperature is a property of the material from which an object is made and represents the amount of heat that is contained in that object.
3. Heat is the total amount of energy in an object.
4. Energy is conserved, but only if no friction is present.
5. Heat can never flow from a low to a high temperature.
6. The specific heat capacity is a measure of the amount of energy that a kilogram of substance can store before its temperature rises by one degree.
7. The absolute best insulator is a vacuum since there are no molecules to pass on energy.
8. An ideal heat engine that works with no friction is 100% efficient.
9. On a bicycle, one form of mechanical energy converts to another form of mechanical energy.
10. According to the Second Law of Thermodynamics, nature always prefers order over disorder.
11. Since time always proceeds from the past to the present to the future, running a film backward violates the Second Law of Thermodynamics.
12. Work, heat, and energy are different names for the same thing.
13. Work can be converted to heat, and vice versa.

14. Solar energy is a higher quality form of energy than fossil fuels.

15. The construction of a time machine is theoretically possible, but will not be technically feasible for a very long time.

16. A machine that creates a net order in the Universe is a PPM of the first kind.

17. All ideal engines operating between two heat reservoirs have the same efficiency.

18. Heat cannot, by itself, flow from a low to a high temperature.

19. Most materials expand upon heating; there are a few (such as rubber) that shrink when heated.

20. The matter continuously degrades as it is recycled.

VI. Fill in the Blanks

1. Heat engines are devices in which thermal energy is converted to _____ energy.

2. A photon is the smallest amount of light that carries energy proportional to its _____.

3. In liquid-in-glass thermometers are best described as _____ amplifiers.

4. It is impossible to construct a heat engine that has the efficiency of unity unless it operates in an atmosphere at _____ temperature.

5. When burned in a gasoline engine, approximately _____ of the gasoline energy ends up in the exhaust pipe.

6. No heat engine can operate with only one heat _____.

7. The ratio of energy delivered to energy used is called the _____ efficiency.

8. Heat pumps usually have _____ ratings greater than one.

9. According to the _____ Law of Thermodynamics, a temperature of zero kelvin can never be attained.

10. To make fusion reactions possible, the gaseous mixture of deuterium and tritium must be heated to 100 million degrees Celsius. Expressing in degrees Fahrenheit, we need a temperature of _____ million degrees.

PROJECT I -- Gas vs. Electricity

In this project, you are asked to examine the electric and gas bills for your home for a month. Find a copy of your gas and electricity bills (if you don't get one, use those from your parents or a friend) and write down:

a. The amount of electricity used in kilowatt-hours.

b. The amount of gas used (in the United States this is usually given in 1000-cubic feet or therms, which is equal to 100,000 Btu).

c. The lowest, highest, and average prices charged during that month. Note that prices may vary depending on location, the month of the year, time of the day, and during peak hours.

d. The total amount of energy consumption (thermal and electrical) in megajoules and kilowatt-hours.

e. The average power consumed by you in kilowatts (divide the total energy used by the number of hours in the month). The average cost of electricity in $/kWh and $/MJ (1 kWh = 3.6x10^6 J).

f. The average cost of gas in $/therm and $/MJ.

g. Which (electricity or natural gas) costs more and why? Is the price differential justified? Explain.

h. How much you would save (or lose) if you switched to all-electric appliances.

PROJECT II — Efficiency and Conservation

Look around your house or your place of work. List all the appliances that consume one or another form of energy. Propose ideas to reduce material and energy consumption. Classify these measures as conservation or efficiency. Estimate the savings in terms of material and energy saved. In terms of money, you spend on utility bills or purchasing materials.

PROJECT III -- Diet and Exercise

In this project, you are asked to keep a daily log of your daily food intake and the tasks you perform. Then, you are asked to estimate your caloric intake and the number of calories you burn as a result of your daily routines. For better estimates, it is recommended that you collect and take the average for three 24-hour periods.

Basic Information:

Sex: _____ (male/female)

Mass: _____ kg

Height: _____ cm

Make a table listing all of the foods you consumed. Categorize them into breakfast, lunch, dinner, and snacks.

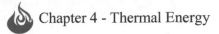
Make a list of the activities you performed and their durations.

1. Find the average daily total intake of food calories. Take the three-day average.
2. Estimate the average daily total calories from carbohydrates, protein, and fat, respectively. Assume 9 Calories per gram of fat and 4 Calories per gram of protein and carbohydrates.
3. Calculate the average power you put out, assuming you maintain a similar diet throughout the year.
4. Calculate your BMR. According to Harris and Benedict[*], BMR can be accurately calculated using the following equations. BMR is the basal metabolic rate in kcal/day; M is body mass in kg, H is height in cm, and A is the age in years.

    Men: BMR = 66 + 13.7×M + 5×H - 6.8×A

    Women: BMR = 655 + 9.6×M + 1.8×H - 4.7×A

5. Estimate the total non-BMR calories burned through various activities. Which of the activities were aerobic and which ones were anaerobic?
6. Calculate your total daily energy expenditure by adding total BMR and non-BMR calories. What is the power per mass (kW/kg)? Carry the energy balance by taking the difference between your daily energy expenditure and energy from your food intake. Calculate your daily calorie needs by multiplying your BMR by:
    a. 1.200, if you are inactive (do little or no exercise).
    b. 1.375, if you are somewhat inactive (light exercise 1-3 times per week).
    c. 1.550, if you are moderately active (moderate exercise 3-5 times a week).
    d. 1.725, if you are active (extraneous exercise 5-7 times a week).
    e. If you maintain a fairly similar routine for the entire year, how much mass should you expect to gain or lose?

PROJECT IV -- Energy balance

In this project, you are asked to estimate your total daily energy consumption.

7. Make a table showing your daily food intake and the total food calories you consume. Convert this energy to joules.
8. Make a table showing all the electrical appliances you routinely use (electric oven, refrigerator, heater, stereo, lights, hairdryer, etc.). Estimate the number of hours you use each device. Multiply time by the power consumption (wattage) to calculate the total energy consumption in kilowatt-hours. If there is more than one person in your household, correct the result by dividing this number by the number of people sharing each device.
9. Assuming electricity was produced in a power plant with an efficiency of 33%, how much thermal energy was needed to meet your electric power requirement?
10. Estimate the total energy requirements for all the gas appliances in your house.
11. Estimate the total energy required for your transportation needs. This can be done by dividing your daily travel in miles by the gas mileage your car gets (in mpg) and multiplying the results by the energy contained in one gallon of fuel.
12. Add items 1-5 to estimate your total daily energy consumption.

[*] https://www.bmi-calculator.net/bmr-calculator/

Work Sheet for Project IV				
I. Food	Person 1	Person 2	Person 3	Total
- Daily food calories				
- Energy to grow food (kcal/d)				
Total annual food energy				MJ
II. Appliances	Watts	Number	Hours on	Total
- TV				
- Refrigerator				
- Microwave oven				
- Electric oven				
- Gas range				
- Others (list) _____				
Total annual energy use by appliances				MJ
III. Lighting	Watts	Number	Hours on	Total
- Incandescent				
- Fluorescent				
- Others				
Total annual energy use for lighting				MJ
IV. Transportation	Car 1	Car 2	Car 3	Total
- Model				
- Annual mileage (or kilometers)				
- Fuel efficiency (mpg or 100 km/L)				
- Gasoline consumption (gallons or liters)				
Total annual energy for transportation				MJ
V. Others (not included)				MJ
Household total (I–V)				MJ
U.S. Total				MJ

Saving by	Proposed action	Saving
a. Changing diet		
b. Changing to energy-efficient appliances		
c. Changing lighting		
d. Others (list)		
_____		
_____		
_____		MJ
Total household savings	Barrels of oil	MJ
Total U.S. Savings		
Impact on U.S. economy	*The U.S. will save $ _____ billions from reduced dependence on foreign oil.*	
Impact on environment	*There will be a reduction in emission of _____ million metric tons of CO_2.*	

CHAPTER 5

Electricity

Electricity ~ Flickr/IPetr Kovár

If it weren't for electricity, we'd all be watching television by candlelight. ~
George Gobal (1919-1991)

When Thomas Edison worked late into the night on the electric light, he had
to do it by gas lamp or candle. I'm sure it made the work seem that much
more urgent. ~ George Carlin (1937-2008)

E lectricity is another elusive word meaning different things to different people. Power companies use electricity to mean electrical energy; many trade books talk of electricity as the flow of electrons, while others talk of electricity as being synonymous with an electric charge. Whatever electricity is, it is closely associated with the imbalance between positive and negative charges within matter.

Unlike other forms of energy, electricity is not a source of energy but requires energy to be produced. Once electrical wires carry the electricity to our homes, it can be used to provide thermal energy through an electric heater, give off light through an electric light bulb, emit sound energy through a speaker, or power an electric motor to pump water or run an elevator. Along the way, a small portion of the energy is lost to the atmosphere as waste heat. The versatility of electricity, exhibited by its ability to carry out so many tasks, is one reason it is considered to be a very high-quality form of energy. Electricity, however, is not available to all people. It is estimated that about one and a half billion people lack electricity, most of them living in rural areas far from electrical grids.

The choice of fuel for the production of electricity in power generating facilities depends on four factors: conversion efficiency, land requirement, cost, and carbon content. Two-thirds of all electricity is generated by fossil fuels (40% from coal, 22% from natural gas, and 5% from petroleum). Renewable sources produce another 22%, and the remaining 11% was by nuclear.

Worldwide, 40% of all the energy consumed is used to produce 21.6 trillion kilowatt-hours of electricity, and in the process, emits 8.8 billion tons of carbon. In the United States, half of all energy consumed is in the form of electrical energy, for a total installed capacity of one terawatt, or about one-quarter of the world's total.

In this chapter, we will become familiar with the laws governing the flow, production, storage, and transmission of electricity.

Electricity and Magnetism

The word "**electricity**" is derived from the Greek word *electron*, meaning amber. The Greeks knew that a piece of amber rubbed against a cat's fur would collect charges. Furthermore, they observed that identical objects touching the amber repelled each other. The same thing happened if the amber and the fur were replaced with another pair of materials -- glass and silk. However, if the glass was brought next to amber, or if the fur was brought next to silk cloth, the pairs would attract.

Benjamin Franklin (1706-1790) suggested that an imbalance results when objects having an excess of an invisible fluid (amber, glass) were brought next to objects deficient in this fluid (fur, silk); in an attempt to reach equilibrium, this invisible fluid would move from one object to the other, and the two would attract. We had to wait another century until it was discovered that this fluid was, in fact, a stream of electrons that flows from one object to another when they rub. However, Franklin erroneously presumed a lack of the invisible fluid rather than a surplus of electrons; opposite to his assertion, electrons transferred from fur and silk to amber and glass.[*]

We can transfer electrons from one place to another in two ways: by contact as is done by rubbing substances and by induction, a phenomenon described in 1831 by Michael Faraday, who showed he could generate electricity in a material by bringing an electrically charged object near it. Lightning is a sudden electrostatic discharge between the top and bottom of a polarized storm cloud, two clouds of opposite charge, or between a cloud and the ground. Franklin's electric rod is a convenient tool to transfer electricity generated by lightning safely to the ground.

Today, we understand that atoms consist of negatively charged electrons orbiting a nucleus composed of positively charged protons and neutrons with no charge. For an atom to be neutral, the total numbers of protons and electrons are equal, resulting in a net-zero charge. We also know that, just as with energy, **electric charges are conserved --**

---

[*] When Benjamin Franklin made his conjecture regarding the invisible fluid, he assumed that fluid flowed from glass to silk. In reality, silk has an excess of electrons and glass is deficient in electrons. If we had designated electrons as having positive charges, the flow of current would have been from higher to lower concentration of electrons, in line with the assertion that excess fluid moved from one object to the other.

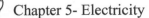

Electrical and Gravitational Forces

There is a striking resemblance between the way electrical and gravitational forces function. Gravitational force follows Newton's Law of Universal Gravitation and is proportional to the product of the two masses and inversely proportional to the square of the distance between them. Electrical force follows Coulomb's Law, which states that the electrical force between two charged objects is directly proportional to the product of the quantity of charge on the objects and inversely proportional to the square of the separation distance between the two objects. In the same way gravity is responsible for a satellite orbiting the earth, electrical force is responsible for electrons orbiting the nucleus. Unlike gravitational forces that are always attractive, electrical forces can be either attractive or repulsive.

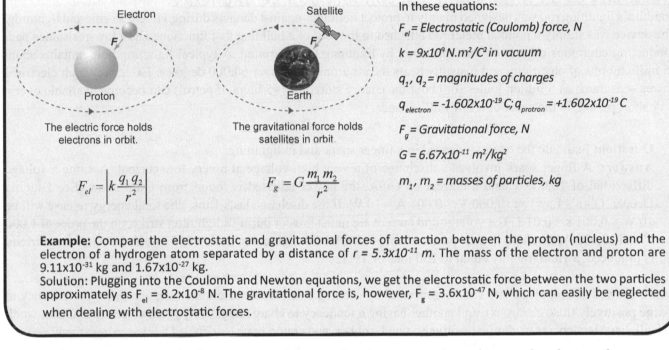

The electric force holds electrons in orbit.

The gravitational force holds satellites in orbit.

In these equations:

F_{el} = Electrostatic (Coulomb) force, N

$k = 9 \times 10^9 \, N.m^2/C^2$ in vacuum

q_1, q_2 = magnitudes of charges

$q_{electron} = -1.602 \times 10^{-19} \, C; q_{protron} = +1.602 \times 10^{-19} \, C$

F_g = Gravitational force, N

$G = 6.67 \times 10^{-11} \, m^2/kg^2$

m_1, m_2 = masses of particles, kg

$$F_{el} = \left| k \frac{q_1 q_2}{r^2} \right|$$

$$F_g = G \frac{m_1 m_2}{r^2}$$

Example: Compare the electrostatic and gravitational forces of attraction between the proton (nucleus) and the electron of a hydrogen atom separated by a distance of $r = 5.3 \times 10^{-11}$ m. The mass of the electron and proton are 9.11×10^{-31} kg and 1.67×10^{-27} kg.

Solution: Plugging into the Coulomb and Newton equations, we get the electrostatic force between the two particles approximately as $F_{el} = 8.2 \times 10^{-8}$ N. The gravitational force is, however, $F_g = 3.6 \times 10^{-47}$ N, which can easily be neglected when dealing with electrostatic forces.

---

i.e., electric charges can transfer from one material to another, but no new charge is created or destroyed.

Electric charges may remain stationary or flow through an electrical conductor. *Electrostatic* (stationary) charges may be caused by friction (shuffling one's foot across a carpeted floor), by contact (touching a metal doorknob), or by induction (lightning). Electrostatic charges are not of concern in this study and will not be discussed further. When the motion of charges is involved, electric currents flow through circuits, powering devices ranging from simple battery-operated toys and home appliances to state-of-the-art electronics. Electrostatic and gravitational forces are similar in many ways (See Box: Electrical and Gravitational Forces).

Unlike gravity, which always is shown to be attractive, the electric force could be either attractive or repulsive.

Magnetism is the ability of certain objects to attract iron and certain other materials. Such objects are called magnets. According to legends, the discovery of magnets goes back 4000 years when a Cretan shepherd by the name of Magnes found the metallic tip of his staff was stuck to a piece of rock. This rock was identified as ferrous oxide and called *lodestone* (meaning the stone that attracts). Ever since we have found many materials that exhibit similar behavior. Iron, nickel, and cobalt are among the materials that are commonly used.

Today, we understand that electricity and magnetism are two phenomena that occur hand in hand; in fact, they are different parts of a single force called the

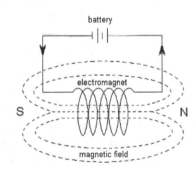

Figure 5-1
Moving electric charges create a magnetic field.

electromagnetic force. This was demonstrated by Hans Christian Oersted (1777-1851), who showed that a compass needle brought near a wire carrying electrical current deflects. Similarly, if an electric current is passed through a looped wire (called an electromagnet), a magnetic field is created around the wire (Figure 5-1). The greater the current and the higher the number of loops in the coil, the stronger the magnetic field will be. Electromagnets are used in many devices, including simple on/off switches and practically every electromechanical devices, from small toys and hair dryers to loudspeakers and large electric motors in elevators and cable car trolleys.

Electricity as a Primary and a Secondary Source of Energy

Franklin's lightning rod was designed mainly to protect buildings against dangers during violent storms and lightning. The device was simply a pointed metal rod attached to the roof of a building that functioned as a low-resistance path conducting enormous electric current discharge by lightning to the ground. A typical lightning bolt contains about 15 million volts of electricity and instantly heats the air around it to over 60,000 degrees. Extremely high electrical power -- as much as 5 billion joules (or about the energy stored in 145 liters of petrol) can become available over a very short period, in the order of a few milliseconds.

> **Question:** Estimate the energy released in a finger spark and in lightning.
> **Answer:** A finger spark involves a discharge of a very high voltage at a very low current. Assume a voltage differential of 10,000 V and a current of 1 mA, the power released is found from Ohm's law (See Digging Deeper, Ohm's Law) as 10,000 V × 0.001 A = 10 W. If the discharge lasts 1 ms, the total energy release will be 10 W × 0.001 s = 0.01 J. The voltage and current are much greater during a lightning strike, on the order of 1,000 V and 10,000 A, resulting in total power equal to 10 GW. For lightening lasting 100 ms, about 1 GJ of electricity is produced, a yield roughly equal to 250 tons of TNT.

As we showed above, electricity can be generated by rubbing two triboelectric materials, one having a tendency to charge positively (lose electrons), and another having a tendency to charge negatively (gain electrons). Glass, wool, and silk have tendencies to charge positively; vinyl, rubber, and cotton have tendencies to charge negatively.

Several schemes have been proposed to harvest energy from a lightning bolt, although nobody has suggested a practical way of utilizing electricity from a thunderstorm yet. However, absorbing lightning and converting it to useful energy proved to be an extraordinary challenge, as it required complex capture and storage supercapacitor facilities. Besides, predicting when and where thunderstorms will occur seems almost impossible. Until such technologies become available, utilizing lightning as a primary source of energy has to wait.

No single source of energy is enough to satisfy all of the electricity needs of any country. Each country combines a mix of various sources to satisfy its need for electricity generation. Australia, China, U.S., and countries with the highest electrical capacity rely heavily on fossil fuels and, therefore, also are the greatest contributors to the emission of carbon dioxide, a major precursor to global warming. There are exceptions, however. France, Belgium, and a few other European countries rely heavily on nuclear energy so they have relatively small carbon footprints. Sweden relies on nuclear, hydro, and other renewable sources of energy to generate 97% of its electricity. Solar is not a major contributor yet, as its cost of electricity production is still higher than other resources. As the prices fall, more countries are moving to make solar an important component of their electricity portfolio. Practically all of the electricity generation in Iceland is from geothermal resources. Norway, with 99% of its electricity generated by hydro resources, is the cleanest country in the world. Canada also gets most of its energy from hydroelectric generating plants. Denmark and China are rapidly expanding their shares of electricity from the wind.

To evaluate the contribution of the energy mix utilized by each country to its carbon footprint, one can calculate the oil-equivalent of various energy resources. Table 5-1 gives examples of this energy mix for several countries, as well as the amount of oil needed to generate one kilowatt-hour of electricity from each resource in terms of kilograms of oil equivalent. Also given is the average release of carbon dioxide per kWh of electricity generated.

Table 5-1 Electricity Generation Mix (%)							
Country	Fossil Fuel	Nuclear	Hydro	Biomass	Other Renewables	koe*/ kWh	CO2/ kWh
Australia	86	0	7	1	6	0.24	0.71
China	68	4	18	neg.	10	0.22	0.66
India	62	2	14	3	19	0.26	0.77
U.S.	64	19	7	2	8	0.17	0.50
France	10	78	12	neg.	neg.	0.02	0.06
Norway	1	0	99	neg.	neg.	0	neg.
Russia	64	18	17	0	1	neg.	0.02
Denmark	70	0	0	6	24	0.26	0.78
Sweden**	3	36	47	5	2	neg.	neg.
Iceland	0	0	74	neg.	26	0.0	0.0
World	**63**	**16**	**16**	**5**	**24**	**0.16**	**0.48**

*kg oil-equivalent (~ 42 MJ)
** Balance is imported.
Source: EIA Annual Reports 2018. U.S. data from EIA, 2018.

Motors and Generators

Electric motors are devices that convert electrical energy into useful mechanical energy. The principle of operation is simple. When a wire carrying an electric current is placed in a magnetic field, it experiences a force that is normal to the direction of the current (Figure 5-2a). If the wire is bent into a loop, then the opposite sides of the loop experience forces that are in opposite directions to each other (Figure 5-2b). The force pair creates a torque that rotates the coil. To increase the magnitude of the torque, and produce a smoother operation, practical motors use an armature consisting of multiple loops (Figure 5-2c). The magnitude of the torque depends on the strength of the magnetic field -- the stronger the magnet, the higher is the torque. Everyday magnets, (such as those used to attach notes to the refrigerators) are made from iron, cobalt, and nickel. They are not strong, however. Stronger magnets can be made from alloys of such rare earth materials as neodymium and dysprosium, with iron and boron. These magnets help generate sufficient torque in the motors of electric and hybrid cars and convert torque to electricity in large wind turbines.

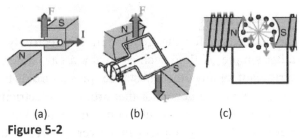

Figure 5-2
Principle of operation of an electric motor.

Electric motors can be driven by either direct current (DC) or alternating current (AC). The difference between DC and AC motors is in the way the magnetic fields are created. In DC motors, this is done through an electromagnet or a permanent magnet. In AC motors, the magnetic field is created by passing an alternating current through a stator, such that the polarity changes just when the armature is lined up with the poles of similar polarity. AC motors are generally considered to be more powerful and generate higher torque AC motors are generally considered to be more powerful than DC motors because they can generate higher torque than DC motors. However, DC motors are typically more efficient and make better use of their input energy. DC motors, on the other hand, are typically more efficient.

One of the main features of electric motors is their ability to produce torque as soon as they start. This is in contrast to internal combustion engines, where no torque is delivered until the engine attains a certain speed. In fact, this is why all cars running on petroleum require starter motors to operate. Furthermore, with only one moving part, electric motors are much simpler and have a much longer lifetime than internal combustion engines. Because of their ability to deliver peak torque at or near stalls, electric motors are widespread in trolley cars, elevators, cranes, forklifts, and electric railroad locomotives. We will discuss the application of electric motors in electric and hybrid vehicles in Chapter 6.

Electric generators (also called alternators) are devices that convert the rotational energy of turbines or spinning shafts into electrical energy. Electric generators work in a manner opposite to motors -- a magnet is turned by some external means to induce a current through a wire.

Depending on their applications, there are different types of generators on the market. In *synchronous generators,* the rotor turns at exactly the same frequency as the electric grid; for a 60-Hz grid, it makes 60 revolutions per second, or 3,600 rpm (50-Hz or 3,000 rpm in Europe). These generators often are used in coal, oil, or nuclear power plants where fuels can be burned at a controlled rate, making the turbine rotate at a fixed velocity. In *asynchronous generators*, the magnetic field of the rotor and the electric field of the stator do not synchronize, but the rotor falls behind (slips). Wind turbines take advantage of variable-speed generators by adjusting the resistance in the rotor winding (slip), or by changing the number of stator poles, to allow the turbine to run faster as wind speed increases.

Generation, Transmission, Distribution, and Storage of Electricity

The delivery of electricity from production to consumption requires efficient generating facilities, access to reliable networks, powerful transformers and relaying stations, accurate metering, adequate storage, and other procurement services such as scheduling and dispatching (Figure 5-3). At all points, the quality of electricity must be assured to maintain its frequency and voltage stability. This is particularly important in large networks in which electricity is continuously added and consumed at various nodes within the grid. Without this, a potential failure can propagate quickly, damaging a large part of the network and causing a blackout over a large geographical area.[†]

Generation

The procedure for the generation of electricity is rather simple. A fluid such as steam, a gas, water, a refrigerant, or any other substance spins a turbine that is connected to a generator that produces electricity. The propulsive force could come from the kinetic energy of the wind, current in a river or stream, the potential energy of falling water, temperature and salinity gradients in oceans, lakes, and ponds, or heat released by uranium fission or burning of woods, biomass, coal, oil, natural gas, or even Earth's geothermal resources. No matter which approach is used, there must always be a potential difference that supplies the work to run the turbine-generator assembly.

The generation of electricity by **conventional thermal power plants** is accomplished in three

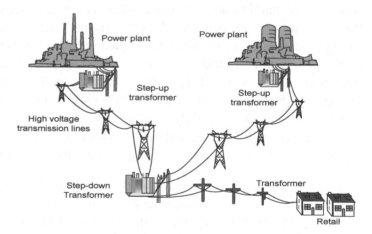

Figure 5-3

Electrical power distribution from generating plants to customers.

---

† The largest power failure in U.S. history occurred in August 2003, following a problem resulting from a fallen tree in Ohio, on an unusually hot summer day, when demand was especially high. This created an overload that triggered a series of power failures across the grid. To prevent equipment damage, more than a dozen nuclear power plants and over 80 fossil-fuel-generating stations in the United States and Canada were automatically shut down within nine seconds. Over 50 million people lost power.

steps: 1) the conversion of chemical or nuclear energy into thermal energy of a fluid inside a combustion chamber or a reactor core; 2) the conversion of thermal energy into mechanical (rotational) energy of a gas or steam turbine; 3) followed by the conversion of mechanical energy into electrical energy by an electric generator.

In coal, oil, gas, and biomass power plants, the source of energy is the energy trapped in the chemical bonds of the fossil fuel or biomass. In nuclear power plants, the binding energy of the nucleus provides the energy. In solar-thermal plants, thermal energy is directly available.

Geothermal plants use the steam generated as a result of natural radioactive decay and molten rocks deep in the earth's crust to run a steam turbine and, therefore, do not need boilers, and step one is eliminated. Hot water also can be used to boil a refrigerant fluid before sending the steam to turn a turbine.

Magnetohydrodynamic (MHD) power generators omit the intermediate step by converting the thermal energy of fossil fuels directly into electrical energy, without first converting it to mechanical energy (turning the turbines). Hot, supersonic gases from coal combustors are "seeded" with strong magnets, it separates the charges, which drift toward, and are collected by electrodes on opposite channel walls. An external circuit can be set up to take advantage of the charge gradient and produce electricity (See Figure 5-4). Because of the low level of heat rejection, efficiency is higher than that of the conventional thermal power plants, and demand for the cooling water is lower. The hot exhaust gas also can be used to boil water to steam and produce additional electricity by conventional methods.

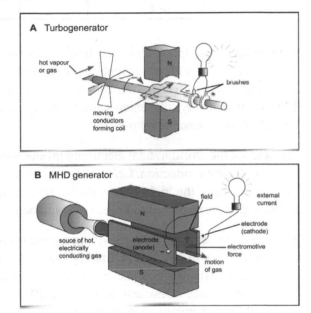

Electricity generated by the **wind, waterfalls, and ocean waves** does not require the first two steps, as they directly utilize the kinetic energy of air streams, falling water, or river streams, ocean waves, and underwater currents to rotate a water wheel or to compress a column of air and drive a gas turbine.[‡] Wind farms are advantageous over hydroelectric plants in the sense that they do not need reservoirs and create no pollution. The disadvantage is that air carries much less energy than water, so to generate a similar amount of electricity, wind turbines must be considerably larger than water turbines.

Figure 5-4
Magnetohydrodynamic can produce power directly without the need for a turbine or generator.

In addition to mechanical and thermal means, electricity can be generated directly. **Fuel cells** produce electricity from electrochemical reactions between hydrogen and oxygen. **Photovoltaic** cells convert the energy in sunlight directly into a flow of electrons through an external circuit, in effect replacing the generator. **Thermophotovoltaic** works in a similar fashion except that, instead of using the visible light from the sun, it converts infrared radiation or heat from furnaces into electricity (See Chapter 10).

Table 5-2 summarizes the steps required to generate power from various energy sources.

Electricity Generation Around the World

Electricity is the world's fastest-growing form of end-use energy consumption, as it has been for many decades. The capacity is expected to increase by another 70% by 2040, with the bulk of growth in non-OECD countries, mainly China, India, and Brazil. Coal and natural gas will continue to be the main sources of fuel for much of this expansion.

---

‡ The major difference between thermal, hydroelectric, and wind power plants is that in hydroelectric and wind plants, water or air flows directly through water or wind turbines, whereas with thermal power plants, a working fluid is heated to its boiling temperature before it is passed through a steam turbine.

Table 5-2 Steps required to generate electricity by various sources.						
Source	*Light*	*Nuclear*	*Chemical*	*Thermal*	*Mechanical*	*Electrical*
Fossil Fuels, Biomass			X	X	X	X
Nuclear		X		X	X	X
Solar thermal				X	X	X
Geothermal				X	X	X
MHD			X	X		X
Wind, Hydro, Waves					X	X
Fuel Cells			X			X
Solar PV	X					X
Thermo-PV				X		X

Liquid fuel consumption will remain relatively flat or may even decline as a source of fuel for electricity generation, as it is substituted with unconventional resources, such as oil sands, shale oil, biodiesel, and synthetic oil. The fastest growth in electrical generation capacity, however, comes from renewable sources, mainly hydro, wind, and solar. The overall capacity still remains small, satisfying only 18% of the total demand. Wind and hydroelectricity account for half of all renewable output.

China leads the world in total electricity production from renewable sources -- thanks to its recent massive additions to hydroelectric production. China is followed closely by the United States, Brazil, and Canada. Wind and solar are expected to have the highest growth; tidal/wave/oceanic energy is not currently competitive, but rapid changes in technologies are expected to lower costs and help accelerate their production.

The fate of nuclear fission in providing a large portion of electricity is rather uncertain and may be forced to slow its expansion. Lack of progress in finding suitable sites for disposal and long-term storage of radioactive waste, rising construction costs, issues associated with the transport of nuclear fuel, proliferation, and safety are all impediments to large acceptance of nuclear power. The 2011 nuclear accident in Fukushima, once again, has flamed debate on the suitability of nuclear energy and forced many governments to reevaluate their nuclear programs. Germany is the first country that formally announced freezing the construction of the new nuclear plants, and the dismantling of all nuclear reactors by 2022. Switzerland is taking similar steps to become nuclear-free by 2034. Other European countries are reevaluating their nuclear policies but are expected to phase out a large fraction of their power plants by 2050.

Thermal Power Plants

As is the case for any heat engine, thermal power plants are devices that convert heat to rotational shaft work, which can be coupled to a generator to produce electricity. Unlike internal combustion engines, where the heat of combustion comes from fuel burned inside the engine, power plants use external heat – most often from fossil or nuclear fuels.

Most baseload thermal power plants follow a thermodynamic cycle, which consists of a high-pressure boiler, a steam turbine, a condenser, and a pump. Water is commonly used as the working fluid, although there are instances where ammonia and other refrigerants serve the purpose best. The cycle operates using a feed-water pump to introduce water into a boiler or steam generator, where it boils and turns into high-pressure, superheated steam. To boil water, energy is required. The source of this energy could be fossil fuel, nuclear fuel, solar heat, or a geothermal reservoir (See Figure 5-5). The superheated steam subsequently enters a steam turbine, where it is expanded and cooled to a saturated mixture of vapor and liquid. To close the cycle, the mixture is condensed into liquid before it is reintroduced back into the boiler. Recycling the same water not only conserves water but also saves on the cost of filtering. This is essential to avoid corrosion and prevent the buildup of mineral deposits in the system.

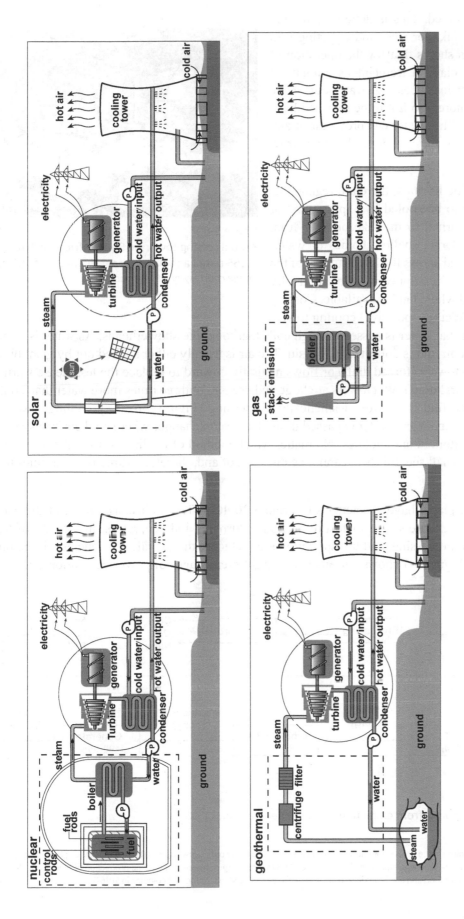

Figure 5-5

Thermal power plants consist of a boiler (or steam generator), a steam turbine, a condenser and a recirculating pump. Water boils in a boiler and turns into superheated steam. Steam will then expand in a steam turbine and delivers shaft work. The steam is condensed back to liquid water before being pumped into the boiler, repeating the cycle.

To condense steam, it must be cooled. This is done by pumping cold water from a nearby ocean, lake, or river and diverting it to the condenser. A simple analysis shows that for the operation of even a moderately-sized power plant, a tremendous amount of cooling water is needed. In most instances, the water out of the condenser is hotter by 20°C or more, too hot to be returned back to its source. The thermal shock of hot water can prove especially harmful to aquatic organisms whose survival depends on a narrow range of temperature fluctuations.[§]

Figure 5-6
Kendal cooling towers in South Africa; each tower is 165 m tall and has a throat diameter of 102 m. *Image courtesy of DB Thermal.*

To safeguard fish and other marine habitats, there are regulations that require the condenser water to be cooled in a spray pond or a cooling tower before being returned to the lake or river from which it came. Spray ponds are large, shallow bodies of water. Water from the condenser is sprayed across the large surface of the pond, where it is cooled by evaporation. Spray ponds are normally used in areas of low humidity and where land is available. Cooling towers can be either wet or dry. Wet (evaporative) cooling towers are similar to spray ponds except that water is passed through coils that look like showerheads. As water is dripped down, it is cooled by the ambient air and is collected in a basin. The air is usually either sucked out by giant blower fans placed on top of the cooling towers (forced draft) or flows naturally upward to replace the less-dense warm air that is rising out of the tower (natural draft). Wet towers are large and use two to three times more water than cooling ponds. Furthermore, many people find the towers aesthetically displeasing (Figure 5-6). Dry cooling towers are cooled by conduction and convection. Warm water is passed through a heat exchanger where cold air is passed over the coils, very much like the radiators in automobiles. No matter which method of cooling is used, the heat always ends up in the atmosphere. As we shall see, this heat cannot be disposed of and, therefore, directly contributes to the warming of the atmosphere.

Depending on the type, practical plants have efficiencies of around 30-40%. This is because much of the energy is used to raise water to high-temperature steam, or lost to friction in turbines and generators. In the case of fossil plants, if losses due to extraction, processing, and transportation are included, the overall efficiencies will be much lower -- in the order of 10-20%. Figure 5-7 shows various losses at different stages of power generation from fossil resources.

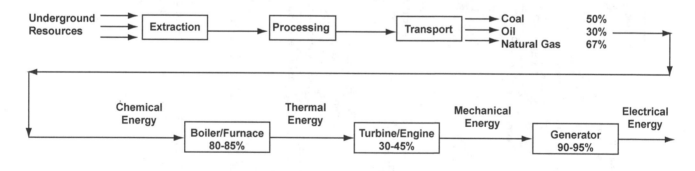

Figure 5-7
Fossil plant energy losses at various points from extraction to power generation.

---

§ The optimal temperature for plankton, the major source of food for many aquatic ecosystems, varies by only a few degrees. For example, the optimum temperature for the growth of green algae is 30°C, whereas blue-green algae thrive at about 30-35°C. Thermal discharges, therefore, favor the production of blue-green algae over green algae. Blue-green algae are a poorer source of food and can be toxic to fish. "Estimated cost of new generating technologies in 2016."

Cogeneration

Cogeneration or Combined Heat and Power (CHP) is the simultaneous production of electricity and heat. When steam also is produced, the system is called **trigeneration**. Natural gas turbines are particularly advantageous over conventional oil and coal plants because there is no emission of sulfur and negligible emission of particulates; nitric oxide and carbon dioxide emissions are also significantly cut. In a typical CHP, the primary power plant produces electricity but, unlike the simple power plants in which exhaust is dumped into the atmosphere, the thermal energy left in the exhaust is used to produce additional power, or used directly for heating purposes. Because much of the waste heat is not dumped into the atmosphere, these practices result in greater conversion efficiencies and lower pollution than the traditional generation methods. When waste heat is used directly for industrial processes, efficiencies as high as 85% have been found to be possible. Cogeneration has another advantage -- that power can be distributed. This means that small-scale power generation facilities can be constructed using hybrid systems consisting of solar panels, microturbines, and wind turbines that can produce enough electricity for small communities such as shopping malls, large office buildings, etc. When power is not needed, the excess electricity could be sold to utility companies, reducing their peak loads. Figure 5-8 shows the schematic of a typical CHP generation system.

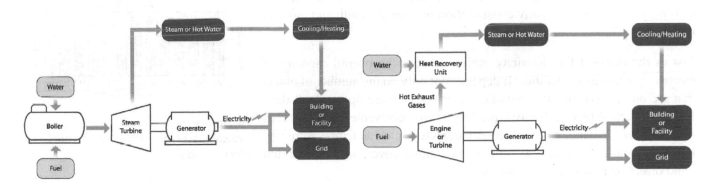

Figure 5-8
The two most common CHP system configurations: left) Natural gas turbine or diesel engine is coupled with a generator to provide the power while the hot exhaust heats water to provide hot water and steam. right) The steam turbine directly provides both steam and power.
Image courtesy of U.S. EPA.

Example 5-1: A cogeneration plant uses combined gas turbines and steam power plants. Assuming that a total of 200 kg of natural gas is burned every second, what is the plant's overall efficiency? The gas turbine has a thermal efficiency of 40%, whereas the efficiency of the steam power plant is only 33%. Assume methane has a heating value of 50,000 kJ/kg.[¶]

Solution: The total heat input into gas turbines is equal to the mass flow rate of the fuel multiplied by its heating value $200 \times 50,000 = 10$ MW.[**] The power output from the primary cycle (gas turbine) is equal to heat input times the efficiency, $10 \times 0.40 = 4$ MW$_e$ (megawatts electric), and heat rejected in the exhaust is $10 - 4 = 6$ MW$_{th}$ (megawatts thermal). In simple cycles, this heat is normally rejected into the atmosphere. In cogeneration cycles, we can generate additional electricity by using this heat to drive a second steam turbine. Since the thermal efficiency of steam turbines is only 33%, we have an additional $6 \times 0.33 = 2$ MW$_e$ from this turbine, for a total of $4 + 2 = 6$ MW$_e$. The addition of the

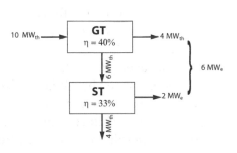

[¶] A challenge problem for the more mathematically inclined: A cogeneration plant combines a gas turbine with efficiency η_{GT} with a steam turbine with efficiency η_{ST}. Show that the cogeneration plant has a combined efficiency of $\eta_{CC} = \eta_{GT} + \eta_{ST}(1 - \eta_{GT})$: What is the overall efficiency of a combined plant if gas turbine and steam turbine efficiencies are 40% and 33%, respectively?

[**] It is common to distinguish between electrical power generated as MW$_e$, and heat (thermal power) as MW$_{th}$.

second turbine boosts combined efficiency to about 60%, which is superior to conventional coal and nuclear power plants with efficiencies of around 33%.

Load and Capacity

The electricity demand called a load, is not always constant and changes with location, season, even time of the day. In most countries, daily electricity demand usually follows a pattern called "the load curve," which is low at night and early morning, gradually increasing during the day. It peaks in the early afternoon when industrial activities are at their highest and drops back in the late afternoon or early evening when manufacturing slows and people retire from work (Figure 5-9 top). On an annual basis, depending on the climate, different regions of the world may experience their peak loads during either summer or winter months. In the United States, overall demand is higher in summer, when large numbers of air conditioners are operating. The opposite is true for Canada, where extreme cold winters demand more electricity for heating. In addition, some regions show curves with two maximums, one in summer and another in winter (Figure 5-9 bottom). The annual load curve can be constructed by summing up the average daily consumption over each month and plotting it over one year.

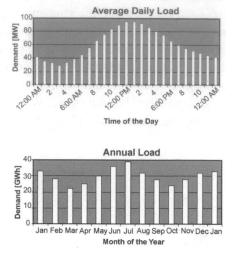

Just as the demand for electricity varies, so does the overall capacity of electricity generation facilities. It depends not only on the number of plants that are operational but also on whether or not they are operating at their full capacities. When electricity is produced from renewable energy sources such as solar or wind, environmental parameters such as temperature and humidity, and factors such as time of day, cloud cover, wind speed, and wind direction also become important.

Figure 5-9
Typical average daily and annual electrical loads.

Example 5-2: A utility company must meet the electricity demand for a community with daily and annual loads represented in Figure 5-10. Calculate:
a. The total daily energy production in kWh
b. The average daily power in MW
c. The baseload capacity in MW
d. Average monthly electrical load

Solution:
a. Total daily electrical output can be calculated by adding hourly productions. Mathematically, this is the area under the average daily load curve. Referring to the figure and adding the hourly loads, daily consumption is determined to be 1,520 megawatt-hours.
b. The average daily power is calculated by dividing the total daily consumption by 24; i.e, 1,520 MWh/24 h = 63.3 MW.
c. The baseload capacity is the power generation capacity that satisfies minimum demand, in this case, 30 MW.
d. The monthly load is calculated by multiplying the average daily load by the number of hours in a month: 63.3 MW × (24×30) h = 45,576 MWh = 45.6 GWh.

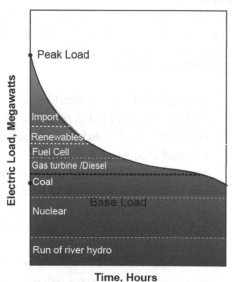

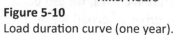

Figure 5-10
Load duration curve (one year).

Optimal Size of the Power Plants

Power plants' total electrical output is measured in megawatts and expressed as installed, peak, baseload, or reserve capacity. **Installed capacity** (also known as the *rated capacity, nominal capacity*, or *nameplate capacity*) is the maximum electricity that can be generated if all power plants are operated simultaneously and at their full capacities. The installed capacity in the U.S. exceeded one terawatt in 2013. **Peak capacity** is the maximum amount of electricity that is needed at any instant. **Baseload capacity** is the minimum amount of electricity delivered continuously at any time during the year. **Reserve capacity** is the additional capacity that is needed during periods of unusually high demand or during a period of maintenance when some equipments are not operating.

One way to meet the maximum load is to design a large power plant capable of satisfying the peak demand. This obviously is not acceptable because the cost is prohibitively high and much of the power plant's capacity would remain idle most of the time. The other extreme is the baseload capacity; power would seldom drop below it and the plant's capacity wouldn't go unused. This is the minimum capacity a power plant must meet at all times and sets the low limit for power plant size. It is, therefore, reasonable to size a plant to meet, at a minimum, the baseload demands, with additional power generation capabilities to meet peak demands.

To reduce stresses on the system it is common to reduce peak loads and redistribute them to off-peak hours. This approach, called **load leveling**, is done most effectively by restricting access while providing customers with incentives to cut demand. For example, a utility company may offer its customers a cheaper rate if they shift usage from peak hours to hours when demand is lower. Another option, energy storage, is attractive when the marginal cost of the energy storage system is lower than the marginal cost of constructing additional plants. This is usually done by storing the excess capacity during periods of off-peak production and using it during times of peak demand. The last, and possibly the best option is to reduce consumption through conservation. Energy conservation measures alleviate stress on the grid, reduce load and emissions, and indirectly reduce the chance of power blackouts. Federal and state agencies can encourage conservation by providing tax incentives, rebates, and subsidies to companies that invest in energy-saving practices or allocate funds for energy-related research, or to individuals who purchase cleaner, more energy-efficient appliances.

Normally, nuclear, coal, or hydro powerplants supply the baseload demands. These plants have low variable costs for fuel and operation but are not suitable for rapid shutdowns and startups, and except for regularly scheduled maintenance, they remain continuously operational throughout the year. Geothermal and concentrated solar thermal plants also have the potential to provide baseload power. Because peak demands last only a few hours at a time and often occur with little or no warning, the additional power should be brought online or taken offline quickly. Tidal, wave, solar photovoltaic, and electricity wind are intermittent and cannot be part of the baseload. In these instances, gas turbines and diesel are much smaller in size and capacity, and any variation in demand can be satisfied easily by adding or removing one or more of these pieces of equipment. The cost of electricity production from these devices, however, is higher than that of conventional power plants. Every year, there may come times when demand exceeds the installed capacity (that of the baseload power plants and all available gas turbines and diesel combined). In such instances, the power company buys power from other large utility companies or individual farmers, homeowners, and other independent generation producers. If total supply is still not enough and the shortage persists, the power company may be forced to stop or limit power delivery to some customers until demand stabilizes and full capacity is restored. To stabilize demand, power utilities adjust prices according to a predetermined schedule. Elaborate algorithms can be envisioned where prices are changed according to the time of day and the quality of power (e.g., the current in the line). Furthermore, the end-user could program the gadget to schedule its operation.

Capacity Factor

Power plants do not utilize 100% of their capacity all the time. In addition to occasional downtime for repair and maintenance, there are times that demand is not sufficient for a plant to run at full capacity. Other factors, such as a lack of necessary resources, moderate weather conditions, or economic sluggishness, also can affect the demand.

The capacity factor represents the degree of utilization of a particular power plant over a certain period. It is defined as the ratio of the actual amount of electricity produced within a specified time and what would have been produced if the machinery had operated at full capacity during the same time period.[††]

$$Capacity\ Factor = \frac{Actual\ power\ produced\ in\ a\ given\ period}{Maximum\ power\ that\ could\ have\ been\ produced\ during\ the\ same\ period}$$

A common practice used to calculate power generation capacity requirements is to calculate the number of hours that power plants must meet a particular demand and plot it in descending order. Hydro, nuclear, and coal power plants provide the majority of baseload demand. Gas turbines are most often used during peak loads. During short periods when demand is extremely high and during emergencies, *other* plants -- diesels, fuel cells, accumulators, or pumped storage facilities are used. If a power plant cannot generate sufficient power to meet with the demand, it may purchase power from neighboring plants, or even cut off power temporarily to certain consumers (**load shedding**).

A sample of such a graph, called the annual load duration curve (LDC), is shown in Figure 5-10. The horizontal axis is the time in hours (T = 8,760 hours or one year), and the vertical axis is the total electrical load measured in megawatts. The actual amount of production is calculated as the area under the load curve. The maximum electricity that the plant could produce is calculated by multiplying the peak capacity by the number of hours in the period under consideration. In the United States, the average capacity factors for electricity generation by nuclear, coal, solar, and onshore and offshore wind plants are 90%, 64%, 25%, 30, and 40%, respectively.

> **Example 5-3:** A 500-MW power plant operates at full power 45 percent of the time, 80% capacity for 50% percent of the time, and is shut down for the remaining 5 percent of the time. What is the capacity factor for this power plant?
> **Solution:** The total power produced is:
> (500 MW) × [(1.00×0.45) + (0.80×0.50) + (0.0×0.05)] = 425 MW
> The capacity factor for this power plant is 425/500 = 0.85 (or 85%).

> **Example 5-4:** To meet peak capacity demand, a power plant is equipped with an additional 10 MW from gas turbines. Assume that, on average, each gas turbine operates at full power ten hours per day for two months in summer and eight hours per day for one month in winter. What is the capacity factor for each additional turbine?
> **Solution:** Capacity factor can be calculated by dividing the actual energy use by the energy use if turbines operated 100% of the time.

$$C.F. = \frac{(10\ MW) \times [(10 \times 60 + 8 \times 30)h]}{(10\ MW) \times [24 \times 365\ h]} = 9.6\%$$

Transmission

After electricity is generated, it must be sent through transmission wires. Transmission lines, when interconnected with each other, become a transmission network. The transport of electricity across an electrical network is fundamentally different from the transport of goods along with a transportation network. In transportation networks, cargo moves from one location to another along specific routes, usually the most direct one. Any interruption along a particular cargo route will affect only that route and possibly a few routes in its vicinity. Unlike cargo, electrical signals travel along the paths of least resistance, not necessarily along the shortest line connecting the two geographical locations; sometimes many thousands of miles are covered before a signal reaches its destination. An interruption along an electrical transmission line can affect power delivery at a point that is a long distance away from the original failure. In addition, as different generating stations go on and off the grid, either by choice or due to equipment malfunctions,

---

[††] Instead of "Capacity Factors," power companies often give the "Utilization Factor," which is the ratio of the actual energy produced and the energy produced during the time the machines operated at partial load capacity, not counting the downtimes.

available power suddenly changes, possibly affecting the stability of the system and causing fluctuations in the frequencies and voltages at various points on the grid. Furthermore, because wires link everything, all generators must spin at exactly the same rate and in complete sync with each other.

To prevent the overload of power lines, a reliable control strategy and power conditioning system must keep the current in each line within safe limits. Also, it must allow for additional capacity to absorb the extra flow, in the case of a sudden failure somewhere else on the network. A generator located in the wrong place will not be able to meet an increase in demand because to do so would push the flow on some lines over their safe limits.

According to Ohm's Law, power lost as heat in a wire is proportional to its resistance and the square of current in the wire, but not on the voltage. Thus thicker cables made of materials of lower resistivity are beneficial. For the same power, voltage and current are inversely related; therefore, to lower the electric current, we must raise the voltage (See Digging Deeper: Ohm's Law). This is commonly done using a step-up transformer, which raises voltages to 110 kV and above before power is transmitted through the grid (See Figure 5-3). At the point of destination, voltages are dropped back to convenient levels (around 14-24 kV) using a step-down transformer and further reduced to 120V (220V in Europe) before being distributed to various end-users.

Today, long-distance power transmission is carried out through overhead power lines made of aluminum. Aluminum is lighter and much cheaper than copper, and only marginally of lower performance. Underground transmission is more reliable, takes up less right-of-way than overhead lines, has no or low visibility, and is less affected by bad weather. However, the cost of insulating cables and excavation is considerably higher, and maintenance is more difficult.

> **Worth Remembering** -- When current flows through a solid conductor (as in a copper wire), electrons creep like grains of sand through interstices between (relatively) huge atoms of the solid. Individual electrons do not move very fast or very far, however. They jostle their neighbors (like the flow of marbles in a narrow tube) and, by doing so, send impulses that travel many thousands of kilometers in a second (300,000 km/s to be exact). The message, whether it is light or Morse code, is transmitted virtually instantaneously.

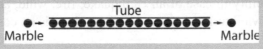

AC or DC?

Direct current (DC) refers to the flow of charge along a conductor in one direction. A current that changes its direction in an oscillatory manner is called an **alternating current (AC).** The current produced by a battery, by a flashlight, or a solar cell is a direct current, whereas the current used to operate our light bulbs and most other devices in our home are of an alternative type. Whether AC or DC was more suitable for power transmission was the subject of sharp disagreement between Edison, who favored DC, and Westinghouse, who preferred Tesla's AC transmission. To reduce losses, the voltage had to be raised. Stepping up and stepping down DC voltages was not easy and required expensive transformers and accompanied great losses. Furthermore, different dedicated voltage lines were required for different applications, such as cable cars, street lights, and electric motors. Because with the high voltage, the low-current transmission was inefficient, generators had to be near their loads.

Edison cited AC transmission as dangerous and, therefore, must be avoided at all costs. Westinghouse argued in favor of AC transmission because of its cheaper price and ability of long-distance transmission (See Box "The Current War"). Ultimately, Westinghouse won the debate, and AC transmission was accepted as the dominant method for long-distance transmission; DC application was limited to short distances. Today, almost all electric power generated in the United States is in the AC form.

The recent advances in technology, however, have made the DC transmission more efficient over long distances of many hundreds of miles, and are more suitable for underground and underwater, outperforming the AC lines that dominate transmission grids now and eliminating the need for the unsightly transmission towers. Furthermore, it provides a higher degree of reliability in case of an earthquake, fire, wind, and other natural disasters. Because power generated by solar cells and wind turbines are in DC form, there is no cost associated with DC/AC and AC/DC conversions.

Wireless electricity will be the way of the future. The technology has the potential to make power cords and disposable batteries obsolete. The idea is not new. Nikola Tesla toyed with the idea over a century ago when he was able to turn on a lightbulb, no matter where it was placed in the room and without being electrically connected to anything. Ever since scientists have developed several techniques to transfer power without a power cord. Briefly, a transmitter converts DC power to radio frequencies (RF) in the range of 904-927 MHz, and a receiver collects this signal and converts it back into DC power. The technology is currently used in office buildings to power temperature sensors that regulate air conditioning and other low-power applications. Power transmission via radio waves is possible for longer-distance power beaming, with shorter wavelengths of electromagnetic radiation, typically in the microwave range. We will discuss one such application -- solar power satellites -- in Chapter 10. The technology called *magnetically coupled resonance* uses a coil with an attached capacitor that resonates and creates a magnetic field. A second resonator, pulsating at the same frequency and placed a distance away, converts the magnetic field back into electricity. The technology is most suited to power home electronics, computers, and robots, or to charge cell phones, laptops, and other electronic gadgets, remotely. Another application is for charging electric cars, whether they are parked in garages fitted with wireless mats or are driving on smart freeways equipped with similar devices, along the way.

Distribution

The distribution network refers to the last mile delivery of electricity to homes and offices. Many household appliances use AC directly, although there are instances when DC power is needed. The digital world is a prominent example, as computers, telephones, digital satellites, and other communication devices all work by direct current. Automobile accessories and all other battery-operated devices also use direct current. Power generated by photovoltaics and fuel cells is in the form of DC and is, therefore, more convenient to use when operating these devices. On the other hand, when electricity is generated for transmission over commercial networks, it must undergo DC/AC conversion using inverters, before it can be connected to the grid. To convert AC to DC power, we need rectifiers which are essentially diodes that allow current to flow in one direction, but not the opposite.

The electrical operator matches electricity consumption with production mostly by bringing new generation capability online when needed and taking it offline when demand falls. The operators also can decide to get electricity from certain power companies to lower costs and improve performance.

Storage

As was explained above, electricity is an energy carrier, and so it cannot be stored as such. The only way to store electricity is to convert it to a form of energy that can be stored, and when needed, this energy is converted back into electricity. Obviously, there are some losses during both conversion and reconversion. Electrical utilities take advantage of lower demand during off-peak periods (when electricity is the cheapest) by storing excess electricity in temporary storage sites and using it during peak periods when the load exceeds the generators' capacities. This reduces the load on the system during peak hours, allowing the main generators to work at constant power, near full capacity, and under optimal conditions, thus reducing the average capital and operating costs by cutting the number of power generating stations.

There are three major mechanisms for storing electrical energy: electrochemical, electrostatic, and electromagnetic. The prime method of storing electricity as chemical energy is in *batteries*. The electrical energy is stored in the form of DC, which can then be used directly or converted to AC by an inverter. Unlike batteries, which release energy slowly, *capacitors* store energy in the form of electrostatic charges and are convenient when there is a large demand for electric power instantly. This makes them particularly suitable for emergencies, and when there are short temporary power interruptions. *Superconducting magnetic energy storage* (SMES) devices are capable of storing enormous amounts of energy within a magnet and are capable of releasing megawatts of power instantly to replace a sudden loss in line power. They store energy in the magnetic field generated by a DC current flowing through a coil of superconducting material that has been cryogenically cooled. At these temperatures, superconductors have near-zero resistance, and so there is no dissipation of heat when energy is stored.

Electricity can also be stored as the potential energy of springs, water pumped to higher elevations, weight raised to higher altitudes, and air compressed to higher pressures, the kinetic energy of a rotating shaft (flywheel), and thermal energy of a substance heated to a higher temperature (hot bricks), or a more dispersed phase (molten salt). The energy can be converted back when water flows to a lower elevation, air expands to a lower pressure, a flywheel stops, or material is cooled or changed phase from vapor to liquid, or liquid to solid. In another scenario, electricity can be used to produce hydrogen that later can be recovered when it burns or operates a fuel cell. Various methods of energy storage are discussed in greater detail throughout the book.

Smart Grids

The origin of the electric power industry goes back to 1880 when Thomas Edison developed the light bulb and established a few power stations to deliver electricity to customers. The demand increased substantially with the invention of the steam engine that could be powered by readily available coal. The invention of the transformer allowed power to be transported over long distances with relative ease and acceptable efficiency. As demand grew, power plants were forced to bring various generating equipment on- and off- line to supplement base power generation, to meet the peak demand. By 1930, the electric network had covered most cities in the United States and Europe, and power reached farther and farther to rural distances. Electric generation was limited to a few companies that controlled all aspects of power generation, transmission, and distribution. The growth in demand eventually

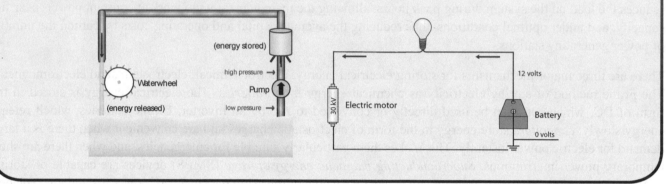
prompted a major shift from the monopolist nature of the electricity infrastructure and, in 1978, the U.S. energy market became deregulated. The U.K. and other European countries soon followed the lead of the U.S. As new generators entered the market competition, many utilities were forced to unbundle the infrastructure. Now, any utility could use the existing grid lines to sell power. Also, there was the possibility of pricing electricity in real-time; customers could choose when to use the power and from which company. This not only helped to alleviate some of the problems associated with load-leveling but also put additional stress on the antiquated electrical network that caused occasional blackouts and major interruptions.

The structure in place today is outdated, overloaded, inefficient, and highly unreliable, or is too far from many rural areas where electricity is needed the most -- primarily designed to transmit a steady flow of power from fossil fuel and nuclear plants, and have trouble dealing with the variable nature of renewables such as wind and solar power. So far, grids can absorb such fluctuations because solar and wind are responsible for a tiny percent of electricity produced in the United States. The grid is bound to fail, however, when solar and wind account for a significant fraction of the electricity generation. The design of a modern smart grid that effectively utilizes the new advances in various information and renewable energy technologies has become more urgent.

A smart grid refers to the infrastructure required to deliver efficient, reliable, environmentally friendly, high-quality power from a broad range of generating sources to multiples of users on-demand. The public at large can be both the end-user and provider of electricity. The smart grid does not refer to a single task assigned to a single company, or a single technology, but consists of many tasks performed by multiples of companies, using an aggregate of techniques and resources. The efficient operation of the grid is controlled by a network of supercomputers that allow real-time monitoring and management of electricity flow, assuring reliability, load management, and pricing. Among the main features of a smart grid are:

Modern IT Infrastructure: New progress in information technology makes it possible for fast data transfer and data storage enabling the acquisition and processing of huge quantities of real-time data from multiples of nodes. New computer models can be developed that respond to disturbances by breaking up a large section of the grid into smaller "islands." Each island can be stabilized by balancing supply and demand using local resources, and creating controlled brownouts. Sensors placed along the transmission grid will be able to check for leakages, vibrations, and even meteorological conditions such as wind speed, lightning, and heavy snowfall and make adjustments to prevent potential blackouts and disruptions. This allows near real-time monitoring of the changes in demand, and two-way communications between producers, transmission companies, distributors, and even consumers. Thus, making it possible to switch away from traditional systems, where electricity flowed in one direction only, to one in which electricity can flow in multiple directions.

Smart Meters: Advanced microprocessor-based metering systems can collect, transmit, and analyze real-time information about total energy usage in large areas, in a particular neighborhood, or even a single household or a manufacturer. Sensors on transmission lines assure power carried on each line does not exceed the maximum allowable at a given temperature, maintaining grid stability. The data can be used to warn the operators of problems before they occur, and for dynamic pricing, that changes with the time of day, application, or load. These meters, combined with smart sensors placed in refrigerators, ovens, and various other appliances, will provide an instant map of how electricity is used and make real-time decisions on how to reduce the cost and prevent grid overload. Smart grids give additional flexibility so that smart devices can be programmed to charge their electric car and use certain appliances such as washers and dryers when the rates are low, or to utilize only renewable resources to reduce carbon footprint and toxic emissions.

Demand-Side Management: As described in Chapter 1, demand-side management refers to various strategies to reduce demand or shift peak load to off-peak periods. The traditional approach is to offer lower prices during off-peak periods, or to customers who agree to have limited access to electricity, or even have their electricity completely shut off during peak hours. The government also can provide tax incentives or rebates that encourage adopting measures that promote conservation or encourage the purchase of more energy-efficient appliances.

Distributed Generation: Also called *decentralized generation* is the generation from multiple sources and multiple locations over a large geographic area. Currently, much of our electricity is produced by large, centralized plants -- mostly coal, oil, gas, and nuclear. Fossil plants are the main sources of carbon dioxide responsible for global warming. Nuclear plants do not produce these emissions, but the disposal of wastes and the potential risks of the accidental release of radioactive materials are impediments to large-scale use. Distributed and hybrid generation allows power to be generated from multiple local sources that include wind turbines, photovoltaics, small hydro generators, microturbines, diesel, and fuel cells. The power can be distributed using microgrids that can cheaply extend the grid to rural areas where most of the people are without electricity.

Virtual Power Plant: A virtual power plant consists of clustered, decentralized installations on-site that can be linked together to act as a single, central plant that meets the emergency needs of an organization of modest size. These units are normally on standby status but can be brought online quickly as a backup in hospitals, universities, manufacturing, and industrial processing firms. The virtual power plant is especially useful during grayouts or blackouts and/or when high demand makes electricity from the grid excessively expensive.

Energy Storage: Just as generators are distributed, energy storage systems may take different forms and are housed in many geographical locations. In addition to the various forms of energy storage described above, excess energy can be used to charge batteries in electric and hybrid vehicles in a concept dubbed *vehicle-to-grid* (V2G). The approach is to allow electric, fuel cell, and plug-in hybrids to be charged beyond their full-charge capacity at night when electricity is cheaper. The vehicle can transmit the extra charge to the grid when parked at the office or at home. Alternatively, these vehicles can be charged during the day using solar cells, in effect serving as a distributed battery storage system. Because the majority of vehicles are parked an average of 95% of the time, V2G can play an important role in stabilizing the intermittency of wind and solar energy. Grid energy storage is particularly important in matching supply and demand over any 24-hour period.

Smart Buildings: Just like smart appliances, buildings can incorporate technologies that allow them to play an important role in increasing energy efficiency while minimizing environmental impacts. Technologies are under development that allow better integration of electric, heating, and even transportation systems. For example, residential natural gas fuel cells can produce electricity, and at the same time, use the waste heat to warm the house. Sensors are being developed that can detect when the building, or a portion of it, is occupied, and adjust thermostats in those areas accordingly, reducing both overall heating and cooling loads. Smart window glass is available that can detect the solar light intensity and electronically adjust the glazing and change light transmission properties. In the near future, building skins can be covered with thin-film solar cells that can directly transmit electricity to the nearby grid. Building materials are being developed that can store solar energy by changing their phase from solid to liquid, releasing the energy at night by returning to their solid-state.

Summary

Electrical energy is the driving force behind much of our technological innovation. Not only does it provide lighting and heating for our rooms, but it is also essential in running our household appliances, as well as the heavy industrial machinery that powers modern societies. Most of the electricity generated today uses coal, nuclear, or hydropower. As demand for electricity continues to increase, new resources must be exploited. Designing more efficient appliances and better utilization of existing resources also can help extend the lifetime of our valuable fossil fuel reserves and maintain the quality of the air and the environment. Upgrading the power grid to a smart grid will allow tapping into a variety of exciting technologies that have just started to become available.

Microgrids can play an important role by providing power to remote areas where electricity is inaccessible. In the long run, microgrids could be connected to form larger grids that can be fed into the national grid. Storage may be an issue; to store power at night, microgrids must rely on diesel or large arrays of batteries that have a limited life. Proper maintenance is also important as solar panels often break, become molded, and become covered with leaves and dirt.

ⓐ *Digging Deeper: Ohm's Law*

The simplest electrical circuit can be envisioned as a small light bulb connected to both ends of a battery, via wires. It is found, experimentally, that the current flowing through the light bulb is directly proportional to the voltage across the battery -- the greater the driving force, the greater the current. The constant of proportionality is called resistance. Ohm's law establishes a relationship between the voltage across the battery, resistances of wires and filament, and the current flowing through the wiring as the following:

voltage [V] = resistance [Ω] x current [A]

[Ohm's Law] $\qquad\qquad\qquad V = IR$ $\qquad\qquad\qquad\qquad\qquad$ (5-1)

The electrical energy supplied by a generator or battery is either converted to work (as in an electric motor) or is dissipated to heat (as in an electric heater or an iron). The higher the number of charges flowing through the wire (current), and the larger the electric potential between the two points in the wire, the higher will be the power transmitted through the wire. In other words:

power [W] = voltage [V] x current [A]

Alternatively, since $V = IR$, power can be expressed in two other, equivalent forms:

[Electric Power]
$$P = \frac{V^2}{R} = RI^2$$
(5-2)

If electric potential and current are given in volts and amperes, resistance will be in ohms, and power will be in watts. One watt equals the energy used, in joules in one second; one kilowatt is 1,000 W, 1 megawatt is 1,000 kW or 1,000,000 W, and 1 gigawatt is 1,000 MW or 1,000,000 kW. Because voltage is the product of current and resistance, this equation implies that power is dissipated as the square of the current. In a resistance heater, the goal is to maximize the amount of heat that can be dissipated, so we would prefer to draw a high current. Conversely, to minimize losses during power transmission over long distances, the current should be reduced as much as possible, while voltage is kept at a maximum. Power companies try to minimize the current in long-distance transmission lines in order to avoid generating excessive heat. Typically, they step up the voltage to 120,000 volts before being sent across high-voltage transmission lines. Higher electrical voltages are considered to be too dangerous since they may result in possible arcing (i.e., dielectric breakdown of air) similar to a lightning strike between two power lines or between a power line and the ground.

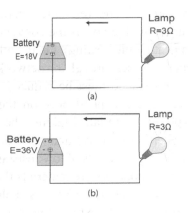

Example 5-5: Calculate the power dissipated by the lamp in the circuits shown at the right.
Solution: For the 18-V battery, $I = V/R = 18/3 = 6$ A; $P = VI = 18 \times 6 = 108$ W.
For the 36-V battery, $I = V/R = 36/3 = 12$ A; $P = VI = 36 \times 12 = 432$ W.
Note that increasing the battery voltage by a factor of two, from 18V to 36V, increased the current by a factor of two and power by a factor of $2 \times 2 = 4$.

Question: How does a high voltage allow for the economical transmission of electric power?
Answer: Energy losses in a wire are calculated as RI^2; therefore, to minimize resistive heating in the power lines, we must minimize the current. For a given quantity of power $P = IV$, a low current means a high voltage.

When discussing electricity consumption and production, it is customary to express power in kilowatts and time in hours. Since energy is the product of power and time, electrical energy is often expressed in kilowatt-hours.

energy [kWh] = power [kW] x time [h]

Example 5-6: A 1200-W electrical heater, ten 100-W electric light bulbs, a 300-W refrigerator, and a 1500-W microwave oven operate simultaneously. Assuming that the household circuit is 120 volts and all appliances are placed in parallel, what is the total current drawn?
Solution: Applying Ohm's law ($I = P/V$) for each device, we can write:

Electric Heater:	$1200/120 = 10.00$ A
Ten 100-W light bulbs:	$10 \times 100/120 = 8.33$ A
Refrigerator:	$300/120 = 2.50$ A
Microwave Oven:	$1,500/120 = 12.50$ A
Total current drawn:	33.33 A

This is a large current and maybe a fire hazard. Houses are usually equipped with 10-20 amp circuit protection. If current exceeds these values, a fuse will burn out or a circuit breaker will trip, disconnecting the circuit. In house wiring, several circuits are used, each equipped with a separate circuit breaker. In the example above, at least two circuits, each capable of carrying 20 A maximum, are needed if all appliances are to be used simultaneously. Indeed, U.S. electric codes require a microwave, garbage disposal, and refrigerator to have a 20-A circuit each, separate from

10-A lighting circuits and wall outlets for other appliances.

Electrical Resistance

Just as there is a resistance to the flow of water in pipes, there is a resistance to the flow of electricity in wires or other conducting materials. The electrical resistance, R, not only depends on the intrinsic properties of the material, but also on the geometry involved: a large cross-section, A, for the current to flow through, and a short distance, L, over which to flow, both contribute to a smaller resistance. This leads to

[Electric Resistance] $$R = \rho \, L/A \qquad\qquad (5\text{-}3)$$

Where ρ is called resistivity and is a property of material only. A good conductor has a low resistivity, for a good insulator, resistivity is large. Resistivity is the inverse of conductivity. The unit of resistance is the ohm (Ω) which is equal to:

$$1\,\Omega = 1\,\text{V/A}$$

We prefer higher resistances in resistance heaters when our main objective is the conversion of electric energy to heat (Joule heating). On the other hand, to minimize energy losses through the network, both the current and the resistance must be reduced as much as possible. Resistances depend only on the cable diameter and type of material. Making the transmission cables thicker is expensive and not practical beyond a point. Selecting materials of low resistance is our best option. Superconductors are materials that lose their electrical resistance at temperatures below a certain limit. Most materials exhibit this behavior at temperatures very close to absolute zero, although some alloys of yttrium, barium, and copper become superconductors at much higher temperatures. If room-temperature superconductor materials are found, much of the losses due to long-distance transmission would be eliminated.

Table 5-3 Power Consumption For Typical Household Appliances			
Appliance	**Power, W**	**Appliance**	**Power, W**
Alarm clock	1 - 2	A/C (one ton)	1200 -2000
Radio	70 - 400	Coffee Maker	900 - 1200
Television (color)	65 - 200	Iron	1200 - 2400
Freezer/Refrigerator	600 - 1000	Dishwasher	850 - 1400
Hair Dryer	1200 - 1800	Toaster	800 - 1400
Washer (clothes)	350 - 500	Microwave	750 - 1100
Vacuum Cleaner	1000 - 1400	Dryers (clothes)	1800 - 5000
Home Computer	100 - 400	Hair blow dryer	1000-2000

Source: U.S. DOE Office of Energy Efficiency and Renewable Energy, (http://www.eere.energy.gov).

Example 5-7: A 100-W light bulb operates in an American household for four hours every night.
a. How much current is drawn by the light bulb?
b. What is the resistance of the light bulb filament?
a. What is the monthly cost of operating this light bulb if the electricity is charged at a rate of $0.20/kWh?
Solution: American electrical power is delivered at 120 volts.
a. The current drawn is: $I = P/V = 100\text{ W}/120\text{ V} = 0.833\text{ A}$
b. The resistance is calculated as: $R = V/I = 120\text{ V}/0.833\text{ A} = 144\ \Omega$
c. Monthly energy consumption by the light bulb is: $E = (0.1\text{ kW})\times(4\text{ h/day})\times(30\text{ days}) = 12\text{ kWh}$. The monthly electrical cost is $12\times\$0.20 = \$2.40$.

Question: In the example above, which draws more current: the wire leading to the light bulb, or the bulb filament? Which gets hotter?
Answer: The flow of electrons is exactly the same in all parts of the circuit. As the electrons try to overcome the greater resistance in the thin filament, they heat it. The wires connected to the outlet are significantly thicker than the filament and are, therefore, barely warm as they allow the same amount of current to pass through.

Example 5-8: Calculate the resistance of 1 km of copper wire, 1-mm in diameter.
Solution: Resistivity of copper is $\rho = 1.7 \times 10^{-8}$ ohm-meter. Noting that
$A = \pi d^2/4 = 7.85 \times 10^{-7} \, m^2$
Substituting in Equation (5-3), the wire resistance is calculated as $R = 1.7 \times 10^{-8}$ ohm-m $\times 1{,}000 \, m \, / \, 7.85 \times 10^{-7} \, m^2$
= 21 ohms, which is compared to the resistance of an ordinary 100-W light bulb (about 100 ohms) is relatively small.

Question: A light bulb is connected through a long extension cable to the wall. Where is most of the resistance -- in the wire cord or in the light bulb?
Answer: The wire in the cord is much thicker than the wire in the light filament. Unless the cord is very, very long, it has a much lower resistance than the filament. If the cord had more resistance than the bulb, the cord would be hot while the lamp would stay relatively cool.

Series and Parallel Resistors

Different electrical devices can be assembled in a circuit in series, in parallel, or in a combination of the two. In a *series configuration*, the output current of one device will be the input current of a second device, and so on; the same current passes through all devices. In series circuits, voltages add up.

$$V_{total} = V_1 + V_2 + ... + V_n \qquad (5\text{-}4a)$$

In a *parallel configuration*, the same voltage potential is applied to all devices. The current necessarily divides. Since the same voltage is supplied to all electrical devices, each device works independently of the others and a burned-out device does not affect the operation of the other devices. In a parallel circuit, currents add up:

$$I_p = I_1 + I_2 + ... \qquad (5\text{-}4b)$$

In other words, series resistances act to divide the voltage, whereas parallel resistances act to divide the current. As far as the net current and voltage difference between two points is concerned, any complex arrangement of resistors can be replaced by one effective resistor. The recipe for doing this involves replacing in series combinations with

$$[\text{in series}] \qquad R_s = R_1 + R_2 + ...$$

and in-parallel combinations with

$$[\text{in parallel}] \qquad 1/R_p = 1/R_1 + 1/R_2 + ...$$

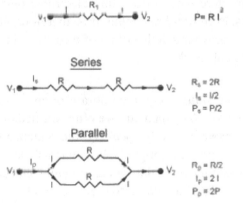

Figure 5-11
Ohm's law applied to series and parallel resistances.

The main disadvantage of a series configuration is that if one of the devices burns out, we have an "open circuit," in which current stops, and none of the devices in the series circuit will work.

Question: To reduce the energy bill, you are interested in insulating your house. Would you be better off adding insulation to the interior walls or to the exterior walls of the house?
Answer: It doesn't make any difference. Thermal resistances (like electrical resistances) are in series and, thus, they add up.

Example 5-9: Compare the resistance of two identical wires, connected in parallel (side-by-side), and in series (end-to-end).

Solution: Referring to Equation 5-3, for a given material, resistance is linearly proportional to the resistor's length and inversely to its cross-sectional area. Side-by-side, A doubles, and R falls by a factor of two, compared with one wire. End-to-end, the two wires effectively have twice the length of one wire, and R increases by two. Thus, end-to-end resistance is four times greater than side-by-side resistance.

Question: A small light is lit by a battery. If a second identical light is added in series, how would the battery's current and voltage outputs be affected? What if the lights were placed in parallel? Which arrangement puts out the most light?

Answer: When lights are placed in series, the resistance doubles, the voltage does not change, and the current drops by a factor of two. Power used, and the amount of light will be reduced by half, also. When lights are placed in parallel, the combined resistance will be only half as much, whereas the current going through each bulb remains the same. The light brightness, therefore, is not affected. The overall power consumption is twice that of a single light.

Question: To measure voltage and current in a circuit, scientists use a voltmeter and ammeter. How should they be placed in a circuit? Do we want these devices to have high or low internal resistances?

Answer: We are normally interested in the electrical potential difference between two points. A voltmeter must be placed across these points and so must be placed in parallel. To measure current, we need to place the ammeter in series. To prevent current leakage from the main circuit, a good voltmeter obviously must have high resistance. An ammeter must have a resistance as small as possible. This will assure little voltage drop across the device. ⓐ

ⓐ *Digging Deeper: Electrical Safety*

Although electricity appears to be the cleanest form of energy, there are a number of health and safety issues that must be considered. Electrical power lines produce magnetic and electric fields that may pose health problems or interfere with surrounding electronic devices. Inappropriate use of electricity also could be dangerous and, at times, even life-threatening. It is, therefore, necessary to understand the harmful effects of electricity and the proper procedures for safe handling of electricity in a manner that can minimize long-term health problems and the risk of electrical shock.

Question: A common phrase often heard concerning electrical safety is, "It's the current, not the voltage that kills." Why then, are we often warned of the danger of high voltage?

Answer: Strictly speaking, the sentence is correct. It is the current that is dangerous. The voltage only pushes the current through the bodily resistance. The question is where do all those currents come from? High voltages mean the potential for creating high currents for a given resistance path through a body -- higher voltages can be translated directly into higher currents.

Health Effects of Electromagnetic Radiation

The health effects associated with overhead power lines and household electrical appliances have been among the most controversial topics debated by scientists. Strong magnetic forces are associated with thick wires and equipment that draw high currents. A current passing through a wire creates a magnetic field that encircles the wire (Ampere's Law), strongest closer to the wire, and drops off as the square of the radial distance from the wire. Strong electric fields are associated with the presence of strong electric charges, such as around high-voltage equipment. A person standing underneath a power line experiences an electric field perpendicular to the ground. The closer the power line is to the ground and the higher its voltage, the higher the electric field's strength. For example, a single 115-kV

> **Safety Tip: The Third Prong**
>
> Faulty electrical devices can deliver dangerous and sometimes lethal shocks. In the most common scenario, frayed insulation causes the high-voltage wire of the device to short (become connected) to the device case. If a person standing on the ground touches the case, he completes a path for the current to reach the ground. Since a person's resistance is typically much less than the resistance within the device, the person presents the path of least resistance and will, therefore, draw a large current. This kind of hazard can be avoided by the use of a three-wire system. A wire to the case of the appliance connects to the third prong of a plug, while the third hole in the outlet is connected to the ground. In the event of faulty wiring in the appliance, the current is routed to the ground through the prong and not through the person, because there is essentially no resistance between the case and the ground.

cable running 100 m above the ground causes an electric field of E = 1,150 V/m, near the ground. Depending on the frequency of the AC line, the direction of the field lines reverses 50-60 times per second, causing rapid changes in the direction of the electric field through a body and exposing it to ionization radiation. Unlike magnetic fields, electric fields can be shielded by conductors such as metals. We will discuss the effect of ionizing radiation on human health and material in Chapter 8. Although the connection between power line fields and cancer is an area of continuing research, so far there are no scientific studies that point to a consistent, significant link between cancer and power lines.

Physiological Effects

When current passes through a living tissue, it experiences resistance and dissipates its energy as heat. Depending on the magnitude of current and tissue involved, electricity can manifest itself in several forms, from low heat and slight tingling to severe burns, paralysis, and even death.

The most significant hazard associated with electric shock is its damage to a person's nervous system. The nervous system consists of a series of nerve cells called neurons that are responsible for coordinating all of the body's movements – from the beating of the heart to the blinking of the eyes – that pass information from various organs to the brain and vice versa. Currents from external sources can be strong enough to override the electrical activity of neurons, preventing them from carrying out their normal functions. If this happens, volitional signals cannot be transmitted. Furthermore, electric shock can cause sustained and involuntarily muscle contraction. This effect is particularly dangerous when a person touches a bare electrical wire. Fingers have the least resistance to current flow and easily can bend involuntarily, clenching into a fist that grabs the wire. The victim becomes immobilized and unable to let go of the wire, making the shock even more dangerous. The state of sustained contraction of a muscle during which muscle cannot relax is called tetanus in medical terminology. The condition persists as long as the current flows.

Shock Severity

The best way to reduce the electrical shock from a live circuit is to add resistance to the path of the current. The length of time, the type of tissue involved, and the magnitude of the current determine the severity of the hazard associated with electrical shock and the extent of damage it causes. The current passing through the victim's body is determined by the body's resistance, which varies greatly from one organ to another and whether the skin is dry or wet. Rubber gloves and boots increase the resistance, thus reducing the current for the same voltage difference. Grounding makes an excellent means of protection by providing a path of least resistance through the ground (and not the body). When the path of current is from hand to hand or from hand to foot, vital organs such as the heart, lungs, or spinal

Table 5-4 Health Effects of Electrical Shocks*	
Current through the body trunk	*Effect on average human*
< 1 mA	No sensation.
3-10 mA	Tingling, person can let go.
10-30 mA	Muscle contraction, person cannot let go.
30-50 mA	Painful, severe muscular contractions. Breathing difficulty.
50-100 mA	Ventricular fibrillation, probable death.
> 100 mA	Fatal.

*Center for Disease Control & Prevention website, (http://www.cdc.gov/niosh/).

cord are affected, and the shock effect is the most severe. A summary of the health effects associated with electrical shocks is given in Table 5-4.

Question: When is the effect of electrical shock most severe? With 120 V or 220 V? With direct current (DC) or alternating current (AC)?

Answer: If everything else is the same, higher voltages result in higher currents; therefore voltages in U.S. outlets are safer than those in Europe. It is difficult to quantify whether DC or AC is more dangerous. Direct current is generally considered to pose less of a shock hazard, but it produces more severe burns. A person shocked with an alternating current is more likely to go into heart fibrillation.

Question: A bird is sitting on a piece of bare copper wire carrying 100 amperes. It is estimated that the copper cable has a resistance of 20 ohms/kilometer. Assuming the bird's feet are 10 cm apart, what is the voltage potential established through the bird's body?

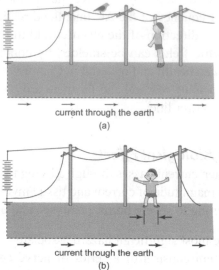

current through the earth
(a)

current through the earth
(b)

Answer: The resistance between the bird's feet is calculated as 0.10 m × 20 Ω / 1000 m = 0.002 Ω, and the potential difference is ΔV = I × R = 100 A × 0.002 Ω = 0.20 V; this is not enough to do any harm!

Question: In the diagrams at the right, determine which instance provides the safest situation for the bird or person involved.

Answer: For current to flow through a circuit, an electrical potential is required. A bird sitting on the wire experiences practically no voltage drop between its feet and is, therefore, immune to potential danger, no matter how high the voltage is. On the other hand, if the bird were to touch both the high- and low-voltage cables at the same time, it then would draw a lethal current through its body. To assure birds' safety, the separation distance between the power cables is chosen to exceed the wingspans of most birds.

This is not true for the boy, however. In diagram (a) the boy holds the bare wire with one hand. Since he is standing on the ground (which by convention has zero voltage), there is a voltage difference between his hand and foot. As a result, electricity flows through his hands and body and eventually reaches his feet, closing the circuit and shocking the boy. The downed power line in diagram (b) causes a large electric potential between the points where the wire touches the ground and the nearest pole where the transmission line is grounded. Thus, there is a voltage differential between the feet of the boy standing somewhere in between, and he would be shocked. Probably the best way to avoid shock is to keep your feet close together, stand on one leg, or run away from the power line. Running has the same effect of having one foot on the ground, preventing a large voltage drop between the victim's feet.

Question: In the previous example, would it make a difference if the boy was barefoot? What about if he touched the wire with both hands?

Answer: If the boy wears shoes with thick, insulated rubber soles, then he is protected from electric shocks. The problem arises if any moisture, dirt, or other conducting substances (such as a metallic strip) provide a path of least resistance and allow the electricity to bypass the sole directly to the body. Leather soles provide much less resistance and are not nearly as effective. Some ground surfaces are better insulators than others. Asphalt contains some oil, which makes it a better insulator than most dirt, concrete, and rocks.

If the boy holds the wire with both hands, the contact area doubles, and two parallel pathways are available for the current to flow. The overall resistance is only one-half of the resistance from one hand, and twice as much current would flow through the body. It is a good practice to keep one hand in a pocket when working around electrical devices! ⓐ

Endnotes

1   US DoE. (2012). Energy Information Administration, https://www.eia.gov

2   International Energy Agency, Global status on modern energy access, Retrieved from http://www.worldenergyoutlook.org

3   Malavikal, S. and Vishal, S. (2013). Harnessing Electrical Energy from Lightning, *International Journal Of Application Or Innovation In Engineering & Management, 2*(9).

4   Glassie, J. (2007). Lightning Farms, *The New York Times*, December 9, 2007.

5   International Energy Outlook, (2016). Retrieved from http://www.eia.gov/forecasts/ieo/table5-1.cfm

6   Manufacturing Energy Consumption Survey (1996). Energy Information Administration, U.S. Department of Energy, Institute for Energy Research, Retrieved from http://www.instituteforenergyresearch.org

7   Thomas, B. and Hall, D. (1992). Probabilistic production costing under integrated operation agreements and joint power agency financing. *Energy Economics, 14*(3), 200-208. doi: 10.1016/0140-9883(92)90013-4.

8   IEEE (2021). IEEE Smart Grid Experts Roundup: AC vs. DC Power - *A New Battle of the Currents*, Retrieved from http://smartgrid.ieee.org

9   Cannon, B., Hoburg, J. Stancil, D. & Goldstein, S. (2019). Magnetic Resonant Coupling As a Potential Means for Wireless Power Transfer to Multiple Small Receivers, Tucker, C., Warwick, K. & Holderbaum, W. (2013). A contribution to the wireless transmission of power. International Journal of Electrical Power & Energy Systems, *47*, 235-242. doi.org/10.1109/tpel.2009.2017195

10   Masters, G., (2004). *Renewable and efficient electric power systems*. Hoboken, N.J.: John Wiley & Sons.

11   Wissner, M., (2011). The Smart Grid – A saucerful of secrets? *Applied Energy, 88*(7), 2509-2518.

12   The Smart Grid. (2011). *MIT Technology Review,* Jan/February 2011, p. 65.

13   Schuler, R. (2010). The Smart Grid -- A bridge between Emerging Technologies, Society, and the Environment, *The Bridge, 10*(1), 44-49.

14   Talbot, D. (2012). *MIT Technology Review*, October 2012, p. 28.

15   For more information on effects of EMF exposure on health, see the World Health Organization's International EMP Project, http://www.whch/programmes/peh/emf/emf_home.htm

🕴 Exercises

I. Discussion Questions

1. What are the primary and secondary sources of electrical energy? Give a few examples of each.
2. How does an electric motor work? What is its advantage over a gasoline engine? How can a motor be used to act as a generator?
3. Define installed, peak, baseload, and reserve capacities. What kind of power plant is suitable to meet the needs of each of these?
4. Why is electricity not considered a source of energy?
5. When is electricity a primary and a secondary source of energy? Give examples of each.
6. What are the main advantages of high-voltage transmission? What are the drawbacks?
7. What is cogeneration? How is it used?
8. What is the Ohm's Law? What is the relationship between voltage, current, resistance, energy, and power?
9. What is the relationship between electricity and magnetism? What are the health effects associated with each?
10. What are the dangers associated with electricity? Which kills -- a high voltage, a high current, or both?

II. Problems

ⓐ Generation

1. A typical 600-MW electric plant is to supply power to a large community. The plant is designed to operate at 100% capacity for 12 hours every day. Assuming that the maximum power demand of an average household is 1.5 kW:
   a. What is the total annual electrical capacity in kWh?
   b. To how many households can this plant supply power?
   c. What is the average monthly bill of each household, if the utility sells power at $0.20 per kWh?

2. A room is to be maintained at a constant temperature during a cold wintry night. The heat losses from the room are estimated to amount to 6,000 kJ/h. Determine the power rating of the heater in kW.

3. A household power demand is approximated by the figures below. Calculate:
   a. Total daily energy required in kWh
   b. Average daily power in kW
   c. Average monthly electrical load in kWh

   d. Monthly electrical bill if the power company charges electricity at a flat rate of $0.15 per kWh
   e. Monthly electrical bill if the power company charges electricity at a rate of $0.27 per kWh during peak hours (10 a.m. to 8 p.m.), and $0.10 per kWh during off-peak hours (8 p.m. to 10 a.m.)

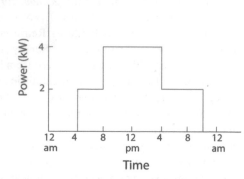

4. What is the annual cost of using an 1800-W hair dryer, if it is used for 20 minutes every day? The utility charges electricity at the rate of 15 cents per kilowatt-hours.

5. ⓐ A cogeneration plant consists of a gas turbine with an efficiency of 55% and a steam turbine with an efficiency of 35%. Determine the overall efficiency of the plant.

ⓐ Ohm's Law

6. To reduce your energy bill, you are interested in insulating your house. Would you be better off adding insulation to the interior walls or the exterior walls of the house?

7. To measure voltage and current in a circuit, scientists use voltmeters and ammeters. How should they be placed in a circuit? Do we want these devices to have high or low internal resistances?

8. Consider two resistances, a 10-ohm resistor and a 20-ohm resistor connected across a 12-volt battery. What is the current, voltage drop, and power dissipated through each resistor, if:
   a. Resistances are placed in series.
   b. Resistances are placed in parallel.

9. A flashlight uses three volts to drive a current through a thin wire of resistance R, to produce a current of 0.4 A in the wire. The wire heats up from the frictional flow of charge through it and produces light. What is the resistance of the wire?

10. A cigarette lighter in a car is a resistor that, when activated, is connected across the 12-V battery.

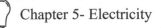

If the lighter dissipates 33 W of power, find the resistance in the lighter and the current that it draws from the battery.

11. A 500-watt toaster, a 900-watt microwave, and a 100-watt lamp all operate on the same circuit. When a 300-watt coffee maker is connected to the same circuit, the fuse melts. What is the amp rating of the fuse?

12. The power is to be transmitted at a rate of 1 MW from an electric generating station to a small residential community, one mile away. Assuming the electrical resistance of 0.0001 ohms/foot of transmission line, calculate the power loss through the wires if the voltage is maintained at a) 1,000 volts, and b) 10,000 volts.

13. A pump is used to draw water that is passed through a valve and used to turn a paddle wheel. Draw an equivalent electrical diagram. Can you draw the mechanical analog of two light bulbs in series lit up by a battery? How about two parallel light bulbs?

14. A three-way light bulb can be constructed by putting two resistances in parallel. Whether the first, second, or both resistances are placed in a circuit, the light can be dim, bright, or very bright. What are the values for the two resistances if the light bulb can be operated to dissipate 50/100/150 W of electricity?

III. Match the List

1. Match the list of variables from the column to the right with the units given in the column to the left.

a.	Force	watt
b.	Charge	ohm
c.	Power	joule
d.	Weight	volt
e.	Mass	coulomb
f.	Electric Potential	ampere
g.	Electrical Resistance	pascal
h.	Current	kilogram
i.	Heat	newton
j.	Pressure	newton

2. Match the components found in typical thermal power plants to energy transformation accomplished by that component:

a.	turbine	1. mechanical to electrical
b.	boiler	2. electrical to mechanical
c.	generator	3. chemical to thermal
d.	feed-water pump	4. thermal to mechanical

3. Match the letters of the components in the figure with the following terms:

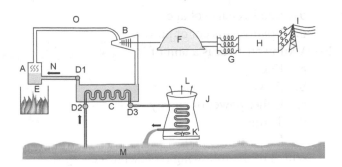

- ☐ Ambient air
- ☐ Water
- ☐ Steam
- ☐ Boiler
- ☐ Condenser
- ☐ Turbine
- ☐ Cooling tower
- ☐ Fan
- ☐ Generator
- ☐ Transformer
- ☐ Heat sink
- ☐ Low-voltage line
- ☐ High-voltage line

IV. Multiple Choice Questions

1. Which of the following statements is not correct?
   a. Atoms are made of negatively charged electrons and positively charged protons.
   b. In neutral atoms, there are as many protons as there are electrons.
   c. The total number of charges in the universe is constant.
   d. Charge and mass are two properties of matter.
   e. Depending on the atoms, electrical and gravitational forces can be either attractive or repulsive.

2. A step-up transformer
   a. Steps up the power.
   b. Steps up the current.
   c. Steps up the voltage.
   d. Steps up the energy.
   e. Transforms current from DC to AC.

3. A magnetohydrodynamic power generator
   a. Is a magnet used to direct the flow of water in rivers.
   b. Uses a magnet to direct the flow of electrons in a wire.
   c. Converts the heat of combustion of coal directly to electrical energy.
   d. Is another name for a fuel cell.
   e. None of the above.

4. A load curve is a plot of
   a. load versus generation capacity.
   b. Load versus time.
   c. Load versus current.

   d. Load versus voltage

   e. Load versus cot of power.

5. A kilowatt-hour is a unit of

   a. Energy.

   b. Power.

   c. Either power or energy.

   d. Torque.

   e. Electric potential.

6. Which of the following represent(s) energy?

   a. Electric voltage

   b. Electric current

   c. Electron-volt

   d. Electric charge

   e. None of the above

7. Which of the following represent(s) power?

   a. Kilojoules

   b. Kilovolts

   c. Kilowatts

   d. Kilowatts/h

   e. Kilowatt-hours

8. What is the unit used by *most* utility companies when they sell the electricity to our homes?

   a. Kilowatts

   b. Btu

   c. Volts

   d. Kilowatt-hours

   e. Therms

9. How much of the energy of coal burned in a typical power plant is discarded as heat?

   a. An insignificant amount

   b. 30-50%

   c. 50-70%

   d. 70-90%

   e. More than 90%

10. In the United States, most electricity is generated by

   a. Burning coal.

   b. Burning oil.

   c. Burning natural gas.

   d. Nuclear power.

   e. Hydro, solar, wind, and biomass.

11. The baseload of daily energy consumption represents

   a. The fraction used in the early morning.

   b. The average energy consumption during the day.

   c. The load supplied by nuclear or fossil fuel.

   d. The load required to provide minimal needs of consumers.

   e. The load reserved for times of an emergency.

12. Baseload power plants are used

   a. Primarily during the nighttime.

   b. Primarily during the daytime.

   c. Day and night.

   d. During peak times.

   e. During emergencies.

13. Gas turbines are best suited for power generation

   a. At all times.

   b. Only during the daytime.

   c. Only during the nighttime.

   d. During peak hours and emergencies.

   e. For baseload power production.

14. In the U.S., when is peak electricity demand in the summer?

   a. 6:00 a.m. - 9:00 a.m.

   b. 9:00 a.m. - noon

   c. Noon - 3:00 p.m.

   d. 3:00 p.m. – 6:00 p.m.

   e. 6:00 p.m. – 9:00 p.m.

15. Most electrical power transmission is in the form of an alternating current because

   a. It can be transmitted with less transmission loss.

   b. Direct current cannot be transmitted in electrical wires.

   c. It is less noisy.

   d. It is safer to use.

   e. It can travel faster.

16. To maximize power dissipation through a given resistance heater, we must

   a. Increase current.

   b. Increase resistance.

   c. Decrease current.

   d. Decrease resistance.

   e. Increase both current and resistance.

17. Electrical power can be calculated by multiplying

   a. Current by voltage.

   b. Current by resistance.

   c. Current by resistance-squared.

   d. Resistance by voltage.

   e. Resistance by voltage-squared.

18. The relationship between voltage to current in an electric line is like

   a. Flow rate to the volume of the fluid in a hydraulic line.

   b. The pressure to flow rate in a hydraulic line.

   c. The flow rate to pressure in a hydraulic line.

   d. Flow rate to pipe diameter in a hydraulic line.

   e. Flow rate to pipe length in a hydraulic line.

19. The function of the transformer in a transmission line is

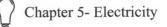

a. Transforms AC to DC.
b. Transforms electric fields to magnetic fields.
c. Changes from high voltage to low voltage, and back.
d. Transforms energy to power.
e. None of the above.

20. What function does a circuit breaker serve in your home?
    a. It protects your home against lightning strikes.
    b. It increases the voltage from the power lines outside your home.
    c. It disconnects the circuit in case of excessive current flow
    d. It disconnects the circuit in case of a sudden surge in the voltage
    e. It provides a barrier against electromagnetic radiation.

21. How does an electric utility company prepare its customers' monthly electricity bills?
    a. By the amount of current drawn at different time
    b. By the number of electrical devices in the household
    c. By the number of occupants in the household
    d. By the amount of electricity and time of the day
    e. By the change in atmospheric conditions

22. Homeowners pay their monthly electric bills in units of dollars per
    a. Therms
    b. kilowatts
    c. Btu
    d. kilowatt-hours
    e. Barrels of oil equivalent

23. If you halve the voltage across an electric heater,
    a. You double the current
    b. You reduce the current by half
    c. You double the resistance
    d. You reduce the resistance by half
    e. None of the above.

24. A typical 100-W incandescent bulb costs $0.50 and burns out after 100 hours of operation. A compact 100-W fluorescent bulb costs $6.00 but lasts 1,200 hours. Which one is a better buy?
    a. The incandescent bulb
    b. The fluorescent bulb
    c. Both are equivalent buys
    d. There is insufficient information to decide
    e. It depends on the price of electricity

25. A bird sitting on an electrical power line

a. Never gets electrocuted.
b. Always get electrocuted.
c. Gets electrocuted, only if it touches both wires
d. Gets electrocuted if it is a DC power line
e. Gets electrocuted if it is an AC power line

V. True or False?
1. An alternating current results from the back and forth movement of electrons in a wire.
2. For the most economical way of transmitting power, it is best to use very high voltages.
3. Blackouts occur when load outstrips generation, either because of the loss of a generator or problems with major transmission lines.
4. Baseload energy is the cheapest to produce; peak-load electricity is the most expensive.
5. Most thermal power plants have efficiencies between 50-60%.
6. In commercial thermal generating power stations, it takes about one unit of electricity to produce three units of thermal energy.
7. It is primarily the current that kills; voltage does not matter.
8. The best approach to electrical safety is to add resistance to the path by wearing rubber gloves, boots, and other safety gear.
9. You can get a shock by touching just one live conductor or even a charged object, such as a fence.
10. You should not unscrew a light bulb with a wet hand, no matter the wattage.

VI. Fill in the Blanks
1. The study of charges at rest is called _____.
2. The product of electric potential across a resistor and the current passing through the resistance gives the _____ dissipated by that resistance.
3. To transmit power over long distances, it is best to use _____ current.
4. The simultaneous production of electricity and heat is commonly referred to as _____.
5. The technology that utilizes hot ionized gases to generate electricity is called _____.
6. _____ uses the chemical energy of water dissociated from its components to extract power.
7. Trigeneration is the simultaneous production of _____, _____, and _____.
8. The work needed to pull a unit charge a given distance is called _____ potential.
9. When resistances are placed in parallel, _____ add up.

10. According to Ohm's Law, for a given voltage difference, the greater the resistance, the _____ the current.

PROJECT I – Electrical Power Generating Station

The migration of new industries and increased population requires the construction of new power generation facilities with a capacity of 10 MW_e near your city. A panel consisting of consumer groups, oil and gas company representatives, coal miners, economists, scientists, business leaders, regulatory agencies, electric utilities, and environmentalists is meeting to debate the merits of various proposals. Several options are being considered:

1. Purchase necessary additional power from a neighboring state or country.
2. Use a combination of renewable energy alternatives such as wind, wave, and solar.
3. Expand the existing power plant facilities using coal, oil, or natural gas.
4. Build a new fossil fuel plant in the city suburbs, away from major population centers.
5. Construct a 15-MW combined heat and power (CHP) geothermal power plant.
6. Construct a nuclear fission power plant.

You are assigned the task of assuming the role of a reporter who is to cover the various arguments being made in favor of, or against, each option. Please detail the findings by writing a report summarizing the following:

a. What are the geographical considerations that preclude using one or more of these options?
b. Which remaining options make the most economic sense? Consider the initial costs of construction, power production, distribution, maintenance, and impact on employment.
c. Which option makes the most environmental sense?
d. What are the political implications of this decision, if any?

PROJECT II – Health Hazards Associated with Power Lines and Mobile Phones

There has been a wide array of studies on possible risks associated with the long-term health effects from electrical systems, which were previously assumed to be safe. Some studies have claimed an increased rate of cancer among those who live in proximity to high-voltage power lines, or use mobile phones frequently. None of these studies is conclusive, in part because of the difficulty in carrying out laboratory experiments or in isolating the effects from many other factors that may contribute to health risks. In the case of mobile phones, data are limited, as these devices found their way into our daily lives only about a decade ago. In light of the long latency period for developing tumors, the linkage of these devices to cancer can be only marginally documented.

In this project, you are asked to search the Internet for scientific studies that link or unlink electromagnetic radiation to safety and health. Write a one-page report outlining the recent findings and answer the following questions:

a. How do electricity and magnetism interact with matter, specifically on various human tissues?
b. Would you expect a greater effect at higher currents? At higher voltages?
c. Is there a need for concern? If so, are there steps that can be taken to minimize the health risks? What are they?

CHAPTER 6

Transportation

A 100-km long traffic jam in China in 2010 lasted 10 days. ~ Jason Lee, Reuter

We have met the enemy and he is us. ~ Pogo

My father rode a camel. I drive a car. My son rides in a jet airplane. His son will ride a camel ~ A Saudi saying

The world's transportation systems are expanding every day, and with expansion comes the rapid depletion of natural resources, ever-increasing traffic congestions, and a higher rate of collisions. Worldwide, there are 1.4 billion vehicles on the road today, and the numbers are expected to increase to two billion by 2050. It is also estimated that during the same period, the global demand for transportation energy will continue to increase by more than 40 percent. The rise is attributed entirely to commercial sources such as trucks, planes, and ships. The number of personal vehicles will increase, but also are becoming significantly more energy-efficient, keeping energy demand for personal transportation relatively flat.

The United States -- with four million miles of highways, railroads, and waterways, 250 million passenger cars, buses, and trucks, 206,000 aircraft, 2.6 million miles of oil and gas pipelines, 40,000 ships, numerous railroad cars and boats, and 20,000 airports -- has the largest transportation system in the world. Every day, about 12 million barrels of petroleum, more than 2/3 of total daily U.S. petroleum consumption and 27% of its entire daily energy use, are required to operate this huge system (Table 6-1). Because most of these fuels are imported, the U.S. must seek ways to reduce its reliance on foreign oil, either by increasing fuel efficiency and switching to alternative fuels or by reducing total miles traveled by investing in mass transit systems and carpooling, bike riding, and walking.

Although most transportation issues are global in nature, because of the sheer size of the U.S. transportation system, its role as a major technological powerhouse, and because it is the biggest contributor to environmental pollution, we will limit our discussion to the United States. The trend is expected to change; however, as population and with it, vehicle ownership in the developing countries continues to increase. Chinese ownership of passenger cars increased 10 fold between 1985-2005, and another ten-fold again since then; India was second with similar growth.

Table 6--1 U.S. Transportation Energy Use by Mode, 2013

Modes	Trillion BTU	Percent of total
Highway	**21,310**	**81.5**
- Automobiles	7,121	27.2
- Light Trucks[i]	8,180	31.3
- Motorcycles	59	0.4
- Buses	214	0.8
- Heavy Trucks	6,151	23.5
Non-Highway	**5,036**	**18.5**
- Air	2,037	7.8
- Water	1,055	4.0
- Rail	611	2.3
- Pipeline	1,141	4.4
Total	**26,153**	**100**

[i] *Including SUVs*
Reference: Davis, S. C., Diegel, S. W., and R.G. Boundy, Table 2.10 "Transportation Energy Data Book," ORNL-6991, Edition 34, 2015.

Power Requirements

We discussed the concept of energy and power in some detail in Chapter 2. Briefly, energy is what is needed to carry out a given task without concern for the time it takes to accomplish it. Power is the rate at which the energy is used and, therefore, determines the speed at which the task is performed. Without sufficient energy, we cannot drive very far before having to refuel. With everything else remaining the same, a larger fuel tank (more energy) makes it possible to drive longer distances. In contrast, a larger engine (more power) allows a vehicle to reach its destination faster, carry a greater load, or climb steeper roads. A major concern in any design of land, air, or marine vehicles is the power required for operation under various conditions.

Power is calculated as the product of the force required to propel a vehicle and speed.* The force must be sufficient to overcome all resistive forces called drag, which itself, can vary, depending on various parameters such as vehicle shape, road conditions, atmospheric parameters, and also speed.

$$\textbf{\textit{Power = Drag} × \textit{Speed}}$$

So, drag is equal to power divided by speed. Since speed is the distance traveled per unit time, drag can be interpreted as the energy per meter of distance traveled.

---

* $P = W/t = F.d/t = F.v$

The actual useful power of any traction engine is calculated as the product of torque (measured by a dynamometer) and rotational speed.

Land Vehicles

The most popular method used to power a vehicle is to burn fuel (mainly fossil fuels) in an onboard engine. Alternatively, energy can be stored in some other forms (batteries, fuel cells, flywheels, or compressed air) and used as needed. No matter which approach is used to propel land vehicles, power is needed for four purposes.[†]

1. *Overcoming the rolling friction of the tires* – A heavier vehicle, a rougher road, and faster movement all result in greater rolling resistance. Other parameters that affect rolling friction are the size and inflation pressure of the tires and the type, material, and age of the threads. At low speeds, a vehicle's rolling resistance is large, relative to other resistances, and most power is dissipated at the wheels. For tracked vehicles such as tanks, heavy construction equipment, and rail systems, rolling friction is much greater and dominates all other types of resistance. Newer trains using magnetic levitation have no contact with tracks and the rolling friction is virtually eliminated.

2. *Overcoming aerodynamic (wind) resistance* – Aerodynamic resistance is the result of the interaction between a moving vehicle and the fluid through which it travels. The magnitude of the force increases with the air density, the square of the vehicle's velocity relative to the oncoming wind, the projected area of the vehicle in the direction of travel (called the frontal area), and the shape of the vehicle. Because power is the product of force and velocity, the power needed to push a vehicle through air increases with the cube of the velocity. The effect of body shape on drag is usually expressed in terms of the coefficient of the drag. Streamlining reduces the coefficient of drag and is particularly effective at high speeds where wind resistance is dominant. For most passenger cars, drag coefficients vary from 0.3 to 0.7 and aerodynamic resistance becomes significant at speeds exceeding 30-50 km/h (20-30 mph). For most public transportation modes, the frontal area per passenger is rather small, making the drag force per passenger small and most often a negligible fraction of the overall drag. The most aerodynamic car designed, so far, is the 2011 prototype hybrid, VW-XL1, with a drag coefficient of 0.19, which has a similar aerodynamic drag of the production record-holder, the GM's EV1. The drag coefficients for some common vehicles and body shapes are given in Table 6-2.

Table 6-2 Drag Coefficients			
Car	C_D	Shape	C_D
Trucks	0.70	Flat Plate	1.17
Sedans	0.55	Cylinder	1.10
Porsche 924	0.34	Sphere	0.41
GM Precept	0.16	Teardrop	0.04

3. *Climbing (overcoming gravitational resistance)* – As a vehicle climbs a slope, it must overcome gravity. The resistance increases with the grade of the road and the weight of the vehicle. When the vehicle is going downhill, this force is negative; therefore, the total power required is actually less than what is needed on a flat surface.

4. *Accelerating* – The acceleration force is equal to the vehicle's mass times the acceleration (See Chapter 2- Newton's Second Law of Motion). When the vehicle is decelerating (braking), this force is negative, which helps to reduce the overall power requirements. We will see later that electric and hybrid vehicles can regain a large fraction of the energy that would otherwise be lost during deceleration by regenerative braking.

5. *Accessories* -- In addition, engines must provide enough power to operate many accessories such as the heater, air conditioner, lights, wipers, horn, power steering, and a variety of microprocessors.

Of the four types of resistance, only the first two contribute significantly to power requirements during cruising. Acceleration drags are mainly important during city driving, in stop-and-go traffic, and when passing other vehicles on highways. Gravitational resistances play a role when climbing a mountain. During idling, the engine provides no useful work, and all energy goes to overcome engine friction. Whether a vehicle is cruising at a constant speed on a flat plane or accelerating over an incline, to reduce power, it is desirable to reduce various resistances. This can be done:

    a. *By making vehicles lighter* – Heavier cars waste energy by flexing and heating the tires. Both rolling and

---

[†] Here we concern ourselves mainly with passenger cars. Similar analyses can be carried out for other types of land vehicles such as buses, trucks, tanks, or railcars.

acceleration forces increase with vehicle mass and, therefore, are proportionally smaller in the lighter vehicles. There are fiber composites (carbon, glass, and Kevlar foam) that are many times stronger than steel and weigh only one-third to one-half as much. Composites also make it possible to build a frameless[‡] "monocoque" making manufacturing easier with considerable savings in both material and energy. Reducing the frame weight by a certain amount makes the vehicle lighter by more than that amount; the synergistic effect resulting from lighter frames makes it possible to have a lighter suspension to carry the weight, a smaller engine, and less fuel to move it.

b. *By making vehicles more aerodynamic* – Sleeker, sportier shaped bodies and smoother underbodies reduce air friction, allowing cars to move faster and consume less fuel. Convertibles, cars with rolled-down windows and protruded mirrors, and cars with large frontal areas are considerably less aerodynamic.

c. *By proper maintenance* – Fuel economy can be improved by keeping tires inflated, air filters clean, and engines tuned. Driving at cruising speeds, using accessories less frequently, and avoiding fast braking can also help.

d. *By using hybrid technology* – Hybrid vehicles have two modes of propulsion, usually an internal combustion engine and an electric motor. The vehicle operates as an electric car during city driving and in stop-and-go traffic, but is, essentially, a conventional gasoline or diesel vehicle during cruising and highway driving. Since the power required during cruising is low, a much smaller engine is needed. The electric motor delivers additional torque when accelerating or climbing steep grades. Thus, the fuel economy of these vehicles is significantly improved.

e. *By using alternative fuel* – Contemporary automobiles are highly inefficient; almost 80% of the fuel energy is lost in the exhaust and dissipated to the environment as waste heat. Certain fuels have been shown to have marginally better efficiencies than gasoline and diesel oil but are of interest mainly due to their reduced emissions.

Rail

The tractive effort of a locomotive is similar to that of a road vehicle and depends on several factors such as friction in the axle bearings, air resistance, grade resistance, and the rolling resistance between the wheel and the track. At low speeds, the tractive effort is to overcome grade and the wheels but gradually increases with speed as aerodynamic drag becomes more significant. Experimental data show that the tractive resistance for locomotives is nearly constant up to a certain speed (about 30-40 km/h) and drops with speed afterward. The maximum speed a train attains is the point where maximum tractive effort is just enough to balance the drags (See Figure 6-1). In the example given, the maximum speed train will attain is 95 km/h on a level track and 75 km/h if the train moves up a 1% slope.

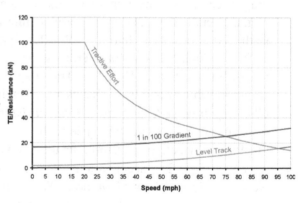

Figure 6-1
Tractive effort versus speed for a typical rail locomotive.

The best way to increase the maximum speed is by reducing rolling resistance. Better yet, if we can make the train move on a cushion of air instead of a metallic track, the resistance can be reduced to a minimum. **Maglev** (short for magnetic levitation) technology provides such an opportunity, enabling trains to reach operational speeds of 500-600 kilometers per hour. If the train could be operated in partially evacuated tubes, much higher speeds can be attained. The first commercial maglev system started operation in Shanghai in 2003 at a maximum speed of 440 km/h -- the fastest speed ever reached by train.[§]

---

‡ A type of vehicle construction in which the body is integrated with the chassis.

§ The world record for conventional high-speed rail is held by the Japan's L0 superconducting Maglev, which was clocked at 603 km/h (375 mph) -- on a test run on 21 April 2015. However, with a top speed of 440 km/h (273 mph), China's maglev train is considered to be the world's fastest, in-service commercial train. The United States does not have any maglev trains but is considering one to be built between large cities in California and Las Vegas (See http://www.magneticglide.com).

Aircraft

The resistance forces acting on aircraft consist mainly of pressure and viscous forces. *Pressure drag* acts normal (perpendicular) to the surface and arises from differences in air pressure along the body. *Viscous or shear drag* is the surface resistance (skin friction) acting on the body as it moves in a viscous fluid.[¶] The magnitudes of these resistances vary widely, depending on the airplane's shape, size, speed, and altitude. Normally, the resultant aerodynamic forces are resolved into two components: that perpendicular to the relative wind direction (lift) and that parallel to the relative wind direction (drag). During cruising, the engine must be able to overcome drag forces. Maximum power required is during takeoff and increases with the lift and the rate of the climb. At very high speeds, another form of drag -- wave drag -- enters the equation. *Wave drag* is caused by the formation of shock waves and usually is associated with supersonic flights. They also can form at subsonic speeds where the flow has locally accelerated to supersonic flow. This is why commercial aircraft (except for the now-retired Concord) travel at a cruising speed of 900 km/h in what is normally called "transonic regime." Planes break the sound barrier at the expense of massive increases in drag and power consumption.

Question: Are there optimum speeds at which birds learn to fly?

Answer: Low-speed flight is uneconomical because birds have to push the air surrounding them downward to stay airborne. The same is true for high-flying birds and aircraft since little air flows around their wings. To sustain their own weight, birds and planes must give that little air a powerful impulse. That requires a lot of energy. High-speed flights require a lot of power to overcome wind resistance, so there is an optimum speed at which a bird can sustain its energy and an optimum speed and altitude at which a plane can minimize its rate of power consumption. This is not the case for automobiles and trains, for which greater and greater power is required at faster and faster speeds. Birds soon learn how to minimize power to stay airborne for the longest time, and minimize energy per unit meter of flying (drag), when they migrate the long distances between sanctuaries.

Question: To ferry a space shuttle from the Edwards Air Force Base in California to its launching site at NASA's Kennedy Space Center in Florida, the shuttle must be bolted on the back of a modified Boeing 747-400 jumbo jet.[**] The volume of fuel used for this journey is huge, as it will take one gallon of fuel to travel only one length of the plane (231 feet). Because of many refueling stops along the way, the trip takes two days to complete. Calculate the amount of fuel it takes the jumbo jet to complete the 2,600-mile journey.

Answer: The fuel efficiency of the Boeing 747-400 is around 0.2 mpg. Because of the heavy payload and loss of much of the aerodynamic advantages with the space shuttle piggybacked, the fuel efficiency drops to only 231 feet per gallon (0.04 mpg); requiring 65,000 gallons of fuel to complete the 2,600-mile journey. The Boeing 747-400 can carry 32,750 gallons of fuel, which is about half the fuel required. For safety reasons, planes carry at least twice the amount of fuel they need to complete a trip. This means the plane has to make at least three or four stops for refueling.

Question: Which one is a more efficient (economical) mode of transportation, a car or an airplane?

[¶] Unlike common presumptions, (viscous) drag is not the same thing as friction. Friction is a resistance force that arises when two objects move relative to each other. Drag appears as a result of interaction between molecules of a solid and liquid or gas adjacent to it. As fluid comes in contact with the solid, it sticks to it, so fluid becomes stationary (zero slip condition). In a very thin region next to the surface called the boundary layer, fluid gains back its momentum approaching its free-stream velocity. Friction and drag are similar, however, in the sense that both forces are non-conservative, meaning they cannot be stored, but turn into waste energy heating the interface.

[**] Due to budgetary constraints, NASA shuttle program was cancelled in 2011.

Answer: Jet aircraft use huge amounts of fuel but also carry a lot of passengers at a very fast speed. Cars, on the other hand, are relatively slow and carry only a few passengers; although, they are not big gas-guzzlers, like jet aircraft. A Boeing-747 needs 12,000 liters of kerosene per hour to lift its 300-ton body. Assuming a density of 0.8 kilograms per liter of kerosene, the Boeing-747 uses about 3% of its weight in fuel every hour it flies. The aircraft can carry 400 passengers at a speed of 560 mph (900 km/h). This is about $12,000/(400 \times 900) = 0.033$ liters per passenger-km. A typical passenger car, on the other hand, gets about 30 mpg (9 km/L). Even if four passengers ride together in the car (which is very rare in the United States), we consume $1/(4 \times 9) = 0.03$ liters per passenger-km. This is roughly the same as the airplane, though it travels at a much slower speed. Therefore, *flying is a more efficient way to travel.* Haven't birds known that for a very long time?

Marine Vehicles

As ships and other marine vehicles move through water, they experience both water and air resistance. The resistance through water is the greater of the two and depends on many factors, including ship speed, hull form, and water temperature. The air resistance is a function of wind direction and speed, and the aerodynamic of the portion out of the water.

The total hull resistance consists of several components:

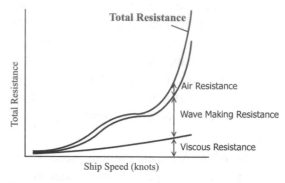

Figure 6-2
Components of hull resistance.

a. Skin friction drag due to friction between the hull and water
b. Form drag due to pressure forces acting on the hull
c. Wave drag due to energy lost in creating and maintaining waves and that is required to push the water out of the way of the hull
d. Wind resistance

Frictional losses are the function of the hull's wetted surface area, surface roughness, and viscosity. At low speeds, viscous resistance is dominant and can account for up to 50-80% of total resistance. Form drag is caused by turbulence and can be reduced by hulls having smoother curves. As speed increases, the wave-making resistance becomes more pronounced. At a certain speed – commonly known as "hull speed" – the resistance increases sharply and dominates all other resistances. This is a major barrier to building fast ships, just as the speed of sound is for aircraft. For small hulls, such as sailboats or rowboats, wave-making resistance is the largest source of drag. Air drag also can play a role, and depending on speed, the shape of the ship above the waterline and the area of the ship exposed to the air may contribute up to 10% to total ship resistance. The wind and current resistances can be significant in rough waters and when a ship runs into strong headwinds.

The total resistance is not proportional to velocity, but increases as the square of velocity at low speeds and more rapidly, as velocity to the fifth power, at higher speeds (Figure 6-2). The power required to propel a ship through water is the product of total hull resistance and ship speed. **That is, for fast ships, power increases by as much as ship speed to the sixth power!** A 10% increase in speed requires an increase of 77% in power. The fuel consumption rate also increases accordingly; i.e., for marine transport, it takes much more fuel to travel a given distance at a faster speed than traveling the same distance at a slower speed.

Specific Energy, Specific Power, and Energy Intensity

The rate at which energy is consumed is not always of our prime interest. If you are waiting for a red light during a city drive or stuck in a traffic jam on a Southern California freeway, you are consuming energy, although no distance is traveled. The energy consumed per mile traveled is infinity (zero mpg), although the energy consumed per unit time (power) is some finite value.

In addition to total power, power-per-unit mass (called specific power or power loading) is important in evaluating the energy costs of various modes of transportation. The power-to-mass ratio is a measure of vehicle acceleration. A Hummer weighs 2.5 times that of a Toyota Prius, produces three times the power, and uses five times the energy, although both have roughly the same power-to-mass ratio (whether we need that much power or not, is a different question, however!). A rocket is usually associated with a high power loading during liftoff (as a large

Table 6-3 Power Loading For Several Power Plants					
Engines	Application	Peak Power (kW)	Peak Power (hp)	Specific Power (kW/kg)	Specific Power (hp/lb)
Electric traction	French TGV	20,000	26,800	0.026	0.02
Two-stroke diesel	Containership	80,000	110,000	0.03	0.02
Gasoline engine	Toyota Prius	73	98	0.53	0.32
V8 turbo diesel	Automobile	250	335	0.65	0.40
V8, 6.6 L gasoline	Hummer H1	224	300	0.63	0.38
Gas turbine	Cruiseship	30,000	40,000	1.3	0.80
Turbofan	Boeing 747	44,700	59,900	5.67	3.46
LH_2/LO_2 rocket	Space Shuttle	53,700	72,000	153	93

amount of energy has to be used to carry a payload into orbit, in a very short time), but rapidly drops to zero, once it attains orbit. Table 6-3 gives the peak power and power-to-mass ratios for several types of engines.

A better way of evaluating the efficiency of different modes of transportation is by comparing their energy intensities, evaluated as kilowatt-hours per passenger-kilometer (or Btu per passenger-mile), or kilojoules per ton-kilometer (or Btu per ton-miles). A plane uses a lot more power to operate, but it travels faster and carries a lot more passengers than your small sedan. Trains are even better, in terms of energy expenditure, when they're nearly full or carrying heavier cargo. The advantages would disappear as fewer passengers opt to use the train, or the train travels with only a fraction of its capacity. For example, it takes a lot more energy to carry a ton of lumber a distance of 100 miles, than it does to carry 100 tons of lumber a distance of one mile -- although they both require the same amount of work. In the United States, energy intensities in Btu/passenger-miles are 3,144 for automobiles, 4,071 for transit buses, 2,455 for commuter rails, and 2,800 for commercial airplanes (See Table 6-4). Similar figures for Japan are 3,700 for cars, 1,000 for buses, 320 for trains, and 2,406 for planes. 730 Btu/passenger-miles for trains and 1,050 Btu/passenger-miles for buses are common in most European countries. It is interesting to note that, although the energy intensities for personal cars and airplanes are within 10% of each other, the lower-energy intensities for Japanese and European buses and trains are striking. Public transportation in these countries is significantly more efficient since trains and buses run with much heavier occupancy rates. In Japan, buses run four times more efficiently than those in the U.S., and trains are eight times more efficient.

The discrepancy between Japanese and U.S. data can be explained by noting that in the years following WWII,

Table 6-4 U.S. Passenger Travel and Energy Use (2013)						
Mode	Number of Vehicles	Passenger-miles (billions)	% of total travel	Load Factor (persons/ vehicles)	BTU/ passenger-miles	kWh/ 100 passenger-km[d]
Automobiles	114 million	2,241	47	1.5	3,144	57
Light trucks	106 million	1,900	39	1.8	3,503	64
Motorcycles	8.4 million	24	0.5	1.2	2,475	45
Buses[a]	792,000	22	0.5	9.2[c]	4,071[c]	74
Planes[b]	200,000	580	12	105	2,406	44
Rails	20,200	39	1	27	2,455	45

[a] Includes transit, intercity, and school; [b] General aviation; [c] Transit buses ; Derived.
Source: Davis, S. C., Diegel, S. W., "Transportation Energy Data Book," ORNL-6991, Edition34, 2015, Table 2.14.

Japanese (and Europeans) and Americans followed different paths. American policymakers, under pressure from the booming automotive industry, promoted private car ownership. Some American car companies went as far as buying and dismantling streetcars and replacing them with diesel buses, effectively forcing the public to purchase private cars. Much of the infrastructure focused on building freeways and promoting private cars as the ultimate measure of personal freedom, literally paving the way for automobiles as the principal source of transportation. In 2013, Americans traveled five trillion miles, about 85% of which was by automobiles, sport utility vehicles (SUVs), and other light trucks. Japan and Europe, on the other hand, devoted significant resources to building the public transportation infrastructure, heavily invested in trains, trams, trolleys, and subways,[††] while discouraging the use of private vehicles.

The total number of vehicles operating in different regions of the world varies widely. The solid line is the number of vehicles for the U.S. in different years -- 838 cars per 1000 persons in 2018.[‡‡] The car ownership for China and India are 188 and 22 Although the number is relatively low compared to the U.S., the rate of growth is substantial. For example, car ownership in China jumped from 18 per thousand to 80 per thousand in only one decade from 2003 to 2013. Today, it tands at 173.

Internal Combustion Engines

Internal combustion engines have found major applications in many industries -- particularly in transportation, home appliances, and stationary power-generation systems. Depending on their size, they can deliver power in the range of a few to several thousand kilowatts. The principle of operation of internal combustion engines is simple -- a mixture of fuel and air is burned inside a combustion chamber and the product of the combustion is expanded, turning the energy of fuel into useful (shaft) work. Examples of internal combustion engines are gasoline engines, diesel, and gas turbines. There is no single person who can be named as the inventor of the internal combustion engine; the process was an evolutionary one that started with Christian Huygens in 1680, who designed (but never built) an internal combustion engine, that used gunpowder. Over the next two centuries, many inventors perfected combustion engines, among them Nicholas Otto (1876), who proposed a four-step "Otto" cycle, Gottlieb Daimler (1885), who

1 Trams (also called streetcars) are rail vehicles which run on fixed tracks along public urban streets. Trolleys are electric buses with wheels that draw power from two overhead electric wires.

‡‡ Although, the trend seems to suggest that China and other developing nations are demanding higher and higher percentages of the world automobile market. For example, only in the last 10 years, the number of vehicles per thousand people has quadrupled (from 9 to 36) in China, tripled in Indonesia (from 12 to 35), and nearly doubled (from 8 to 13) in India, (Ref: Transportation Data Book, vol. 29, Table 3-4).

invented the prototype gas turbine, and Karl Benz (1889), who built the first practical four-stroke, two-cylinder engine, and the first four-wheeled automobile. Wilhelm Maybach (1890) then used Benz's design to build the first four-cylinder, four-stroke engine (Figure 6-3).

The first automobile manufacturing company in the United States was established by Henry Ford in 1903. In 1908, he mass-produced the Model-T vehicle and at one-third the price of electric cars, affordable to many people. The company named its automobiles according to the letters of the alphabet. With increased reliability and cheap and widely available petroleum, the number of privately owned cars increased rapidly.

The most common internal combustion engines in use today are gasoline engines, diesel, and gas turbines; their basic operations are described below:

Figure 6-3
Karl Benz's Velo, patented in 1894 was the first commercially manufactured automobile.

Spark Ignition (Gasoline) Engines

Most passenger cars operating today are spark ignition (also called gasoline or Otto engine); the engines work by allowing a mixture of fuel and air prepared in a carburetor to burn and expand inside the cylinders. The downward motion of a piston is converted to the rotational motion of the crankshaft using a connecting rod and, eventually, by way of a transmission to the wheels.

The *rotary (Wankel)* engine is a special type of spark ignition engine in which the piston-cylinder assembly is substituted by a three-edged rotor that is mounted off-center of a specially designed housing. Unlike conventional engines, in which the four strokes are accomplished by linear, up and down motions of the pistons, rotary engines work by varying the volume as the rotor rotates in the housing. The main advantages of rotary engines are their lower mass and volume as compared to reciprocating engines of comparable power rating and their simpler construction. Furthermore, because rotary engines deliver power directly in the rotational form, their overall efficiency is higher. The main disadvantage is that rotors are more difficult to seal, which makes hydrocarbon emissions higher.

We learned in Chapter 4 that for better thermal efficiencies, combustion must be carried out at high temperatures. This is accomplished by using better fuels and by higher compression ratios. In gasoline engines, however, there is a limit to the amount that a mixture can be compressed before the temperature exceeds the ignition point, and the engine misfires (knocks). In addition to the uncomfortable noise, it creates, knocking reduces the life of the engine. Most modern gasoline cars have compression ratios of 8 to 10 and thermal efficiencies of around 20-25%; that means that roughly three-quarters of the fuel energy is lost through the exhaust, releasing a substantial amount of air pollutants into the atmosphere. One way to reduce knocking in gasoline engines is by switching fuels, or by mixing gasoline with fuels of high octane numbers. Another approach is the use of turbochargers to pre-compress air, allowing more air to be ingested by the cylinders. The fuel burned will be proportionally higher and more power is obtained. Gasoline engines have been around more than one hundred years, and have undergone major improvements, with a significant gain in efficiency. Further gains appear to be limited and require modifying the existing design that requires lowering frictional losses between the pistons and cylinders and adjustment to valve timing to reduce the energy that escapes in the exhaust.

Charged Ignition (Diesel) Engines

Instead of compressing the air/fuel mixture to high temperatures and pressures, as is done in gasoline engines, diesel engines operate by compressing air alone. Because there is no fuel present, air can be heated to pressures and temperatures well over the ignition temperature of the fuel, without concern for ignitin and engine knock. Unlike gasoline engines, diesel requires no carburetors or spark plugs. Instead, tiny droplets of diesel fuel are injected directly into the cylinder, where they mix and burn with already heated air. Since injection times are relatively long,

Four-stroke Gasoline (Otto) Engine

Intake stroke: The intake valve (port) opens and the air-fuel mixture is sucked into and fills the cylinder.

Compression stroke: The intake valve closes, and the crankshaft helps the piston to move up, compressing the mixture to a high temperature and pressure.

Power stroke: A spark plug ignites the mixture. The pressure suddenly rises, forcing the piston to move down, expanding gases and providing the shaft work. At the end of the power stroke, the exhaust valve opens and the pressure suddenly drops to near atmospheric conditions (blow-down).

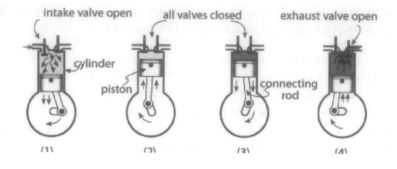

Exhaust stroke: The piston moves upward (or the rotor continues its rotation and clears the exhaust port), exhausting the burned gases.

Four-stroke Diesel Engine

Intake stroke: As the piston slides down, the intake valve opens and pure air is sucked into and fills the cylinder.

Compression stroke: The intake valve closes, and the crankshaft helps the piston to move up, compressing the air to a high temperature and pressure. The temperature is now above what is necessary for the self-ignition of the fuel.

Power stroke: When the piston is at the top, an injection pump gradually injects fine fuel droplets into the combustion chamber. As fuel droplets meet particles of hot air they burn, increasing the pressure and forcing the piston to move down, expanding gases and providing shaft work. At the end of the power stroke, the exhaust valve opens and pressure suddenly drops to near atmospheric conditions (blow-down).

Exhaust stroke: As the piston makes the second round of upward motion, burned gases are exhausted. The exhaust valve then closes in preparation for the cycle to begin again.

Figure 6-4
Four-stroke internal combustion engines for reciprocating engines.

the piston travels an appreciable distance before fuel is cut off, keeping the pressure in the cylinder nearly constant.

Strictly speaking, diesel is less efficient than gasoline engines with similar compression ratios. However, because diesel is designed to operate at higher compression ratios (20-22 compared to 8-10 for gasoline engines), they have higher efficiencies (~ 40% compared to ~30% for petrol engines). Their main drawbacks are that they are dirtier, bulkier, accelerate more slowly, and are generally more expensive. These characteristics make diesel particularly attractive in stationary applications and for buses and large trucks. Because of the stricter air pollution standards, diesel is less common in the United States than in Europe.

Gas Turbines

The basic operation of a gas turbine is relatively simple and resembles that of diesel, except compression and expansion of gases take place in compressors and turbines instead of the cylinders. Air is drawn through a diffuser and compressed in a compressor to very high pressure and temperature before entering a combustion chamber. Fuel is injected through a fuel injector into the combustion chamber, where it mixes with the air and burns. Depending on the application, kerosene, natural gas, or jet fuel can be used. The product of combustion is expanded to run a turbine that can power a helicopter, a jet engine, a tank, or a generator that produces electricity (Figure 6-5).

The main advantages of gas turbines over gasoline and diesel engines are their relatively low emissions, very high power density (kW/m^3) and specific power (kW/kg), multi-fuel capability, and smooth, vibration-free power delivery. New ceramic materials allow gas turbine operation at higher temperatures and greater efficiencies.

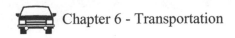

ⓐ Transportation Fuels

The most common fuels used for automobiles are gasoline and diesel oil. They are liquid, are relatively inexpensive, and have good combustion characteristics. Furthermore, the necessary infrastructure for the production, storage, and distribution of these fuels is fully in place. These fuels, however, are associated with most of our air pollution problems.

To increase efficiency, improve air quality, and reduce dependence on foreign oil, the U.S., Japan, and many European governments have passed laws and enacted taxes and other incentives to promote the use of alternative fuels in vehicles. These fuels have not, however, found wide acceptance and their use has been limited to fleets and government vehicles. They can find wide appeal among consumers, only if they meet many of the same requirements as gasoline and diesel fuels.

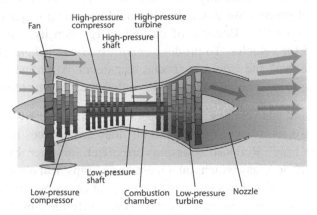

Figure 6-5
Gas turbine operation follows the Brayton cycle, consisting of four processes: intake, compression, combustion, and expansion.

As of 2015, only about 329,000 alternative-fuel vehicles were in operation in the United States (Table 6-5). Another 20 million were using various blends of biodiesel fuels. The most common fuel, by far, was ethanol, followed by propane (LPG), and compressed natural gas (CNG). In addition, about 67,000 electric vehicles were on the road, mainly in California and Arizona.

Probably, the most positive impact of alternative fuels is the relatively lower emission of greenhouse gases, measured by the ratio of the net amount of carbon dioxide per kilogram of fuel burned; the improvement is, at best, marginal.

Below is the list of various transportation fuels and known advantages and drawbacks:

Gasoline (Petrol) is the most common fuel used in vehicles. It is a colorless and volatile liquid made up of many hydrocarbons but is conveniently represented as a single compound with a molecular structure approximated as C_8H_{17}. Like most other liquid fuels, gasoline is derived primarily from crude oil. To aid combustion and reduce hydrocarbon emissions, it is advantageous to add some oxygen to gasoline. The product, called *reformulated gasoline*, has been found to reduce smog in cities with large concentrations of cars. Adding some detergents to gasoline helps to prevent the build-up of deposits, keeping engines work smoothly.

Diesel oil like gasoline is a mixture of light distillate hydrocarbons. Its boiling point is somewhat higher than that of gasoline, allowing for engine operation at an increased compression ratio, with less concern over the engine knock common in gasoline engines.

Kerosene is a mixture of heavier hydrocarbons; it is used mostly as heating oil. Kerosene is lighter than gasoline and has a higher heating value. It is used as jet fuel in pure distillate (JP5) or is blended with gasoline (JP4). Kerosene often is represented as a single hydrocarbon with the formula $C_{12}H_{26}$.

Natural gas is about 90% methane and 10% heavier hydrocarbons. Natural gas is

Table 6-5 Number of Alternative Fuel Vehicles, and Refueling Stations, 2015		
Fuel Type	**# Vehicles**	**# Refueling Sites**
E85	863	2,914
LPG	139,477	3,146
CNG	118,214	1,549
LNG	3,436	111
Hydrogen	~ 0	45
Electric	67,205	39,659,275
Total	**329,195**	*48,177*

Source: Davis, S. C., and Diegel, S. W., "Transportation Energy Data Book," ORNL-6961, Edition 34, 2015, Tables 6.1 and 6.8.

Table 6-6 Direct Carbon Dioxide Emissions from a Gallon of Fuel	
Fuel	**Grams**
Gasoline	8,887
Diesel	10,180
E85	1,340
B20	8,120
LPG	5,805
Propane	5,740
Jet fuel (kerosene)	9,751

Source: Davis, S. C., and Diegel, S. W., "Transportation Energy Data Book," ORNL-6961, Edition 34, 2015, Tables 6.1 and 6.8.

generally considered a relatively clean fuel, as the emission of carbon monoxide, hydrocarbons, and particulate matter is substantially less than that of gasoline or diesel fuel. At this time, methane emission accounts for 13% of all greenhouse gases, but it would become a major concern if natural gas were to become a dominant fuel for transportation. Because of its low energy density, natural gas must be compressed or liquefied before it can be used for vehicles. To produce *compressed natural gas* (CNG), methane must be compressed to 15-25 MPa (2,300-3,800 psi) and stored in special containers. At ordinary room temperatures, it is impossible to liquefy methane by compression alone and must be cooled to cryogenic temperatures (-162°C).

Natural gas vehicles (NGV) operate similarly to conventional gasoline- or diesel-powered vehicles in that they burn a gaseous mixture of fuel and air; they are less costly to operate, produce 30-40% less pollution than gasoline or diesel fuel. Reduced emissions are offset, however, by an increase in the emission of unburned methane, a potent greenhouse gas which, on a mass basis, traps heat about 20 times more than carbon dioxide. Its high octane number (ON = 130) allows engines to operate at compression ratios as high as 12:1, compared to 8:1 for gasoline engines. Methane-powered cars have, however, inferior power and energy densities, resulting in roughly 20% lower fuel efficiency and a shorter cruising range. Furthermore, passenger cars stand idle more often, which accompanies high evaporative losses.

Worldwide, there were 14.8 million natural gas vehicles by 2011, with more than half in only three countries Iran, Pakistan, and Argentina. There were about 118,000 CNG ad 3,400 LNG alternative fuel vehicles in use in the United States in 2015. Natural gas vehicles are not available on a large scale in the U.S. Honda Civic GX is the only CNG dedicated car. Liquefied natural gas (LNG) can be an attractive alternative for heavy duty vehicles and passenger buses, which travel long distances with a single fill-up.

Liquefied petroleum gas (LPG) is natural gas leftover after methane is removed. It is mostly propane, but some butane and higher hydrocarbons are also present. Unlike methane, propane can be liquefied at room temperature and relatively low pressure; this makes LPG suitable for storage in light fuel tanks, with a driving range comparable to that of gasoline.

Methanol (also called *methyl* or *wood alcohol*) is the simplest alcohol. It is liquid, like gasoline, has a high octane rating (ON = 100), and can be produced by a variety of methods from gasoline, natural gas, and other fossil fuels, or from the distillation of wood chips, garbage, and animal manure. Since methanol has a high H/C ratio, it is a relatively clean fuel, and except for aldehydes, methanol emissions are considerably lower than those of gasoline. Unfortunately, methanol is so toxic that even ingesting a small amount can cause blindness or death. It is also corrosive to aluminum and other materials commonly used in seals and pipe fittings for transporting gasoline, and therefore, cannot be transported through existing pipelines. Methanol has only half the energy density of gasoline, which means for a given driving range, about twice the amount of fuel will be needed. Because of these limitations, the number of methanol vehicles has declined steadily in recent years, and its use as a transportation fuel all but eliminated. Methanol use has been mainly in fuel cells or being converted to hydrogen and operate fuel-cell vehicles.

Ethanol (also called *ethyl* or *grain alcohol*) is made through the biochemical conversion (fermentation) of sugar and perennial grasses, or by the hydration of ethylene from petroleum. Ethanol can be used directly in fuel cells or as a transportation fuel in either the pure form or mixed with gasoline. Ethanol has a very high octane rating (ON = 113) and, therefore, is most suitable for use in high-compression engines. Ethanol has a lower heating value than gasoline and burns at a lower air/fuel ratio (9:1 as compared with 15:1 for gasoline). So, for a given engine, more fuel can be introduced per cycle, compensating for its lower heating value, and overall higher power output is possible. Ethanol burns with an invisible flame; to increase visibility, it often is blended with gasoline to produce gasohol (a mixture of 10% ethanol, 90% gasoline), E85 (85% ethanol, 15% gasoline), and E95 (95% ethanol, 5% gasoline). E85 is usually used for light-duty applications, whereas E95 is best for heavy-duty vehicles.

Biodiesel is derived from vegetable oils, seeds, animal fats, and algae (See Chapter 11). Biodiesel is, however, more viscous than gasoline, which makes cold-temperature starts more difficult. Because biodiesel is biomass, it

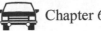

is biodegradable, less toxic, has fewer hydrocarbon and particulate emissions, and does not contribute to global warming. Biodiesel. however, emits more NOx than petroleum-derived diesel fuel. NOx emissions are precursors in the formation of smog and acid rain. Some studies have field-tested and showed that the NOx emission is reduced if B20 diesel is emulsified with various degrees of water content; at the same time, particulate matter emission was also reduced. Biodiesel is marketed as pure biodiesel (B100) or as a blend of 20% biodiesel and 80% petroleum diesel (B20).

> **Example 6-1:** Estimate the amount of carbon dioxide emission per mile traveled for typical gasoline passenger cars. What is the annual average carbon dioxide of a gasoline vehicle on U.S. roads today? According to Federal Highway Administration Highway Statistics, the average gasoline vehicle has a fuel economy of about 21.6 miles per gallon (mpg) and drives around 11,400 miles per year.
>
> **Solution:** From the data given in Table 6-6, the average gasoline passenger car produces 8,887 grams of carbon dioxide. We have:
>
> $$CO_2 \text{ emissions per mile} = \frac{8,997 \text{ grams of } CO_2 \text{ per gallon}}{21.6 \text{ mpg}} = 411 \text{ g}$$
>
> $$\text{Annual } CO_2 \text{ emissions} = 411 \text{ g/mile} \times 11,400 \text{ mile} = 4.7 \times 10^6 \text{g} = 4.7 \text{ metric tons}$$

Hydrogen

Hydrogen is the simplest and most abundant element in the universe; it has the highest energy density (energy per unit mass) of all fuels.[§§] When combusted with oxygen, produces water, making it, also, the cleanest form of energy. Because of its superior energy-to-weight ratio, liquid hydrogen has been the fuel of choice for rocket engines and has been utilized in the upper stages of launch vehicles on many space missions, including the Apollo missions to the moon, Skylab, and the Viking. Hydrogen can produce electricity through fuel cells -- directly eliminating carbon dioxide and other pollutants that are associated with the burning of fossil fuels.[¶¶] In addition, it has a higher ignition temperature, and wider flammability range than gasoline, allowing engine operation at a higher compression ratio and leaner mixture, both increasing the thermal efficiency. One kilogram of hydrogen contains about the same amount of energy as one gallon of gasoline.

Earlier combustion engines used a synthetic producer gas with a large hydrogen fraction. With the development of the carburetor, hydrogen was replaced with liquid fuel as it carried a lot more energy in the same volume of the fuel tank. Existing distribution channels used for the transport and delivery of gasoline are not suitable for hydrogen. A number of manufacturers, including GM, Mercedes, and BMW, have developed hydrogen-powered concept cars. None, however, have committed to full production of these vehicles until there are practical ways to store adequate hydrogen onboard, build refueling infrastructure, and train technicians to repair and maintain these vehicles. Figure 6-6 shows a BMW vehicle modified to burn hydrogen.

Figure 6-6
BMW 745-hl. The first hydrogen-powered car using liquid hydrogen.

Hydrogen Storage

The major impediment to the development of hydrogen vehicles is that hydrogen storage is difficult. Because at

---

[§§] Contrary to what some might think, hydrogen is not a fuel, but a carrier and a means of energy storage. To produce hydrogen, one requires at least as much energy as is produced when it is burned in a combustion process, or the electricity it generates when it is used in a fuel cell. In other words, we store the energy contained in other energy sources in the form of hydrogen and then use the hydrogen to produce power.

[¶¶] If hydrogen is burned in an internal combustion engine then, besides water vapor, some NOx also will be produced. The high temperatures of hydrogen flames cause air to be ionized into atomic nitrogen and oxygen, which subsequently react to produce nitric monoxide. When hydrogen is used in fuel cells, the reaction is at low temperatures, and the only product is water vapor.

ambient temperature, hydrogen has a low volumetric energy density, it is stored onboard a vehicle as a compressed gas to achieve the driving range of conventional vehicles. Two methods are compressing hydrogen to very high pressures (5,000-10,000 psi) or cooling to cryogenic temperatures (-253°C), both requiring a substantial amount of energy. With the current technology, about 15% of the energy content of hydrogen goes into its compression; liquefying the gas requires even more energy -- as much as 30-35% of the stored chemical energy. To make it practical in transportation applications, the Department of Energy has set a goal of 50 kg of hydrogen per cubic meter of storage space. This seems to be possible only if hydrogen is stored on the surfaces of solids (by adsorption) or within solids (by absorption). Unfortunately, these methods add considerable weight to the storage container. Metal hydride and carbon nanofibers are two promising technologies:

Nanofibers and nanotubes are hollow materials weaved in the shape of fibers 1-30 nm in diameter, stacked as nanoscale cylindrical rolls of graphite that provide many thousands of times more surface area per mass of solid material. Carbon is particularly suitable because of its high absorption capacity, small pore sizes, and low mass; the large surface area enhances the adsorption rate allowing a significantly larger amount of hydrogen gas that can be stored.

Metal hydride systems consist of aluminum or stainless steel cylinders filled with a metal powder -- typically a rare earth material capable of absorbing a large amount of hydrogen. The powder is recharged by introducing gas at elevated pressures. Metal hydride storage has the advantage that there is no need for high-pressure tanks -- a safety concern for most hydrogen systems. The disadvantage is the extra weight, making it unsuitable for use in passenger cars.

Aside from these considerations, some concerns have been recently raised in regard to the environmental effect of potential gas leaks. Due to the small size of its molecules, hydrogen is prone to leakage, causing pipes to deteriorate faster. Hydrogen embrittlement is also of some concern. Being so light, hydrogen can rapidly rise through the atmosphere, eventually reacting with oxygen to form water vapor, making the stratosphere wetter, cooling the lower atmosphere, particularly in the polar regions. This would disrupt the ozone layer, causing 7-8% more depletion over the poles.

Time = 0 min, 0 sec

Time = 0 min, 3 sec

Time = 1 min, 0 sec

Figure 6-7
Fuel-leak simulation. Hydrogen-powered vehicle is on the left, and gasoline-powered vehicle is on the right. Notice that after 1 minute, the hydrogen flame is subsiding, whereas the gasoline flame is engulfing the entire vehicle. (Ref. 17)

Hydrogen Safety

Hydrogen is highly explosive and burns easily with an invisible flame, and over a wide flammability range. Images of the catastrophic explosion of the hydrogen-propelled Hindenburg, 1937, are still alive in many people's minds[***] -- even though some recent studies have shown that the cause of the explosion was not the hydrogen, but the electrostatic charge accumulated by an oily substance used to treat the cotton skin of the airship. The lack of flame visibility can be resolved easily with certain additives. New advances in composites allow the design of hydrogen tanks that can withstand major crashes and falls from buildings several stories tall. In addition, hydrogen sensors are available that can detect and shut down flow as the smallest leaks are detected. Finally, since hydrogen is the lightest of all gases, hydrogen flames are highly buoyant and spread in the form of jets diffusing upward and away from the body of the car and its occupants, in case of a major accident, as demonstrated by several crash and fire simulations (See

---

[***] The Hindenburg was a giant, hydrogen-filled airship (at 245-meters length, it was the largest ever to fly) that operated regularly in the 1930s, taking transatlantic passengers between Germany and both North and South America, before it was destroyed by a fire in 1937. A total of 35 people died.

Figure 6-7). Table 6-7 compares the ignition characteristics of hydrogen with those of methane and gasoline.

Hydrogen Production

Unlike petroleum and methane, hydrogen cannot be mined but must be produced in a number of ways, ranging from hydrocarbon reformation to coal gasification and pyrolysis, to the electrolysis of water. If hydrogen is produced by reforming ethanol, then a large amount of energy required for the distillation of ethanol will take away most of the hydrogen advantage; if hydrogen is produced by reforming fossil fuels, then most of its environmental benefits disappear. Renewable sources such as solar, wind, and hydropower are ideal because they can electrolyze water in large quantities without polluting the atmosphere. Nuclear sources are another option.

Table 6-7 Ignition Characteristics of Various Gaseous And Liquid Fuels			
Car	*Hydrogen*	*Methane*	*Gasoline*
Ignition Temperature	585°C	540°C	230-480°C
Flammability Limit	4-75% by vol.	5-15% by vol.	1.4-7.6% by vol.
Explosion Limits	20-65% by vol.	6-14% by vol.	1-7.6% by vol.
Energy Density	120 MJ/kg	50 MJ/kg	44 MJ/kg
Ignition Energy	8.5 MJ/L	40 MJ/L	21 MJ/L

Source: Flynn, T., Cryogenic Engineering, Second Ed., CRC Press, 2005.

The least costly approach to hydrogen production is through a **water-gas shift reaction**, where steam is sprayed over a bed of hot coal. The product is a mixture of hydrogen and carbon monoxide, known by some as **coal gas**.

$$C + H_2O \rightarrow CO + H_2$$
$$CO + H_2O \rightarrow CO_2 + H_2$$

Unfortunately, the carbon monoxide produced along the way is highly poisonous. To extract additional energy and get rid of the dangerous gas, carbon monoxide is burned to produce carbon dioxide.

Currently, most commercial hydrogen is produced by *steam reformation* of natural gas. Natural gas is a particularly good candidate for producing hydrogen at the wellhead. Instead of piping crude or natural gas, large reformers can be installed to strip off the hydrogen and ship it through the pipelines. The by-product of the reformation process, mainly carbon dioxide, then, can be sequestered by injecting it back into the gas field, raising the pressure and improving extraction efficiency (See Chapter 3, Enhanced Oil Recovery). Methanol and gasoline also have been used to produce hydrogen using steam reforming. @

@ Emissions from Internal Combustion Engines

When automobiles were marketed in the early twentieth century, they were seen by many as a clean form of transportation, doing away with the nuisance of horse feces in large urban cities. In the decades that followed, as the number of vehicles increased, the impact of this technology on air quality and health became more pronounced and cars became the main source of environmental pollution. The high concentration of air pollutants is directly linked to many adverse health conditions, notably reduction in the body's ability to fight diseases and in aggravating asthma. In the U.S. today, motor vehicles are responsible for more than half of all carbon monoxide and nitrogen oxide emissions and nearly one-quarter of all hydrocarbons released into the atmosphere (Table 6-8). In addition, motor vehicles produce carbon dioxide, a potent greenhouse gas. Most emissions are released through the exhaust pipes. In addition, some hydrocarbons are from the crankcase, carburetor, and fuel tanks. Compared to reciprocating engines, gas turbines produce lower emissions. This is because gas turbines operate under ultra-lean combustion. Furthermore, gas turbines do not respond well to transient operations and usually operate in a continuous mode.

Exhaust pipe emissions are largely a result of incomplete combustion and are affected by many factors. Three parameters have profound effects on how combustion proceeds and how much pollution is formed; these parameters are referred to as the three Ts of combustion -- Temperature, Time, and Turbulence. *Temperature* determines the rate of reaction and heat release. If everything else remains the same, higher temperatures increase the production of nitric oxides and limit the production of hydrocarbons, carbon monoxide, and soot. Temperature is highest near stoichiometric conditions and for fuels with high hydrogen-to-carbon (H/C) ratios. Stoichiometric conditions occur when an air/fuel mixture burns to completion and when, under equilibrium conditions, the only products of combustion are molecular nitrogen, carbon dioxide, and water. The *time* that reactants have in a flame reaction zone determines the extent to which reactions go to completion. Greater residence times generally favor more stable molecules (carbon dioxide, nitrogen, water vapor) and lower overall emissions. *Turbulence* affects the rate of mixing of fuel and air molecules. Better mixing prevents localized pockets of very rich or very lean mixtures, thus allowing the reaction to complete and produce fewer contaminants.

Table 6-8 U.S. Total Emission of Criteria Pollutants in 2014					
Source	Total Emission[b]	Mobile	Stationary	Industrial	Others[a]
CO	61	54%	7%	3%	36%
NOx	11	58%	29%	9%	14%
HC (VOC)	16	23%	4%	41%	32%
PM10[c]	19	2%	5%	5%	88%
PM2.5[c]	6	6%	14%	7%	73%
SO_2	5	2%	82%	11%	5%

[a] Waste disposal, recycling, etc.
[b] Million metric tons
[c] Particulate matters smaller than 2.5 and 10 microns.

Source: U.S. EPA, National Emission Inventory Air Pollutant Emission Trends, (http://www.epa.gov/oar/oapqs).

A brief discussion of major pollutants from automobiles and other internal combustion engines, and factors affecting their formation is given below. The health and other environmental effects associated with these pollutants are discussed in Chapter 7.

Oxides of nitrogen result from a reaction between oxygen and nitrogen heated to combustion temperatures. Over 90% of all oxides of nitrogen are in the form of nitrogen monoxide (NO), and the rest is in the form of nitrogen dioxide (NO_2). However, soon after entering the atmosphere, NO is oxidized to NO_2; therefore it is common to quote the sum of the two components, called NOx (and pronounced *nocks*). As we may expect, maximum NOx occurs near stoichiometric conditions where the temperature is at its peak and sufficient oxygen is available. The best way to reduce NOx emissions is by lowering the combustion temperature and adjusting the mixture ratio. Too much air dilutes the mixture and reduces the flame temperature; with too much fuel, little oxygen is left over for reacting with nitrogen. Recirculating a portion of exhaust gases back to the intake manifold is shown to be effective in reducing NOx emissions by lowering the air-to-fuel ratio and cooling the flame. Unfortunately, exhaust gas recirculation (EGR) valves must operate with a rich mixture, which promotes the production of hydrocarbons and carbon monoxide. Another method to reduce NOx emissions is to add some hydrogen to the gasoline/air mixture. The drawback is backfiring, a result of hydrogen's low ignition temperature and lower power rating. The main sources of nitrogen dioxide are transportation and stationary power plants, but some also are released from fertilizers and other chemical plants.

Carbon monoxide results from incomplete reactions. It is formed when there is insufficient oxygen, low temperature, or a short time to oxidize all carbons to carbon dioxide. The obvious way to reduce carbon monoxide emissions is by maintaining a mixture lean in fuel. Advancing the spark, or increasing the compression ratio, raises peak temperatures and increases the time available for reaction, both of which inhibit the formation of carbon monoxide. The overwhelming majority of all carbon monoxide emissions are from cars. Other major contributors include stationary power plants and solid waste disposal.

Hydrocarbon (also referred to as volatile organic compounds) emissions can be divided into two categories, unburned and partially burned. Roughly half of all hydrocarbon emissions come from the unburned vapor during fill-ups, evaporation from the carburetor, and from other hot surfaces when the engine is shut off. Other sources of hydrocarbon emissions are crankcase blow-by and emission from leaky valves, piston rings, and gaskets. The hydrocarbon release during fueling is reduced by installing vapor recovery nozzles on gas pumps. Crankcase emissions are practically eliminated by closing off the vent to the atmosphere and installing a positive ventilation valve (PCV) to recycle blow-by back into the engine's intake. In addition to cars, industrial chemicals such as benzene, solvents such as toluene and xylene, and many other chemicals used as dry-cleaning solvents, are major contributors to hydrocarbon emissions.

Particulates include soot, lead, dust, ocean salt, and metal debris. ***Soot particles*** are large aggregates of carbon atoms generated in the combustion chambers. Soot also can be formed from the lubrication oil adjacent to cold surfaces and from the rapid expansion during the power stroke. The main sources of particulates are power plants and diesel cars, although smaller sources such as wood stoves, agricultural burning, and dust also contribute. Particulates can vary in size from a fraction of a micron to many hundreds of microns. Those below 10 microns (PM-10) become airborne and may be inhaled, diffused, and be adsorbed and deposited on the interior of the lungs, potentially contributing to lung damage and cancer. Particles larger than 10 microns are entirely blocked by the nose. These particles are responsible mainly for reduced visibility and, eventually, will settle. ***Lead*** is a poisonous metal emitted from the old automobile exhausts, paints, storage batteries, and pipes. During the 1970s, lead was routinely added to gasoline to reduce knocking and to allow for the construction of higher compression engines, but due to its adverse health effects, lead eventually was removed from gasoline and, therefore, is not of environmental concern, any longer. Dust and ocean salt is present naturally, and thus not considered pollutants. They may, however, present nuisances by forming fog and influence secondary reactions in the atmosphere.

Sulfur oxides (SO_2) are generated by the combustion of sulfur-rich fuels. Sulfur dioxide emissions are not a major concern in passenger cars and other vehicles, as they are removed from gasoline and diesel fuel before they are sold. The main sources of sulfur emissions are stationary power stations, refineries, and industrial processing plants.

Catalytic Converters

Vehicular exhaust emissions contain not only carbon dioxide and water vapor, but also a significant amount of carbon monoxide, nitrogen oxides, and hydrocarbons. Generally speaking, nitric oxides are produced during cruising and acceleration (driving mode), where the mixture burns at its maximum temperature near stoichiometric conditions. On the contrary, during braking and when the engine idles (stopping mode), some exhaust enters the intake manifold, causing carbon monoxide, hydrocarbon, and particulate emissions to be high. For the best performance -- maximum efficiency and minimal environmental pollution -- it is ideally desirable to convert all carbon into carbon dioxide, all hydrocarbons into water vapor, and all nitrogen into molecular nitrogen. To convert carbon monoxide and

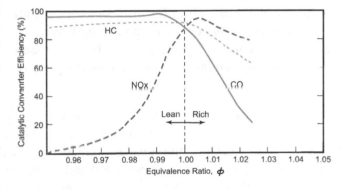

Figure 6-8

Conversion efficiency of the catalytic reactors as function of the fuel/air ratio.

hydrocarbon, we need a high temperature and an oxidizing atmosphere. The problem is that these same conditions provide a favorable environment for the oxidation of nitrogen into nitric oxides. Three-way catalytic converters can achieve successful modifications of CO and HC while at the same time reducing NOx to molecular nitrogen. This is achieved in two steps:

1. Convert all nitric oxides into nitrogen in a reducing atmosphere (fuel-rich).

$$NO \xrightarrow{Rh} N_2 + O_2$$

2. Convert all hydrocarbons (HC) and carbon monoxide into carbon dioxide and water in an oxidizing atmosphere (air rich).

$$CO + HC \xrightarrow{Pt, Pd} CO_2 + H_2O$$

Generally, catalytic converters are made of stainless steel canisters filled with porous ceramic honeycombs or small particles of alumina coated with catalytic materials. Three-way converters employ redox (for reduction/oxidation) catalysts, which are essentially made of two reactors, a reducing reactor (with a rhodium catalyst), followed by an oxidizing reactor (with platinum or a palladium catalyst).

Figure 6-8 shows the conversion efficiencies of the catalytic converter for CO, HC, and NOx at different fuel/air ratios. As can be seen, for redox reactors to work, they must operate within a narrow range of air/fuel ratios (around stoichiometric). When in good working conditions, these reactors reduce in excess of 98% of CO and 95% of HC and NOx emissions.

$$CO + HC + NO \rightarrow \boxed{\text{Reducing Reactor}} \rightarrow CO + HC + N_2 \rightarrow \boxed{\text{Oxidizing Reactor}} \rightarrow CO_2 + H_2O$$

Compare to gasoline engines, diesel exhausts' temperatures are considerably lower; thus diesel emits eight to ten times more particulate matter than comparable SI engines. A *trap oxidizer* works by filtering particulate matter and burning it periodically. Both gasoline and diesel catalytic converters are poisoned by sulfates, which can be avoided by removing sulfur from the fuel.

Fuel Economy and Emission Standards

Following the Arab oil embargo of 1973, the U.S. government has introduced the "**Corporate Average Fuel Economy** (CAFE) standard for passenger cars, light trucks, and SUVs weighing 8,500 pounds or less[†††] to a combined average of at least 38 mpg in 2020, and eventually expanded to 48.7 mpg by 2025. Also, the new rules contain incentives for manufacturers to earn credits by over-complying, or by producing alternative or dual-fueled vehicles. These credits can be sold or used to balance the non-compliance of other model years or classes.

Table 6-9 Cafe Standards (in miles per gallon for model year vehicles)					
	2013	**2014**	**2015**	**2020**	**2025**
Passenger Cars	34.4	35.2	36.4	44.2	55.3
Light Trucks	25.6	26.2	27.1	30.6	39.3
Combined	30.6	31.4	32.6	38.3	48.7

Source: Annual Energy Outlook, 2013, http://www.eia.gov/forecasts/aeo/ [Accessed August 1, 2020]

Even though cars are becoming consistently more efficient, the savings in fuel has, so far, not translated into reduced consumption. Instead, better fuel efficiency, along with the low price of petroleum, has triggered an upsurge in the use of SUVs, pickups, and minivans (cumulatively called light trucks). For example, the U.S. Department of Transportation reported that between 1990 and 2009, the share of midsize and large SUVs increased from 1.3% to 31%. During the same period, the share of small cars reduced by half. Also during that period, the total vehicle miles traveled increased around 15% by passenger cars and 60% by light trucks. The 1980-2000 census data point to an ever-worsening situation, as the share of workers driving alone to work increased from 64% to 76%, while the percentage of those who carpooled reduced from 20% to 11%. Although the current data does not lead us to believe that efficiency alone makes much of a dent in the fuel savings, many industry insiders suggest that by 2040, advanced transportation technology and more efficient automobiles will result in doubling of fuel economy, and a considerable reduction in total auto emissions.

U.S. emission standards are indirectly linked to fuel economy standards. Table 6-9 shows the minimum EPA standards for vehicles in the United States. California has devised its own standards, which always have been more stringent than Federal standards. Europeans and Japanese standards are generally comparable to U.S. standards.

[†††] CAFE standards are set and administered by the National Highway and Traffic Safety Administration (NHTSA); the Environmental Protection Agency (EPA) provides the fuel economy data and calculates the average fuel economy for each manufacturer..

Electric Vehicles

The second half of the nineteenth century and the early twentieth century marked the dawning of transportation innovation, as horse-drawn carriages were replaced with steam locomotives, petrol engines, and electric trolleys. In 1900, of the 4,200 automobiles sold in the U.S., 40% were steam, 38% electric, and 22% were powered by gasoline. By 1912, electric cars dominated the automobile market, surpassing all other vehicles equipped with internal combustion engines.

The demise of electric cars came with the invention of the starter motor by Charles F. Kettering in 1911. The Kettering starter was a small electric motor that produced enough power to crank an engine for a very short time, eliminating the need for much more tedious hand cranks. The popularity of gasoline engines continued to increase as they become more reliable, eventually making the steam engine obsolete and electric vehicles (EV) inferior. Mass production of Ford's Model-T, with affordable prices and a range twice that of the best electric cars, helped make internal combustion engines even more popular.

As electric vehicles became less and less attractive and the number of internal combustion engines grew, so did the concern for automotive pollution. The sudden increase in the price of gasoline in early 1970, following the Arab oil embargo, revived the interest in electric vehicles. The main problems that have precluded a wide acceptance of electric vehicles are their higher cost, limited range, and the inconvenience these vehicles present in comparison to internal combustion engines. Batteries used in electric vehicles are heavy and of relatively low power density. This means that, for the same weight, EVs have a much shorter range than gasoline and diesel engines. One kilogram of the lead-acid battery delivers 25 Wh of electrical energy. Compare this with 12,200 Wh of thermal energy (4 kWh electrical) delivered by 1 kg of gasoline.

Another problem with the batteries is their long charging time. Furthermore, unlike gasoline filling stations that are widely available throughout the world, battery charging stations are few and far between. The obvious challenge to electric vehicles' popularity is to develop compact batteries with similar energy density to gasoline and at a reasonable price. As the price of gasoline rises, it is expected that electric cars claim a larger fraction of the total vehicle market. Out of 250 million cars operating in the United States, about 40% are used as second cars, and 87% of automobile trips are less than 50 kilometers. Electric vehicles can satisfy these needs when used as town cars and as fleet vehicles for inner-city, short-route bus lines, delivery vehicles, in airports, and mail-delivery services.

Battery-operated Electric Vehicles (BEV)

The first mass-produced electric car was EV1, manufactured by General Motors (GM) and inspired by its earlier success in producing a limited number of electric concept cars called the "Impact." Although strongly endorsed by the public, GM did not see the car as a good economic investment, and stopped production in 1999, after only three years and production of 1,117 vehicles. The EV1 program subsequently was discontinued, and all cars on the road were repossessed and crushed; only a few were donated to museums. In 2004, Tesla Motors began the development of the Tesla Roadster, the first production automobile that married the light, low drag Lotus body with the advanced motor and inverter of the EV-1 electric car and lithium-ion battery cells (Figure 6-9). It is the first all-electric car to travel 200 miles (320 km) on a single charge. Other nations are catching up fast -- China and India are expected to be among the major exporters of electric and other low-emission vehicles in the near future. China has rapidly created the world's largest electric vehicle market, and it today accounts for half of the world's electric cars and more than 90% of electric buses and trucks. India's efforts in penetrating the EV market are equally ambitious.

Figure 6-9
Tesla Roadster.
Image Courtesy Tesla Motors.

Cost of Operating an Electric Vehicle

The number often quoted as the cost of owning an electric vehicle is the **miles per gallon of gasoline-equivalent (mpg-e),** which is the miles driven with the amount of electricity having the same energy as one gallon of gasoline (33.7 kWh). It does not reflect the cost of depreciation (replacing) of the battery. Adding the cost of battery replacement to the cost of charging, it may not be immediately apparent that electric vehicles make economic sense when compared to gasoline and diesel vehicles. The cost saving of avoiding environmental and health effects is, however, significant.

Advantages and Disadvantages of Electric Vehicles

The major advantages of electric over conventional vehicles are:

1. *Better torque characteristics.* Electric motors are simpler and have torque characteristics that match those demanded by vehicles more closely (high torque at low speeds and acceleration, relatively low torque during cruising). Internal combustion engines, on the other hand, deliver maximum torque at optimum cruising speed (Figure 6-10). Because little or no torque is delivered during start-ups and at lower speeds, internal combustion engines need starter motors. Electric motors, on the other hand, produce the highest torque at startup and therefore, can be attached directly to the drive wheels (direct-drive, in-hub motors) and can accelerate the vehicle from rest to the desired speed without the need for a transmission. In electric vehicles that have no in-hub motors, transmission systems are required. The power trains are simpler, however, and don't usually need more than one or two gear ratios. Reverse gears are also absent because their function can be achieved simply by reversing the polarity of the electrical input.
2. *Regenerative Braking.* Electric motors can run as generators by running in reverse. Electric vehicles take advantage of this feature by employing regenerative braking, where up to 50% of the kinetic energy of the vehicle can be reclaimed during urban stop-and-go traffic to recharge the battery. The experimental data show that, depending on the design and the driving cycle, regenerative braking extends the driving range between 5-15%.
3. *Lower noise and emission.* Electric vehicles are much quieter during operation and do not consume any power or produce any emissions when stopped. This is not true with gasoline cars, which continue to consume a substantial amount of fuel and produce pollution, even when they idle. Some emissions, such as hydrocarbons, are actually higher during idling than when cruising at optimal speeds.
4. *Superior efficiencies.* Electric vehicles have efficiencies in the range of 40-45%, compared to efficiencies of 18-25% common for most conventional vehicles. However, when losses associated with the generation of electricity and transport are considered, efficiency advantages are only 10-30%.

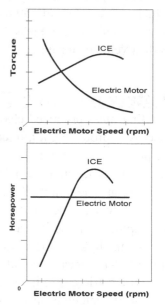

Figure 6-10
Power and torque characteristics of an ICE and an electric motor.

The major disadvantages of electric vehicles over conventional vehicles are:

1. Batteries have a relatively small capacity to store energy. Compared to gasoline, which has an energy density of 12,000 watt-hours per kilogram, lead-acid batteries have only 50 watt-hours per kilogram, i.e., one kilogram of gasoline, does what 240 kilograms of battery. Lithium-ion batteries common in today's electric vehicles have an energy density of 250 Wh/kg, five times higher than that of lead-acid batteries. Lower battery storage capability results in limitations on the distance electric vehicles can travel before they must be recharged. More batteries add to vehicle weight, which indirectly limits performance. The EVs available on the market are, on average, 300 to 1,000 kilograms heavier than similar conventional vehicles. Batteries used in the Tesla Roadster account for

188

1/3 of its total weight.[‡‡‡]

2. *Infrastructure does not exist.* There is no network of recharging stations. Charging must be accomplished in much faster times than are currently possible and in all types of weather conditions.

3. *Electric vehicles cost more.* Costs of ownership (initial purchase price, plus costs associated with maintenance and repair) are higher for electric vehicles.

ⓐ *Batteries*

Batteries are devices that store electric energy as chemical energy (during charging) and release it as electric energy during discharge. A battery consists of a number of voltaic cells. Each cell produces a certain voltage that depends on the type of cell and materials used. When several cells are arranged in a series configuration in a plastic casing, they are collectively called a **battery**. The energy stored in a battery is the difference between the available energy between chemical components in the charged and discharged states that can be converted to electricity on-demand.

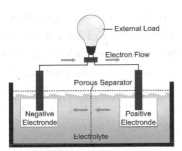

Figure 6-11
Lead-acid battery.

Each cell consists of two unlike metal electrodes immersed in an electrolyte that reacts with them. The positive electrode (cathode) produces negative ions (molecules with extra electrons in their outer shells), while the negative electrode (anode) produces positive ions (molecules that lack electrons in their outer shells). If the two ends of the electrodes are connected through a wire and external load, an electric current path is established that allows electrons to flow from the negative to the positive electrodes, called terminals (Figure 6-11). In small batteries, electrodes are small rods inserted in a pool of electrolytes. In larger batteries, electrodes are in the shape of thin metal plates. The circuit is closed by a flow of ions through the electrolytes. In an ideal battery, the electrons travel only through the external circuit. When the circuit is disrupted, electron flow stops and the battery retains its state of charge. Unfortunately, batteries are not ideal, and there are always electrons that migrate (diffuse) across the separator through the electrolytes, and so there is an inherent *self-discharge* of the battery with time, a factor that gives batteries limited capability as long-term storage devices.

Depending on whether the cells can be recharged or not, batteries are classified as primary and secondary. In **primary batteries** (such as those used in most flashlights, watches, calculators, cameras, etc.), the chemical reactions that supply current are irreversible. Once these batteries are discharged, they must be replaced. In **secondary batteries** or **accumulators**, chemical reactions are reversible; by supplying current in the opposite direction, the chemical reactions are reversed and depleted electrode materials are restored. Batteries used in transportation are of the secondary types. The most widely used secondary battery is the *lead-acid battery* (Pb-acid), where the electrolyte is a solution of sulfuric acid and water and electrodes are pure lead and lead dioxide. These batteries are relatively inexpensive, the materials needed for their

Table 6-10 Advanced Storage Technology Comparison				
Technology	**Specific Energy (Wh/kg)**	**Specific Power (W/kg)**	**Cycle life 80% depth of discharge**	**Primary Use**
Advanced lead acid	50	140	500	ICE
Nickel-Cadmium	60	200	2000	Camera
Nickel-Metal Hydride	80	220	600+	Laptop
Lithium-Ion	150	500	1200	Electric car
Zinc-Air	200	100	---	Hearing aid
Ultracapacitor	5	500	108	Hybrid car
Flywheel	10	400	---	Hybrid bus

manufacture are abundant, and the technology is mature; lead-acid batteries have low specific energy, and short calendar and cycle life and, therefore, are not suitable for electric and hybrid vehicles. *Nickel-cadmium* (NiCd)

[‡‡‡] It should be noted that the efficiencies quoted here are first law efficiencies, the fraction of the input energy (electricity for EV and petrol for ICE) that is used to drive the vehicle (See Chapter 4)..

and *nickel-metal-hydride* (NiMH) have 2-3 times the energy densities as lead-acid batteries, perform better in low temperatures, and have a much longer life. They are more expensive, however. The best candidate for electric and hybrid electric vehicles is the *lithium-ion* (Li-ion) battery; it has higher specific energy and power, good temperature performance, and low self-discharge; the cost is higher, however. Lithium-ion batteries have also been used in laptop computers, cell phones, and a large number of other applications. *Metal-air* batteries have been investigated, and some show potential for a much longer range between charges. Table 6-10 gives a comparison between various battery technologies.

Depending on the application, batteries are classified as deep-cycle or shallow-cycle. **Deep-cycle batteries**, such as those used for golf carts, electric vehicles, backup power, or renewable energy systems, are allowed to deplete up to 80% of their charge, many hundreds of times. Automotive batteries (also called SLI, for starting, lighting, and ignition) are **shallow-cycle batteries** and cannot be allowed to discharge more than 2-5% of capacity without being damaged. In addition to deep- and shallow-cycle batteries, there also are **marine (hybrid) batteries** used on boats and other marine applications, which can be discharged up to 50%. ⓐ

Ultracapacitors

Depending on whether electric vehicles operate under steady (cruising), or transient (accelerating/decelerating) load conditions, their power requirements vary by an order of magnitude. Batteries must be designed to perform a trade-off between the conflicting requirements of high energy density, high power density, and cycle life. A possible solution is that EVs be powered by two sources of energy -- a battery as its primary (main) energy source, and an ultracapacitor as a secondary (auxiliary) source for acceleration and hill-climbing. This auxiliary source can be recharged from the primary source and during regenerative braking.

Unlike batteries, which store energy by chemical reactions, ultracapacitors (also called supercapacitors) store energy as static energy (Figure 6-12). A capacitor is made of two conducting plates filled with an insulator called the dielectric. The major differences between a battery and an ultracapacitor are their energy and power densities. Typically, batteries are best suited for storing a lot of energy (but delivering little power), whereas capacitors can provide large amounts of power, but store little energy. Because there are no chemical reactions, the negative environmental impacts associated with battery use, do not exist. Furthermore, they allow virtually unlimited amounts of charging and discharging -- an important feature for hybrid vehicles and electric cars that deploy regenerative braking.

Figure 6-12
Ultracapacitor.
Image courtesy of Maxwell Technologies, Inc.

Fuel-Cell Vehicles (FCV)

Fuel-cell cars are essentially battery-operated electric cars, except that the batteries are continuously charged by hydrogen supplied through a fuel tank, or produced in onboard reformers. Many automotive manufacturers have developed prototype fuel-cell passenger cars and buses that are being field-tested. In 2005, GM developed the drive-by-wire concept car, the "Sequel," which integrates fuel cells with its chassis, called the skateboard (Figure

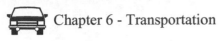

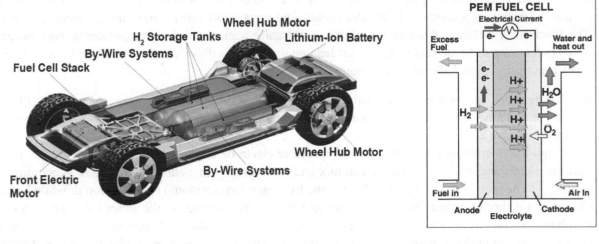

Figure 6-13
GM skateboard chassis for Sequel.
Image courtesy of General Motors.

PEM FUEL CELL

Figure 6-14
Principle of operation of a PEM fuel cell.
Source: World Fuel Cell Council

6-13). All the parts required to move the car are housed in the skateboard. The frame sits on the skateboard and, in principle, can be built by different designers. The first FCV commercially in the U.S. market is the Toyota Mirai (from *mirai* Japanese for the future) sold in 2016 with a range of 500 km (311 miles). Today, only three companies, Toyota, Honda, and Hyundai are dominating the fuel cell global market.

Fuel Cells

Fuel cells produce electricity through a chemical reaction between hydrogen and oxygen. In contrast to a battery, the fuel cell generates electrical energy rather than stores it and continues to do so as long as the fuel supply is maintained. The fuel cell was invented in 1839 by the British physicist, Sir William Grove, but, because of inherent problems associated with its operation, it was soon forgotten. It was only in the 1960s that the first fuel cell was employed aboard Gemini and Apollo capsules to replace the heavy batteries used in previous space missions. Since then, fuel cells have many applications, such as in airplanes, stationary power generators, and now automobiles.

The advantages of fuel cells are many. They are efficient, operate virtually vibration-free and silently, have a high energy density, have no moving parts, and produce little or no emissions. They can be customized to any shape and for any power demand, which makes these devices ideal for numerous applications. It is expected that they will eventually replace a major portion of internal combustion engines and power future cell phones, computers, camcorders, and other cordless devices. The major barriers to the wide-scale commercial development of fuel-cell cars are the public's concern over safety and cost. If hydrogen is used directly as the "fuel" instead of being produced by an onboard reformer, then other issues such as hydrogen distribution, delivery, and storage would also become a concern.

To make fuel cells a viable alternative to batteries and internal combustion engines, their cost must be brought down; they must work virtually maintenance-free, and their safety must be improved. The prices cannot fall unless fuel cells can be mass-produced, which happens only when prices are already low and sufficient infrastructure (such as hydrogen filling stations) is in place -- a classic chicken and egg problem!

ⓐ **The Principle of Operation:** Fuel cell operation can be described accurately as reverse electrolysis. In electrolysis, an electric current is passed across two electrodes immersed in an electrolyte solution,

Hump-Back Stations

Braking energy can be stored as gravitational energy. Instead of mechanical braking, as is done in most conventional vehicles, it is possible to drive a vehicle up a ramp. Often, this is done to slow down run-away trucks. It also has been successfully implemented as a means of energy storage in London Underground Victoria Station. As much as 50% of the motoring-input energy can be recovered when compared with non-regenerative methods.

splitting water into its constituents – hydrogen and oxygen. The fuel cell works in the opposite direction; hydrogen and oxygen (usually from air) recombine in an electrochemical reaction to form water, and an electric current is produced. The reaction is different from combustion, as it usually occurs at lower temperatures, and electricity (instead of heat) is the output. Since fuel cells are not heat engines, their efficiencies can be quite high and are not constrained by Carnot principles. Efficiencies of around 50% are typical.

The most common fuel cell for passenger cars and light-duty trucks is the *Proton Exchange Membrane* (PEM). It consists of a positive and a negative electrode separated by a membrane or electrolyte (Figure 6-14). Hydrogen gas is introduced at the negative electrode (anode), where a catalyst strips electrons from the hydrogen atom. Hydrogen ions migrate through the membrane toward the positive polymer electrode (cathode) and react with oxygen to form water. Without the membrane, hydrogen and oxygen mix and react directly in a chemical reaction, generating heat, instead of electricity. The membrane works by allowing the hydrogen ions (protons) to pass through while blocking electrons. Electrons are then diverted through an external wire before arriving on the other side, where they are recombined with protons and oxygen to complete the reaction. As long as the flow of hydrogen gas is not interrupted, the electrical current is maintained, which can turn a light on or be used to power an electric motor. The PEM operates best at temperatures of around 80°C. The major drawback is that it has little tolerance for contaminants, and so requires pure hydrogen for proper operation.

To summarize, the reaction at each electrode and the overall reaction can be written as:

Anode : $2H_2 \rightarrow 4H^+ + 4e^-$

Cathode : $O_2 + 4e^- + 4H^+ \rightarrow 2H_2O$

Overall Re*action* : $2H_2 + O_2 \rightarrow 2H_2O$

Besides PEM fuel cells, three other technologies show promise for various transportation applications. The *Phosphoric Acid Fuel Cell* (PAFC) is most appropriate for locomotives, two-cylinder trucks, and urban transit buses. These fuel cells already are used for stationary power generation. *Solid Oxide* and *Direct Methanol* fuel cells are mainly of interest for medium to large-scale power generation. The main advantage of these fuel cells is that they can take methane gas or methanol liquids directly without the need for reformers. The major problem with all of these fuel cells is that they operate at much higher temperatures and very high costs.

Reformers

Fuel cells suitable for a car must be small, have a high power density, refuel in a short time, store sufficient hydrogen for a range of 500 kilometers or more, and be available at a cost comparable to conventional internal combustion engines. To travel 500 kilometers, three kilograms of hydrogen are needed; if stored at 20 MPa (3,000 psi) – the pressure tanks currently used -- the hydrogen occupies a volume of 190 liters. Furthermore, the current lack of convenient refueling stations is a big impediment in marketing fuel-cell vehicles using pure hydrogen.

Rather than relying on storing hydrogen and using it directly, a number of car companies are concentrating on developing onboard reformers. Reformers use a variety of fuels, such as gasoline, methanol, or methane. Reforming **methane gas** does not seem to be economical for personal automobiles. **Methanol** is the favorite for transportation, because it is liquid at room temperature, has a high hydrogen content, and can be produced from biomass or by conversion of natural gas. The methanol distribution system is also lacking at this time. **Gasoline** does not have this problem, but has a lower H/C ratio, and is more difficult to process. Reformers available today are bulky and the cost is prohibitive.

Electric and Fuel-Cell Cars: How Clean Are They?

Electric and fuel cell vehicles don't have tailpipe emissions. If nuclear energy or renewable sources such as wind, solar, or hydropower are used to produce hydrogen, these vehicles would be truly zero-emission vehicles (ZEV).

Even in the instances that fossil fuels are used to reform hydrogen or produce electricity, pollution is considerably lessened. According to one study, if all conventional vehicles were replaced with electric vehicles overall hydrocarbon and carbon monoxide emissions would drop by 95-99%, nitric oxides by up to 90%, and ozone and volatile organic compounds (VOC) are eliminated altogether. Sulfur dioxide and particulate emissions may drop or rise depending on what percentage of electricity is from coal and oil power plants.

This point of view is not, however, shared by all investigators. For example, it is not enough to look at only tailpipe emissions and charging and operation of vehicles, but any analysis must include the vehicle's entire life cycle, from its construction through its operation and on to its eventual dismantling and disposal. Furthermore, the environmental cost is not limited to global warming but also a large number of other pollutants, not generally, considered as greenhouse gases. Manufacturing EV and FCV parts require a substantial amount of heavy metals and the release of other pollutants. What's more, fossil fuels are burned in every step of the way from the extraction of the raw materials, to fabrication, assembly, maintenance, and disposal. Materials used in lithium-ion and nickel-cadmium batteries, commonly used today, need substantial energy to extract and release toxic substances that eventually find their way into air and groundwater.

No matter which point of view is accepted, one thing is clear. Unless hydrogen is produced from non-fossil sources, moving from internal combustion engines to electric and fuel cell vehicles, results in the transfer of pollutants from local neighborhood streets to suburban areas. The debate is not settled by any means, and the final verdict will become only when a number of other technologies are matured and the true environmental costs of intermediary processes are known.

Hybrid Vehicles

The much greater range offered by gasoline engines, and the much cleaner operation of battery-electric and fuel cell vehicles, are the major impetus for the development of hybrid vehicles. A hybrid vehicle is defined as a vehicle with at least two modes of propulsion. Today, most hybrid cars combine an internal combustion engine (either gasoline or diesel) and an electric motor powered by batteries. The choice is not, however, limited to those and other primary sources of power, such as gas turbines and fuel cells, and other types of storage devices such as flywheels and ultracapacitors are also possible. In addition to **full hybrids**, a new class of hybrids (called **mild hybrids**) is emerging that provides some of the benefits of the full hybrids with fewer weights and lower prices. These models utilize small and relatively inexpensive electric motors that capture some of the energy during braking and use it to restart the car when stopped behind the traffic lights. In 2016, hybrid vehicles constituted less than 2.4% of total U.S. car sales but are expected to pick up reaching 35% of all vehicles by 2040.

The idea of hybrid vehicles is not new. The French Kriéger Company, originally established to produce electric cars, introduced the first alcohol-electric hybrid car in 1902, a gasoline version in 1904, and a turbine-electric hybrid shortly before it went bankrupt in 1909. With the advent of the starter motor in 1911, much of the lure of electric and hybrid vehicles vanished and, until the oil crisis of 1973, no major research was carried out. In recent years, however, the rapid rise in the price of liquid fuel, political instability in much of the oil-producing countries, along with raising concerns on global warming, has initiated new interest in developing new hybrid technologies that improve transportation fuel economy.

Hybrid vehicles take advantage of the best features of both ICE and EV by selecting the proper mode of operation. During start-ups and at low speeds common in early morning traffic and in city driving, when the gasoline engine is the least efficient, only the electric motor powers the vehicle. When an automobile is cruising at freeway speeds, the gasoline engine drives the wheels and helps operate the generator, which charges the battery. When an extra load is placed on the car, such as climbing a hill or accelerating, both the engine and electric motor work simultaneously. When braking, the electric motor runs as a generator to convert the kinetic energy of the car into electricity and charges the battery.

Efficiency

Hybrid vehicles offer superior efficiencies over both petrol and electric vehicles because they are operated at their most efficient modes. Let's consider two cars, one conventional and another hybrid, as depicted in Figure 6-15. The conventional car (1×) consumes 100 units of fuel, losing 73 units through the exhaust, radiator, friction, and other accessories and another 11 units during standby, delivering the remaining 16 units of energy to propel the car. The hybrid car with twice the efficiency of a gasoline car (2×) deploys an internal combustion engine half the size, using 50 units of fuel and losing 37 units to the ambient. The standby losses are eliminated because the vehicle operates electrically when the car stops and no motor is left running. An additional three units of energy are restored when the vehicle brakes and energy goes back to charge the batteries. Like the gas-powered car, the net useful energy is 16 units. In short, we have doubled the fuel efficiency by using an engine only half the size and supplemented the power by recovering much of the losses through regenerative braking.

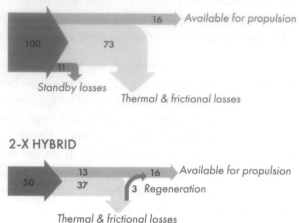

Figure 6-15
Comparison between a pure internal combustion engine and a 2× hybrid vehicle.

Configurations

Almost all hybrid vehicles operating today utilize a prime mover or hybrid power unit (HPU), such as small, spark-ignition engines, diesel, or gas turbines to complement batteries in providing power directly, or by acting as generators to charge batteries. HPUs can be fueled by gasoline, diesel fuel, or any number of alternative fuels and are operated near optimum conditions to produce simultaneous low emissions and high efficiency.

Hybrid vehicles are classified as either series or parallel. The main distinctions between the two configurations are in the way the HPU transfers power to the wheels and whether batteries become fully discharged (charge-depleting) or retain their charge by continuous charging (charge-sustaining).

In a series configuration, all motive power comes from the electric motor powered by batteries. With series hybrids, there is no mechanical connection between the engine and the wheels; power is transferred electrically to an electric motor that drives the wheels. Since electric motors deliver power instantly, there is no need for the gradual buildup of torque through revving (as is unnecessary in internal combustion engines), and series hybrids have simpler transmissions or no transmissions at all (Figure 6-16a). A series hybrid can attain a long-range with an engine only a fraction of the size of a conventional engine, and with a battery pack weighing far less than those of pure electric vehicles. In the simplest configuration, the vehicle operates as a pure electric vehicle, until batteries are depleted to their preset thresholds, at which time the internal combustion kicks in and begins to recharge the batteries. Since the engine does not have to meet changing power demands directly, it can be set to operate in a narrow speed range *(sweet spot)* where it has the highest efficiency, the lowest emissions, or a combination of both. Alternatively, control strategies can be devised where a small internal combustion engine operates continuously at its optimal point, so as to keep the battery at, or near, its full charge.

In a parallel configuration, the engine, the electric motor, or both, supply power to the wheels (Figure 6-16b). Parallel hybrids are primarily used in electric-only mode for short trips and city driving, and engine-only mode for long trips and highway cruising. The prime mover is to be sized to meet average power demand, so it is much smaller than those in conventional vehicles, which must be designed for peak-power demand. The electric motor is used to help overcome hill climbs, to accelerate quickly, and in instances when the engine cannot single-handedly meet the power demand.

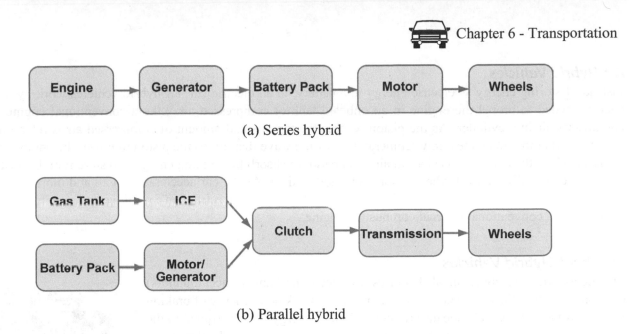

(a) Series hybrid

(b) Parallel hybrid

Figure 6-16
Hybrid configurations; (a) series hybrid, and (b) parallel hybrid

The main advantage of the series over the parallel hybrid configuration is that the engine never idles and does not necessarily need a transmission. The main advantage of the parallel over series is that vehicle can simultaneously draw power from both the engine and the motor, which can be used more efficiently. Because the engine, electric motor, or both must deliver the power, a clutch/transmission assembly is necessary. New advances in continuously variable transmission (CVT) enable continuous delivery of a variable speed ratio, allowing the engine speed to be completely independent of the vehicle speed. The Toyota Prius, the best-known hybrid vehicle to date, uses a parallel configuration with a CVT technology.

Plug-in Hybrid Electric Vehicles (PHEV)

Plug-in hybrids are essentially electric vehicles with gasoline range extenders. (Figure 6-17). Because they can tap into gasoline once the onboard batteries are discharged, they are dubbed anxiety-range removers! In contrast to regular hybrids, in which batteries are kept nearly fully charged at all times, PHEV allows batteries to become fully discharged before they switch to gasoline mode.

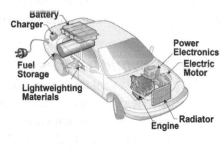

PHEV can be charged via one of the three modes: 1) slow charge (6-8 h) at home and office by connecting to the electric grid (10A/220V); 2) fast-charge (0.5-1 h) in charging stations (32A/400V); and 3) battery-pack change-overs for long trips. Like regular hybrids, PHEVs come in parallel (Prius and Ford Escape), in series (Chevrolet Volt), or both (Mitsubishi).

Figure 6-17
Plug-in Hybrid.
Source: NREL (Http://www.nrel.gov)

Example 6-2: The Chevrolet Volt is a series PHEV with a 175-kg, 16-kWh battery pack, and an onboard 1.4 L-IC engine to extend the range when the battery is depleted. Assuming that the battery is discharging at the rate of 0.2 kWh/mi and a 50% depth of discharge, determine the car's all-electric range. If the battery pack is charged during off-peak hours when electricity costs $0.20/kWh, what is the cost of fuel for operating this vehicle?
Solution: The battery's useful capacity is 0.5×16 = 8 kWh, giving a range of 8/0.2 = 40 mi = 65 km range when operated as a pure EV. The fuel cost of operating this vehicle under all-electric conditions (distances shorter than 65 km), is $0.20 × 0.2 kWh/mi = $0.04/mi (4¢ a mile, or 2.5¢ a kilometer). Comparing this to an ICE with a fuel economy of 30 mpg, and a gasoline cost of $3 per gallon, the cost is 10¢ per mile. Everything else being the same, the electric car saves 60% in fuel costs.

Air Hybrid Vehicles

Instead of storing energy as electric energy in a battery, in an electric car, air hybrid vehicles work by storing the energy needed to propel the engine in an onboard tank of compressed air. Like a conventional engine, a piston compresses air in a cylinder. As the piston reaches the top, a small amount of compressed air is released into the expansion chamber to create a low-temperature pressure wave that drives the piston to power the engine. When the vehicle brakes, the engine is used as an air compressor to absorb the braking energy and store it in the air tank. The engine is essentially shut off when it stops for a traffic light. As the car accelerates, more and more air is allowed into the cylinder until the compressed air is depleted. The tank can be refilled in a refilling station or by a compressor operated by a conventional internal combustion engine.

Flywheel Hybrid Vehicles

Flywheels (dubbed mechanical batteries or electromechanical accumulators) eliminate much of these conversion losses by storing the kinetic energy of braking in a fast-rotating flywheel. Because rotational kinetic energy is proportional to the square of the rotational speed, fast-speed flywheels are preferred. Traditionally, flywheels have been used for energy balance in internal combustion engines, but recent advances in material technology have made it possible to design flywheels from lighter composite materials that can run at much higher speeds -- up to 100,000 rpm -- making them ideal for storing surplus energy from power plants. Flywheels can provide up to 50 times the energy storage capacity of a conventional lead-acid battery. Currently, small flywheels are available that provide power up to 1 kW for three hours and 100 kW for 30 seconds. Larger flywheels are being developed that delivers approximately 250 kW for up to 15 minutes (Figure 6-18).

Figure 6-18
Flywheel.
Image courtesy of CCM (http://www.ccm.nl).

Flywheels can be used to charge batteries, making them suitable for providing steady power to electric and hybrid vehicles or to produce bursts of energy during acceleration and on steep grades. Flywheels also have found applications in fuel cells, gas turbines, and other prime movers. They are advantageous over conventional lead-acid batteries because they have a much longer cycle life, rapid charge rate, higher storage efficiencies, and are capable of operating in any ambient conditions, delivering energy over a very short time.

Hydraulic Hybrid Vehicles

In this type of vehicle, hydraulic accumulators replace batteries. Hydraulic accumulators are oil-filled pressure vessels in which energy is absorbed by a non-compressible hydraulic fluid. The fluid is held by a spring, a heavyweight, or compressed gas. The energy is released when the external force is removed. The energy recovery rate is higher and, therefore, the system is more efficient than battery-charged hybrids. The drawback is that the accumulators are bigger and require more space than batteries.

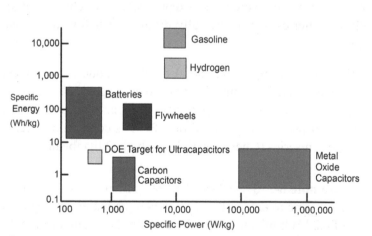

Figure 6-19 compares various energy storage devices being tested with hybrid vehicles.

Figure 6-19
Specific power and energy for several energy storage systems.

Advantages of Hybrid Vehicles

One of the main advantages of a hybrid vehicle is its ability to use two separate power sources, the main power unit to provide continuous power, and a surge power unit to take care of transient loads (such as when the vehicle accelerates or climbs a mountain). Engines and fuel cells are in charge of supplying the main power, whereas batteries generally are tasked with providing the surge power. Regenerative braking works on the principle that when vehicle brakes, the kinetic energy is stored in a battery and used when it is needed. This conversion is, however, quite costly and, at best, is performed with low efficiencies not exceeding 30-40%. The reason is that the conversion must take place in two steps -- the conversion of kinetic energy into electrical energy, followed by conversion of electrical energy into chemical energy in the battery. When energy is needed, reverse conversions take place. At each step of the way, part of the energy is lost.

For example, ICE performance is a strong function of engine speed, designed to operate optimally at cruising speeds around 90-100 km/h (roughly 50-60 miles per hour), and producing relatively less pollution; efficiency drops rapidly at both very high and very low speeds. On the other hand, electric motors have their highest efficiency at low speeds, generate no onboard emissions, have favorable torque characteristics, and can utilize regenerative braking. Key components of the car, like the air-conditioning, horn, and lights can run directly off the battery. These characteristics make conventional engines ideal for freeway driving and constant speed operation, and electric vehicles best suited for city driving and transient conditions.

Not only is the engine size smaller, but also, individual components can be sized to fit different driving conditions. In most designs, the engine is sized to meet only the cruising demands, whereas power for acceleration and hill-climbing is offered by batteries and other storage devices. Since the engine is not directly coupled to the wheels, the engine can run at a more constant load and near its optimal conditions at all times. The major disadvantages of hybrid vehicles are the additional complexity of dealing with two power systems and potentially higher capital cost.

Social Costs of Transportation

Many of the costs associated with driving have little to do with fuel use. Traffic congestion, excessive noise, lost productivity, air pollution, stress, damage to roads and other properties, accidents, and health costs are among many indirect costs attributed to driving. In 2002 alone, Americans lost over 3.5 billion hours and wasted 5.7 billion gallons of gasoline because of traffic delays. Furthermore, during the same year, there were over six million accidents, resulting in about 43,000 deaths. The loss of productivity due to traffic delay alone was estimated at 62 billion dollars. If costs associated with stress and health effects were included, the cost of car ownership would be much higher.

To address the increased demand, car manufacturers, politicians, and policymakers promote heavier and bigger cars, pack cars with more air pollution control devices, add lanes, build more roads and parking structures, and move many industries and large corporations away from metropolitan areas and large population centers. The solution may actually be the exact opposite. What is needed most is better-designed neighborhoods that reduce our need for commuting. Unfortunately, Americans have opted for decentralization -- moving away from population centers to the suburbs, causing a heavier reliance on personal transportation and an increase in the number of miles traveled. In fact, 87% of trips are by private cars, and only 3% are by transit.

Unlike Americans, European cities have become more centralized. The larger population density is accommodated by better architectural planning and reducing the need for cars and transits. A more efficient and cheaper public transportation system and, at the same time, higher sales taxes, insurance fees, and fines, have made personal car ownership costlier and less convenient. Some countries have enacted laws to restrict driving to reduce congestion and improve air quality, making certain parts of large metropolitan areas off-limits to passenger cars. People are to leave their cars outside the restricted zones and take public transportation to downtown areas and populated city centers; police cars, ambulances, and other emergency vehicles are exempt. In another scenario, drivers are given access to certain regions during certain hours or days, and only on an as-needed basis. For example, cars with license plates that end with an odd number can travel in a city only on Sundays, Tuesdays, and Thursdays, or they have to pay an extra toll charge during rush hours.

Office managers and business owners can encourage their employees to carpool or to use public transportation by providing free parking spaces to carpools or by paying for their bus or train fares. They also may help in paying part of the home mortgages of employees who live within a short distance of the place of employment. Some companies and organizations have successfully implemented flex-hours, allowing some employees to shift their work hours, or even work part of their time at home. The local city government can participate in the effort by providing bikes to the general public that can be used, free of charge, in central districts, where most government offices are located. Architects and city planners can be especially effective in this effort by designing convenient shopping centers and large office buildings to satisfy multiple needs, thus reducing the need for frequent visits.

Future of Transportation

Transportation systems have come a long way, from dug-out canoes, draft horses, wheelbarrows, and driving carriages and wagons, to large ships, supersonic planes, and even space vehicles. Early trolleys and cable cars gave way to large diesel trucks and buses. Steam locomotives were replaced with modern fast trains, and automobiles went through phases, from hybrid and electric to petrol, and now back to electric and hybrid again.

What will the future of transportation look like, depends on whether we continue our path on an oil-based economy or switch to technologies that move away from petroleum? In the first instance, we would expect a rising demand for oil, along with intense regional and international conflicts that may lead to economic hardship and a large decline in transportation activities. Alternatively, we can put our resources into developing technologies that reduce our dependence on petroleum in a sustained manner that assures both economic growth and environmental stewardship.

A technological revolution is underway, which makes future transportation systems even more efficient. New advanced polymer and carbon-fiber composites are being developed that are lighter and safer to use. Composites can be made for frame-less "monocoques" that cost less, are many times stronger than conventional frames, are lighter than steel by two to three times, and upon impact, absorb five times more energy. This helps not only in designing safer cars but also in reducing rolling resistance and power requirements for climbing and accelerating. The reduction in required power results in smaller engines, transmissions, and other components which, in turn, make the vehicle even lighter.

It is expected that future transportation systems will rely less on the internal combustion engine and more on electric and hybrid propulsion (Figure 6-20). Future travels by marine and air vehicles will be by larger ships and airplanes that carry more passengers while increasing the occupancy ratios. Rail travel will also be more common, as more and more countries are moving toward faster electrification of their roads and railways. China with more than 100,000 kilometers of electrified rail is first: India is second. Many cities around the world are bringing back trolleybuses, light rail (trams), and heavy rail (metro) powered by overhead wires. In addition to rail and fleet vehicles, passenger cars can also be connected to grids. A major portion of the weight of today's electric vehicles is from batteries. These batteries occupy a large space and make BEVs unnecessarily heavy. If they are grid-connected, there is no need to carry the batteries, and weight is substantially reduced, which reduces energy consumption. Electric power can be generated from a variety of sources including, renewable sources and can be transferred wireless or from wires stretched along major highways.

Autonomous (self-driving or driverless) cars are going to soon be ubiquitous in American and European roads and freeways. These cars rely largely on the very high-speed internet capabilities of 5G cellular technology, equipped with a multitude of sensors that monitor traffic and watch for behaviors of adjacent vehicles (vehicle-to-vehicle, or V2V). Data on traffic, road conditions, and the weather that are continuously being updated (vehicle to infrastructure, or V2I), guiding the vehicle to drive itself safely and in a timely fashion. According to the National Highway Traffic Safety Administration, in 2011 alone, there were 5.5 million crashes in the U.S., causing 32,000 death and 300 billion in economic damage. Ninety-three percent of the fatalities are caused by human error, the majority could have been avoided if conventional cars were replaced with driverless cars. It is projected that by 2025, the number of EV exceeds 10 million in the world; by 2050, all cars will be electric and self-driving.

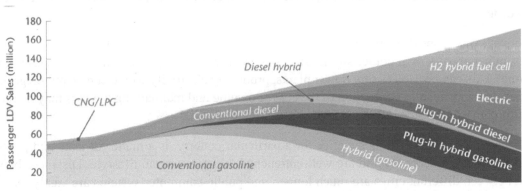

Figure 6-20
IEA roadmap for future transportation system.
Source: https://www.iea.org/publications/freepublications/publication/EV_PHEV_brochure.pdf

Summary

To cope with the ever-increasing problems associated with transportation, various approaches have been proposed. Among the options considered are 1) reducing vehicle use, 2) increasing efficiency and reducing the emissions of conventional gasoline-powered vehicles, 3) switching to less noxious fuels, and 4) using cleaner alternative systems. The first choice calls for developing a large-scale mass transit system, carpooling, reducing travel by working from home, and removing the need for excessive driving by implementing more effective community designs. This also will reduce much of the social costs, such as traffic congestion and delays, pollution, accidents, repair costs, and other social ills, such as fatigue and stress. Although this option helps with many social and environmental problems, by itself, it seems to have limited success.

The second and third options are to make existing transportation systems better by designing more efficient cars or vehicles that use better and less polluting fuels. Internal combustion engines have been around for a long time and their efficiencies have been greatly improved. It seems that improving efficiencies beyond current levels only comes in small steps and no major breakthrough is imminent. Alternative fuels like methanol and natural gases have been tried by a number of investigators with marginal improvements in emissions and fuel efficiencies. Hydrogen seems to be the obvious alternative fuel -- largely on the belief that there exist vast amounts of untapped natural gas reserves that can be used to manufacture the hydrogen. Problems associated with hydrogen storage, safety concerns, and the lack of a hydrogen distribution infrastructure have been major obstacles to the commercial development of hydrogen-propelled internal combustion engines, although a number of automotive manufacturers have developed prototype units.

The fourth option is to do away with current technologies in favor of newer and cleaner alternatives. Electric vehicles appear to partially provide an answer. They don't use any hydrocarbon fuel, have zero tailpipe emissions, and their operating cost is relatively small. Long-term effects of vehicle construction, fuel extraction, refining, and disposal on climate and health may not be insignificant, and according to some, actually exceeds those of gasoline-powered vehicles.

Hybrid vehicles have advantages over both electric and conventional vehicles by combining features and enhancing performance to a degree not possible using either propulsive systems alone and without their limitations. In order for electric, hybrid, or any other types of cars to find mass-market acceptability, they must meet certain requirements. They must have full-size trunks, be able to travel great distances, recharge in a short time, have all the comfort and luxury of conventional cars, and be offered at costs comparable to conventional internal combustion engines. Currently, in the United States and elsewhere, there is a major move toward making plug-in hybrids and battery-operated electric vehicles more efficient and cost-effective. Fuel-cell cars are not expected to be competitive for at least another decade.

As U.S. data shows, Americans drive their cars only 4% of the time. The remaining 96% of the time, cars sit idle in parking garages, either at work or at home. Similar statistics are true for Europe and other countries around the globe. During these times, cars can be used as tiny power plants, producing electricity which can be put on grids and sold to utility companies. In this way, a large fraction of the cost of owning and maintaining the cars may be recovered, and our reliance on foreign oil and other nonrenewable resources reduced.

Which of the transportation strategies is superior for a particular country, is a matter of taste and public policy. In the United States, cars are a necessity and are well-entrenched in the American lifestyle. Distances between homes and offices and between different cities are much longer, and public commuter systems are vastly inadequate. As a result, the use of public transportation is largely limited to low-income and disadvantaged citizens. In Europe, on the other hand, distances are shorter -- often within walking distances, the infrastructure is more developed, and a vast network of railways and other public transportation systems for commuting and long-distance travel already exists. Affordable and easily accessible public transportation has removed the need for personal vehicles for most people, making cars a luxury -- nice to have for special occasions, leisurely evening activities, and weekend excursions.

ⓐ Digging Deeper: Energy Efficiency in Transportation

Walking and Bicycling

Studies of metabolic rates of adults undergoing various physical activities show that a person walking at a moderate pace, on level ground, uses roughly 3.3 times the energy he/she would exert while sitting quietly, reading, or watching TV. The rate at which an average adult burns calories at rest (sedentary activity) is approximately 1 kcal per kg of body mass, per hour. This normally is referred to as metabolic equivalent or MET.

$$1 \text{ MET} = 1 \text{ kcal/kg/h}$$

The equivalent value in U.S. units is 1 MET = 0.45 kcal/(lb-h).

By this definition, we can say that a moderate walk on a flat surface has a MET of 3.3. Other MET values of interest in transportation are 4.0-5.0 for fast walking, 4.0 for bicycling at speeds less than 10 mph, 6.0-8.0 for bicycling at moderate efforts, 8.5 for mountain biking, and 16.0 in bicycle racing (>20 mph). MET values for running can vary significantly from 6.0 to 18.0, depending on the speed.

Example 6-3: How many calories does a 200-lb man walking at a speed of 3.5 mph, for one hour, burn? How much would he burn if he walked for one mile?

Solution: The total calories burned are: (0.45×3.3 kcal/lb/h) × 200 lb × 1 h = 297 kcal. Note that this value includes the basal metabolic rate (the calories the person would have burned anyway, just by sitting or lying in bed). The sedentary metabolic rate is 0.45×200×1 = 90 kcal/h; the extra energy burned by walking is 297 - 90 = 207 kcal. To calculate energy expenditure in one mile, we must multiply this number by the number of hours it takes him to walk that distance. At a rate of 3.5 mph, it will take 1/3.5 = 0.286 h. The additional energy expenditure for one mile of walking is 0.286×207 = 59 kcal per mile (4 kWh per 100 kilometers).

Example 6-4: Redo the example above, if the same person, instead of walking, bikes at 10 mph.

Solution: Using a bike, he burns energy at a rate twice as fast as a brisk walk (MET~6.6), or about 600 kcal/h, or 510 kcal/h over his normal metabolic rate. At a speed of 10 mph, it will take him 0.1 h to cover the one-mile distance or 51 kcal. The energy expenditure is 51 kcal/mi = 32 kcal/km (3.6 kWh per 100 km).

Traveling by Cars

For the automobile to be practical, its engine must be strong enough to overcome all resistive forces from the air and the ground, as well as from transmission losses, and still have enough power left to run various accessories, climb a steep road and accelerate, when necessary. The total tractive effort is:

$$F_{TR} = F_{aero} + F_{rr} + F_{gr} + F_{acc} \qquad (6-1)$$

Aerodynamic resistance is the force required to overcome wind resistance or push the car through the stagnant air. Aerodynamic resistance is given by:

$$F_{aero} = \frac{\rho V^2}{2} C_D A_f \qquad (6-2a)$$

Where:

ρ is air density [$\rho = 1.23$ kg/m3]

A_f is the frontal area, equal to the projected area in the direction of travel [m^2]

V is car speed relative to the wind [m/s]

C_D is the drag coefficient, and is a strong function of the vehicle shape and model, whether it is a convertible or a sedan, whether windows are rolled up, or if the lights are recessed; Table 6-11 gives values of drag coefficients for several cars. Reference values for some common shapes are also given.

Because power is proportional to the cube of velocity, aerodynamic resistance is a major component of total drag for passenger cars at speeds exceeding 40 mph (See Figure 6-21). Drag can be reduced in passenger cars by closing windows and covering the tops, by choosing recessed lighting, and by avoiding mounting mirrors that protrude too much from the body of the vehicles.

Early buses and trucks had huge radiators, many sharp corners, protruding lamps, and exposed pipes. Newer models have improved fuel efficiency by installing smaller radiators, rounded corners, recessed lamps, and avoiding exposed gas tanks, piping, and other accessories. Adding wheel and underbody skirts, covering wheelbases, and eliminating

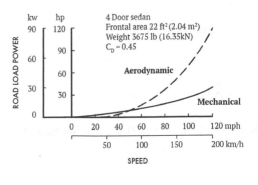

Figure 6-21
Drag force versus vehicle speed.

Table 6-11 Drag Coefficients				
Car	C_D	$A_f (m^2)$	*Shape*	C_D
Boeing 747	0.033	180	Person (upright)	1.0-1.3
Trains	1.8	10	Dolphin	0.004
Buses and Trucks	0.7-1.3	10	Airfoil	0.045
Sedans	0.5-0.7	1.7-2.2	Flat Disk	1.28
Sport Cars	0.3-0.4	1.8-2.0	Cylinder	1.1
Electric Cars	0.2-0.4	2.2-2.4	Sphere	0.07-0.50
GM Solar Car	0.14	1.35	Bullet	0.295
Bikes	0.9-1.1	0.43	Teardrop	0.04
Reference: https://www.grc.nasa.gov/www/k-12/airplane/shaped.html				

gaps between cabins and trailers will reduce aerodynamic drag even more.

For trains, aerodynamic drag accounts for 40% of the total drag at a speed of 120 km/h but rapidly climbs to 75% when the speed reaches 160 km/h.

Rolling resistance is the force required to overcome friction on the road. Rolling resistance is approximated as:

$$F_{rr} = C_{rr} m_{eff} g \qquad\qquad (6\text{-}2b)$$

In this equation:

C_{rr} = Rolling coefficient, and depends on the air pressure inside the tires, the type of thread, the age of the tires, and the footprint. C_{rr} is about 0.015 for bias-ply tires and 0.010 for stiffer tires under recommended pressure. Under-inflated tires add additional resistance.

m_{eff} = Effective mass, equal to the vehicle mass and the rotational inertia of wheels, drive trains, flywheels, etc. For passenger cars and light-duty vehicles, take $m_{eff} = 1.06\ m$, where m is the vehicle mass.

g = Gravitational acceleration [g = 9.81 m/s^2].

Rolling resistance for cars constitutes about 25%-50% of the engine's power and is used to push the tires down the road as it bends, deforms, and rolls. Trains are many hundreds of times heavier than automobiles and, thus, rolling resistance is a very important part of the total drag. To reduce drag, it is critical to making the rolling coefficient as small as possible. Trains have steel wheels and have little contact patch (footprint) with the track. With high-quality steel, the deformation is minimum, which reduces the rolling drag. One major factor that can significantly increase the drag coefficient is when wheels are not aligned, which causes lateral motion, the rapid wearing of the bearings, and higher energy dissipation at the wheel.

Grade resistance is the gravitational resistance equal to the force required to overcome gravitational acceleration and climb a grade.

$$F_{gr} = mgs \qquad\qquad (6\text{-}2c)$$

Where:
m is vehicle mass [kg]

s is road grade *(s = sin ϕ)*

It can be shown that the energy needed for a vehicle to climb a grade is equal to the change in its potential energy.

$$\Delta E = mg\ (z_2 - z_1) \quad ; z_1 \text{ and } z_2 \text{ are elevations before and after the vehicle has climbed.}$$

Acceleration or inertia force is the product of mass times the acceleration.

$$F_{acc} = ma \qquad\qquad (6\text{-}2d)$$

It can be shown that the energy needed for a vehicle to accelerate from velocity V_1 to V_2 is equal to the change in its kinetic energy.

$$\Delta E = (m/2)(V_2^2 - V_1^2);$$

The power requirement for a typical four-door sedan is given in Figure 6-22. What is striking to note is that for speeds below 40 mph (city driving), aerodynamic resistances are rather low and so the shape of the vehicle does not play a critical role in mileage efficiency. The aerodynamic forces vary as the square of the velocity and increase rapidly at freeway speeds. Because power is force times velocity, the power requirement increases as velocity cubed ($\sim V^3$), and aerodynamic resistances dominate.

Example 6-5: A 2,000-lb car equipped with a 20-kW engine is traveling at 30 mph on a road with a grade of 4%. For $C_D = 0.55$ and $C_{rr} = 0.015$, $A_f = 2.1$ m^2, determine the total tractive effort and power requirements. If the car uses the full power of the engine to suddenly accelerate (full-throttle), what would be the car's speed after 10 s?
Solution: The rolling, aerodynamic, and grade resistances are:

$$F_{rr} = C_{rr}W = 0.015 \times 906 \times 9.81 = 133 \text{ N}$$

$$F_{aero} = \frac{\rho V^2}{2} C_D A_f = 0.5 \times 1.23 \times (13.4)^2 \times 0.55 \times 2.1 = 127 \text{ N}$$

$$F_{gr} = mgs = 906 \times 9.81 \times 0.04 = 356 \text{ N}$$

The power to overcome these resistances is equal to total resistance forces times velocity.

$$P = \frac{(133 + 127 + 356) \text{ N} \times 13.4 \text{ m/s}}{1000 \text{ W/kW}} = 8.25 \text{ kW}$$

The remaining power 20-8.25 = 11.75 kW can be used to accelerate the car.

$$P_{acc} = \frac{KE_2 - KE_1}{t}; \quad 11,750 = \frac{\frac{1}{2}(906) \times [V_2^2 - 13.4^2]}{10}$$

The car accelerates to the final velocity of 21 m/s (47 mph).

Example 6-6: In the example above, how much energy is required for the car to travel a distance of 100 km at a cruising speed of 30 mph? Compare results with the manufacturer's claim of 20 mpg in combined city/freeway driving.
Solution: At cruising speed, the engine has only to overcome the rolling and aerodynamic resistances. The energy required is (133+127) × (13.4/1000) = 3.48 kW. The time to travel a distance of 100 kilometers is (100,000 m)/(13.4 m/s) = 7,463 s = 2.07 h. The consumption rate is 2.07×3.48 = 7.2 kWh/100 km.

The car is reported to consume one gallon of petroleum for every 20 miles it travels. Converting to SI units:

$$20 \frac{\text{miles}}{\text{gallon}} = 20 \frac{\text{mile}}{\text{gallon}} \times \frac{1.609 \text{ km}}{1 \text{ mile}} \times \frac{1 \text{ gallon}}{3.785 \text{ L}} = 8.5 \frac{\text{km}}{\text{L}}, \text{ or } 11.76 \text{ L per 100 vehicle-km.}$$

Gasoline has an energy content of 32.2 MJ/L (8.95 kWh/L); that gives the gasoline a consumption rate of 105 kWh/100 vehicle-km. With an occupancy rate of 1.6 persons per vehicle, the energy expenditure is 66 kWh/100 person-km, in close agreement with the average U.S. published results of 63 kWh/100 person-km (See Table 6-3). For full-capacity vehicles (four persons), this number is reduced to 26 kWh per 100-km.

This calculation shows that the average power expenditure per vehicle is roughly 15 times the power needed at its cruising speed. Where does all this excess power go? Answer: losses in transmission, the drivetrain, and exhaust, numerous accelerations/decelerations during city driving, in climbing grades, running the air conditioner, and charging the battery for operating various accessories, such as radio, heater, and windshield wipers.

Maximum Speed of a Vehicle
The maximum speed achieved by a vehicle depends on the power produced by vehicle engines and various

resistances. For a vehicle cruising at a constant speed on a flat road, acceleration and grade resistances are zero, and engine power is entirely used to overcome aerodynamic and rolling resistance.

Coast-Down Velocity

Coast-down velocity refers to the maximum speed a vehicle achieves on a downhill with the engine shuts off. Under these conditions, the rolling resistances are small, and aerodynamic resistances balance the force of gravity.

$$\frac{\rho V_{coast-down}^2}{2} C_D A_f = mgs$$

or:

$$V_{coast-down} = \sqrt{\frac{2mgs}{\rho C_D A_f}}$$

Where $s = \sin \varphi$ is the road grade.

Gradability

The maximum grade that the vehicle is able to climb (called gradability) is found by assuming constant speed and that no accessories are operating. Furthermore, for most instances, the speed is low enough that aerodynamic resistances are also negligible. Thrust (motive power) provided by the engine is:

$$P_{engine} = (F_g + F_{rr}) . V = mgV(s + C_{rr})$$

Rearranging the equation yields to:

$$\phi = \sin^{-1}\left(\frac{P_{engine}}{mgV} - C_{rr}\right)$$

Traveling by Trains and Planes

Because trains are high-occupancy vehicles (HOV), the frontal area and, thus, the aerodynamic resistance per passenger, are small, making trains one of the most efficient modes of transportation. High-speed rail has the potential to be the most efficient form of transportation if it consistently travels at near-full capacity. Planes flying at subsonic and transonic speeds can be efficient if they carry a sufficient number of passengers. Supersonic transport is not efficient since the penalty for breaking the sound barrier is quite high. ⓐ

Endnotes

1   Davis, S. C. & Diegel, S. W. (2015). *Transportation Energy Data Book*, Edition 34., Oak Ridge National Laboratory, ORNL-6991.

2   Deng, Xin. (2016). "Private Car Ownership in China: How Important is the effect of Income?" Retrieved from https://esacentral.org.au/images/Deng.pdf

3   Wong, J., (1993). *Theory of ground vehicles. Second edition*, New York, N.Y.: John Wiley & Sons, Inc.

4   See Volkswagen Announcement at http://www.volkswagen.co.uk/volkswagen-world/news/282/volkswagen-unveils-the-xl1-super-efficient-vehicle-in-qatar.

5   Katz, J., (1995). *Race Car Aerodynamics*, Robert Bentley, Inc.

6   Schaufele, R. (2000). *The Elements of Aircraft Preliminary Design*, Santa Ana, CA: Aries Publications.

7   Tennekes, H. (1997). *The Simple Science of Flight*, pp. 22, Cambridge, Massachusetts: MIT Press.

8   The U.S. data are from the 2015 Transportation Energy Data Book (Reference#2, Table 2-13); the Japanese figures are converted from the 2001 edition, pp.112 of EDMC Handbook of Energy & Economic Statistics in Japan by The Energy Data and Modeling Center, The Institute of Energy Economics, Japan, and published by The Energy Conservation Center, Tokyo, Japan.

9   Kay, J. H. (1997). *Asphalt Nation: How the Automobile Took over America and How We Can Take It Back*, pp. 171, New

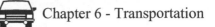

York: Crown Publishers.

10   Highway Statistics, (2018). Retrieved from https://www.fhwa.dot.gov/policyinformation/statistics/2018/pdf/mv1.pdf.

11   Britannica Online Encyclopedia, Retrieved from http://www.britannica.com

12   Bullis, K. X. (2006) Better Than Hybrids, *MIT Technology Review*, March/April 2006.

13   Miller, S. (2012) *MIT Technology Review,* September/October 2012, pp. 10.

14   DOE Technical Targets for Onboard Hydrogen Storage for Light-Duty Vehicles, <https://www.energy.gov/eere/fuelcells/doe-technical-targets-onboard-hydrogen-storage-light-duty-vehicles>

15   .Houlihan,T. (2012) Knocking the NOx out of Biodiesel, *Mechanical Engineering*, May 2012, pp. 38-41.

16   Tromp, T., et al. (2003) Potential Environmental Impact of a Hydrogen Economy on the Stratosphere, *Science*, 300, pp 1740-1742.

17   Follows, M, (2015). What ignited the Hindenburg? *Education in Chemistry*, 2 July 2015, Retrieved from https://edu.rsc.org/feature/what-ignited-the-hindenburg/2000137.article

18   Swain, M. R. (2001). Fuel Leak Simulation, "Proceedings of the 2001 DOE Hydrogen Program Review", NREL/CP-570-30535.

19   Environmental Protection Agency, Retrieved from http://www.epa.gov/otaq/climate/regulations.htm

20   Shacket, S. (1981) *The Complete Book of Electric Vehicles*, Domus Books.

21   Chan. C C., Electric Vehicles, in Electrical Engineering, [Ed. Wong Kit Po], in Encyclopedia of Life Support Systems (EOLSS), Developed under the Auspices of the UNESCO, Eolss Publishers, Oxford, UK. Available online at http://www.eolss.net

22   Jin, L., et. al. (2021). Driving a Green Future: A Retrospective Review of China's Electric Vehicle Development and Outlook for the Future, Cina EV100, Retried from https://theicct.org/sites/default/files/publications/China-green-future-ev-jan2021.pdf

23   Quiroga, T. (2006). "Driving the Future," *Car and Driver*, Hachette Filipacchi Media U.S., Inc. August 2006, pp. 52.

24   Wilkinson, D. T. (1985). Electric Braking Performance of Multiple Unit Trains, *Proc. Instn Mech Engrs*, 199(D4), 309-316.

25   Valentine-Urbschat, D. W. B. M. (2009). Powertrain 2020 - the Future Drives Electric. Roland Berger.

26   Laminie, J. and Dicks, A. (2001). *Fuel Cell Systems Explained*, John Wiley & Sons.

27   Hidden Costs of Energy: Unpriced Consequences of Energy Production and Use, National (2010) *Academies Press*.

28   Boschert, S. (2006). *Plug-in Hybrids*, New Society Publishers.

29   IEA (2021), Electric and Plug-in Hybrid Vehicle Roadmap,Retrieved from https://www.iea.org/publications/freepublications/publication/EV_PHEV_brochure.pdf

30   Satcon Technologies, Cambridge, Massachusetts, http://www.satcon.com

31   Hearn, C. S. et al. (2007). "Low-Cost Flywheel Energy Storage for a Fuel-Cell Powered Transit Bus,", *Vehicle Power and Propulsion Conference*, VPPC 2007, IEEE, Sept 9-12,

32   Rosen, H., & Castleman, D. R. (1997). Flywheels in Hybrid Vehicles, *Scientific American*, October 1997, pp. 75-77.

33   Hawken, P. Lovins, A. & Lovins, L. H. (1999). Natural Capitalism: Creating the Next Industrial Revolution, Rocky Mountain Institute, pp. 41.

34   Schrank, D., & Lomax, T. (2004). The 2004 Urban Mobility Report, Texas Transportation Institute, Texas A&M University, September 2004.

35   Wayt Gibbs, W. (1997). Transportation's Perennial Problems. *Scientific American*, 277(4), 54-57. doi: 10.1038/scientificamerican1097-54

36   Preparing a Nation for Autonomous Vehicles (2013). ENO Center for Transportation, https://www.enotrans.org/wp-content/uploads/2015/09/AV-paper.pdf

37   Ainsworth, B. Haskell, et al. (1993). Compendium of Physical Activities: classification of energy costs of human physical activities. *Medicine & Science In Sports & Exercise,* 25(1) 71-80. doi: 10.1249/00005768-199301000-00011

38   Tian, H. (2009). Formation mechanism of aerodynamic drag of high-speed train and some reduction measures, *Journal Of Central South University Of Technology,* 16(1) 166-171. doi: 10.1007/s11771-009-0028-0.

Exercises

I. Discussion Questions

1. How do spark-ignition engines, diesel, and gas turbines work?
2. Describe the operation of a catalytic converter. How does it simultaneously reduce NOx, CO, and HC emissions?
3. What are problems associated with hydrogen storage, delivery, and safety?
4. How does a fuel cell work? Why is it advantageous, compared to batteries and other modes of propulsion?
5. What are the major impediments to the large-scale production of fuel-cell vehicles?
6. What are the characteristics of a good battery suitable for electric vehicles? Compare the advantages and disadvantages of lead-acid and lithium-ion batteries for this application.
7. What is the difference between a series and a parallel hybrid? What are the advantages and disadvantages of each configuration?
8. What are the differences in emission requirements in various countries? At a minimum, compare the requirements in the U.S., UK, EU, and Japan.
9. How does a hybrid vehicle work? What is the difference between a hybrid and a plug-in hybrid?
10. What major changes in the future transportation system are forecasted? How do they change the quality of life as we know it today?

II. Problems

1. A gasoline engine is modified to run on hydrogen. Assuming hydrogen releases heat at the rate of 120 MJ/kg when burnt,
   a. Write the chemical reaction involved in the burning of hydrogen in the air.
   b. Determine the ratio of the mass of air to fuel (A/F ratio).
   c. What is the fuel consumption rate if the engine produces 100 kW? The engine operates between a combustion temperature of 585°C and an exhaust temperature of 50°C.
   d. What is the mass flow rate of water in the exhaust pipe?
2. You have a sports utility car that gives you 20 miles per gallon. You are trading your car for a hybrid car with a fuel efficiency of 50 miles per gallon. If the distance you travel each year is 20,000 miles and the average price of gasoline is $2.40 a gallon, how much do you save annually in fuel costs?
3. What is the energy expenditure of a 50-kg woman during a 10K run, with an average speed of 10 km/h? What is the power used by the woman during a 100-m dash traveled in 10 s?
4. A typical American household consumes 3 kW of electrical power. To supply this power during a two-hour blackout, two options are considered; a) store electricity in a bank of lead-acid battery, or b) generate electricity using a gasoline or diesel engine. Determine the weight of battery or gasoline fuel required.
5. Consider that a 2,000-lb car equipped with a 20-kW engine is cruising at 30 mph on a flat road when it suddenly experiences a steep grade. What is the maximum angle that this car can negotiate? Assume $C_D = 0.55$ and $C_{rr} = 0.015$, $A_f = 2.1$ m^2.
6. What is the terminal velocity that a 40-hp car will attain when it coasts down a 10% grade? What is the maximum velocity it reaches on a flat road? Assume that the car weighs 3,200 lb, has a frontal area of 30 square feet, and a rolling resistance coefficient of 0.015, and an aerodynamic drag coefficient of 0.55.
7. In the previous problem, find the specific fuel consumption rate (mpg) if the car travels on a flat road with no wind at a steady speed of 50 mph. Assume the engine has an efficiency of 15%.

III. Multiple Choice Questions

1. The efficiencies of various modes of transportation in carrying cargo over long distances are measured in terms of
   a. Horsepower per ton-mile.
   b. Btu per ton-miles.
   c. Horsepower per ton.
   d. Btu per ton.
   e. Tons per mile per hour.
2. The main strokes of a four-stroke, internal combustion engine are
   a. Intake, expansion, compression, and exhaust.
   b. Compression, ignition, expansion, and exhaust.
   c. Intake, compression, power, and exhaust.
   d. Intake, compression, ignition, and expansion
   e. Intake, ignition, expansion, and exhaust.
3. To increase the efficiency of a spark-ignition engine, we must
   a. Increase the compression ratio.

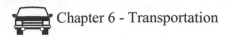

b. Use fuels with higher ignition temperatures.

c. Reduce exhaust temperature.

d. Maintain proper tire pressure.

e. All of the above.

4. The power required to propel a vehicle over a given distance can be calculated as

a. Power divided by distance.

b. Work times distance.

c. Speed times distance.

d. Force times distance.

e. Force times speed.

5. The <u>main</u> barrier to the widespread use of fuel-cell vehicles is

a. Finding or developing light electric motors and generators.

b. The high price of hydrogen.

c. Developing lighter and stronger chassis.

d. Developing a better hydrogen storage system and reducing cost.

e. Developing batteries with higher energy and power densities.

6. Aerodynamic resistance exceeds all other resistances in vehicles

a. When cruising at speeds below 40 km/hr (25 mph).

b. Only during the stop-and-go traffic.

c. Only during acceleration and climbing.

d. At speeds exceeding 40 km/hr (25 mph).

e. At all speeds.

7. Nitric oxides in the exhaust are mainly a result of

a. Incomplete combustion.

b. Quenching by cold surfaces.

c. The reaction of nitrogen and oxygen in the air at high temperatures.

d. Burning a very rich mixture.

e. All of the above.

8. Which of the following emissions <u>cannot</u> be controlled by catalytic converters?

a. Carbon monoxide

b. Carbon dioxide

c. Nitric oxide

d. Hydrocarbons

e. Particulates

9. The main function of catalytic converters is:

a. To raise fuel economy

b. To raise power

c. To reduce pollution

d. To reduce exhaust noise

e. All of the above

10. LPG is mainly

a. Natural gas with some propane and butane.

b. A blend of methanol and ethanol.

c. Distilled gasoline.

d. Leftover natural gas after methane is removed.

e. Same as the jet fuel.

11. The major disadvantage of methanol as an alternative fuel is that

a. It has an invisible flame.

b. It is toxic.

c. It is corrosive.

d. It has a low energy density.

e. All of the above.

12. What is the main advantage of hydrogen over fossil fuels?

a. Hydrogen can be stored at very high pressures so we can store a lot in a small volume.

b. Hydrogen can be easily liquefied, so it is easy to transport.

c. The hydrogen flame is invisible, so it is relatively safe.

d. When produced from renewable sources, hydrogen is the cleanest of all fuels.

e. Because of its lower density, hydrogen-powered vehicles are lighter, requiring less power to run.

13. Which of the following is <u>not</u> considered an internal combustion engine?

a. Diesel using synthetic biofuels

b. Gasoline engines

c. Gas turbines

d. Steam locomotives

e. All are internal combustion engines

14. Which of the following is <u>not</u> considered an external combustion engine?

a. Stirling engines

b. Steam engines

c. Jet engines

d. Solid-fuel rockets

e. Both c and d.

15. Most gasoline and diesel vehicles operating today, use

a. Lead-acid batteries.

b. Iron-nickel batteries.

c. Nickel-cadmium batteries.

d. Nickel-metal hydride batteries.

e. Zinc-air batteries.

16. Diesel engines are superior to gasoline engines in the following ways:

a. They can operate at higher compression ratios,

so efficiencies are higher.
  b. They lack carburetors, so they weigh less.
  c. Diesel fuels are substantially cheaper than gasoline.
  d. Diesel does not knock.
17. Which of the following can be said about fuel cells?
  a. The fuel cell is a well-developed technology with most infrastructure already in place.
  b. Fuel-cell vehicles can go thousands of miles between charges.
  c. Fuel cells are relatively cheap to manufacture.
  d. Their efficiency can be higher than those dictated by the Carnot efficiency.
  e. All of the above.
18. Fuel cells are regarded as a promising technology because
  a. They were used in the space program.
  b. They use fossil fuels.
  c. Their only by-product is water.
  d. They are cheap to produce.
  e. We have huge reserves of hydrogen.
19. Hybrid cars
  a. Are designed so they can run on any type of liquid or gaseous fuel.
  b. Use regenerative braking for faster stops.
  c. Have two or more distinct modes of propulsion.
  d. It may not need transmissions.
  e. All of the above.
20. Which of the following can be said about electric vehicles?
  a. The main disadvantage of electric vehicles is the danger associated with electrical shock.
  b. The number of battery-powered electric vehicles is expected to increase to 20% of all vehicles by 2020.
  c. Electric vehicles have a limited range.
  d. Most electric vehicles are powered by fuel cells.
  e. Electric vehicles are superior during highway driving and at cruising speeds.
21. Which of the following increases a vehicle's fuel efficiency?
  a. Using the right kind of oil
  b. Making the vehicle lighter
  c. Increasing the compression ratio
  d. Properly inflated tires
  e. They all increase efficiency
22. Air hybrid vehicles
  a. Use air as the fuel.
  b. Use methane as fuel and air as the oxidizer.
  c. Use compressed air for propulsion.
  d. Use compressed air to boost power.
  e. There is not such a thing.
23. Reformulated gasoline
  a. Is lower in carbon monoxide and particulate emissions, because of additional oxygen dissolved in the gasoline.
  b. Makes combustion more efficient,
  c. Provides better lubrications because it deposits a thin film of hydrocarbon on the walls of cylinders.
  d. Is the same as regular gasoline, with some oxygen added.
  e. All of the above.
24. Which of the following statements is false?
  a. A catalyst is a substance that accelerates a chemical reaction by raising the energy needed for it to proceed.
  b. Catalytic converters are chambers mounted in the flow system through which the exhaust gases pass.
  c. Catalytic converters are called three-way converters because they are used to reduce the concentration of carbon dioxide, soot, and water vapor in exhaust gases.
  d. Catalytic converters are called three-way converters because they are used to reduce the concentration of CO. HC, and NOx in the exhaust.
  e. None of the above.
25. Which of the following is true of methanol as a fuel?
  a. Because it has a higher H/C ratio than gasoline, it is relatively clean.
  b. It is not corrosive so that it can be transported through existing pipelines.
  c. It has a higher energy density than gasoline.
  d. Unlike gasoline, it does not produce formaldehyde.
  e. It is relatively nontoxic.
26. An air hybrid vehicle
  a. Is a lightweight hybrid car.
  b. Is similar to a conventional engine except that compressed air from a tank provides the power stroke.
  c. Is a type of internal combustion engine that operates without any fuel.
  d. Violates the First Law of Thermodynamics because it gets energy without burning any fuels.

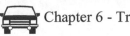

e.   Violates the Second Law of Thermodynamics because it compresses air without doing any work on the pistons.

27. What does CAFE stand for?
  a.   Combined Average Fuel Economy
  b.   Composite Average Fuel Efficiency
  c.   Comparable Average Fleet Efficiency
  d.   Corporate Average Fuel Economy
  e.   Both c and d

28. For the same frontal area, which shape has the smallest drag?
  a.   Sphere
  b.   Airfoil
  c.   Cylinder
  d.   Teardrop
  e.   Flat disk

29. A 50-hp engine can accelerate a car from rest to 60 mph in 16 s. It can be deduced that
  a.   This same car can accelerate from rest to 30 mph in 8 s.
  b.   A 100-hp engine can accelerate this car from rest to 60 mph in 4 s.
  c.   A 100-hp engine can accelerate this car from rest to 60 mph in 8 s.
  d.   a and c but not b.
  e.   None of the above.

30. Which of the following(s) can be done to raise the efficiency of transportation systems?
  a.   Raise fuel efficiency standards.
  b.   Offer incentives for buying fuel-efficient cars such as hybrid and electric.
  c.   Add pollution tax to older and bigger cars.
  d.   Encourage the use of public transportation by lowering fares.
  e.   All of the above.

31. Carbon dioxide is considered an air pollutant because
  a.   It reduces human immunity to disease.
  b.   It is a precursor to photochemical smog.
  c.   It has an unbearable smell.
  d.   It reacts with the hemoglobin of the blood.
  e.   All of the above.

32. Complete combustion of gasoline (C_8H_{17}) with air gives rise only to
  a. CO, CO_2, and H_2
  b. CO, NO, and CO_2
  c. CO_2, H_2O, and N_2
  d. CO_2, HC, and NO.
  e. CO, H_2O, and N_2

33. Nitric oxide is produced in a gasoline engine as the result of
  a.   The reaction of oxygen with nitrogen in the fuel.
  b.   Catalytic converter
  c.   The reaction of molecular nitrogen and molecular oxygen in the air at high temperatures
  d.   Dissociation of nitrogen dioxide at combustion temperatures
  e.   None of the above

IV. True or False?

1.   To reduce rolling drag, it is best to keep tires under-inflated.
2.   For ships and boats moving at low speeds, viscous drag accounts for most of the resistance.
3.   A rotary engine works similarly to a reciprocating engine, except the piston is substituted with a triangular rotor.
4.   Gas turbines have relatively lower emissions than gasoline and diesel engines.
5.   Electric motors produce maximum torque at cruising speeds.
6.   Gasoline engines are most efficient at cruising speeds.
7.   In a series hybrid configuration, all motive power comes from the electric motor powered by batteries.
8.   Electric vehicles are much quieter during operation and do not consume any power or produce any emissions when stopped.
9.   Fuel cell cars are essentially electric cars with an onboard charging station.
10. The energy intensities for trains and buses are smaller in the U.S. than in Europe.

V. Fill in the Blanks

1.   _____ is the dominant drag force for automobiles at slow speeds.
2.   _____ is the result of energy lost in creating and maintaining the ship's characteristic bow and stern waves.
3.   Electric motors produce the highest torque at _____ speed when it is most needed.
4.   In a _____ hybrid configuration, the engine, the electric motor, or both supply power to the wheels.
5.   What's needed to reduce the travel time is _____; what's needed to cover a longer distance is _____.

PROJECT I - Auto Emission from Passenger Cars

In this assignment, you are asked to estimate the total petroleum consumption by passenger vehicles in the U.S. and their contribution to the air pollution problem.

1. What kind of car do you drive? What year and model?
2. What is the power rating for the engine?
3. How many miles per gallon do you get in city driving? In highway driving?
4. What is the average price of gasoline in your area?
5. How many people usually ride in your car?

Now answer the following questions:

a. How many gallons of fuel do you use annually? What is the mass of fuel?
b. What is the annual cost of petroleum? Compare this with the cost of bottled water or soda you consume every year.
c. How many kilograms of air do you pollute for every mile traveled? Gasoline is a mixture of many hydrocarbons, but the chemical formula can be adequately represented as C_8H_{16}. Assume complete combustion.
d. How much carbon dioxide does your car produce? Give your results in grams/mile. What are the yearly emissions of carbon dioxide in kilograms?
e. What are the total annual emissions of carbon monoxide and nitric oxides for your car? The CO, NOx, and particulate emissions Federal Standards set by the EPA are 3.4, 1.0, and 0.2 grams per mile, respectively, for cars less than five years old, and 4.2, 0.6, and 0.10 for cars older than five years (See Table 14-8).
f. What are the emission rates per person per year?
g. Extend your calculations to estimate the total amount of gasoline consumed by Americans every year. How do your estimates compare to published data by the Department of Transportation? How much pollution is from cars? Assuming that there are 120 million vehicles in the United States, what is the average amount of petroleum used per vehicle? Is it higher or lower than your rate of consumption?
h. Assume that you are converting your car to run on methanol (CH_3OH), a synthetic liquid produced from wood. How are the emissions affected?
i. Repeat the calculation, assuming a switch from gasoline to natural gas. Assume natural gas is primarily methane gas with the chemical formula CH_4.
j. What is the impact of natural gas vehicles on global warming if there is a leakage of 1% of methane gas into the atmosphere? As a greenhouse gas, methane is about 40 times more potent than carbon dioxide.
k. The lower heating value (LHV) of gasoline is 44 MJ/kg, and one U.S. gallon of fuel has a mass of 2.85 kg.

Hint: Assume stoichiometric reaction:

$$C_8H_{16}+12 (O_2 + 3.76 N_2) \rightarrow 8 CO_2 + 8H_2O + 45.1 N_2$$
$$1 \text{ kg HC}+14.7 \text{ kg air} \rightarrow 3.1 \text{ kg } CO_2+1.3 \text{ kg } H_2O +11.3 N_2$$

PROJECT II - Cars versus Bikes

In this project, you will compare the amount of energy used to travel from your home to school and back, by either driving your car or by riding your bike.

a. What is the round-trip travel distance between your house and school or work?
b. How long does it take you to get to work or school if you ride a bike? Assume an average speed of 20 km/h.
c. How much muscle energy do you use to make the round trip by bike?
d. How much food energy do you need to take this trip?
e. How long would it take you to travel the same distance by car?
f. What is the fuel efficiency (mpg) of your car?
g. How much money do you save annually on gasoline and other car expenses, if you bike to work or school?
h. What are the advantages and disadvantages of driving over bicycling? Discuss in terms of convenience, energy efficiency, health benefits, etc.

PROJECT III - Fast Trains vs. Slow Trains

The French TGV (*train à grande vitesse*) holds the record for high-speed trains at 575 km/h (357 mph) and seats 794 people. It weighs 752 tons and has a total traction power of 12,200 kW (16,300 hp). A conventional train weighs 120 tons, has a top speed of 180 km/h, seats 100 passengers, and takes 6,400 kilowatts to operate. Determine the power-to-mass ratios for each train. Which of the two trains is more energy-efficient?

CHAPTER 7

Environmental Consequences of Fossil Fuel Use

UN Photo/Mark Garten.

All substances are poisons. There is none, which is not a poison.
The right dose differentiates a poison from a remedy. ~ Paracelsus
(1493-1541)

Concentrate on what cannot lie -- the evidence... ~ Gil Grissom (1951-)

ossil fuels were the agents of change that made our civilization possible. They powered our factories during the Industrial Revolution and made much of the amenities of our current life possible. The use of fossil fuels has not been without consequences, however. Many of the activities associated with mining, transportation, and processing of fossil fuels and other minerals contributed to land, water, and air pollutions. Coal mining (and to a lesser extent, petroleum and gas recoveries) results in the emission of a huge amount of dust and the release of a wide range of toxic metals that eventually find their way into the atmosphere. Strip mining results in deforestation, animal displacement, and soil degradation. Open coal mines have the highest level of sulfurs; when it rains, the exposed seam leaches sulfur that mixes with water and produces sulfuric acid, making the subsoil infertile, acidifying lakes and rivers, and killing fish, plants, and aquatic animals that are most sensitive to a shift in water acidity. Non-conventional sources -- tar sands, and oil and gas shales are even more damaging to the environment and remain highly controversial.

After fuel is excavated, it is transported by trucks, rail, or ships to refineries for processing – each step accompanied by the release of large amounts of toxic chemicals into the atmosphere. Once the fuel is refined, it is burned or processed further into useful products. Combustion is dirty; it produces hydrocarbons, particulates, and various oxides of nitrogen, sulfur, and carbon. Exhaust entering the atmosphere reacts to form acids, smog, and various toxins that not only affect human health but also endanger plant and animal life, damage materials, affect visibility and contaminate the air, water, and soil.

Carbon dioxide, the major byproduct of fossil fuel burning, is not considered a pollutant, but its presence in the atmosphere provides a blanketing effect by preventing the terrestrial infrared radiation to escape. According to the World Health Organization (WHO), an estimated six to seven million people die of air-pollution-related diseases annually, mostly in developing countries where healthcare facilities are often inadequate, environmental laws are seldom enforced, and the high costs of air pollution control equipment are largely prohibitive. According to data recently released by NASA, mostly as a result of burning fossil fuels, the earth is becoming hotter than it has been in the last 12,000 years. Globally, 2020 was the hottest year on record, effectively tying 2016, the previous record. In fact, the ten warmest years since 1860 (when measurements began) have occurred after 2003. Worse yet, if the current global warming pattern continues, by the middle of this century, temperatures will exceed the highest level, ever, in the last million years.

Issues associated with the extraction, processing, and transportation of fossil fuels were discussed in Chapter 3. In this chapter, we will look at the effect of fossil-fuel burning and various toxins on climate change and indoor and outdoor air quality.

Thermal Pollution

Laws of thermodynamics provided the foundation to design and improve various useful thermal devices. In these devices, either heat is used to produce mechanical (automobiles) and electrical (power plants) work, or work is used to move heat between a colder to a warmer space (refrigerators and heat pumps). In all cases, some heat must be discarded into the atmosphere as *thermal pollution*. Thermal pollution is not limited to mechanical devices, however. Any human activity, even the simple act of breathing, involves the dissipation of a substantial amount of heat into the surrounding air. Forest fires, radioactive decay of isotopes, volcanic ash, and other natural phenomena may also contribute.

Earth's Energy Balance

In Chapter 4, we discussed solar and terrestrial radiation balance, and concluded ignoring minor seasonal variation in incoming solar energy, the earth's atmosphere is in thermal equilibrium. i.e., the sum of all energy entering the atmosphere is equal to that which leaves the atmosphere. Of the 342 W/m^2 of solar radiation reaching the surface nearly half is absorbed by land and water surfaces (See Figure 4-4). This, combined with direct terrestrial radiation, is returned to the atmosphere as sensible heat, as latent heat of evaporation, and as long-wave infrared radiation. Unless additional energy is generated and released into the earth's atmosphere, the equilibrium is maintained, and the average atmospheric temperature remains constant at around 15°C.

The planetary energy balance has been affected by two phenomena, both the result of human activities associated with extensive use of fossil fuels: the blanketing effect of greenhouse gases in the atmosphere, and an increase in the incoming solar radiation emission as a result of depletion of the stratospheric ozone layer.

Question: What is the impact of global warming on temperatures of atmospheres of venus and mars?
Answer: The atmospheres of both Mars and Venus are mostly carbon dioxide (97% in Venus and 95% in Mars, with the remaining being mostly nitrogen). Venus has a dense atmosphere, some 100 times thicker than the Earth. The greenhouse effect imakes Venus at 467°C the hottest planet in the solar system. Mars is about 50 million miles farther away from the Sun than Earth and has a very thin atmosphere, only 1/100 of that of the earth and as result, cannot hold the heat. Its average temperature is only -63°C. The greenhouse effect had made Venus a furnace, while the lack of atmosphere had locked Mars in a deep freeze.

Weather and Climate

The distinction between weather and climate is crucial in the study of any climate science. Weather is the day-to-day or week-to-week changes in atmospheric conditions in a limited area such as a city or a state. Weather can change within a few minutes or hours. When we tell it is hot today, or what we should wear tonight, we talk about the weather.

Climate refers to weather over a long period, years to decades, and a wider area such as a country or even globally. Different regions can have different climates. The following statements all refer to climate. Chicago is called "the windy city." Antarctica is getting warmer and warmer each year. New York has four seasons. The tropical rainforest experiences a humid season throughout the year.

Earth's Carbon Balance

Carbon is being continuously recycled through the earth and its atmosphere, among plants, animals, and between soil, air, and oceans. Carbon appears in two forms: organic and non-organic; *organic compounds* are produced by and are associated with living organisms, whereas *inorganic compounds* are created by non-living natural processes or human intervention. Examples of organic compounds are fats, sugars, nucleic acids, enzymes, proteins, and other molecules the organism uses for food. Carbon dioxide, carbon monoxide, carbides, cyanides are inorganic. As we shall see in Chapter 11, through the process of photosynthesis, carbon dioxide and water react in the presence of light to form carbohydrates. In this reaction, inorganic carbon turns into organic carbon (i.e., carbon is fixed!).

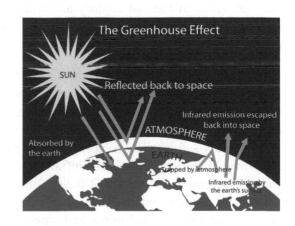

Oceans hold 80% of all carbon in the form of dissolved carbon dioxide and bicarbonates; another 10% is stored in various forms of fossil fuels, primarily coal, and the rest are in the air, soil, and

Figure 7-1
Energy balance in the atmosphere and the greenhouse effect.

in the form of terrestrial biomass.

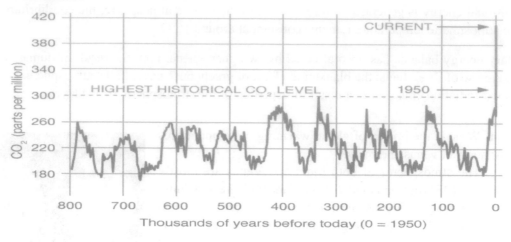

Figure 7-2
Background carbon dioxide concentration over Antarctica for the past 400,000 years. During these cycles, changes in carbon dioxide concentrations track closely the changes in temperature, and rise in the sea-level.
Image courtesy of Oakridge National laboratory (ORNL).

Greenhouse Effect

Global warming is a natural phenomenon, part of the long cycle of repeated heating and cooling that could last many thousands of years. The last ice age began about 2.6 million years ago and lasted until 11,000 years ago when the ice sheets melted, and the climate warmed and became similar to what we have today. This period also coincided with the migration of homo sapiens across the planet and a time when gatherers and hunters could finally settle down. The warmer, wetter, and more stable conditions, particularly in tropical and temporal regions made agriculture possible.

The latest cooling period was during the Little Ice Age of 1300-1850. During this period, there were fewer sunspots, and the temperature dropped, destroying crops that caused half the people in Europe to die of starvation, reducing immune systems while allowing rats to flourish. Some blame the Bubonic Plague or Black Death of mid 14th century on the changing climate. In 1484, Pope Innocent VIII recognized the existence of witches and echoed the popular sentiment by blaming them for the cold temperatures and resulting misfortunes that plagued Europe.

Human activities in the last century and a half, however, have been responsible for alterations in atmospheric composition, changes in weather patterns, and raising the global temperature by about 0.8°C. During the past 25 years, the rate of temperature increase has been even greater and totals about 2°C, if extrapolated over 100 years.

To understand the global warming phenomenon, we must understand **the greenhouse effect**. Greenhouses heat to temperatures exceeding their surroundings because window glasses (and some plastics) are transparent to incoming solar radiation, but block most of the reflected infrared radiation from plants and surroundings. Certain gases, such as water vapor, carbon dioxide, methane, nitrous oxides, and several fluorinated organic compounds (CFCs and HFCs), behave similarly -- they allow solar radiation to pass through to reach and heat the ground and air above it, but absorb and reradiate the reflected terrestrial infrared radiation blanketing the earth (Figure 7-1). Carbon dioxide is the main product of the combustion of fossil fuels. Cattle and termites produce methane as the byproduct of breaking down plant bacteria in their guts. Methane is also produced in wetlands, municipal waste dumps, and rice patties, and leaked into the air from coal mines and pipelines; nitric oxides (NO and NO_2) come primarily from fertilizers and animal wastes. Nitrous oxides (N_2O) come from fossil fuel consumption and agriculture. CFCs are widely used in fire extinguishers, refrigeration systems, and aerosol spray cans; ozone and halogenated substances that contain fluorine, chlorine, or bromine also contribute. Carbon monoxide, non-methane volatile organic compounds, aerosols, and

214

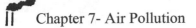

liquid droplets do not have a direct impact on global warming but indirectly affect terrestrial and/or solar radiation absorption by influencing the formation or destruction of greenhouse gases.

Why carbon dioxide? An analysis of the air bubbles trapped in Antarctic ice caps provides evidence that for hundreds of thousands of years, carbon dioxide concentration in the atmosphere has been essentially constant, at around 240 ± 40 parts per million (0.024% by volume). The temporal variations in carbon dioxide concentrations have correlated closely with that of the average surface temperatures and the rise in sea levels (Figure 7-2). Note that the CO_2 concentration never exceeded 280 ppm until the mid-twentieth century. Following industrialization and the rapid increase in the rate of consumption of fossil fuels (Figure 7-3), man-made carbon dioxide has caused these levels to increase. The concentration reached 385 ppm in 2007, and continued to increase to 417 parts per million in May 2020. The trend is expected to continue at an alarming rate of 1.5 to 2 ppm every year, to over 500 ppm by the middle of this century as more and more fossil carbon is brought to the surface and burned.

It should be noted that contrary to what some may suspect, carbon dioxide is not the most damaging greenhouse gas, and depends not only on the nature of the gases and their concentrations but also on the length of time that they remain in the atmosphere. Over a 100 year period, each gram of methane has the same effect on climate change as the emission of 21 grams of carbon dioxide; nitric oxides are 289 times more effective, and CFC's global warming potential (GWP) can be as much as 12,000 times that of the carbon dioxide.* Carbon dioxide has been cited as the most important greenhouse gas merely because it is the most abundant. Methane and nitric oxide concentrations in the atmosphere have been increasing as a result of human activities since 1750 and now far exceed pre-industrial values determined from ice cores spanning many thousands of years.

It is instructive to note that if we dug up and burned all the fossil fuel deposits in the earth, the concentration of carbon dioxide in the atmosphere would increase by four to eight folds. According to some climate scientists, each doubling of atmospheric CO_2 will result in an increase of an average of 3°C in the mean

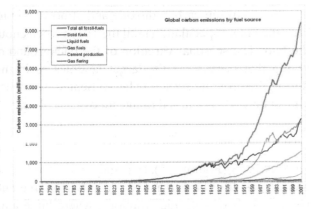

Figure 7-3
World carbon emission, 1750-2012.
Source: Carbon Dioxide Information Analysis Center. U.S. Department of Energy.

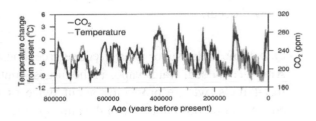

Figure 7-4
Seasonal background carbon dioxide concentration and average global surface temperature 2016-2020.
Source: NOAA, 2020

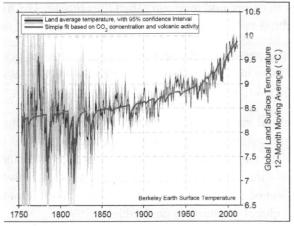

Figure 7-5
Average surface temperature of Earth 1750-2011.
Image courtesy of Berkeley Earth (http://berkeleyearth. org).

surface temperature of the earth, therefore burning all fossil reserves can potentially raise the temperature by as much as 12°C. The severity of the consequences can only be appreciated in light of the fact that the earth's temperature was only 6°C to 9°C above today's temperature during the time that dinosaurs roamed the earth and only 5°C colder during the last Ice Age.

---

* Recent data *(International Herald Tribune, June 20, 2007)* suggests that, for the first time, China surpassed the United States in total emissions of greenhouse gases. Per capita production remains well below the U.S., however.

The link between carbon dioxide and atmospheric temperatures was presumed as early as the late 19th century but remained mere speculation until the 1980s when enough data had been collected to show a strong correlation between the two. The seasonal variation of the background carbon dioxide concentration (Figure 7-4) can be explained by noting that because of the larger landmasses in the Northern Hemisphere, photosynthesis is more predominant during the growing season (May to September) when plants remove large amounts of the carbon dioxide from the atmosphere. It is returned to the atmosphere from fall until mid-spring, as plants die.

Richard Muller, a physics professor at the University of California, Berkeley and until recently a prominent critic, conducted his independent research, extending IPCC's (Intergovernmental Panel on Climate Change) data as far back as 1753 (Figure 7-5). His study convinced him that not only global warming is real, but also it is exclusively a direct result of human activity mainly from the burning of fossil fuels. The small dips in temperatures are during short periods of volcanic eruptions, where large amounts of volcanic ashes reduced the amount of solar light that penetrated the atmosphere. The solar sunspots, cited by some as the main cause of global warming, did not correlate with data and could safely be ignored without any change in the final outcome. The study also confirmed that the global land temperatures have increased by 1.5°C over the past 250 years, and if the current pattern of energy use continues, the model suggests that by 2050, a temperature increase as high as 1.1°C overall, and 1.6°C over land masses will occur.[†]

> **Question:** Water vapor is an effective greenhouse gas. Why isn't it cited as the main cause of global warming?
> **Answer:** Indeed, water vapor is the largest contributor to greenhouse gases in the atmosphere. When we burn fossil fuels, we are producing about twice as much water vapor as carbon dioxide. However, water vapor concentration does not control the atmospheric temperature, but it is the temperature that determines how much water vapor the atmosphere can hold. Unfortunately, some politicians and lobbyists cite the role of water vapor as proof that global warming is a natural phenomenon having nothing to do with human activity.

Causes of Climate Change

Both nature and man can affect the climate. The **natural causes of climate change** are variations in solar irradiance, orbital variation, volcanic eruptions, forest fires, and biological activities.

Solar irradiance changes somewhat as the sun goes through a cycle every 11 years. During each cycle, the number of sunspots and volume of materials ejected into the space change. The effect on the earth's global warming is, however, insignificant.

Orbital variation of the earth and its tilt also changes the total radiation received by the earth. Earth is rotating on an elliptical orbit around the sun, having the farthest distance from the sun on July 4 and nearest to the sun on January 3. The earth's axis makes an angle of 23.5° with the plane of rotation of the earth about the sun, causing the seasonal variation. The tilt angle changes somewhat between 22.1 and 24.5 degrees for every 40,000 years. Although the effect of tilt on solar irradiation between northern and southern hemispheres at any time is significant, the net effect on global warming is negligible.

Volcanic eruptions have the most effect on the climate. A massive amount of volcanic ashes with a huge volume of aerosols and carbon and sulfur oxide gases enter the atmosphere. The effects are multitude; ash particles have a blanketing effect preventing some of the light from reaching the earth; carbon dioxide traps heat and therefore has a positive impact on global warming. Sulfur dioxide reacts with water vapor to produce a sulfuric acid cloud that reflects some of the sunlight back to the sky. The overall effect is cooling. The most impressive volcanic explosion in the modern age was the cataclysmic 1991 eruption of Mount Pinatubo in the Philippines. The ashes caused a reduction in the amount of radiation reaching the earth causing a drop in the average global temperature of about 0.6°C (1°F) for 15 months. The temperature went back to normal, so no long-term effects are attributed to the atmospheric cooling.

---

† Another stark conclusion was that the additional greenhouse effect of the CO_2 is not proportional to CO_2 concentration, but the logarithm of the CO_2 level. For example, a doubling from 500 to 1000 ppmv would have approximately the same climatic effect as an increase from 300 to 600 ppmv.

The **anthropogenic causes of climate change** are the extensive use of fossil fuel burning, deforestation, and farming/agricultural practices. As it was discussed in some detail in Chapter 3, our economy is strongly dependent on the use of fossil fuels. The global consumption of fossil fuels was increased 16 fold during the twentieth century, and again, by an additional 50% between 2000 -2019. During this same time, deforestation was accelerated and more croplands were converted to pastures. The data is closely correlated with the rise in temperature. How much of the warming since 1850 can be attributed to human emissions? According to the recent report by the Intergovernmental Panel on Climate Change (IPCC), *"Anthropogenic greenhouse gas emissions have increased since the pre-industrial era, driven largely by economic and population growth, and are now higher than ever. This has led to atmospheric concentrations of carbon dioxide, methane and nitrous oxide that are unprecedented in at least the last 800,000 years."*

Causation and Correlatin

It should be stressed here that in the strictest sense, correlation does not mean causation. For example, paleoclimate data reveal a strong correspondence between temperature and the concentration of carbon dioxide in the atmosphere. When the carbon dioxide concentration goes up, the temperature goes up. When the carbon dioxide concentration goes down, the temperature goes down. As carbon dioxide has changed in the past, many other aspects of climate have also changed, and the overall result has been a strong correlation between carbon dioxide and temperature.

Question: According to a highway traffic report, there is a strong correlation between the number of traffic accidents and the number of cars with at least one umbrella in them. Does this suggest that to avoid accidents, it is best not to carry an umbrella in the car?

Answer: Of course not! People carry umbrellas only when it rains, or there is a high probability of rain. Rain causes roads to get slippery, which implies more possibility of an accident. Although there exists a correlation, there is no causal relationship between the two.

Role of Feedback Mechanisms

The composition of gases in the atmosphere is determined from an interplay of many reactions involved in their destruction and formation. Feedback mechanisms are either negative or positive. It is called a ***negative feedback loop*** when a change in one variable triggers a response that brings back that variable its initial value. A popular example of negative feedback is the population of different species in an ecological system that competes for limited resources. Let's consider a farm that houses only two species, rabbits and foxes. As long as there is enough grass for the rabbits, they multiply and the population of rabbits goes up. More rabbits mean more availability of food for foxes, and the population of foxes will increase until they run out of food and their population decline. This means fewer predators, allowing the rabbit population to increase again. Another example of negative feedback is the homeostasis in our body. As we become ill and our body temperature rises, or when ambient air temperature exceeds the normal body temperature of 37°C (98.6°F), the blood flow to the skin increases, resulting in additional heat loss to the environment. At the same time, sweat glands secrete fluid. As the fluid evaporates, our bodies lose more heat, forcing our body temperature to drop to a healthy level. Similar mechanisms are triggered if body temperature falls. These include constricting the blood vessel to maintain heat and stops the feedback. Prolonged exposure to a cold environment can potentially lead to hypothermia because of excessive heat loss. In this case, shivering helps in the involuntary contraction of muscles to generate heat bringing back the body to normal temperatures.

Negative feedbacks try to restore the earth's equilibrium by adjusting the degree to which low-altitude clouds form. Higher temperatures increase the rate of ocean water evaporation, thereby expanding the cloud cover. Also, the burning of fossil fuel releases particles that act as condensation nuclei and increases the cloud cover. More clouds increase the blanketing effect, both by keeping the reradiated terrestrial radiation in (positive effect) and by reflecting the incoming solar radiation out (negative effect). Clouds' net contribution in heating or cooling the atmosphere is debated. Another stabilizing mechanism involves the loss of longwave radiation to space from the surface. Since this radiative loss increases with increasing surface temperatures (See the Stefan-Boltzmann law presented in chapter 4), it acts to reduce the near-surface air temperature.

A positive feedback loop is a process that exacerbates the effects of a small disturbance. That is, the effects of a perturbation on a system magnify the perturbation (snowball effect). Positive feedback systems are often associated with an undesirable outcome, and in the case of human homeostasis can be deadly. For example, when a body is injured, it releases chemicals that activate blood platelets, which in turn, activates more platelets and stops excessive bleeding. Typically, our body will naturally dissolve the blood clot after the injury has healed. Another example is childbirth during which, the body releases the hormone oxytocin that induces labor. As the number and intensity of contractions increase, more and more oxytocin is released and stops when the child is born.

Several positive feedback mechanisms are at play in processes involved in global warming. For example, as the temperature of the atmosphere increase, so does the amount of water vapor. Since water vapor is a potent greenhouse gas, the net greenhouse effect becomes stronger, which leads to even greater warming. In this case, we have a positive feedback loop, the higher the temperature, the higher is the concentration of water vapor that leads to an even higher temperature, and so on. Other positive feedbacks reinforce the warming effects; i.e., with the increasing temperatures:

a. Warmer oceans dissolve less carbon dioxide and raise carbon dioxide concentration in atmospheric air.
b. Less nutrient biomass (plankton) becomes available, reducing the atmosphere's capacity to remove the CO_2.
c. A warmer climate causes organic matter to decay faster, adding to carbon dioxide already in the air.
d. Arctic permafrost and tundra will melt, releasing methane and carbon dioxide.

Consequences

There is considerable disagreement as to the severity of global warming and its long-term effects on the environment. Although environmentalists and the scientific community blame human greed and non-restricted use of fossil fuels, many politicians, oil companies, and even some researchers claim that the natural variations of solar activity have a much larger influence on climate change. This point of view is, however, in the clear minority, and many discards it purely as a political ploy to support the hidden agendas of special interest groups.

One thing that scientists agree on -- and data confirms -- is that global warming, whatever the cause, can lead to major changes in regional climates, or local weather, increased frequency of extreme events, unprecedented hot summers, more intense heat waves, heavy rainfall, and severe droughts. The human toll, in terms of a rise in regional and global conflicts, disease, hunger, and lack of access to drinking water, and other natural resources, is hard to determine, but the majority of economists and social scientists point to a dramatic and unpleasant outcome.

Depending on how much GHGs we produce and strategies we undertake to combat it, earth temperature can rise by a couple of degrees, or we push ourselves to the point of no return -- the *tipping point* where positive feedback reactions cause the earth to warm more and more even if humans stopped dumping more carbon dioxide and other greenhouse gases into the atmosphere. Some even go further, believing that it is already too late to prevent catastrophic climate change by only reducing GHG emissions, but also must develop technologies that remove much of what is already in the atmosphere. What science tells us is that unless we implement strict policies for immediate phase-out of all GHG emissions, as a result of global warming:

1. *Air temperature close to the earth's surface increases, whereas the stratosphere cools.* It is expected that, as a result of global warming, the earth will warm somewhere between 1.4-5.8°C by the end of the twenty-first century. Rising temperature causes acceleration in the rate of decay of organic matter, and melting of Arctic permafrost and tundra, both producing methane which is, itself, a major greenhouse gas.
2. *Ocean water gets warmer.* Global warming also results in the warming of ocean waters and, possibly, even the collapse of the conveyor belt. The conveyor belt is a system of water currents that circulate between the Atlantic and Pacific oceans. It is the shallowest in the Indian Ocean, where the water is the warmest. As water moves north, it cools, becomes denser, and sinks to the bottom near Greenland. The Gulf Stream is part of the conveyor belt that moves north, bringing warm salty water from tropics to higher altitudes in the North Atlantic. The warm water, coupled with prevailing westerly wind helps moderate much of the European climate.; if weakened, it will cause the temperature in much of Europe to drop.
3. *Frequency of forest fires increase.* As the temperature rises and the air dries up, the danger of large-scale fire increases. In the past three decades only, the area burned by forest fires has doubled.
4. *Warmer oceans also affect the diversity of marine life.* As oceans warm, fish body temperatures, metabolism, and oxygen consumption rates will rise. Lake-locked species are especially affected as they have no recourse to move to colder regions. Unfortunately, the solubility of gases is also reduced and less oxygen is available, causing many species of fish to disappear. As water loses its capability to dissolve carbon dioxide, some of the stored carbon dioxides are released back into the atmosphere.[‡] Furthermore, water viscosity and density are reduced, causing an increase in the rate of settlement of suspended particles in the water – possibly affecting aquatic food supplies. Finally, warmer oceans mean fewer nitrates, an important ingredient for the production of carbon-absorbing phytoplankton.

It should be noted that the amount of carbon dioxide in the atmospheric air is a tiny fraction of that dissolved in oceans. Without water, the atmospheric carbon dioxide concentration would have been much higher, making the atmosphere much hotter and unsuitable for most forms of life. The planet Venus retains much of its carbon dioxide in its atmosphere, keeping its surface temperature at a searing 470°C (880°F), today (See Box "Venus").

Venus

Compared to the Earth's atmosphere, which except for some trace gases, is composed entirely of nitrogen and oxygen, Venus' atmosphere is 96% carbon dioxide. Much of the carbon dioxide on earth is dissolved in ocean waters, sequestered in plants, or locked up in carbonate rocks, releasing only trace amounts of carbon dioxide to the atmosphere. Venus does not have any liquid water and almost all carbon dioxide has out-gassed into its thick atmosphere. As a result, runaway greenhouse gases play a much more dominant role on Venus, maintaining its temperature in excess of 470°C.

‡ The decrease in solubility of carbon dioxide with temperature is also the main reason that soda, beer, and other carbonated beverages become flat shortly after they are opened. Soda cans are filled under pressure. When opened, their pressure drops to atmospheric levels. Carbon dioxide is less soluble and leaves the beverage. Similarly, when the beverage warms up, its ability to dissolve carbon dioxide reduces and the beverage goes flat.

5. *Ice caps in Greenland and Antarctica break up and melt.* Rising temperatures cause the melting of continental glaciers, snowfields, and permafrost, thus further reducing the fraction of sunlight that is reflected back to the sky. The data shows that in the last 30 years alone, there has been a considerable loss in Greenland's glaciers surface area and a 40% thinning of the northern ice cap. The rate of melting has been increasing in recent years. It is believed by some scientists that a 2-3 degrees centigrade rise in the ambient temperature will result in the complete melting of the entire ice sheet and a global sea rise of 7.2 m (24 ft). Even a rise in the sea level of only a few feet will bury many of the smaller Pacific islands underwater. In low-lying countries, such as Bangladesh and the Netherlands, millions of people will be displaced. Many coastlines and beaches, including some in the United States, Australia, and Europe will be lost. As a result, the atmospheric temperature rises even further, causing more ice to melt.

6.

 Melting glaciers have other unexpected consequences. As glaciers slowly flow downhill, they grind up underlying rocks, releasing mercury into their meltwater. Analysis of runoff water from the Greenland ice sheet, shows ten times more mercury present in glacier's freshwater samples.

7. *The climate becomes even more unpredictable.* As the upper layers of seawater warm, the intensity of hurricanes, typhoons, and tornadoes increases.[§] The rising global temperature does not, however, mean that all regions will experience warmer weather. In fact, some regions may actually cool as a result of a change in the climate. Furthermore, the change in rainfall patterns will result in droughts in some regions and floods in others. Forests and other natural resources will also suffer from changes in the climate.

8. *Agriculture will suffer.* Saltwater will damage much of the low-lying coasts, cause an increase in the pest population, crop failure, growth in weed population, reduce farmland, thus affecting the grazing of farm animals and the production of food.

9. *Weather-related diseases will increase.* Global warming can dramatically increase pests and outbreaks of infectious diseases, such as yellow fever, tuberculosis, malaria, asthma, and other respiratory illnesses.

10. *Animal migration is severely affected.* Rising temperatures on land and sea are increasingly forcing species to migrate to cooler climes, pushing disease-carrying insects into new areas. Also, animals may get lost as they try to return to their natural habitats.

11. *Conflict over natural resources will increase.* As glaciers melt and its freshwater mixes with salty ocean water, the availability of clean water needed for drinking, cooking, and bathing declines. This, in turn, increases competition for freshwater and other natural resources, which results in increased regional conflict, and triggers mass migration. According to one estimate between 200 million and one billion people may have to displace by 2050.

12. *There will be less drinking water.* Climate change is disrupting the hydrological cycle, exacerbating water scarcity and contaminating water supplies. Rising temperatures can lead to deadly pathogens in freshwater resources.

13. *There will be a huge influx of immigrants.* Global warming results in large-scale human migration due to resource scarcity and increased frequency of extreme weather events such as floods, droughts, particularly in the earth's low latitudinal band. This will negatively impact the job market, putting additional stress on the economy, and potential conflict between the citizens of the host country and the new arrival

---

§ Recent studies suggest that much of the violent weather behaviors of the last decade, such as the 1991 cyclone in Bangladesh, the 1992 floods in Pakistan, China, and Australia, and 1990-1995 El Nino and La Nina in the United States, are related to global warming. Some scientists warn against rushed judgment, however, that the frequency at which violent storms such as Katrina (which hit New Orleans in 1995) can be entirely coincidental. There are now better devices to predict hurricanes, and at far-out locations at sea, so the higher number of hurricanes neither supports nor rejects a link to global warming phenomena; the hurricane's destruction of New Orleans is also partly coincidental, and partly due to the fact that the city lies below sea level and the fact that the levy protecting the city was poorly designed.

Air Pollution

Air pollution occurs when substances are present at concentrations well above their normal ambient levels that have harmful effects on man, animals, vegetation, or materials. The severity of effects depends on the nature and concentration of the pollutants, the length of time they remain in the atmosphere (residence time), and their reactivity with other chemicals in the atmosphere. Atmospheric conditions, such as wind speed and atmospheric stability also can play key roles. According to a recent report published by the United Nations Children's Fund (UNICEF), in 2012 alone, air pollution was linked to around seven million deaths, 600,000 of those children under five years old. Most of these children live in low- and middle- income countries, especially in Africa and Asia.

Outdoor air pollution consists of solid wastes, pesticides, herbicides, fertilizers, and tobacco smoke. Indoor air pollutants are those emitted from the burning of coal and natural gas for cooking and heating, as well as household chemicals and volatile organic compounds used in solvents, paints, lightners, paints, solvents, spray cans, personal care products, and building materials.[¶]

Classification

The major sources of outdoor air pollution are transportation, generating stations, and industrial processes. They are commonly characterized as either **stationary** (large diesel engines, coal power plants, and refineries), or **mobile** (cars, trucks, boats, and planes), and either as **point source** (stack plumes from power plants), as **line source** (tailpipe emissions from cars on freeways), as **area source** (forest fires, and large oil or chemical spills), or as **volume source** (smog). Depending on the nature of the contaminants, air pollutants are divided into two categories: the so-called criteria air pollutants and hazardous (toxic) air pollutants.

Criteria air pollutants are those common in mobile and stationary sources (tailpipe and smokestack emissions), which are thought to cause heart and respiratory problems, and may cause cancer. They are sulfur dioxide, carbon monoxide, nitrogen oxide, ground-level ozone, particulate matter, and lead. Carbon dioxide is not considered a pollutant, but because of its effect on global warming, it is sometimes treated as such. EPA is charged to set National Ambient Air Quality Standards (NAAQS) for criteria air pollutants and their monitoring. Table 7-1 shows the total U.S. emissions of criteria air pollutants by sector in 2010

Hazardous air pollutants are less common but they are carcinogenic or may cause damage to the immune or neurological systems. These include volatile organic compounds (unburned hydrocarbons), ammonia, and a wide range of chemicals used as solvents, sterilizers, and components in industrial processes. Whether directly emitted into the atmosphere, or formed by reaction with other species in the atmosphere, pollutants can be considered as primary or secondary:

Primary pollutants are those coming directly from the source and maybe natural or anthropogenic. Natural sources include dust, pollen, sea salt nuclei, volcanic ash, smoke, and particulates from forest burning. The anthropogenic source of pollutants results from fossil fuel combustion and includes carbon monoxide, the oxides of nitrogen (mainly NO and NO_2), the oxides of sulfur (mainly SO_2), unburned hydrocarbons, and particulates (mainly soot, ash, and metal traces). Because almost all air pollutants come from combustion sources, the amounts of emissions correlate closely with the amount of fossil fuel consumption.

Secondary pollutants are those produced as a result of the reaction between primary discharges and the atmosphere. Ozone is not directly released into the ambient but formed as a result of a photosynthetic reaction of primary pollutants within the atmosphere. Sulfuric acid mist and smog also are considered secondary; smog is a result of the reaction of hydrocarbons with nitric oxides; acid rain is a result of the reaction between sulfur dioxide with water or with trace elements emitted alongside other pollutants.

¶ The EPA does not list VOCs as criteria pollutants, but because of their impact on the formation of smog, they are included here.

Table 7-1 Total U.S. Emission of Greenhouse Gases and Criteria Air Pollutants by Sector, 2018.												
Sector	GHG		CO		NOx		VOC		Particulate**		SO₂	
	Tons*	%	Tons*	%	Tons*	%	Tons*	%	Tons*	%	Tons*	%
Transportation	1,871	29.2	30.32	52.1	5.95	57.6	3.23	20.2	0.72	3.1	0.10	3.5
Stationary Sources	2,003	31.2	4.06	7.0	2.80	27.1	0.52	3.3	1.62	6.9	1.96	71.5
Industrial	1,916	29.9	2.03	3.5	1.17	11.3	7.32	45.8	1.2	5.1	0.50	18.4
Others	621	9.7	21.74	37.4	0.40	3.9	4.90	30.1	19.91	85	0.18	6.6
Total	6,410	100	58.15	100	10.33	100	15.97	100	23.45	100	2.74	100

*million short tons
** PM-2.5 + PM-10

Source: Davis, S. C., Diegel, S. W., US Department of Energy, "Transportation Energy Data Book, Edition 36," ORNL-6987, 2012 Tables 12.4 and 13.1.

Ozone

Ozone is a pale blue gas with a pungent smell that allows it to be detected even in very low concentrations. In fact, the word ozone is derived from the Greek word *ozein* meaning "to smell." A molecule of ozone contains three atoms of oxygen bound together (Figure 7-6). The extra oxygen makes ozone highly reactive, attacking and oxidizing almost anything it contacts. Ozone appears both in the upper and lower layers of the atmosphere. In the upper atmosphere (stratosphere), ozone is produced naturally from the reaction of oxygen with ultraviolet radiation from the sun. In the lower atmosphere (troposphere), ozone is formed from the reaction between nitrogen oxides and volatile hydrocarbons in the presence of sunlight, mostly as a result of human activities. Most of the ozone (about 90%) is found in the upper atmosphere (commonly referred to as the *ozone layer*) at around 15-35 km above the ground (Figure 7-7). As a result of large-scale meteorological weather systems, the ozone layer somewhat varies in thickness from one day to the next and greatly fluctuates with the seasons.

Figure 7-6
Molecular structures of oxygen and ozone.

The Good Ozone and the Bad Ozone

The stratospheric ozone may be regarded as the earth's sunglasses. It serves as a shield, protecting the earth from the harmful effects of ultraviolet radiation. Depending on its frequency, ultraviolet light can be classified as UV-A, UV-B, or UV-C (Figure 7-8). UV-A (320-400 nm), also known as *black light*, is responsible for skin tanning and has the lowest energy. It is generally considered to be harmless, although some new studies have linked damage to the retina with long-term exposure to this type of radiation. UV-C (100-290 nm) has the most energy, but is entirely absorbed by the outer layers of the earth's atmosphere and, under normal circumstances, is not of concern. Because it is highly effective in killing germs, bacteria, viruses, mold, fungi, and spores, UV-C is used in hospitals and some industrial applications. UV-B (290-320 nm) has lower energy than UV-C and most is absorbed by the ozone layer in the upper atmosphere, however, even the small amount that reaches the ground results in long-term cataracts, skin cancer (malignant melanoma), and breakdown of the immune system in a large number of people. A 1% reduction in the thickness of the ozone layer will

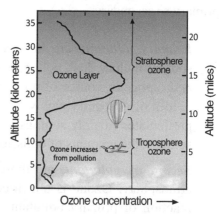

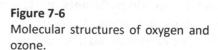

Figure 7-7
Atmospheric ozone.

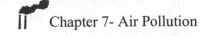
result in a similar increase in the intensity of UV-B radiation and a 2% increase in the probability of skin cancer.[**] The effect is more severe at higher latitudes (such as in Scandinavian countries) and higher altitudes.

Although the presence of ozone in the upper atmosphere is considered "good," its presence in the lower atmosphere is "bad," and detrimental to health. Major health problems associated with elevated levels of ozone in the atmosphere are coughing, headaches, nausea, and chest pains. Ozone also causes shortness of breath, chronic bronchitis, and fatigue. Asthma epidemics, especially in children in industrialized countries, can be directly attributed to ozone.

Figure 7-8
Ozone acts as a protective shield against ultraviolet radiation.

Ozone Formation

Stratospheric ozone (O_3) is produced by the process of *photolysis*. Photolysis begins when an oxygen atom absorbs ultraviolet light and split into two oxygen atoms. The oxygen atom consequently reacts with an oxygen molecule to form ozone. The basic steps are:

$$O_2 + UV \rightarrow 2O$$

$$2O + 2O_2 \rightarrow 2O_3$$

The net reaction is that three molecules of oxygen are destroyed and two molecules of ozone are produced.

$$3O_2 \rightarrow 2O_3$$

The Ozone Hole

The reduction in the amount of ozone in the stratosphere is another environmental problem widely attributed to the increased use of fossil fuels. This reduction commonly referred to as the "**ozone hole**," was first reported over Antarctica in 1985. Since then, it has been recorded over the Arctic and elsewhere around the globe. Since 1978, in areas where ozone concentration routinely has been measured, there has been a 4-5% loss of stratospheric ozone over the continental United States.

Among the chemicals, most threatening to the ozone layer are chlorofluorocarbons (CFCs). CFCs are odorless, non-toxic, non-flammable, and inexpensive chemicals originally introduced in the 1920s and used as a substitute for ammonia, which was the primary coolant in refrigerators. Marketed under the trade name Freon, it quickly found its way into a large number of other products such as paints, propellants, insulation, seat cushions, solvents, and a foam-lowering agent for aerosol cans. Supersonic passenger aircraft, rockets, and space shuttles release chlorine and nitrous oxides directly into the atmosphere and, thus, contribute to the depletion of the ozone layer.

In addition to CFCs, methyl bromide (a product mainly used in pest control and fire extinguishers) and nitrogen oxides (produced during combustion and a common component of fertilizers) also are shown to have similar destructive properties. These materials are highly stable and can stay in the atmosphere, eventually migrating to the stratosphere where they interfere with the natural ozone cycle. Although ozone depletion is widespread over the entire globe, it is of particular significance in the Antarctic. The severity of depletion in the Antarctic is due to its extremely cold temperatures and the presence of ice crystals that hover over Antarctica and act as catalysts to break up CFCs. There are no such ice clouds around the North Pole and so the ozone hole is smaller.

The mechanism responsible for ozone destruction was first investigated by Rowland and Molina, who showed that the depletion is a result of chlorine compounds transported from the lower to the upper atmosphere. Once in the stratosphere, these chemicals are broken down by high concentrations of ultraviolet rays releasing chlorine that, in turn, decompose ozone molecules into molecular and monatomic oxygen. The reaction responsible for ozone depletion can be summarized as UV rays of the solar radiation breaks CFC molecules to form chlorine monoxide

---

[**] For a summary review of the dangers associated with the depleting ozone layer, http:// http://www.theozonehole.com

$Cl + O_3 \rightarrow ClO + O_2$, followed by reaction of chlorine monoxide with oxygen radical to form chlorine and molecular oxygen $ClO + O \rightarrow Cl + O_2$. The net result is the continuous destruction of ozone to form molecular oxygen $O_3 + O \rightarrow 2O_2$.

Similar processes occur in the presence of bromine and fluorine molecules. Rowland and Molina received the 1995 Nobel Prize in chemistry for this pioneering work.

Acid Rain

Acid rain refers to any kind of acid precipitation such as acid fog, snow, mist, or any other acidic particles or aerosols that fall to the ground or remain suspended in the atmosphere. The main components responsible for their acidity are oxides of sulfur and nitrogen that are dissolved in water and deposited on the surfaces of suspended particles.

The measure of the acidity of a solution is its **pH value**. The pH scale ranges between 0 and 14; the lower the number, the more acidic the substance is. Pure water has a pH of 7 and is considered to be neutral. Acids have pH values lower than 7, and alkalines have pH values higher than 7. The scale is logarithmic, which means a drop of one in the pH level represents a tenfold increase in acidity. Thus a pH of 6 is 10 times more acidic than water; a pH of 5 is 100 times more acidic. Even unpolluted rainfall has a pH of around 5.6 because it includes dissolved carbon dioxides. Precipitation with a lower pH than this is considered acid rain.

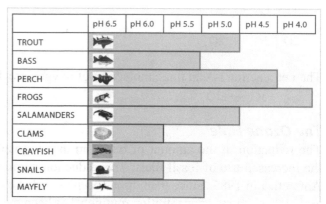

Acid rain has a detrimental effect on human and animal health, endangers plant and marine lives, and degrades materials. Green algae disappear at a pH of 5.8. Clams, snails, salmon, trout, salamander, and bass can survive in rivers that are a bit more acidic (Figure 7-9). Many marine species, such as frogs and toads, die in acidic lakes with a pH lower than 4.

Figure 7-9
Lethal acidity for marine life.

The health problems associated with acid rain include lung and other respiratory ailments. Its primary effect on plants is the leaching and blocking of the uptake of nutrients and essential minerals, such as calcium and magnesium, from the plants' roots. Acids are also highly corrosive and attack metals and other construction materials (Figure 7-10).

Acid rain adversely affects lakes and ponds. The severity of the problem depends on the nature of the lake. In some parts of the world, lakes are in limestone (calcium carbonate) that neutralizes the acid and, therefore, provides a buffer against acid rain. In other regions, including the northern U.S., Canada, and most of Europe, lakes are in granite and have a smaller buffering capacity. Therefore, acid rain poses a greater threat to fish, salamanders, and frogs in these areas. At higher levels of acidity, bacteria and water plants also die. Under these conditions, lake water looks pure, while a healthy lake might appear cloudy because of the natural plant life in it. To increase the alkalinity of the soil and water, some people have proposed liming them; however, this process has proven prohibitively expensive.

Figure 7-10
The sandstone statue at Castle of Herten in Germany is strongly defigured by acid precipitation in the atmosphere. The figure at left taken in 1908 shows relatively little damage after 206 years of exposure since creation in 1702. The picture at right was taken in 1960, shows loss of most details after only 52 years.

The best method to combat acid deposition is by preventing its formation; it can be achieved mainly by burning low-sulfur coal, substituting natural gas for coal in generating electricity, increasing the use of renewable energy sources, and improving energy efficiency. Many nations have enacted laws to limit their sulfur emissions, mainly by installing scrubbers. Scrubbers remove sulfur dioxide by spraying power plants' exhausts with a limestone mist to produce sludge that can be dumped or used to make boards suitable for home building.

Smog

Smog is a result of physical and chemical activities between various pollutants released from smokestacks *(smoke)* in the presence of *fog* (thus the word *smog*). **Classical smog** refers mainly to the plume of sulfur oxides and particulate matter generated from the combustion of coal and petroleum products. It is formed primarily in the early morning, during winter months, and in places of high humidity where condensation of water vapor over smoke particles is easier. The infamous London Smog of December 5, 1952, is probably the worst air pollution episode ever recorded. High concentration of sulfur dioxide from dirty coal-fired power plants along with soot from a large number of diesel buses and generators blown across the English Channel from industrial areas of Continental Europe formed a persistent blanket over a windless foggy London, causing a temperature inversion (See below) with cold, stagnant air trapped under a layer of warm air. When inversion was finally lifted, at least 8,000 and perhaps as many as 12,000 people had been killed.

Photochemical smog is very different from classical smog because it is formed under specific meteorological conditions and only when a large amount of sunlight is available. It forms when nitric oxides and hydrocarbons react in the presence of sunlight to produce ozone; this ozone can be further oxidized to produce nitrogen dioxide and other photochemical oxidants.

The Los Angeles Basin is a prime location for photochemical activities because of the large number of cars and power stations, plenty of sunlight, and proximity to water. Furthermore, the basin is surrounded on three sides by mountains, which prevents the dispersion of pollutants. To make matters worse, Los Angeles has many days in which a thermal (or temperature) inversion layer blankets the basin and prevents the upward mixing of pollutants with atmospheric air. The situation can be visualized as having a pot (basin) filled with water (oceans) and other ingredients (pollutants), with the lid closed (the inversion layer) to prepare a stew (photochemical smog). All that is missing is the heat, which is provided by the abundant Southern California sun (Figure 7-11).

The severity of smog is strongly dependent on the concentration of various pollutants, atmospheric temperature

---

Dinosaurs and Air Pollution

Dinosaurs dominated the earth for nearly 130 million years but became victims of an unthinkable mass extinction some 65 million years ago. In 1979, Luis and Walter Alvarez, a father-son scientist team, suggested that extreme pollution was, in fact, a major contributor to the dinosaurs' demise. The scientists proposed that an asteroid or comet had smashed into the earth and caused a series of catastrophic events that wiped out the dinosaurs within a blink of a geological eye. A compelling piece of evidence discovered was an excess of iridium and other rare elements in a rock layer determined to be about 65 million years old. In 1992, further support for the hypothesis came in the form of a giant crater found in Mexico, spanning about 300 km.[i]

The asteroid that possibly produced the crater is estimated to have had a mass of approximately 2×10^{16} kg, which collided with the earth at a speed 10 km/s. This amounts to about 10^{24} J of kinetic energy, which is roughly equivalent to about two billion Hiroshima bombs. The debris from the impact might have risen as high as several kilometers into the atmosphere.

In addition to polluting the air with dust and acid rain, the impact caused huge tidal waves and earthquakes — much larger than anything experienced in recent history. And if that were not enough, the combined effect of a darkened, wintry sky and the release of vast quantities of carbon dioxide (normally trapped in the soil and water) would undoubtedly produce calamitous extremes of cold and/or heat in the climate. Such abrupt environmental changes evidently exceeded the ability of the dinosaurs — and certainly of many other living organisms — to adapt and condemned them to remain forever as spectacles of extinction.

[i] *Alvarez, L., Alvarez, W., Giant Crater Linked to Mass Extinction, Science News, Vol. 142, No. 7, August 1992, pp.100.*

Figure 7-11
The brown coloration in the background is an indication of formation of photochemical smog in Los Angeles.
Source: Wikipeda Commons.

and humidity, and sunlight intensity -- all highly influenced by atmospheric stability and whether it results in the presence of temperature inversion.

Meteorology

The earth's atmosphere can be divided into layers with distinct temperature profiles (Figure 7-12). The layer closest to the ground is the *troposphere* extending from sea level to a height that varies from 10 km over the poles to 16 km over the equator. In this region, the temperature drops with elevation.[††] The troposphere is the region where most climatic activities take place and are by far the most important region for air pollution studies. Above the troposphere, lies the *stratosphere*, which extends to about 50 km in altitude. Temperature is nearly constant for the first 10 km but then rises with altitude, due to the synthesis of ozone from oxygen involving the absorption of short-wave radiation from the sun. The temperature rises from -40°C to -50°C at the base of the stratosphere to about 0°C at the top of the stratosphere. The *mesosphere* extends from the top of the stratosphere to 85 km; the temperature drops one more time, reaching -100°C, the coldest point in the atmosphere. The uppermost layer is the *thermosphere*. Intense ultraviolet radiation causes ionization of the few air particles remaining in the atmosphere, and temperature rapidly rises to exceed 500°C.

Unlike atmospheric temperature that increases and decreases with height, the pressure in the atmosphere always drops with elevation, but the change is not linear. This is because density in the air does not remain constant with height. The farther away from the ground we go, the lesser will be the effect of gravity, and the more the air molecules can spread out. This is not true in water. Water is rather incompressible, so its density remains nearly constant with depth, causing pressure to rise linearly with depth at the rate of roughly one atmosphere for every 10 meters.

Temperature Inversion

Under normal conditions, the air is colder as we go higher and higher in elevation. Warm air by the surface rises and wind allows for mixing of warmer and cooler air. As a result, temperature decreases with increasing altitude (Figure 7-13 left). Under the condition of temperature inversion, the opposite occurs, i.e. temperature increases rather than decreases, with altitude.

Most thermal inversions happen near the surface and at nights when winds are calmer and skies are clear. Once the sun goes down, the ground loses heat quickly and cools the air next to it. Under these conditions, a warm layer is sandwiched between a layer of cold air near the surface and another cold layer in the upper atmosphere (Figure 7-13 right). Winter nights are colder and last longer than summer nights, making surface inversions stronger and more <u>common during</u> the winter months.

[††] The exception is over the polar ice caps, where the temperature actually rises rather than declines for the first 3 km before it begins to drop..

When the sun rises the next day and warms the ground, surface inversion weakens and eventually disappears. During certain meteorological conditions, such as strong high-pressure systems over an area, inversions can persist for several days. In addition, local topographical features can enhance the formation of inversions, especially in valley locations.

Thermal inversions tend to exacerbate the effect of air pollution, making the air unhealthy especially for people with medical ailment and breathing difficulties. The lower the inversion, the smaller the volume that is available for pollutants to mix, and concentrations are greater.

Air Pollution Standards

There are no air pollution standards that are universally adopted by all countries. The World Health Organization (WHO) has provided air quality guidelines for key pollutants (SO_2, NO_2, CO, O_3, and lead) to enable countries to set their national or regional air quality standards within the context of existing environmental, social, economic, and cultural conditions. In the United States, the agency responsible for setting, monitoring, and enforcing air quality standards is the Environmental Protection Agency (EPA). In 1963, Congress passed the Clean Air Act (CAA), requiring EPA to develop **National Ambient Air Quality Standards** (NAAQS) for pollutants considered harmful to public health and the environment. EPA set two kinds of standards for improving average air quality at the federal level: **primary standards** to protect public health, and **secondary standards** to protect public welfare, including protection against decreased visibility and damage to animals, crops, vegetation, and buildings. Individual states could set more stringent standards if they desired. Because air pollution does not recognize any boundaries, various states and governments have established guidelines that regulate interstate and inter-continent pollution transport. Furthermore, it is each state's responsibility to develop *state implementation plans* that set the procedures to achieve state and federal goals.

For areas already cleaner than NAAQS, a three-tiered system was established to prevent significant deterioration of air quality. In Tier 1 regions (mainly national parks), the emission levels were frozen at their 1997 level when air quality standards were established. Tier 2 included most regions and allowed some reduction in air quality, whereas the quality of Tier 3 regions could eventually deteriorate to the minimum air quality standards. Geographical areas that do not meet the emission standards are called *non-attainment* areas.

Table 7-2 compares the current guidelines established by the

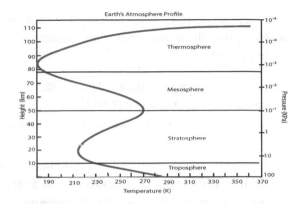

Figure 7-12
Atmospheric temperature profile with height

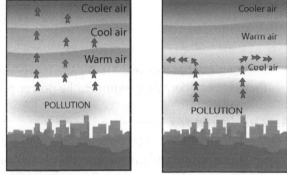

Normal Pattern   Thermal Inversion

Figure 7-13
Effect of thermal inversion on pollution.

Table 7-2 Standards for Common Pollutants (2015)*			
		Concentration	
Pollutant	**Exposure time**	**WHO (μg/ m^3)**	**U.S. EPA**
CO	1 hour	--	35 ppm
	8 hours	10,000	9 ppm
NO_2	1 hour	200	100 ppb
	1 year	40	53 ppb
SO_2	24 hours	125	0.14 ppm
	1 year	50	0.03 ppm
O_3	8 hour	100	0.075 ppm
PM2.5	24 hours	25	35 μg/m^3
	1 year	10	15 μg/m^3
PM10	24 hours	50	150 μg/m^3
	1 year	20	
Lead	1 quarter	---	0.15 μg/m^3

Source:
US EPA: http://www.epa.gov/air/criteria.html
WHO: http://apps.who.int/iris/bitstream/10665/

WHO and the U.S. EPA for various pollutant concentrations and exposure times. In the United States, as a result of implementing these standards, the emission of the criteria pollutants has been consistently reduced and air quality has improved.

In addition to setting the standards for criteria air pollutants, NAAQS has established the National Emission Standard for Hazardous Air Pollutants (NESHAP), which sets safety standards for seven regulated toxic substances -- asbestos, arsenic, benzene, beryllium, mercury, radionuclides, and vinyl chloride.

Example 7-2: A monitoring station near a coal power plant measures sulfur dioxide concentrations of 200 µg/m^3 between the hours of 7:00 a.m. and 5:00 p.m. It drops to 60 µg/m^3 at all other times. Determine whether this power plant satisfies the WHO's guidelines.

Solution: Within any 24-hour period, the power plant emits 200 µg/m^3 for 10 hours of operation and 60 µg/m^3 for the remaining 14 hours. The average 24-hour emission is calculated as:

$$\text{Average daily concentration} = \frac{(10 \times 200) + (14 \times 60)}{24} = 118 \frac{\mu g}{m^3}$$

Although the power plant narrowly meets the WHO's guidelines in any 24-hr average (See Table 7-2), unless there is considerable downtime, the power plant is likely to exceed the one-year average emission guidelines.

Air Quality Index

The Air Quality Index (AQI) was established by the EPA as a simple indication of how clean the air is on a given day and what precautions, if any, need to be taken in carrying out daily activities. The AQI can be viewed as a yardstick to measure the cumulative effects of the criteria air pollutants on human health. It is calculated based on several factors, such as ambient air temperature, wind conditions, and concentrations of various pollutants.[‡‡] The value of 100 is arbitrarily assigned to air that barely meets the national air quality standards. A value lower than 100 means acceptable air quality and successively lower values mean comparatively cleaner air. Values above 100 signify unhealthy air. The higher the AQI number, the more health risks to individuals. Under these conditions, sensitive groups such as children, the elderly, and adults with heart disease, asthma, and other respiratory complications are at higher risk and must limit their outdoor activities. When the AQI climbs above 200, everyone is affected. AQI above 300 is considered hazardous and everyone should avoid prolonged outdoor exposure (See Table 7-3). In the United States, the AQI is usually below 100 for most communities, but may exceed this value a few times per year; in recent years, the AQI has rarely gone beyond 200. Similar standards are set in other major cities around the world. ⓐ

Table 7-3 Air Quality Index	
Air Quality Index (AQI)	**Levels of Health Concern**
0 to 50	Good
51 to 100	Moderate
101 to 150	Unhealthy for sensitive people
151 to 200	Unhealthy
201 to 300	Very unhealthy
301 to 500	Hazardous

Control and Prevention

The best way to control pollutants is to prevent them from forming in the first place. The obvious choice is to reduce fossil fuel consumption and switch to cleaner sources of energy. Short of that, cleaning the fuel and modifying combustion processes are probably our next best options. As a last resort, we may opt to remove gaseous and particulate pollutants from the exhaust before they are released into the atmosphere.

Fortunately, technologies exist today that can help reduce environmental impacts at every stage in the process. New technologies have made many alternative and renewable sources of energy cheaper, and in some instances, competitive with fossil fuels. Several new processes have been developed that show the promise of more efficient

‡‡ You can compare AQI to DowJones Industrial Average, where the health of the economy is measured based on the average price of selected stocks.

combustion and reduced air pollution. Cogeneration and combined-cycle combustion turbines have helped to improve efficiency and reduce pollution considerably.

These technologies can reduce particulate and sulfur emissions to a high degree, but still produce substantial amounts of gaseous and particulate emissions, which must be removed before they are released into the atmosphere (end-of-the-pipe control technologies). Depending on the nature and size of the particulates, they can be removed by cyclones, baghouses, filters, scrubbers, or electrostatic precipitators. Gaseous pollutants can be removed by physical and chemical adsorption. Fuel desulfurization and limestone scrubbing can control sulfur dioxide emissions. Nitric oxides and oxides of carbon are best removed by various flue gas treatment techniques. In fluidized bed combustion, coal is pulverized and suspended on a bed of air, improving mixing while lowering the combustion temperature, which reduces both carbon dioxide and nitric oxide emission. Vehicular emission is controlled by catalytic converters, where small pellets of palladium and platinum transform carbon monoxide and nitric oxides into carbon dioxide and nitrogen. Automotive emissions were discussed in some detail in Chapter 6. Thanks to strict environmental control in the United States, the emission of various criteria pollutants has dropped in the past quarter of a century (Figure 7-14).

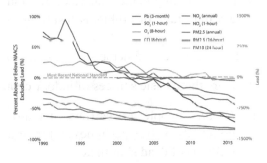

Figure 7-14

Comparison of the emissions for four criteria pollutants in the United States for the period 1980-2008.
Source: EPA, (http://www.epa.gov).

Summary

The degree to which fossil fuels impact our atmosphere and the climate depends on many factors: the rate at which population grows, the world economy, the state of technology, and also the willingness of citizenry to participate in preserving the environment. Various climate change treaties are expected to have only limited success in curbing global warming unless they include provisions that require reducing greenhouse gas emissions by all countries; that scenario will be possible only if industrialized countries help the "less-developed" countries with technologies that enable them to reduce their carbon footprints with little or no economic hardship. In the end, this may prove to be a more economically viable option than costs associated with carbon dioxide removal and sequestration. Attempts to reduce or slow the impacts of global warming fall into one of the following two categories.

a. Reduce the levels of greenhouse gases in the atmosphere. This possibly can be done by enhancing uptake and storage by terrestrial and oceanic biological systems and by various physical, chemical, and biological approaches;

b. Reduce the net incoming short-wave ultra-violet and visible solar radiation received, by deflecting sunlight, or by increasing the reflectivity (albedo) of the atmosphere, clouds, and the earth's surface, allowing outgoing long-wave infrared radiation to escape. Toward this goal, the United Nations (UN) has organized several international conferences to draft contracts and adopt guidelines to fight global warming. The most notable was the 1997 Kyoto Accord that mandated each signatory to reduce its carbon emission by 10% from its 1990 levels by the end of 2012 when the Kyoto Treaty expired. Although overall global emission of carbon dioxide has increased by almost 60% from 1990 until 2014 -- which is contrary to the UN's stated goal of reducing the greenhouse gases, the agreement is generally deemed successful, as, by February 2015, Western European countries, Russia, and Australia had reduced their emissions by over 20 percent—well above the ten percent target they aimed to meet. The United States' rise was moderate, at 6%. China and India, on the other hand, continued to dump carbon dioxide into the atmosphere at fast rates, although China's emission has since stalled, mainly by moving away from coal, by structural changes in the economy, and the energy mix.

ⓐ *Digging Deeper: Indoor Air Pollution*

We spend over 90% of our lives indoors, so the quality of the indoor air we breathe is particularly important. Unfortunately, over the past few decades, indoor air quality has continuously deteriorated. To reduce the heating and cooling loads, many newer buildings have been weather-proofed by insulating walls and ceilings and by sealing windows resulting in inadequate ventilation. Little did we realize that these cost- and energy-saving measures would cause a multitude of problems resulting in what is now commonly known as the "sick-building syndrome." It is estimated that 20-30% of people are exposed to toxins, and losses exceeding $250 billion are attributed to sick buildings. Figure 7-15 demonstrates common contaminants contributing to a house with unhealthy indoor air quality.

There are three basic sources of indoor contaminants:

1. *People:* People are carriers of many contaminants such as bacteria, germs, allergens, and not-so-obvious pollutants such as perfumes and fragrances. Even the simple act of breathing can emit many chemicals and shed millions of dead skin flakes.
2. *Building materials:* These include construction materials such as formaldehyde outgassed from particle boards, paint, glue, wax, fiberglass, paper, dust, lint, carpet fibers, dirt, detergents, and other cleaning materials, and, in the case of old buildings, asbestos from ceiling tiles.
3. *Processes:* Major contributing processes are tobacco smoking and indoor appliances, such as copying machines, computers, gas water heaters, gas stoves, and oven ranges.

There is no federal law to regulate or limit indoor air pollutants. Several states have enacted regulations in terms of building codes and developed mostly voluntary guidelines. In the absence of federal laws, it is best to use common sense and implement strategies that safeguard our health and the health of our loved ones. These may include removing sources by eliminating or reducing the use of toxins and substituting them with more environmentally friendly chemicals, proper maintenance, and increased ventilation.

Toxins in the Environment

Toxins are poisonous substances capable of damage or causing disease on contact with, or absorption by internal and external body tissues. In fact, whether a substance is toxic or not, depends on a large degree on its dosage. As the 15th century Swiss physician, Paracelsus said, at *sufficiently high doses, all substances are toxic.*

Depending on the form that various substances can take in the atmosphere, toxins are classified as:

	Name	Source	Danger		Name	Source	Danger
1	Nitrogen Oxides	Unvented gas and wood stoves, kerosene heaters	Irritated lungs, colds, headache	8	Particulates	Pollen, pet, dander, dust mites, smoke particles	Irritated eyes and lungs, asthma attacks, runny nose
2	Carbon mon-oxide	Faulty furnaces, unvented gas, wood, and kerosene heaters	Headaches, arrhyth-mia, drowsiness, death	9	Benzo-a-pyrene	Tobacco smoke, cigarettes	Lung cancer, respitory ailment
3	Para-dichlorobenzene	Air fresheners, mothball crystals	Cancer	10	Phthalates	Laminate wood, and vinyl flooring	Liver, kidneys, and reproductive system
4	Tetrachloroeth-ylen	Dry-cleaning fluid fumes on clothes	Nerve disorders, damage to liver and kidneys	11	Asbestos	Pipe insulation, vinyl ceiling and floor tiles	Lung disease, lung cancer
5	Styrene	Carpets, plastic products	Kidney and liver damage	12	Radon-222	Radioactive soil and rock, water supply	Lung cancer
6	Chloroform	Chlorine- treated water in hot showers	Cancer	13	Methylene chloride	Paint strippers and thinners	Nerve disorders, diabetes
7	Formaldehyde	Furniture stuffing, particle board, foam insulation	Irritation of eyes, throat, skin, and lungs	14	Dust, pollen, pesticides, and herbicides	Yards (not shown)	Allergies

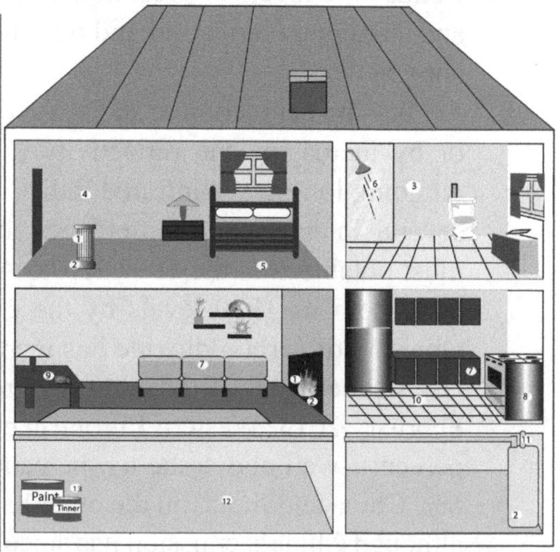

Figure 7-15
Sources of indoor air pollution.

Gases are fluids that can expand or contract to take any shape and volume by changing their temperatures and pressures. Gases can diffuse through other gases and liquids and may react with them to form other substances.

Vapors are the gaseous states of substances that are normally liquid or solid but can be changed to the "gaseous" form by changing their temperatures and pressures. The process that turns a liquid into vapor is called *evaporation*. Under certain conditions, solids are turned directly to vapors without going through the liquid phase *(sublimation)*.

Mists are suspended liquid droplets generated by *condensation* from the vapor into a dispersed liquid state, such as by splashing, foaming, and atomizing.

Fumes are solid particles generated from the volatilization of molten metals.

Dust is solid particles generated by crushing, grinding, and detonating rocks, metal, coal, wood, etc. Unlike fumes that often flocculate or coalesce, dust particles do not, unless they are exposed to electrostatic forces. Dust particles are generally larger than mists and fumes, and settle under the influence of gravity, rather than diffuse in the air.

Toxicity

Toxins and their impacts on human health is a topic of great interest by many researchers, academicians, and policymakers. *Toxicologists* are interested in the type of injuries suffered as a direct result of exposure to toxins, and whether their effects are local or systemic. *Epidemiologists* investigate and describe the short and long-term effects of pollutants, whether they are acute or chronic, examine morbidity and mortality data on such factors as age, gender, and geographical location, and develop the means for prevention or control. *Applied epidemiologists*, who usually work for state health agencies, respond to disease outbreaks, determining their causes and helping to contain them. *Research epidemiologists* study diseases in laboratories and in the field to determine how to prevent future outbreaks.

TOXIC HAZARD

Toxicity is measured commonly by threshold limit values (TLVs) and mean lethal dose (LD$_{50}$).

Threshold Limit Values refer to airborne concentrations and represent conditions under which it is believed most workers can be exposed safely for 8-hours a day, 5-days a week. TLVs are often meant to provide on-the-job safety standards for people who work with toxic or hazardous materials. For gases and vapors, the TLV is usually expressed in parts per million of air. For fumes, mists, and some dust, the TLV is often listed as milligrams per cubic meter (mg/m^3). With few exceptions, TLVs are time-weighted average concentrations, i.e., it is occasionally accepted that, as long as the average concentration remains below the threshold value, the concentration values may exceed the threshold for short periods.

Table 7-4 LD-50 Values for Selected Toxins.	
Compound	*mg/kg*
Potassium cyanide	10
Tetraethyl lead	35
Lead	100
DDT	150
Aspirin	1,500
Table salt	3,000

Source: Sinnott, R. K., "Chemical Engineering Design," Butterworth-Heinemann, 2005.

The median lethal dose (LD$_{50}$) is the statistical estimate of the dosage that kills 50% of a large population of test animals exposed to a toxin. *LD$_{50}$* is usually expressed as milligrams of poison per kilogram of body mass (mg/kg). The assumption is that it takes twice the dose to kill a large animal that is twice the weight of a smaller animal. Table 7-4 lists the LD-50 values for a few substances measured in rats.

Example 7-1: What is the amount of salt that a 75-kg person can ingest before it reaches its toxic limit?
Solution: Referring to Table 7-4, and assuming that toxicity values tested on rats can be extrapolated to humans, we can estimate the toxicity limit as 75 kg x 3,000 mg/kg = 225,000 mg = 225 g.

ⓐ *Digging Deeper: Effects of Air Pollutants*

The degree to which materials are toxic varies depending on whether the exposure is local or over the entire body, and whether is from a single exposure or multiple exposures over an extended period. A **local effect** refers to an effect that takes place at the point or area of the contact. For example, a spill of acid on the skin is a local effect. The point of contact can be external (skin, eyes, or mucous membrane) or internal (gastrointestinal). A **systemic effect** refers to an effect after the material has been ingested or absorbed into the body in either a single dose or in multiple exposures. As an example, the effect of arsenic exposure can become apparent in the bloodstream, nervous system, liver, kidneys, and skin sometimes after only one exposure has taken place. The effect of heavy metals such as mercury and lead might become apparent after multiple exposures.

Effects can be either acute or chronic, depending on the length of time the exposure has occurred. **Acute effects** are those characterized by sudden absorption of the toxic substance during a single large exposure. Acute health effects are often reversible. For example, carbon monoxide or cyanide poisoning can be reversible if the victim is treated immediately. **Chronic effects** are characterized by prolonged or repeated exposures over many days, months, or years. Symptoms may not be immediately apparent. Chronic health effects are often irreversible.

Atmospheric pollution can affect the environment by producing smog, depleting ozone, reducing visibility, and accelerating global warming. It damages plants by destroying their chlorophyll, which causes yellowing and the dropping of their leaves, and damaging crops. It makes lakes, rivers, and aquifers acidic, which kills fish and other marine species, and damages crops. Climate change may indirectly increase the risk of some infectious diseases, particularly malaria, yellow fever, and other diseases that appear in warm areas or are spread by mosquitoes and other insects.

Many of the emissions released into the atmosphere are directly or indirectly *corrosive and attack buildings and materials* at a great cost. Dust and soot particulates, especially in the humid air, cause the erosion and soiling of buildings, paintings, and sculptures. Nitrogen and sulfur oxides cause deterioration of cotton and nylon, corrosion of metals, and fading of dyes.

The health effects associated with air pollution are numerous and depending on their types and concentrations, and the duration of exposure, vary from burning eyes and nose, irritated throat, and pulmonary diseases such as bronchitis and emphysema, to more severe effects such as cancer, birth defects, brain and nerve damage, and death. Even a single exposure can be catastrophic. A testament to this is the notorious London episode of 1952, which, as a result of thick fog and a high concentration of carbon and sulfate particles, caused many thousands of people to become sick and die. The 1984 release of methyl isocyanate from a Union Carbide pesticide plant in Bhopal, India, killed 2,500 people and injured numerous others.

The most important pollutants directly affecting human health are:

Carbon monoxide -- is a colorless, odorless gas produced most principally by vehicles. Other sources include fuel combustion in boilers and incinerators. When inhaled, carbon monoxide diffuses through the lungs into the bloodstream, where it reacts with blood hemoglobin, displacing the oxygen. Consequently, the body will be deprived of oxygen, resulting in headaches, fatigue, impaired judgment, and in extreme cases, suffocation and death. Prolonged exposure to low levels of carbon monoxide has been linked to cardiovascular diseases and premature birth.

Nitrogen oxides -- Combustion sources emit two forms of oxides of nitrogen, nitric oxide (NO), and nitrogen dioxide (NO_2). Nitric oxide is not a health hazard directly but reacts with oxygen to form nitrogen dioxide, which is a major pollutant. As result monitoring stations report only the sum of these two compounds (called NOx and pronounced *nocks*). The most important health effect associated with nitrogen dioxide is the reduction of the body's resistance to infection. Nitrogen dioxide also limits plant growth, causes corrosion

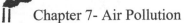

in metals, and is a major cause of global warming, acid deposition, and photochemical smog. In the presence of sunlight, nitrogen dioxide reacts with hydrocarbons to form ozone.

Sulfur dioxide -- The principal source of sulfur dioxide is the combustion of sulfur-rich fuels (mainly coal) in stationary power stations, refineries, and industrial processing plants. Sulfur dioxide is highly soluble in water, and when inhaled, is absorbed easily in moist areas of the nose, throat, or mouth. Some sulfur dioxide recombines with water formed during combustion and forms particulate sulfate. Long-term exposure to sulfur dioxide increases mortality rates, especially among those with cardiac and lung diseases.

Particulates -- The main sources of particulates are power plants and diesel cars, although smaller sources such as wood stoves, agricultural burning, and dust also contribute. Particulates can vary in size from a fraction of a micron to many hundreds of microns. Larger particles are responsible for reduced visibility and will eventually settle, whereas smaller particles become airborne and may be inhaled, diffuse, and be adsorbed, and deposited on the interiors of the lungs, potentially contributing to lung damage and cancer. Particles larger than 10 microns are entirely blocked by the nose. Smaller particles in the range of 0.5-5 microns can travel as far as the bronchioles before they are deposited onto the inner walls or may enter the bloodstream, causing a variety of health problems, including heart disease and other cardiovascular complications. The intermediate size particles pass through the upper respiratory system and exhaled. For the same mass, smaller particles have relatively larger surface areas and, therefore, could absorb a higher percentage of toxins and other carcinogenic materials. Some particles, such as ocean salt and fine soot, can act as nuclei sites for water condensation and fog formation. Particulates with diameters smaller than 10 microns (PM10) are a major component of indoor air pollution and forest fires. Particulates smaller than 2.5 microns (PM2.5) are mostly the result of fossil fuel combustion from vehicle exhaust, industrial production, and power plants, as well as from natural sources such as windblown dust and volcanic activity.

Fly ash, a byproduct of burning pulverized coal in electric generation power plants carries into the surrounding environment 100 times more radiation than a nuclear power plant producing the same amount of energy.

Lead Lead is a poisonous metal emitted from old automobile exhausts, paints, storage batteries, and pipes. Lead has been linked to impairment of brain development in infants and children, and hypertension in adults. Depending on its concentration, lead can damage the lungs and may lead to convulsions, brain damage, and even death.

Mercury -- Mercury is one of the rare metals that remains liquid at atmospheric temperature and pressure. Trace amounts of mercury exist in coal and other fossil fuels. When these fuels burn, mercury vapor is released into the atmospheric air, water, and soil. Prolonged mercury exposure can cause neurological and behavioral dysfunctions.

Volatile organic compounds -- VOCs are the main constituents of fossil fuels, industrial chemicals, solvents, and lubricants, and numerous other petrochemicals, and play an important role in the formation of ozone. Methane is not considered a VOC since it does not significantly participate in ozone formation. In addition to these pollutants, there are pollutants present mostly in indoor environments and include:

Radon is a naturally occurring radioactive noble gas derived from the radioactive decay of radium found in uranium ores and common materials such as granite and limestone. It diffuses through rocks and soil and enters through cracks into concrete and clay basements. When inhaled, a small amount diffuses through the lungs damaging cells that line the lung. According to EPA estimates, about 20,000 persons develop lung cancer as a result of exposure to radon seeping into their homes. Areas with naturally high concentrations of radon are Brazil, China, India, and Iran. The health impacts of exposure to ionizing radiation will be discussed in greater detail in Chapter 8.

Tobacco smoking is a significant contributor to indoor air pollution. Worldwide, between two to three million people die annually of smoke-related diseases such as lung cancer, emphysema, and bronchitis. The number in the United States is around 400,000. It has been reported that even a single cigarette in an office can quickly raise the levels of particulate matter to over 30 times the EPA standards. In addition to tar and nicotine, tobacco smoke produces hundreds of chemicals, most considered to be carcinogenic.

The concern about smoking became significantly greater when it was discovered that smoking was not only a hazard for the smokers themselves but the people around them. As evidence of the dangers of secondhand smoking mounted, smoking was banned in public places such as office buildings, theaters, shopping malls, buses, and airplanes in many U.S. and Canadian cities. Other countries are slowly following the U.S.'s lead.

Asbestos refers to a group of six types of naturally occurring minerals. Because of its insulation properties, asbestos has been widely used in woven fiber mats, fireproof suits, gloves, gaskets, brake shoes, and even gas masks. The structural strength of this material led to the introduction of many products, including thread used by heart surgeons, fireproof mailbags used by U.S. Postal Service workers, filters for purifying orange juice, wine, sugar, and yes, even toothpaste.

The most popular applications of asbestos have been its use as the insulating material in roof panels and corrugated walls. Reports of fibrotic lung damage (asbestosis) among textile workers and WWII-era ship insulators, massive increases in the number of lawsuits, and pressure from labor unions have forced the EPA to ban the use of asbestos in most products. Asbestos is still used in U.S. Navy submarines; the space shuttles' solid fuel boosters carry asbestos-impregnated rubber liners to protect the steel casings from the heat of takeoff. The use of asbestos in new buildings has been banned and there are efforts to remove it from older buildings.

Pesticide is a general term that refers not only to insecticides (for killing insects), but also herbicides (for controlling weeds), fungicides, and fumigants.

Mold refers to the growth of microorganisms on damp surfaces. Much of the mold found indoors comes from outdoor sources.

Ozone is an irritant gas usually associated with photochemical smog. Ozone is highly reactive, attacking and oxidizing almost anything it contacts and is a precursor to the formation of smog. Some office copying machines also produce this chemical and, therefore, can be considered as a potential indoor pollutant. Ozone's major impacts are reduced visibility and damage to vegetation, materials, and human health. Ozone also causes shortness of breath, asthma, chronic bronchitis, and fatigue. Obstructive pulmonary diseases such as chronic bronchitis, lung emphysema, and asthma epidemics, especially in children in industrialized countries, can be attributed directly to ozone.

Other harmful substances found in everyday, household products include formaldehyde, benzene, and chlorinated compounds. Formaldehyde, a component of glue, resins, paint surface coatings, particleboards, insulation foam, and wood paneling, is present in most furniture, shelving, and cabinetry. The major health effects associated with formaldehyde are headaches, dizziness, burning of the eyes and throat, nausea, and dermatitis. Benzene is known to cause leukemia and is present in most petrochemical products, tobacco smoke, and also many household products. Chlorinated substances are found in many dry cleaners, spray aerosols, and paint removers. PCB or polychlorinated biphenyl is used in insulation, lubricants, paint, and fluorescent lights. PCB is carcinogenic and is known to damage the liver, the skin, and cause congenital disabilities. @

ⓐ *Digging Deeper: Unit Conversion*

Emission guidelines for common pollutants are given in Table 7-3 for WHO and EPA. The United States often expresses the emissions in parts per million (ppm), whereas WHO gives similar data in the unit of $\mu g/m^3$. Assuming that the ideal gas approximation applies ($C_i = p_i / RT$), we have:

$$C_i\,(ppm) = \frac{R_u T}{p\,(MW_i)} \times C_i\,(\frac{\mu g}{m^3})$$

Where:

R_u = 8.314 Pa.m^3/K.mol is the universal gas constant
T = Temperature (K),
p_i = Partial pressure of species i (Pa)
MW_i = Molecular weight of species i (g/mol)

At STP, T= 273 K, and p = 1.0133x10^5 Pa, and the equation simplifies to

$$C_i(ppm) = \frac{0.0224}{MW_i} \times C_i(\frac{\mu g}{m^3}) \tag{7-1}$$

Example 7-3: Convert the ambient ozone concentration of 0.05 ppm to $\mu g/m^3$.
Solution: Molecular weight of ozone is MW = 48 g/mol. We have:

$$C_i = \frac{48}{0.0224} \times 0.05 = 107.1\,\frac{\mu g}{m^3} \quad ⓐ$$

📚 Endnotes

1   Climate Central (2020). Retrieved from: http://www.climatecentral.org

2   Kiehl, J. and Trenberth, K. (1997). Earth's Annual Global Mean Energy Budget. *Bulletin Of The American Meteorological Society, 78*(2), 197-208. doi:10.1175/1520-0477(1997)078<0197:eagmeb>2.0.co2

3   Kasting, J. (1998). The Carbon Cycle, Climate, And The Long-Term Effects Of Fossil Fuel Burning, *Consequences, 4*(1), http://gcrio.org/CONSEQUENCES/vol4.no1/carbcycle.html

4   Neftel, A., Moor, E., Oeschger, H., and Stauffer, B. (1985). Evidence from polar ice cores for the increase in atmospheric CO2 in the past two centuries, *Nature, 315*(6014), 45-47. doi: 10.1038/315045a0

5   Tans, P. (2007). Trends in Atmospheric Carbon Dioxide -- Mauna Loa, NOAA/ESRL.

6   The Guardian (*2020*, June 4). Atmospheric CO2 levels rise sharply despite Covid-19 lockdowns

7   Scripps Institute of Oceanography, http://scrippsco2.ucsd.edu

8   Prentice, I. et al. (2001). Technical Summary: F.3 Projections of Future Changes in Temperature. In Houghton J.T. et al (Eds.). Climate Change 2001: The Scientific Basis. Contribution of Working Group I to the Third Assessment Report of the Intergovernmental Panel on Climate Change. Geneva, Switzerland.

9   Muller, R. (2011, October 21). The Case Against Global-Warming Skepticism, *The Wall Street Journal.*

10 Rohde R, Muller RA, Jacobsen R, Muller E, Perlmutter S, et al. (2013) "A New Estimate of the Average Earth Surface Land Temperature Spanning 1753 to 2011," Geoinfor Geostat: An Overview 1:1. doi:10.4172/2327-4581.1000101

11 Trenberth, K., et al. (2007). Observations: Surface and Atmospheric Climate Change, *Climate Change* 2007: The Physical Science Basis. Contribution of Working Group I to the Fourth Assessment Report of the Intergovernmental Panel on Climate Change, edited by S., D Solomon, et al., Cambridge University Press, Cambridge, United Kingdom.

12 NASA Media Resources, (2021). Retrieved from https://www.nasa.gov/mission_pages/sunearth/solar-events-news/Does-the-Solar-Cycle-Affect-Earths-Climate.htm

13 NASA Earth Obsevatory (2021). Retrieved from https://earthobservatory.nasa.gov/features/Milankovitch/milankovitch_2.php

14 Ritchie, H., and Roser, M. (2017). Fossil Fuels, Published online at OurWorldInData.org. Retrieved from https://ourworldindata.org/fossil-fuels' [Online Resource]

15 IPCC (1996). IPCC Climate Change 1995: The Science of Climate Change. Rep IPCC, 2014: Climate Change 2014: Synthesis

Report. Contribution of Working Groups I, II and III to the Fifth Assessment Report of the Intergovernmental Panel on Climate Change [Core Writing Team, R.K. Pachauri and L.A. Meyer (eds.)]. IPCC, Geneva, Switzerland, 151. ort of the Intergovernmental Panel on Climate Change, edited by J. T. Houghton, et al., Cambridge University Press, Cambridge, England, 1996.

16 IPCC (1996). IPCC Climate Change 1995: The Science of Climate Change. Report of the Intergovernmental Panel on Climate Change, edited by J. T. Houghton, et al., Cambridge University Press, Cambridge, England, 1996. See for example the article by Richard Lindzen in the Wall Street Journal, June 11, 2001.

17 NOAA (2011). Retrieved from http://www.noaanews.noaa.gov/stories/s412.htm

18   IPCC (2012). Summary for Policy Makers: Economic and Social Dimensions of Climate Change - IPCC Working Group III (2001), Revised in 2007. Climate Change 2007: The Physical Science Basis. Available for download at http://www.ipcc.ch

19 Environmental News Network (December 13, 2001). Scientists See Threat of Abrupt World Climate (2012). Reuters article by Andrew Quinn, Retrieved from http://www.enn.com/news/wire-stories/2001/12/12132001/reu_45873.asp

20 Hodges, L. (1977). *Environmental Pollution* (2nd ed., p. 312). Holt, Rinehart and Winston.

21 IPCC (2001). Climate Change 2001: The Scientific Basis. Contribution of Working Group I to the Third Assessment Report of the Intergovernmental Panel on Climate Change (IPCC) edited by J. T. Houghton, et al., Cambridge University Press, Cambridge, United Kingdom and New York, NY, USA, pp881, 2001.

22 Shah, K. (2021). Greenland's Ice Sheet Is Releasing Huge Amounts of Mercury into Rivers, *New Scientist,* 24 May 2021.

23 Cline, W. R. (1992). The Economics of Global Warming, Washington D.C. Institute for International Economics.

24 UNICEF (2016). *Clear the Air for Children*, Oct. 2016. Retrieved from http://www.unicef.org/publications/files/UNICEF_Clear_the_Air_for_Children_30_Oct_2016.pdf

25 U.S. EPA (2021). http://nepis.epa.gov/air/urbanair

26 Fahey, D. et al. (2002). Twenty Questions and Answers About the Ozone Layer, 2002 Scientific Assessment of Ozone Depletion, Les Diablerets, Switzerland, 24-28, June 2002.

27 Molina, M. & Rowland, F. (1974). Stratospheric Sink for Chlorofluoromethanes: Chlorine Atom Catalyzed Destruction of Ozone, *Nature*, June 28.

28 Moore, C. (1995). Green Revolution in the Marketing, *Sierra*, vol. 80, January/February 1995.

29 Bell, M., Davis, D., & Fletcher, T. (2004). A retrospective assessment of mortality from the London smog episode of 1952: the role of influenza and pollution, Environmental Health Perspectives. *112*(1), 6-8. doi: 10.1289/ehp.6539

30 Flagan, R. and Seinfeld, J. (1988). *Fundamentals of Air Pollution Engineering*, Prentice-Hall.

31 Air Quality Index (2021). Retrieved from https://airnow.gov/index.cfm?action=aqibasics.aqi

32 Geoengineering the climate: science, governance, and uncertainty, (2009). *The Royal Society*, London, U.K, September 2009.

33 Trends in global CO2 emissions: 2015 Report, PBL Netherlands Environmental Assessment Agency, The Hague.

34 U.S. EPA. (1991). Indoor Air Pollution Facts, Number 4 Sick Building Syndrome, February 1991, Retrieved from http://nepis.epa.gov

35 Sax, N. I. (1984). Toxicological Effects of Non-nuclear Pollutants, Atmospheric Science and Power Production, DoE/TIC-27601, pp. 746-750.

36 Ansari, N. 1994). Plant in Bhopal: Technical Report on Population-Based Long Term Epidemiological Studies (1985-1994), Indian Council of Medical Research, New Delhi, India, Available at: http://icmr.nic.in/final/BGDRC-TEchnical%20Report.pdf

37 Neumann, R. (1973). Smoking and Air Pollution Standards, *Science, 182*, 335-336.

38 Alleman, J. and Mossman, B. (1997). Asbestos Revisited, *Scientific American*, July 1997, pp. 70-75.

39 Hvistendahl, M. (2007). Coal Ash is More Radioactive than Nuclear Waste, *Scientific American*, 13 Dec 2007

Exercises

I. Discussion Questions

1. What are the differences between weather and climate? Describe how the weather was during the last week. How do you describe the climate in the city you were born?
2. What are the natural and anthropogenic causes of climate change?
3. What is a positive and a negative feedback loop? Give an example of each
4. What is the main cause of the ozone hole? How does it relate to climate change?
5. Why do some highly polluted lakes appear to be clean?
6. Is a higher concentration of ozone in the lower atmosphere" good" or "bad? How about in the upper atmosphere? Explain.
7. What is the difference between classical and photochemical smogs? What are the conditions that either one or the other prevail?
8. What are the different layers of the atmosphere? What are the reasons for the strong variation of temperature with altitude?
9. How does pressure change with height above sea level? How does it change with water depth? Explain.
10. What is the impact of lake acidity on humans, animals, and property?

II. Problems

1. The exhaust from an old car contains 1.75% by volume of carbon monoxide. Compute the concentration of CO in milligrams/m^3 at 25°C and 1 atm of pressure.
2. Table 7-3 summarizes the emission standards set by WHO and EPA for various air pollutants. Compare the limit for an 8-hr average exposure to carbon dioxide and determine which agency sets a more restrictive standard?
3. In addition to its main constituents, nitrogen, oxygen, argon, and carbon dioxide, air contains trace amounts of other gases that include 18.2 ppm of neon, 5.2 ppm of helium, and 2 ppm of methane. Express the concentration of these gases in percentages and in µg/m^3.

4. Carbon monoxide concentration near a manufacturing plant was measured every hour during a 24-hr period, and was found to be 20 ppm from 8 a.m. to 6 p.m., but dropped to 5 ppm in the evening hours (6 p.m. to 8 a.m.). Does this factory meet the EPA's air pollution standards?
5. A monitoring station measures the ozone concentration of 80 µg/m^3 of ambient air. Express the ozone concentration in ppm.
6. The latest global carbon dioxide background concentration was measured at 408 ppm under a standard ambient atmosphere. What is the concentration in mg/m^3?

III. Multiple Choice Questions

1. What is the primary constituent of the earth's atmosphere?
   a. Nitrogen
   b. Oxygen
   c. Hydrogen
   d. Carbon dioxide
   e. Sulfur dioxide
2. In which layer of the atmosphere does weather occur?
   a. Troposphere
   b. Stratosphere
   c. Ionosphere
   d. Mesosphere
   e. Hydrosphere
3. In the past century, the average global temperature and background carbon dioxide concentration have increased by _____ °C, and _____ ppm.
   a. 0.8, 80
   b. 0.8, 320
   c. 1.6, 80
   d. 1.6, 320
   e. 1.6, 500
4. The accumulation of greenhouse gases (GHGs) causes global warming by letting sunlight into the atmosphere as _____, but trap the outgoing _____ energy, when the earth re-radiates the heat back to space.
   a. Visible light, ultraviolet radiation
   b. Visible light, infrared radiation
   c. Ultraviolet radiation, infrared radiation
   d. Infrared radiation, ultraviolet radiation
   e. Infrared radiation, visible radiation
5. Negative feedback loop

a. Results in an increase in CO_2 concentration
b. Occurs after a positive feedback system stops
c. Is a reinforcing force
d. Is a re-instating forcex
e. Has no impact on global warming phenomenon

6. The increase observed in atmospheric levels of carbon dioxide over the past 100 years is most likely due to
   a. Variations in the rate of lunar eclipses.
   b. Melting of the permafrost.
   c. The burning of fossil fuels.
   d. Thinning of the ozone layer.
   e. The advent of nuclear reactors.

7. The greenhouse effect would not occur if
   a. We had equal land masses in both the southern and the northern hemispheres.
   b. There were no forests.
   c. The earth had no atmosphere.
   d. The earth didn't have an ocean.
   e. Any of the above.

8. The average global surface temperature depends strongly on the
   a. Concentration of greenhouse gases in the atmosphere
   b. Earth's albedo
   c. Seasonal variation
   d. Solar intensity
   e. All of the above

9. Which of the following does not directly participate in the warming of the earth?
   a. Non-methane volatile organic compounds
   b. Fog and other liquid droplets
   c. Carbon monoxide
   d. Sunspots
   e. All of the above.

10. Which of the following is not a greenhouse gas?
    a. Carbon dioxide
    b. Carbon monoxide
    c. Nitrogen
    d. Nitrous oxide
    e. Methane

11. Venus temperature
    a. Is warmer than the earth because it is much bigger than earth.
    b. Is warmer than the earth because its atmosphere is mostly carbon dioxide.
    c. Is warmer than the earth because it has a very thin atmosphere.

d. Is warmer than the earth because of its close proximity to the sun.
e. Is colder than the earth because of its tilt away from the sun.

12. Carbon dioxide is a strong absorber of
    a. Gamma-ray radiation
    b. Visible light radiation
    c. Ultraviolet radiation
    d. Infrared radiation
    e. Microwave radiation

13. Ozone is a strong absorber of
    a. Gamma-ray radiation
    b. Visible light radiation
    c. Ultraviolet radiation
    d. Infrared radiation
    e. Microwave radiation

14. According to the IPCC report, as a consequence of global warming, by the end of this century
    a. The earth will warm by 10-15°C.
    b. The population of phytoplankton will double.
    c. The stratosphere will warm.
    d. We may experience a strong comeback from tropical diseases such as malaria.
    e. The rate at which carbon dioxide dissolves in water will accelerate.

15. The United States was the only country that refused to ratify the Kyoto Treaty, on the grounds that
    a. It gave unfair advantages to India and China.
    b. It adversely impacted its economy.
    c. It would drive the U.S. companies to move their manufacturing facilities overseas.
    d. The cost of cleanup would be borne solely by the U.S. and other industrialized countries.
    e. All of the above.

16. Ozone has the chemical formula _____, is generally _____ in the lower atmosphere, and is _____ in the stratosphere.
    a. O_3, beneficial, beneficial
    b. O_3, beneficial, detrimental
    c. O_3, detrimental, beneficial
    d. O_3, detrimental, detrimental
    e. O_2, detrimental, beneficial

17. GWP represents
    a. The potential damage by one kilogram of a substance.
    b. The increase in temperature as a result of adding a kilogram of a greenhouse gas.
    c. The relative effectiveness of a kilogram of

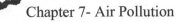

substance to that of a kilogram of carbon dioxide as a greenhouse gas.

   d. The relative effectiveness of a mole of substance to that of carbon dioxide as a greenhouse gas.

   e. The cumulative economic and environmental impacts of global warming.

18. Which of the following group of substances are most responsible for the greenhouse phenomenon?
   a. Sulfuric acid, nitric acid, and carbonic acid
   b. Carbon dioxide, chlorofluorocarbon, and ozone
   c. Nitrogen, sulfur dioxide, and methane
   d. Ozone, chlorine, and bromine
   e. All are equally responsible.

19. Which of the following is not one of the criteria pollutants for which the EPA has set air quality standards?
   a. Lead.
   b. Sulfur dioxide.
   c. Carbon dioxide.
   d. Particulates.
   e. Ground-level ozone

20. Why is carbon dioxide the most important GHG in our atmosphere?
   a. Because, on a mass basis, it is the most damaging.
   b. Because it is highly reactive.
   c. Because it is most difficult to remove from the atmosphere.
   d. Because it is the most abundant.
   e. All of the above.

21. On a per-gram basis, which of these gases is most effective in causing global warming?
   a. Carbon dioxide
   b. Carbon monoxide
   c. Ammonia
   d. Nitrogen
   e. CFCs

22. The "greenhouse effect" is mainly a result of
   a. Occasional solar flares
   b. The transparency of CO_2 and H_2O to infrared radiation.
   c. The opacity of CO_2 and H_2O to infrared radiation.
   d. The transparency of ozone to ultraviolet radiation.
   e. The reaction between carbon dioxide and ozone in upper atmospheric air.

23. A leading cause of global warming is

   a. Increased soot particles in the atmosphere resulting from forest fires.
   b. Increased carbon dioxide in the atmosphere as a result of human activity.
   c. The increased luminosity of the sun as a result of the higher frequency of solar flares.
   d. The earth is getting closer to the sun.
   e. A result of the natural solar radiation cycle.

24. Global warming deniers believe global warming is a hoax because
   a. The temperature records are not reliable.
   b. Antarctica ice sheet becomes thicker
   c. Global warming is a natural phenomenon
   d. Is because of the increase in solar activity.
   e. All of the above.

25. Carbon monoxide is dangerous to human health because
   a. It causes suffocation since it can react with hemoglobin in the blood.
   b. It eventually warms the earth to a point where life will be affected.
   c. It will reside in the lungs which eventually results in cancer.
   d. It is an important ingredient of photochemical smog.
   e. It causes extensive damage to DNA.

26. The primary source of SO_2 in the atmosphere of a large city is/are
   a. Waste disposal.
   b. Incineration.
   c. Automobiles.
   d. Volcanic ash.
   e. Power plants and other stationary sources.

27. The primary source of sulfur dioxide in the atmosphere is from _____; it harms people, animals, vegetation, and material through the formation of _____.
   a. Gasoline burning, particulate
   b. Hot springs, sulfuric acid
   c. Coal-burning, hydrocarbons
   d. Coal-burning, sulfuric acid
   e. Automobile, smog

28. Ozone depletion is a result of the
   a. The reaction between nitric oxides and hydrocarbons in the presence of sunlight.
   b. The reaction between carbon dioxide and ozone in the upper atmosphere.
   c. Leaching mechanisms that remove ozone from

the lower atmosphere.

   d. The reaction between chlorine and bromine compounds with ozone in the upper atmosphere.

   e. Reduction in photochemical activities in the stratosphere.

29. Photochemical smog has its name because
   a. The chemical industry in Los Angeles produces photons.
   b. Sunlight converts O_3 to NO.
   c. Sunlight converts NO_2 to sulfuric acid.
   d. A combination of NO, HC, and sunlight leads to the formation of O_3.
   e. A combination of SO_2 and sunlight leads to the formation of O_3.

30. Thermal inversion refers to
   a. A condition in which hotter air sits on top of cooler air.
   b. A condition in which, as a result of a lot of emissions from cars and smokestacks, temperature increases rather than decreases with height.
   c. Changes in temperature between summer and winter seasons.
   d. Cooling of the atmosphere as we move to higher elevations.
   e. A decrease in the concentration of pollutants in the upper regions of the atmosphere.

31. The most environmentally harmful emissions from gasoline cars are:
   a. CO, SO_2, and NOx.
   b. Hydrocarbon, CO, and NOx.
   c. CO_2, SO_2, and NOx.
   d. CO, O_3, and NOx.
   e. Hydrocarbon, particulates, and CO.

32. Which of the following statements is not correct?
   a. The measure of the acidity of a solution is its pH value.
   b. The pH scale ranges between 0 and 14.
   c. Pure water has a pH of 7 and is considered to be neutral.
   d. Any substance having a pH value higher than 7 is acidic.
   e. None. All are correct.

33. Which of the following is important in forming photochemical smog
   a. Sunlight
   b. Vehicular exhaust gases

   c. Temperature inversion
   d. Water
   e. All of the above

34. The reason skin cancer is caused by an increase in human exposure to the ultraviolet, but not to the visible light, is
   a. It allows high wavelength UV light into the lower atmosphere.
   b. It blocks the high-intensity UV light.
   c. It accelerates the rate of production of ozone in the lower atmosphere.
   d. UV has more energy than visible light and can break up (ionize) biological molecules more readily than light.
   e. All of the above.

35. Which chemicals are most responsible for the breakdown of ozone molecules?
   a. Carbon dioxide and carbon monoxide
   b. Sulfur and nitrogen oxides
   c. Sulfur and carbon oxides
   d. Compounds containing chlorine or phosphorus
   e. Compounds containing chlorine or bromine

36. In which layer of the atmosphere is most of the earth's ozone concentrated?
   a. Exosphere
   b. Mesosphere
   c. Thermosphere
   d. Stratosphere
   e. Troposphere

37. Which of the following statements is correct? As we go higher and higher in the atmosphere,
   a. The pressure drops linearly.
   b. The density drops linearly.
   c. The temperature drops linearly.
   d. The temperature drops exponentially.
   e. Both the density and pressure drop exponentially.

38. Which of the following statements is correct? As we go deeper and deeper in ocean water
   a. The pressure drops linearly.
   b. The temperature drops linearly.
   c. The density drops linearly.
   d. The pressure increases linearly.
   e. Pressure increases first but eventually becomes constant with depth.

39. Radon is
   a. A poisonous gas, produced in many industrial processes.

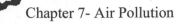

b. A naturally occurring radioactive gas derived from the decay of uranium-238.

c. Mostly absorbed by the atmosphere and is not of particular interest, except for certain regions in the United States.

d. A strong rock mostly used in building foundations.

e. A reference to the photons emitted in the radio frequency range.

40. The adverse health effect after a radioactive material has been ingested or absorbed into the body is

a. A local effect.

b. A distributed effect

c. A systemic effect.

d. An acute effect.

e. A chronic effect.

IV. True or False?

1. The best strategy to slow down the rate of ozone depletion is to ban or reduce the use of products that contain chlorine or bromine.

2. The so-called "greenhouse effect" is due, at least partially, to the opacity of CO_2 and H_2O to infrared radiation.

3. The seasonal variation in carbon dioxide concentration can be traced to changes in levels of photosynthesis activity in plants.

4. Among factors that enhance the severity of global warming is the increase in cloud cover as a result of soot nuclei generated by burning fossil fuels.

5. Chronic health effects refer to those characterized by repeated or prolonged exposure.

6. An example of an acute health effect is gradual radon poisoning from basements of old buildings.

7. According to the EPA guidelines, when the air quality index is above 150, the air is considered to be unhealthy.

8. Solar sunspots have proven to be among major contributors to global warming.

9. Criteria pollutants are harmful substances directly emitted from the source.

10. Ozone in small quantities may be refreshing, but in large concentrations causes discomfort, irritates the eyes, and reduces the human immune system.

V. Fill in the Blanks

1. Long-term storage of carbon in underground storages or in oceans is referred to as _____.

2. The main ingredients of _____ smog are sunshine, hydrocarbon, water, and nitric oxides.

3. It is widely believed that ozone destruction is a result of _____ and _____ compounds transported from the lower to the upper atmosphere.

4. In the United States, the _____ is the agency responsible for developing, monitoring, and enforcing air quality standards.

5. As of 2006, _____ has overtaken _____ as the largest contributor of greenhouse gases.

6. EPA has devised the _____ to protect public health at the federal level.

7. Most species of fish die if the pH level of lakes drops below _____.

8. According to Paracelsus, all substances are poison, at high enough _____.

PROJECT I - A Question of Ethics!

It is often argued that even if the scientific evidence does not entirely point to the extent of the global warming problem, it is best to be on the side of caution. After all, we are not losing much even if we are wrong.

a. Is it ethical to exaggerate the technical/scientific evidence in order to get the attention of the public? Could it backfire? Is it okay to give a true assessment of the problem (to the extent we know at the time), even if there is a danger that the public may not take the problem seriously?

b. Are we willing to deal with the consequence of inaction even if it endangers the lives of many and is to the detriment of the environment?

c. To make our point, is it acceptable to cherry-pick the evidence? What if the other side is doing the same thing?

PROJECT II - Your Environmental Footprint

In this project, you are asked to estimate the environmental and health impacts of the chemicals you regularly use in your home and the number of greenhouse gases produced as a result of your activities.

1. Household chemicals

a. Take an inventory of the chemicals found in your house (kitchen, laundry, garage, etc.). Classify them by their applications as solvents, detergents, paints, etc.

    b. List their chemical compositions and identify them as toxic, non-toxic, volatile, organic, or biodegradable.

    c. Which of these chemicals are carcinogenic, poisonous, or flammable?

    d. Which of these products is causing global warming? Which ones are ozone-depleting? Which ones are considered to be health hazards?

    e. Can you substitute any of these products with more environmentally friendly (green) products? List.

    f. What are the proper methods of disposal for each of these products?

2. Carbon footprint

    a. Estimate the amount of carbon dioxide emissions by listing your daily activities. An online "household emissions calculator" is provided by the U.S. EPA, and can be found at *http://www.epa.gov/climatechange/emissions/ind_calculator2.html.*

    b. How can you reduce your emissions without significant changes in your lifestyle? By how much?

PROJECT III - What is Your Carbon Footprint?

Use EPA's Greenhouse Gas Equivalencies Calculator *(https://www3.epa.gov/carbon-footprint-calculator/)* to estimate your household carbon footprint.

1. Prepare a list of activities that can be reduced/substituted/eliminated with little or no change in your lifestyle. Recalculate the footprint and estimate the savings.

2. Which pieces of equipment can be eliminated, or substituted with a more energy-efficient one? What investment do you have to make to implement these changes? How long is the payback period?

PROJECT IV - Status of International Treaties

In this project, you are asked to carry out a literature survey and comment on the status of various international treaties and what different countries have done to comply with the established guidelines and recommendations.

    a. Highlight major milestones that are to be achieved by the Kyoto Treaty Montreal Protocol, and Paris Summit? As of today, what should have been accomplished and by whom?

    b. What were the responsibilities of the country of your birth in meeting these requirements? Have they been met? If not, why?

    c. How do you rate the overall success of these treaties? Have they achieved their general goals? What were the shortcomings?

PROJECT V - SupersonicTransport

It has been known sometimes that the commercial supersonic transport plane flown in the ozone layer will result in chemical reactions that cause ozone depletion. Nitrogen oxide interacts with ozone according to the reaction

$$NO + O_3 \rightarrow NO_2 + O_2, \text{ followed by}$$
$$NO_2 + O \rightarrow NO + O_2$$

The overall reaction is the depletion of one atom of ozone molecule. Because of the catalytic nature of the reaction, a small amount of nitrogen oxide in the ozone layer can destroy a large number of ozone molecules.

A similar reaction involving CFC molecules can also be responsible for additional ozone destruction. Propose a possible set of reactions that result in similar depletion, and explain how the substitution of CFC with ammonia as a refrigerant can help protect the ozone in the upper atmosphere.

CHAPTER 8

Nuclear Energy

Cooling tower in the evening sun ~ Image Flickr / Andy Rudofer

Each atom of your tender heart you bore, You will see a sun smiling within the core. ~ Hatef Esfehani (18th century Persian Poet)

I ask you to look both ways. For the road to a knowledge of the stars leads through the atom; and important knowledge of the atom has been reached through the stars. ~ Sir Arthur Eddington (1882-1944)

On December 2, 1942, the world's first nuclear reactor went critical on the floor of an abandoned squash court at the University of Chicago. At 3:26 p.m. that afternoon, scientists achieved the first self-sustaining nuclear chain reaction inside what was known as Chicago Pile-1, initiating the atomic age. This opened the possibility of providing power from the energy locked safely inside the atom (Figure 8-1). To promote nuclear energy, electric companies assured the public of a source that provided power so cheap that there would be no need even to meter it. This optimism and excitement were soon tarnished as the hazards, environmental costs, and dangers associated with the intentional and accidental release of radiation became apparent.

Today, the same optimism exists toward the future development of controlled fusion -- that all our energy needs will be satisfied and this source of relatively clean, renewable energy will substitute for all other forms of energy.

The nuclear accidents at Three Mile Island (TMI), Chernobyl, and Fukushima, along with the mounting volume of nuclear waste, have declined the public confidence in the use of nuclear reactors. In the United States, the last nuclear plant that went online was in 1996, and in several European countries, the number of new facilities being constructed has declined. In contrast, in response to their increasing demand for electricity and in an effort to combat global warming, China and several other countries are adding new nuclear power plants. Even though there are currently no fool-proof solutions for the disposal of nuclear waste, the increasing dependence of the industrial world on imported oil, the volatility in prices of crude oil and natural gas, and the concern over environmental issues may tilt the balance in favor of nuclear energy.

Figure 8-1
This 12-foot bronze sculpture by Henry Moore marks the site at the University of Chicago where the first sustained nuclear reaction was achieved.

The Early Atoms

Early Greek philosophers, principally Aristotle, believed that the Universe was made of four elements: earth, air, water, and fire. Each element contained two of the four qualities: hotness, coldness, wetness, and dryness. The fire was hot and dry, water was cold and wet, the air was hot and wet, and the earth was cold and dry. Other elements were a mixture of these four substances, and so, could be transformed from one to the other by modifying the ratios of these substances and their qualities. The alchemists' main interest became turning copper, lead, and mercury into gold.

Aristotle (384-322 BCE) also had other ideas. He refuted the existence of a vacuum and, thus, the atomic theory proposed by Democritus (460-370 BCE), which stated that matter could be divided further and further until it turned into indivisible parts called *atomos* which means indivisible in Greek. He saw heat as a substance with a mass (Chapter 4). Johann Becher (1635-1682), called this substance phlogiston, which had a mass and flowed from a hot object to a cold one. According to this theory, when things burned, they released phlogiston in the air. Since phlogiston had a mass, combustion should involve a loss of the mass. Careful measurement by Antoine Lavoisier (1743-1794) showed that mass remained unchanged during the combustion, and so phlogiston theory was disproved. Not only, he proved mass is conserved (conservation of mass), but also that phlogiston had to be replaced by a massless substance, he called *caloric*.

John Dalton's (1766-1844) passion was experimenting with gases and how different gases combined to make new compounds. He investigated the expansion of balloons as they were heated and argued that, since phlogiston no longer had mass, the only way to explain the expansion of gases was to assume that gases were made of small, solid, billiard-like particles surrounded by nothing but a vacuum... and a new theory of atoms was born. Different elements had different atoms with different masses, sizes, and colors; they could not be created or destroyed – but could be combined to make different compounds.

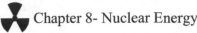

			History of the Atom
Democritus	Greek	425 BC	Suggested all things are made of elementary particles called atoms
Aristotle	Greek	370 BC	Suggested all matter is made of only four elements: fire, air, water, and earth
Joseph Priestley	English	1766	Discovered element oxygen
Henry Cavendish	English	1766	Discovered element hydrogen and that water was a compound made of hydrogen and oxygen
Antoine Lavoisier	French	1777	Formulated conservation of mass and that heat is not made of the substance "phlogiston"
John Dalton	English	1803	Proposed the atomic theory, which states all matter is composed of small and indivisible atoms.
Dmitri Mendeleev	Russian	1869	Constructed the periodic table
Wilhelm Roentgen	German	1895	Discovered x-ray
Henri Becquerel	French	1896	Discovered radioactivity
Marie Curie	Polish	1898	Discovered uranium was transmuted to radium
J. J. Thompson	English	1898	Discovered electron
Max Planck	German	1900	Originated the quantum theory
Albert Einstein	German	1905	Found equivalency of energy and mass, E = mc2
Ernest Rutherford	New Zealander	1909	Developed the first model of atom
Niel Bohr	Danish	1913	Saw electron as a "wave particle"
James Chadwick	English	1931	Discovered neutron
Enrico Fermi	Italian	1938	Succeeded in carrying the first fission reaction
The crew of Enola Gay	American	1956	July 16, 1945 (5:30 am) The first atomic explosion over Hiroshima

The New Atom

A newer picture of the atom was proposed in 1911 by Ernest Rutherford (1871-1937), who suggested a planetary model, which assumed that atoms are made of a number of electrons orbiting a nucleus, much like the motion of planets around the sun. Shortly thereafter, it was discovered that nuclei, themselves, are made of smaller particles called protons and neutrons -- collectively called nucleons (Figure 8-2). The recent model of the atom considers that protons and neutrons are made of even smaller particles called quarks, which are held together by gluons (after the English word glue). Some even postulate that quarks and electrons, themselves, are made up of the tiniest particles called strings. If string theory proves to be valid, then all matter can be thought of as a collection of these strings, that resides at the center of a whirling cloud of electrons. Although the nucleus contains almost all of the mass of the atom (about 99%), the volume it occupies is very small -- like a fly sitting in the middle of a large stadium -- leaving a relatively large, empty space between the nucleus and the electrons. Each proton carries a single positive charge of electricity, exactly balancing the negative charge of an electron, thus making atoms electrically neutral. In other words, charges are conserved. Neutrons, as the name implies, carry no charge. Because different chemicals react by sharing or donating their electrons, neutrons do not play a role in the chemical properties of matter. In other words, it is the number of protons that gives the element its chemical identity, i.e., no two different elements have the same number of protons:

The atom is the smallest particle of a chemical element that still exhibits all the chemical properties unique to that element.

Different atoms make up everything in the universe. Hydrogen, the lightest of all elements, has only a single proton; helium has two. Carbon, the basis of all life and the main constituent of fossil fuels, contains six protons. The uranium atom, with 92 protons, is the heaviest of all-natural elements that make up our planet. Besides these natural elements,

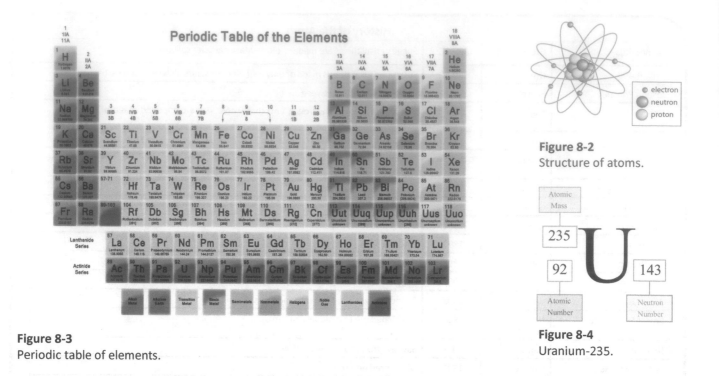

Periodic Table of the Elements

Figure 8-2
Structure of atoms.

Figure 8-3
Periodic table of elements.

Figure 8-4
Uranium-235.

other elements with higher numbers of protons have been discovered, but only in a laboratory environment. These elements, along with their atomic masses and numbers, are summarized in the **periodic table** given in Figure 8-3.

Atoms are represented by two numbers, their atomic numbers, and their atomic masses. The **atomic number (Z)** is the number of protons in the nuclei; the **atomic mass (A)** is the sum of the protons and neutrons. Because electrons have negligible masses (electrons are 2000 times lighter than protons or neutrons), atomic mass essentially determines the mass of atoms. An atom of hydrogen, with only one proton and no neutrons, has both an atomic number and an atomic mass of 1. An atom of uranium, with 92 protons and 146 neutrons, has an atomic number of 92 and an atomic mass of 238 and is represented as uranium-238 or simply ^{238}U. The nuclei of a small fraction of uranium atoms, however, have three fewer neutrons. As will be seen, this form of uranium, called uranium-235, is very unstable and plays an important role in the construction of both nuclear reactors and nuclear bombs (Figure 8-4).

Nuclear Forces

Anybody who has taken any elementary physics course remembers that there are only two kinds of electric charges in nature and that objects of opposite charges attract, whereas objects of like charges repel. Two questions might come to mind: 1) Why don't protons and electrons bump into each other and cancel out each others' charges?, and 2) Why don't positively charged protons, residing side by side in the nuclei, push each other away and cause the nuclei to fall apart? To answer these questions, we must understand how nuclear forces work.

The first question is easy to answer. The electrostatic force between electrons and protons is relatively weak. Electrons revolve around the nuclei at the right speed so that the resulting centrifugal forces just balance the electrical attraction between the electrons and nuclei. The answer to the second question requires some understanding of the weak and strong forces acting between two particles. As it turns out, there are two forces that compete against each other: a very strong, attractive nuclear force that operates at short ranges; and the repulsive Coulomb force operating at long ranges. At short distances, the nuclear force dominates, whereas the Coulomb force is the more important force at large distances. As we saw in Chapter 5 when applied to elementary particles, gravitational forces are much smaller than electrical forces, so they can be safely ignored for our discussion.

For sure, if it were for electrical and gravitational forces alone, nuclei could not be made stable and soon protons

246

> **Atoms: The Facts**
>
> - A row of 100 million atoms of hydrogen would be only about one centimeter long.
>
> - Eight of the elements known to us make up 98.5% of the Earth's crust by weight: oxygen makes up 46.6%, silicon 27.7%, and aluminum 8%, with Fe, Ca, Na, K, and Mg composing the rest.
>
> - Hydrogen is the most abundant element in the universe.
>
> - Of the 92 naturally occurring elements, 76 are solids, 11 are gases, and five are liquids at room temperature.
>
> - Nearly all of the mass of an atom is contained in the nucleus, which has a density of around 100 million tons per cubic centimeter.
>
> - One kilogram of uranium, about the size of a golf ball, stores as much energy as 30 carloads of coal.

would fly apart; the nuclei owe their stability to the presence of the strong forces.

Binding Energy

The binding energy of a nucleus is a measure of how tightly its nucleons (protons and neutrons) are held together by nuclear forces. The binding energy per nucleon -- the energy required to remove a neutron or a proton from a nucleus -- varies with the mass number, and is the highest for iron, implying that when a heavy nucleus (such as that of uranium) splits into two lighter nuclei, or when two lighter nuclei (such as those of deuterium and tritium) coalesce, more stable nuclei form and energy is released. The former example describes fission, while the latter represents the basic mechanism that occurs in fusion reactions. Figure 8-5 shows a plot of binding energy per nucleon as a function of atomic mass.

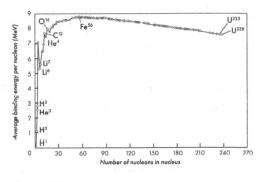

Why iron? As we discussed above, the higher the number of nucleons in a nucleus, the more powerful will be the strong interaction, compared to the much weaker, repulsive electrical force. But this can occur to a limit. As the number of nucleons increases, so does the size of the nucleus, and eventually will exceed the range of the strong interaction -- some of the protons are placed far enough apart to repel each other by electrical forces. As you guessed, the element with just enough nucleons to fit this diameter is iron-56. Heavier particles become exceedingly less stable. The heaviest nucleus occurring naturally is uranium-238. Its isotope uranium-235 is even less stable and is the easiest to break apart.

Figure 8-5
Energy can be liberated when the nuclei of light elements combine (fuse) to form heavier elements, or the nuclei of heavy elements are split to form lighter elements (fission).

Mass Defect

One of the astonishing observations made when studying the nuclei of different elements is that masses of individual components of an atom (protons, neutrons, and electrons) are always greater than the mass of the atom put together. The difference is called the **mass defect**. It's the mass that disappears when nuclei form from elementary particles.

Mass defect = Mass of Nucleons - Mass of Nucleus

This mass is, indeed, very small, and is often expressed in atomic mass units. The atomic mass unit (amu) is defined as exactly:

1 amu = 1/12th the mass of a carbon-12 atom = 1.661x10^{-27} kg

Based on this definition, the mass of an atom of carbon-12 is 12 amu. The atomic masses of elementary particles and a few atoms are given in Table 8-1. Numbers are expressed to six significant digits since the changes are subtle.

Table 8-1 Atomic Mass (amu)	
Electron	0.000549
Neutron	1.008665
Proton	1.007276
Hydrogen atom	1.007825
Helium atom	4.002063
U-235 atom	235.043924

An atom of helium is made of the nucleus (consisting of two protons and two neutrons), and two electrons. If we add these masses together, we get $(2 \times 1.007276) + (2 \times 1.008665) + (2 \times 0.000549) = 4.032980$ amu, which is greater than the measured mass of a helium atom -- 4.002063 amu. The difference of 0.030917 amu is the mass defect.

You must be careful not to mistake the atomic mass with nuclear mass. The atomic mass is the total mass of the atom (including the electrons); the nuclear mass is the mass of the nucleus (protons and neutrons). The nucleus of a helium atom is called an alpha particle and has a mass of 4.001505 amu, slightly less than that of a helium atom.

> **Worth Remembering** – All atoms are lighter than the sum of the masses of their constituents -- protons, electrons, and neutrons.

Energy and Mass

To pull out a nucleon from the nucleus, we have to put in a lot of energy. This energy is put back into the particle as it recovers its missing mass. This energy is called the **binding energy** and can be calculated from Einstein's celebrated equation showing the equivalency between mass and energy:

[Binding Energy] $E = mc^2$ (8-1)

Where m is the mass defect, and E is the binding energy defined as the energy released when a nucleus is assembled from its constituent nucleons (or the energy needed to tear the nucleus apart into its nucleons). c is the velocity of light in vacuum equal to 3×10^8 m/s (300,000 km/s).[*]

> **Example 8-1:** What is the energy equivalent of 1 amu?
> **Solution:** Using Einstein's Equation (8-1), we get:
>
> $$E = mc^2 = (1 \text{ amu}) \times \left(\frac{1.66 \times 10^{-27} \text{ kg}}{1 \text{ amu}} \right) \times \left(3 \times 10^8 \frac{\text{m}}{\text{s}} \right)^2 = 1.494 \times 10^{-10} \text{ J}$$

This is a very small amount of energy. It is customary that when we deal with atoms, we express energy as electron-volts. One million electron-volts is called a mega electron-volt. 1 MeV = 1.6022×10^{-13} J. In other words, the energy equivalent of 1 amu is 931.5 MeV.

Mass-Energy equivalent: 1 amu = 931.5 MeV

1 kg = 25 TWh

> **Example 8-2:** Calculate the defect mass and total binding energy and binding energy per nucleon of U-235? The mass of the nucleus of U-235 is 235.043924 amu.
> **Solution:** U-235 nuclei consist of 92 protons, and 143 neutrons. Its mass defect is:
> $92 \times 1.007276 + 143 \times 1.008665 - 235.043924 = 1.91517$ amu.
> The binding energy is: $(1.91517 \text{ amu}) \times (931.5 \text{ MeV/amu}) = 1,784$ MeV; or, B.E./nucleon = 1,784 / 235 = 7.59 eV/nucleon.

[*] The speed of light is usually denoted by c, from Latin "*celeritas*" meaning rapidity of motion or action.

Units Commonly Used by Nuclear Scientists

- The mass of nucleons is usually represented in atomic mass units.

  1 amu = 1/12 of the mass of atom ^{12}C = 1.66x10^{-27} kg

- The energy of nucleons is usually expressed in *electron volts* (eV or MeV).

  1 eV = energy that an electron would gain if it were accelerated through an electrical potential difference of

  1 volt = 1.6x10^{-19} J; and, 1 MeV = 10^6 eV

Nuclear vs. Chemical Reactions

There is a fundamental difference between chemical reactions (such as the burning of coal or natural gas) and nuclear reactions. Consider the chemical reaction:

$$CH_4 + 2\,O_2 \rightarrow CO_2 + 2\,H_2O$$

methane + oxygen $\rightarrow$ carbon dioxide + water vapor + heat

Note that after the reaction is completed, we still have one atom of carbon, four atoms of oxygen, and four atoms of hydrogen; the molecules, however, do not stay the same. In this reaction, one molecule of methane reacts with two molecules of oxygen and results in one molecule of carbon dioxide and two molecules of water. The total mass of the reactants (methane and oxygen) and products (carbon dioxide and water vapor) also remain the same. Heat appears because of the reconfiguration of atoms and the lower energies in the newly created bonds, as compared to that in bonds that have been broken.

In chemical reactions, the total number of atoms remains constant –
electrons are redistributed to form new bonds and molecules.

In a nuclear reaction, atoms lose their identities. For example, when uranium-235 is hit with a neutron, two lighter elements, such as krypton and barium, are formed and two or three neutrons are released. In this case, the total number of nucleons (protons and neutrons) is conserved. The mass of the product is slightly smaller than the mass of the reactants. Energy is released because the configuration of elementary particles forming the nucleus of the fragments has a lower binding energy (mass) than that of the nucleus of the atom undergoing fission.

In nuclear reactions, the total number of nucleons remains constant –
protons and neutrons are redistributed to form new atoms.

Another notable distinction between chemical and nuclear reactions is the huge difference in the amount of energy each release. This is because the binding energy that holds a nucleus together is far greater than the energy that holds electrons to the nucleus. For example, the fission of one kilogram of uranium provides as much energy as 2.4 million kilograms of the best quality coal. Even though nuclear fuel contains only 3-5% fissionable material, the tremendous energy released from a nuclear reaction is apparent.

Question: How does the energy density of a nuclear fuel compared to that of fossil fuel?
Answer: The nuclear material lacks the empty space that exists in non-nuclear materials. As a result, it has a density of approximately one hundred trillion times greater.

Worth Remembering – In chemical reactions, the mass of both the reactants and the products is exactly the same. In nuclear reactions, whether fission or fusion, the mass of the products is always a bit smaller than the reactants.

Isotopes

To make atoms electrically neutral, all that is required is for the number of protons and electrons to be equal. Although the number of protons (and also electrons) is the same for each element, the number of neutrons may not be, i.e., each element comes in several flavors (same Z, but different A). These different atoms of the same element are known as isotopes. For example, the nucleus of hydrogen may have either 0, 1, or 2 neutrons (Figure 8-6). Similarly, all atoms of carbon have six protons and six electrons. Roughly 99% have six neutrons (carbon-12), 1% have seven neutrons (carbon-13), and a tiny amount has eight neutrons (carbon-14). Uranium and hydrogen, the heaviest and lightest of all the naturally occurring elements and the fuels of choice for nuclear fission and fusion reactions, are both found naturally in three isotopes.

Since different isotopes are only different in the number of neutral charges they contain, they are chemically identical but differ only in their physical properties, notably their mass.

As we will see, these isotopes may have significantly different nuclear characteristics. **Radioactive materials** are those isotopes, which have unstable atomic nuclei and may undergo spontaneous decay, forming lighter isotopes (called *daughters*) and releasing highly energetic ionizing radiation in the process. For example, the isotope of uranium-238 decays into several isotopes before it becomes the stable lead (Figure 8-7).

All elements with atomic masses heavier than bismuth are naturally radioactive. It is, however, possible to artificially produce isotopes of lighter elements. Half-life is an important quantity in measuring the effect of harmful radiation from a radioactive source.

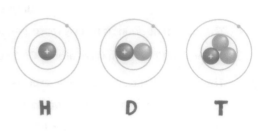

Figure 8-6
There are three isotopes of hydrogen that differ only in the number of neutrons they possess. The hydrogen isotope has only one proton, the deuterium isotope has one proton and one neutron, and the tritium isotope has one proton and two neutrons.

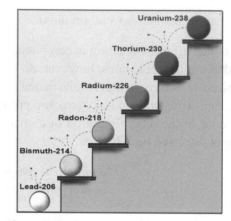

Figure 8-7
Decay chain of isotope of uranium-238.

Half-Life

A half-life is a time in which the concentration of an isotope decays to one-half of its original concentration. The rate of emission from a radiation source reduces to $1/2$ in one half-life, to $1/4$ in two half-lives, to $1/8$ in three half-lives, and to $(1/2)^n$ after n half-lives. Half-lives of some of the isotopes of interest to us are uranium-238 (about 5 billion years), uranium-235 (about 0.7 billion years), plutonium-239 (24,360 years), cesium-137 (30 years), and strontium-90 (28.8 years). Iodine-131 has a half-life of only 8.04 days. Thorium-232 is very long-lived and is considered to be the main source of geothermal heat.

> **Question:** Estimate the concentration of uranium-238 and its isotopes at the time of the formation of the earth, 4.5 billion years ago.
> **Answer:** Earth is still younger than the half-life of uranium-238 (5 billion years), so we expect that it still contains more than one-half the original uranium-238. Uranium-235 is much less abundant, as the elapsed time is between six to seven times its half-life. We expect that the earth still contains only about 1% of the original uranium isotope.

It should be noted that radioactive decay is a statistical occurrence; it does not favor some nuclei over others. All half-life means is that within this period, 50% of nuclei have the possibility to undergo disintegration. The probability does not change, so the remaining nuclei still will have the same chance of decay.

Alchemists and Transmutation

Transmuting metals to gold has been the aspiration of alchemists for over 4,000 years -- and pursued independently by ancient Egypt and China. The origin of the word alchemy is "khem" which means fertility. The Egyptians' original desire was to find a way to preserve bodies in anticipation of the eventual return of their dead to life. *Khem* was the technique used for mummification. The prefix -al was added to the word when Arabs occupied Egypt in the seventh century. The Arabs believed that all metals were made up of mercury and sulfur in different proportions, and gold was the "purest" of all metals. So it was ideal for turning (transmuting) metals from their lowest forms to the most perfect form: gold. Even Newton could not escape the temptation. None succeeded, however.

To understand the dilemma, let's look at the atomic structures of, let's say, mercury and gold. Mercury with an atomic mass of 200 and an atomic number of 80 consists of 80 protons and 120 neutrons. Take one proton away and mercury turns into an isotope of gold. Seems simple enough? Two problems that come immediately to mind are the lack of knowledge about the atomic structure of matters and the availability of a nuclear reactor. The interest in alchemy eventually led to the discovery of new elements and the start of the science of chemistry.

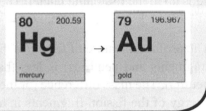

In Chapter 1, we derived the equation for the doubling-time of a quantity that grows exponentially with time. Examples given were population growth, interest accumulating in a savings account, and energy consumption. The same equation can be shown to apply to the radioactive decay of isotopes, except the rate of decay and half-life are used instead of the rate of growth and doubling time. Following the approach used in Chapter 1, we can write:

$$Half\ Life = \frac{70}{Percentage\ Rate\ of\ Decay}$$

Example 8-3: A radiation leak released cesium-137 radionuclide. How long would it take until the radioactivity of cesium drops to 1/1000 of its initial value? What is its rate of decay? The half-life of ^{137}Cs is 30 years.

Hint: $2^{10} = 1,024$

Solution: The concentration of nuclei is ½ after one half-life, ¼ after two half-lives, and continues to drop by half, after each consecutive half-life. About ten half-lives or 300 years; the concentration is $\frac{1}{2^{10}} = \frac{1}{1024} \approx 0.001$ of its initial value. The decay rate is $r = 70/30 = 2.33\%$ per year.

Question: *New Horizons* was launched on January 19, 2006, to study Pluto and its moons, Nix and Hydra. On July 15, 2015, it reached its target point 12,500 km (7,800 mi) above the surface of Pluto. To power various instruments, the satellite carries 11 kg of plutonium-238, to power a generator that provides 460 W of continuous power. What is the advantage of using this isotope over plutonium-239?

Answer: The plutonium-238 used in this generator has a half-life of 88 years, in contrast to the 24,360 years for plutonium-239. This makes plutonium-238 about 277 times more radioactive (and also 277 times more toxic). The satellite would have had to carry three tons of plutonium-239, instead.

Fission

Fission is the splitting of an atom's nucleus. Very heavy nuclei, like isotopes of uranium and plutonium, are easiest to split. The process involves bombardment of these atoms by small sub-atomic particles like neutrons, which split them into two fission products; two to three neutrons and excess energy in the form of gamma rays are also produced. These neutrons collide with more uranium atoms, thus initiating a self-sustaining chain reaction that results in more fission and the continuous release of enormous amounts of energy (Figure 8-8). Any substance capable of sustaining a fission chain reaction is known as a *fissile* material. The materials most suitable for fission are ^{235}U and ^{239}Pu. These radioactive isotopes are fissionable by what is termed as *slow* or *thermal neutrons*. They are called thermal because they have a kinetic energy of only a few eV, similar to the thermal motion of the molecules of gas of the same temperature. The isotopes ^{238}U and ^{232}Th are called **fertile**, but become fissile if bombarded by *fast neutrons* -- i.e., neutrons with kinetic energy greater than one MeV.

The physics of nuclear energy is simple. When a neutron collides with an atom of the isotope uranium-235, a highly excited atom of uranium-236 is formed, which immediately fissions into two or more lighter nuclei. Fission reactions can produce any combination of lighter nuclei, as long as the number of protons and neutrons in the products adds up to the fissioning nuclei. The most likely fragments are isotopes of barium, krypton, cesium, xenon, and strontium.

The profound feature of fission is that the mass of the products (fission fragments and neutrons) is less than the mass of a ^{236}U atom plus a neutron. The mass difference (or the mass defect) appears as the kinetic energy of the fission fragments in an amount determined according to Einstein's formula (Equation 8-1).

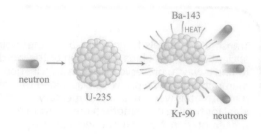

Figure 8-8
The fission process: when U-235 is bombarded by a neutron, it breaks into smaller fragments and 2 or 3 neutrons releasing a huge amount of energy.

Question: One of the likely possible reactions involving fission of uranium-235 is:

$$^{235}U + n \rightarrow ^{236}U^* \rightarrow ^{143}Ba + ^{90}Kr + 3\,n + heat$$

The mass appears to be the same on both sides of the reaction ($235 + 1 = 143 + 90 + 3 = 236$). Thus, it seems that no mass is converted into energy. In this case, where does the energy come from?

Answer: The statement is not entirely correct. Actually, the mass of a nucleus is more than the sum of the individual masses of its protons and neutrons and contains the extra mass equal to the binding energy that holds the protons and neutrons of the nucleus together.

Radiometric Dating

Archeologists use a simple approach to determine the age of fossilized objects buried underground a long time ago. A technique known as carbon dating uses the ratio of an isotope of carbon, carbon-14, to that of common and stable carbon, carbon-12, to estimate the age of a fossil that was buried many decades or centuries before. All living organisms naturally contain an isotope of carbon, C-14, which is produced when the Earth's upper atmosphere is bombarded by cosmic radiation that breaks nitrogen down into unstable carbon-14. Because C-14 is chemically identical to stable C-12, it attaches to complex organic molecules through photosynthesis in plants and enters the food chain. Since all living matter takes up carbon from the atmosphere through respiration, they maintain the same ratio of $^{14}C/^{12}C = 1.28 \times 10^{-12}$. When a tree is cut down or an animal dies, the process stops, and C-14 gradually decays to N-14, whereas stable C-12 remains largely unchanged. The decrease in the ratio of $^{14}C/^{12}C$ can be, therefore, used as a measure of the age of a fossil or an artifact.

Question: A group of British scientists has studied the charcoal remains from Stonehenge and found it to contain the carbon isotope ratio of 8×10^{-13}. Estimate the possible age of the Stonehenge site.

Answer: Assuming that the charcoal is leftover from social activities during the Stonehenge era, we can write:

$$\frac{^{14}C}{^{12}C} = 1.28 \times 10^{-12} \times 2^{-t/5760}$$

Substituting for the carbon ratio ($^{14}C/^{12}C = 8 \times 10^{-13}$), we get t = 3,800 years.

It must be noted that the accuracy of the carbon dating technique decreases with less sensitive instruments and with the age of the sample. With a half-life of 5,760 years, an initial C-14 population will decay to 1/16 of its original value in 23,040 years – about the limit of detection possible with current instruments. For estimating the age of older fossils and rocks, scientists use other radioactive isotopes (See the table to the right).

Parent Isotope	Daughter Isotope	Half-Life
Carbon-14	Nitrogen-14	5,760 years
Aluminum-26	Magnesium-26	700,000 years
Uranium-235	Lead-207	700 million years
Potassium-40	Argon-40	1.25 billion years

Question: Carbon has two stable isotopes, ^{12}C and ^{13}C. The isotope ^{14}C is unstable and decays to ^{14}N, with a neutron changing into a proton. Describe the reaction and how it can be used in dating fossils and other archeological artifacts.[†]

Answer: Both ^{14}C and ^{14}N have the same atomic mass. The difference is in the number of protons and neutrons in their nuclei. ^{14}C, with eight neutrons and six protons, is less stable than tightly bound ^{14}N, which has seven protons and seven neutrons. The half-life of the decay is 5,760 years, which is used in determining the age of fossils and other biological organisms (See Box "Radiometric Dating").

Nuclear Fuel

Most nuclear reactors use uranium as fuel, roughly 3 kilograms per day for an average one-gigawatt reactor. Uranium is a common element on the planet, formed during the earlier stages of the earth's development. At the time our planet was formed 4.5 billion years ago, about 75% of all uranium was in the form of U-238 and the remaining 25% was in the form of isotope U-235. As uranium decayed, the ratio of U-235 to U-238 dropped considerably. Today only 0.7% of the uranium found in nature is U-235. The non-fissile isotope U-238 makes up the rest.

Uranium is scattered throughout the earth's crust in most rocks and soils, as well as in many rivers and in seawater. Uranium is not an unlimited resource and, like fossil fuel, has only a limited lifetime. With 28% of the world's total resources, Australia has the largest reserve and is the leading producer of uranium. Other countries with vast uranium reserves are Kazakhstan (15%), Canada (9%), and Russia (7%). The states with the largest known uranium ore reserves are Wyoming, New Mexico, and Colorado.

Today, half of all uranium fuel used in U.S. nuclear reactors comes from bomb material from dismantled Russian and American nuclear weapons. The remainder is from domestic production or imports, primarily from Australia.

Processing

From extraction to disposal, uranium undergoes many changes. Various stages of the nuclear fuel cycle are shown in Figure 8-9 and consist of:

1. *Mining and milling* -- Like coal and other minerals, uranium must be mined and hauled away to a mill where uranium ore is crushed and ground to a fine slurry that is poured into an acid that dissolves the uranium. The acid solution is dried into a yellow powder called a *yellowcake*. The leftover rock is known as *tailing* and is considered a waste.

2. *Conversion* -- The yellowcake is then shipped to a conversion plant, where it is purified and chemically converted to uranium hexafluoride (UF$_6$) gas.

3. *Enrichment* -- The flow stream has very little uranium-235, the fuel for nuclear fission. During the enrichment process, the concentration of U-235 isotopes is raised from 0.7%, which is naturally present in the ore, to the 3-5% required for use as nuclear fuel.[‡] The two main enrichment processes

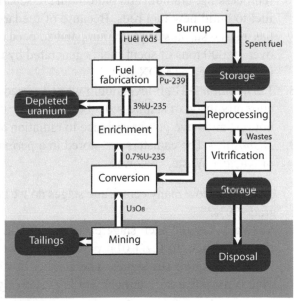

Figure 8-9
Nuclear fuel cycle.

---

† Radioactive dating is not limited to biological systems. For example, a similar technique called potassium-argon dating can be used to determine the age of volcanic rocks. When volcanic liquid -- called lava -- was solidified into rock, it contained an isotope of potassium K-40, which decays into argon gas. The technique works by melting the rock and measuring the concentration of the trapped argon gas to estimate the rock's age.

‡ Enrichment is a physical process that relies on the small mass difference between two isotopes of an atom. Since all isotopes are chemically identical, no chemical methods can separate isotopes apart.

are diffusion and centrifuge. In the diffusion technique, the differences between masses of different isotopes result in different rates of diffusion through a membrane. In the centrifuge, a substrate is spun at a very high speed to separate heavier isotopes. Successive operations allow the production of higher and higher concentrated uranium-235. To achieve sufficient enrichment, many thousands of centrifuges may have to be connected in series. Today, almost all uranium enrichments are centrifuges.

4. *Fabrication* -- The enriched UF_6 gas is sent to a fuel fabrication plant where it is converted to uranium dioxide (UO_2) powder and pressed into small ceramic pellets, which are then stacked inside long zirconium or stainless steel tubes to form the fuel rods before they are bundled together to make the fuel assemblies used in nuclear reactors. Some U-238 remains in the tail and is called depleted uranium (DU). Because of its high density, depleted uranium has been used in yacht keels, antitank missiles, and artillery shells.

5. *Burn-up* -- A reactor core contains several hundred fuel assemblies where the fission process takes place and fuel is "burned," producing heat in a process called a chain reaction. Fission products are plutonium and various fission fragments. A one-gigawatt nuclear power plant produces about 27 tonnes of spent nuclear fuel every year.

6. *Storage* -- Over time, the concentration of the uranium fuel decreases while that of fission fragments builds up. As more and more neutrons are absorbed, a point is reached where fuel is no longer efficient and must be replaced with new ones. The spent fuel and other fission products remain highly radioactive and continue to release heat and radiation long after they are removed from the reactor core. To cool the fuel is placed in a cooling pool where it remains for years. During this period much of the low-level waste is decayed, before it is sent to be reprocessed or dried (vitrified) and stored in interim storage facilities.

Figure 8-10
Storage pond for spent fuel at a reprocessing plant.

7. *Reprocessing* -- Used nuclear fuel can be processed to extract fissile materials for recycling and to reduce the volume of high-level wastes. Recycling is largely based on the conversion of fertile U-238 to fissile plutonium. During reprocessing, uranium and plutonium are separated and returned to the conversion plant as mixed-oxide (MOX) fuel to build new fuel rods. Because of the large quantities of plutonium manufactured during WWII, the U.S. has a large surplus of plutonium, and so needs no new reprocessing plants in the foreseeable future. Each year, over 10,000 tons of spent fuel is generated by the world's operating nuclear plants, of which less than one-third is reprocessed as MOX fuel.[§]

8. *Vitrification* -- High-level liquid waste is dried and stored in special containment vessels called casks. Casks are currently made of stainless steel canisters surrounded by concrete. Ceramics may be a better material, as it does not rust and have good resistance to radiation and heat.

9. *Disposal* -- The canisters are stored in a permanent or semi-permanent underground repository (See "Disposal of Nuclear Waste," below).

Question: How many centrifuge stages do we need to enrich uranium from its natural 0.7% to 3.5%? To weapon-grade 90%?

Answer: Assume each stage enriches the U-235 by 1%, then the concentration increase from 0.7% to 0.77% after one stage, to $0.7(1.01)^2$ percent after two stages, and to $0.7(1.01)^N$ percent after N-stages; i.e., to get to 3.5%, we require 161 stages. The number of stages increases to 452 to produce weapon-grade uranium. This is what is most feared as enrichment is a relatively simple task.

---

§ In the last few years, many European countries have been using mixed uranium with plutonium extracted from their surplus stockpiles of nuclear weapons as a nuclear fuel (called MOX for mixed oxide fuel). The United States has not been using MOX to fuel its nuclear reactors yet, but is planning to build a MOX facility at a DOE site at Savannah River, South Carolina. The project is part of the disarmament process and is aimed at reducing the nuclear threat by minimizing the number of nuclear weapons and disposing of the nuclear-grade plutonium, which has accumulated over many years of weapons manufacturing and reactor operation. Critics of the plan warn that opening the large stockpiles of plutonium to commercial sites makes power plants vulnerable to thieves and terrorists, because the plutonium can be separated from the MOX fuel rather easily and then be used for constructing an atomic bomb.

Plutonium

Plutonium is only slightly heavier than uranium, but unlike uranium that is abundant in mines, there is no plutonium left in nature. This is because, compared to uranium, plutonium has a very short life, and therefore, all is already decayed to lighter, more stable elements. Plutonium, however, can be manufactured in nuclear reactors. When uranium-238 -- which comprises the bulk of nuclear fuel -- is bombarded by neutrons, it turns to highly radioactive uranium-239, with a half-life of only 23 minutes. The resulting isotope is called neptunium-239, which is also radioactive and decays further to the isotope plutonium-239. The sequence of reactions is:

$$^{238}_{92}U + n \rightarrow \ ^{239}_{92}U^* \ \rightarrow \ ^{239}_{93}Np \ \rightarrow \ ^{239}_{94}Pu$$

uranium-238 + neutron → neptunium-239 → plutonium-239

Table 8-2 Countries with Largest Nuclear Generation Capacity as of April 2020				
Country	Reactors in Operation	Under Construction	Capacity GWe	% Electricity
U.S.	95	2	100	20
India	22	7	6	3
Japan	33	2	36	8
China	47	11	46	5
Russia	38	4	28	20
South Korea	24	4	24	26
France	57	0	63	71
World	440	54	392	10

Source: Nuclear Energy Institute, 2016, (http://www.nei.org).

Plutonium is not only the fuel for breeder reactors but is also the fuel of choice for making nuclear bombs. Plutonium is also highly toxic and causes death within a few hours or days if ingested. In bulk quantities, plutonium is not very dangerous, but if vaporized or aerosolized, it can cause great damage and must, therefore, be carefully safeguarded from falling into the hands of terrorist organizations.

Nuclear Reactors

As of April 2020, there are 440 nuclear power plant units in 30 countries with an installed electric net capacity of about 392 GW; another 54 plants are under construction (Table 8-2). The United States with 95 nuclear reactors tops the list, but the fraction of electricity they generate is relatively small, compared to that in some European countries. China is aggressively moving to increase capacity to at least 200 GW by 2030 and 400 GW by 2050.

A nuclear power plant produces electricity in almost exactly the same way as a conventional power plant (See Chapter 5). Fossil fuels (coal, oil, or natural gas) are burned to create heat, which boils water in a boiler and creates steam. The steam is expanded in a turbine, which runs a generator that produces electricity. In a nuclear power plant, the boiler is replaced by a reactor core in which nuclear fuel undergoes fission processes to produce heat. Everything else is the same.

Reactor Core

The reactor core is the heart of any nuclear power generation facility. Inside the reactor core, fission takes place and provides energy to produce the steam required by the power plant. A reactor vessel made of several inches of carbon steel surrounds and protects the reactor core. The vessel itself is housed in a containment structure made of several feet of concrete, reinforced with thick steel bars. The reactor core consists of four main components (Figure 8-11):

1. **Fuel Assembly** -- Nuclear fuel consists of pellets of ceramic uranium oxide arranged in long tubes (fuel rods) which are grouped into bundles (fuel assemblies). The bundles are submerged in a coolant inside a pressure vessel. Depending on the type, nuclear reactors have a number of fuel assemblies that must be replaced occasionally, as they deplete and fission products build up (Figure 8-12).
2. **Moderator** -- In lieu of the much larger concentration of uranium-238, it is unlikely that a fast neutron will hit a uranium-235 atom and cause fission. Slower neutrons have a better chance of being pulled by the nuclei and there is a higher probability for capture. The moderator is the material that slows down

255

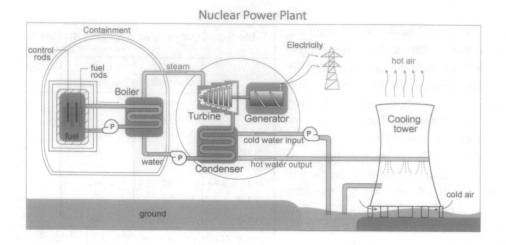

Figure 8-11
A typical nuclear reactor has several primary components: Inside the reactor "core" are the fuel rods, the control rods, the moderator, and the coolant. Outside the core are the turbines, the heat exchanger, and the main cooling system.

the fast neutrons to thermal neutrons. Without a moderator, the fission chain reaction cannot be sustained. With enriched uranium, the probability of neutron collision is higher, and a strong moderator such as ordinary water (H_2O) or graphite is needed. With heavy water (D_2O) as a moderator, there is less affinity to absorb neutrons, and enrichment is unnecessary. Deuterium is a heavier and more stable isotope of hydrogen. It has an excess neutron in its nuclei, leaving more neutrons free to collide with uranium-235, increasing the probability of collision and making fission more likely.[¶] Nuclear weapons function by releasing a large number of neutrons over a very short period, and so no moderator is needed.

3. **Control Rods --** It was previously explained that a fission reaction splits a uranium atom into two smaller fragments and two or three neutrons. To sustain a steady and controlled chain reaction, one neutron is all that is needed to hit the next atom and cause the next fission and continues the chain reaction. This means that in order to prevent a possible runaway reaction, the concentration of neutrons in the reactor must be controlled. Control rods are responsible for removing the extra neutrons and controlling the power output from the reactor. Control rods, made of neutron-absorbing material alloys such as cadmium, hafnium, or boron are placed between the fuel rods; these materials absorb neutrons but do not cause fission. To increase power (power-up the reactor), the rods are raised and more of the uranium bundles are exposed; to create less heat, the rods are lowered. To shut the reactor down in the case of an accident or to change the fuel, the rods are lowered all the way.

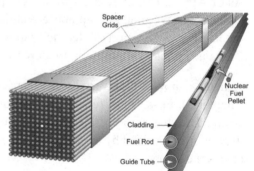

Figure 8-12
Fuel assembly
Guide tube function to support integrity of fuel rods and easy insertion of control rods.

4. **Coolant --** To carry away the heat of the reaction, coolants are needed. Water is usually the material of choice. Some gas-cooled reactors use carbon dioxide or helium gas, while breeder reactors use sodium. Potassium, bismuth, or other liquid metals have been also used.

¶ In other words, the neutron cross-section of heavy water is significantly smaller than that of light water.

Fast Breeder Reactors (FBR)

Like fossil fuel, uranium reserves are limited.[**] It is possible to extend the supply of nuclear fuel if the non-fissionable component of nuclear fuel is converted into fissile materials. The breeder system uses uranium-238 as its fuel, which can transform into fissile plutonium-239 through collision with fast neutrons. By doing so, more fissile nuclei are produced than consumed, hence the term "breeding."

Because neutrons are not slowed down, no moderator is used. Because water tends to slow (moderate) the fast neutrons, water as a coolant is ruled out. A suitable coolant is a liquid metal like sodium, which has excellent heat transfer properties and a very high boiling point, and which provides significantly better cooling and allows operation at essentially atmospheric pressure -- eliminating the need for a heavy-pressure vessel. The main concern with these reactors is that, in the presence of water or even moisture in the air, liquid metals become highly explosive. Therefore, breeder reactors require special care to ensure the safety of their operation.

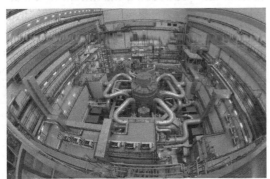

Figure 8-13
A cut-away view of BN-800 Fast breeder reactor (EBR-II).
Source: Word Nuclear Association.

The first large-scale plant of this type, called Super Phoenix, went into operation in France in 1986. From the beginning, the plant was the focus of anti-nuclear and environmental groups, who eventually succeeded in closing the plant down in 1998. As of 2021, there only two reactors of this type, both in Russia, BN-600 with a capacity of 600 MW, and BN-800, producing 800 MW of electricity and using liquid sodium as a coolant (Figure 8-13). India has started the construction of a 500-MW prototype reactor, scheduled to start operation in 2022. Many factors, including the availability of sufficient uranium fuel for the near future, safety concerns, the fear of terrorism, and nuclear proliferation, have greatly dampened the enthusiasm for these reactors and many countries have stopped work on fast breeder technology altogether.

Retiring of Nuclear Reactors

Most nuclear reactors were constructed during the 1960s and early 1970s. Nuclear reactors are usually designed to last about 40 years, after which embrittlement and corrosion of the reactor vessels could pose a danger. By the year 2033, all nuclear reactors currently operating in the United States will have reached the end of their original 40-year-license period and must be shut down or upgraded for new licenses. Nuclear reactors, however, cannot simply be turned off and demolished, as most non-nuclear facilities are. The building, equipment, and the leftover fuel are radioactive and will continue to generate heat and emit radiation long after the reactor has ceased operation. Most often, following the reactor shutdown, the plant enters a storage mode, during which it is left alone, long enough to allow the intense, short-lived radioactive material to decay and become less radioactive. Another approach is to entomb the reactor under heavy protective layers of lead and concrete. The final phase of retirement is the dismantling or decommissioning of the plant by tearing it up using special robots and moving and storing its critical parts in a permanent storage site.

Reactor Safety

One of the most frightening aspects of nuclear power is the possibility of something going wrong, with disastrous consequences. In one scenario, a malfunction of the control rods or a loss of coolant results in a "runaway" reaction and an uncontrolled release of energy that melts the fuel rods and causes them to fuse. The fused rods would then burn through the reactor vessel and the containment floor. Such a meltdown would cause the leakage of dangerous

---

[**] According to at least one report [(OECD. Uranium 2009: Resources, Production, and Demand. OECD NEA Publication 6891. 2010], the world reserve of uranium is estimated to be 5.4 million tons at $130/kg in 2010. The reserves will increase to 6.4 million tons at $260/kg. At the current rate of consumption (69,000 tons per year), the uranium reserves last another 78 to 92 years. The fraction of electricity from nuclear sources is expected to rise sharply, so the lifetime would be substantially shorter. On the other hand, if breeder reactors substitute light water reactors, the same amount of uranium will last by a factor of 143 times to 11,000 years.

radioactive materials into the environment.

The first major nuclear accident in the United States occurred in July 1959 at *Santa Susana Field Laboratory* in Simi Valley, California. The laboratory was run by Atomic International (now Boeing Rocketdyne) to test liquid-propellant rockets and design and operation of the U.S.'s first commercial nuclear reactor. It used sodium as its coolant and produced a maximum of about 7.5 to 20 megawatts of electric power. The incident followed a power excursion that caused severe overheating of the reactor resulting in the partial meltdown of a third of the fuel rods releasing a large amount of radioactive iodine into the air. Because of the top-secret nature of the work conducted at this site, the incident was largely unreported. It wasn't until recently that a lawsuit filed by the environmental activists and accident survivors prompted Boeing to admit to the incident. Three of the most famous (or infamous!) nuclear accidents are those that occurred at Three Mile Island (U.S.), at Chernobyl (Ukraine), and at Fukushima (Japan).

Three Mile Island, USA

Although various safety features make serious nuclear accidents unlikely, an accident did occur on March 28, 1979, at the Three Mile Island Nuclear Power Station near Harrisburg, Pennsylvania (Figure 8-14). The incident was triggered by a malfunction in the secondary cooling circuit, which caused the temperature in the primary coolant to rise. The plant went immediately into a shutdown mode but failed to close a relief valve. Failing to notice the valve malfunction, operators turned off the emergency cooling pumps that led to the loss of coolant, and the reactor suffered a partial meltdown. To prevent overpressure, some of the radioactive gases were vented out. Fortunately, the majority of the radioactive release stayed within the containment structure, and very little radiation escaped the reactor. Although human exposure to radiation was relatively minor, the economic cost and the psychological stress on the public were significant.

Figure 8-14
Three-Mile Island nucear power plant.
Source: Nuclear Regulatory Comm.

The TMI accident is considered the worst nuclear disaster in U.S. history. Under mounting pressure from the public, Congress enacted legislation regarding more stringent regulations for the design, construction, and operation of nuclear reactors. In addition, the nuclear industry formed its own watchdog, the Institute of Nuclear Power Operation (INPO) that oversees safety standards and assures that power plants follow these standards and maintain active and continuous training of nuclear operators.

Chernobyl, Ukraine

On April 26, 1986, about seven years after the TMI incident, another accident made the headlines, this time at the Chernobyl nuclear power plant located about 130 km north of Kiev, the capital of Ukraine. A fire in one of the four reactors followed by an explosion released more than 50 tons of radioactive material -- ten times that of the bomb dropped on Hiroshima -- into the environment. The scientific consensus is that the accident was the product of a flawed reactor design, coupled with inadequate training and serious mistakes made by the operators of the plant. Unlike TMI, the Chernobyl accident was not a result of the loss of coolant but followed a sequence of events that led to a power surge that caused a fire to the carbon moderator. The plant lacked the massive containment structure common in most nuclear power plants operating in Europe and the United States.

The effects of the disaster at Chernobyl were widespread. The immediate casualties were among the clean-up crew, firefighters, and pilots who died from acute radiation exposure. An additional 56 deaths are attributed to radiation exposure from the accident. Environmental damage included the destruction of vast areas of agricultural and farmland and the poisoning of major surface and underground water reservoirs. The economic damage from the accident is

estimated at more than 13 billion dollars. The long-term concern is the contamination of the soil with cesium-137. Since the accident, to contain radiation, a giant sarcophagus is built over the damaged reactor (Figure 8-15). Following the Chernobyl accident, the World Association of Nuclear Operators (WANO) was formed to fulfill a similar role to that of the INPO, on a global basis.[††]

Figure 8-15
Chernobyl nuclear powerplant after the nuclear explosion. A giant sarcophagus prevents radiation leaking from the damaged reactor.
Source: Wikipedia Creative Commons.

Fukushima, Japan

Probably the most serious mishap took place on March 11, 2011, following a 9.0-magnitude earthquake off the coast of Japan and the subsequent tsunami that slammed northeastern Japan. Official reports put the number killed at 15,894; another 2,500 were reported missing.

As the nation struggled to rescue what was left of its coastal cities, it was faced with yet another crisis. Three reactors at Fukushima Daiichi Nuclear Power Station were severely damaged. This triggered an automatic shutdown of the nuclear reactors. Even with fission stopped, the fuel rods continue their disintegration and, thus, must be kept cool. A major flaw in reactor design was that auxiliary pumps, diesel generators, and batteries were kept in the basement of the power station and, thus, were flooded, making it impossible to circulate water to cool the fuel rods. As the water boiled off and more of the nuclear rods were exposed to air, three reactors suffered partial meltdowns, while spent fuel at the fourth reactor caught fire, releasing large amounts of radioactive materials directly into the atmosphere. In a desperate bid to cool the reactors, workers vented the high-pressure steam and hydrogen into the reactors' housing. At sufficient concentrations — roughly 4% or more (See Table 6-7) — hydrogen is explosive if it finds oxygen or a spark. That is exactly what happened at reactor No. 1, where an explosion tore the roof off of the building that housed the reactor. As the crisis escalated, nitrogen was pumped into the reactor vessel to bring down the hydrogen concentration to below its explosivity limit. In addition, the Japanese military began dropping seawater from helicopters onto the reactor cores; firefighters participated by using water cannons to vault cooling liquid into the spent fuel pools. The effectiveness of this approach has been questioned by experts, who point out that seawater is highly corrosive and may insulate fuel rods, impeding their ability to conduct heat away.

The economic impact of the accident is not fully assessed, but expected to exceed several hundred billion dollars. Fortunately, there are no records of anybody being killed immediately as a result of radiation exposure, but many people may eventually die as the number of cancer patients will inevitably arise. A few lessons are to be learned, however -- that power plants must be designed to withstand even stronger earthquakes and tsunamis and, assure backup power and water supplies, in case of accidents and long-term shutdowns, are not disrupted.

Nuclear Wastes

Uranium undergoes several changes as it is mined, processed, burned, reprocessed, and eventually discarded and stored in a repository. Along the way, it leaves a footprint by producing and leaving behind various levels

[††] One fundamental difference between the Chernobyl reactor and the water-cooled reactors operated in the United States, and elsewhere, is the role that steam plays during an accidental loss of coolant. In water-cooled reactors, steam may accumulate to form pockets known as voids. With excess steam, more voids are created and water becomes less effective as a moderator; as a result, the chain reaction is not sustained and less power is produced, which tends to shutdown the reactor. When moderator and coolant are kept separate (as was the case in Chernobyl), any loss of coolant reduces the cooling capacity without affecting the moderator and the rate that neutrons are released. As the reactor heated, the rate of the fission chain reaction increased, until the cooling water turned to steam and exploded. This in turn, accelerated the chain reactions and increased power output. More power means additional steam, less cooling, less neutron absorption, and still more power. With a lack of proper safety precautions, the process may continue to dangerous levels. Water-cooled nuclear reactors are, therefore, inherently safer because they do not face this risk. In addition, the lack of containment structures in the Chernobyl plant, similar to those present in American, European, and Japanese nuclear plants, resulted in substantial releases of radionuclide and added to the severity of the accident.

of radioactive waste. Depending on the amount and type, the waste is classified as a low level, an intermediate level, or a high level. **Low-level** nuclear wastes are those with low doses and relatively short half-lives. They come from hospitals, medical and research laboratories, x-ray machines, and contaminated clothing and equipment. Many commercial products, such as watches, ionization smoke detectors, eyeglasses, dental porcelain, luminescent products, and instrument dials and signs, contain some radioactive materials. Low-level wastes do not need any casks and are suitable for shallow-depth burial or incineration. The sources of **intermediate-level** nuclear wastes are nuclear fuel processing and nuclear power plants before decommissioning. Intermediate-level wastes are usually solidified in concrete and, depending on their type, buried in shallow or deep underground repositories. **High-level** nuclear wastes are spent fuel and other products from the reactor core and if it has been decommissioned, the reactor itself. A typical power plant generates about 20 to 30 tons of high-level radioactive waste each year, mainly cesium-137, strontium-90, and technetium-99. Plutonium-239 is the most serious byproduct of breeder reactors.

Disposal of Nuclear Wastes

Waste management is one of the most controversial and pressing issues tarnishing the image of the nuclear industry. Nuclear waste not only has presented challenges for the present generation but also may endanger the welfare of future generations for many thousands of years. As yet, there is no completely reliable method of permanently disposing of nuclear waste. All current methods are only interim measures. No matter how small or large a role nuclear energy plays in meeting future energy needs, developing technologies that safely can dispose of the intensely radioactive byproducts remains a top priority. Worldwide, more than a quarter of a million tons of high-level nuclear waste is waiting to be disposed of. Below are a few proposals that have been, or are being considered:

Permanent subterranean storage – The most commonly favored method for disposal is the placement of waste into deep geological repositories. Factors affecting this determination are soil stability, proximity to large water reservoirs and runoffs, seismic activity, and the local population. An ideal site must be completely dry, with no possibility of moisture percolating through the cracks and corroding the alloys. Salt has been shown to be an effective barrier to radiation; therefore, lands with large salt deposits, located in geographically stable landmasses, are believed to be the best choice.

The U.S. government has considered many sites and, until recently, had decided on a permanent repository near Yucca Mountain, Nevada. The plan included processing up to 77,000 metric tons of spent fuel that, so far, has been accumulated, storing it in steel canisters, and inserting the canisters into holes drilled in the rock floor of caverns, hundreds of meters below the surface. Residents of nearby communities have vehemently opposed this construction, some jokingly referring to Yucca Mountain as "Yucky Mountain" or "Yuck-a-Mountain." Other opponents charge that the government has overlooked seismic and volcanic activity and other potential dangers in the area, in a rush to find a location. After much debate, suits and countersuits and after spending $9 billion, and under intense pressure from various constituents, in July 2009, President Obama scrapped the project, citing no urgency in finding a permanent repository right away. According to a recent document, the administration plans to implement a program to design, construct and begins operation of a pilot interim storage facility by 2021, and a permanent repository by 2048. As it stands, the ultimate fate of the U.S. nuclear wastes remains as uncertain as ever.

Entombment under the seabed – This plan is similar to the plan outlined above, but in this case, canisters are buried in a tectonic subducting zone under the deep ocean floor, far away from the shore and people. The potential leakage could be catastrophic, however, and there are international treaties that bar the disposal of radioactive wastes at sea.

Nuclear transmutation – This method converts (transmutes) radioactive waste materials with very long half-lives to short-lived or non-radioactive products, by bombarding them with elementary particles, such as neutrons. An intense beam of fast-moving protons produced by a linear accelerator hits a lead or tungsten target and knocks out a large number of neutrons, which then attack the radioactive waste. For example, by absorbing a neutron, technetium-99 ($T_{1/2}$ = 211,000 years) becomes technetium-100 ($T_{1/2}$ = 16 s), which then rapidly decays to stable non-radioactive rubidium-100. Another example is the transmutation of iodine-129 ($T_{1/2}$ = 16 million years) into the stable element xenon-130.

Storage under polar icecaps – The concern surrounding this proposal is that a large amount of heat generation would result in the melting of major icecaps, with irreversible environmental consequences.

Reprocessing – Reprocessing refers to the chemical separation and recovery of fissionable uranium and plutonium from irradiated nuclear fuel. The advanced reprocessing technology was developed during the Second World War when the US attempted to recover fissionable plutonium from irradiated nuclear fuel. The program continued after the war to reprocess the waste and recover plutonium for commercial breeder nuclear reactors and because of a perceived scarcity of uranium. In an attempt to limit the proliferation of nuclear weapons material, the federal support for reprocessing was stopped in 1977.

Taking nuclear waste into space – The major concern over this method is an explosion during the launch of the rocket containing nuclear waste. In light of the explosions of the Space Shuttle Challenger in 1986 and Columbia in 2003, this fear seems ever more relevant. As space launch technology becomes more and more reliable, it may become possible to find a nearly fool-proof method to send the waste products into orbit around the sun or bury them on the moon and other planets.

Example 8-4: The concentration of strontium-90 in high-level liquid wastes is about one curie (Ci) per gallon. If the concentration is to be dropped to 10^{-9} curie per gallon for it to become safe, how long do we need to wait? A curie is a measure of the activity of unstable nuclei of radioactive isotopes.

Solution: Strontium-90 has a half-life of 30 years. The concentration drops in 10 half-lives (300 years) by 1000, in 20 half-lives (600 years) by a million, and in 30 half-lives (900 years) by a billion times -- a drop usually assumed as an acceptable level to be considered safe. Examples like this help us understand the concern environmentalists have for the storage of nuclear wastes.

Non-Electricity Uses of Nuclear Energy

Besides producing electricity, nuclear energy has numerous applications in space exploration, rocket propulsion, and ground-based transportation. Nuclear power is particularly suitable for sea vessels, such as ships and submarines, that may need to stay in water for a long time. It also can provide a convenient alternative for charging batteries for electric and hybrid vehicles, producing hydrogen for fuel-cell vehicles, or delivering process heat for various industrial uses. Radioisotopes are used in industrial radiography, flow tracing, and mineral analysis. Gamma radiation is used for luggage screening in airports, smoke detectors, sterilization of medical instruments, and medical research for the treatment of cancer and other diseases. Similarly, x-rays are used for medical screening and diagnostics, tomography, leak detection, process control, and food preservation, among numerous other industrial applications. Nuclear technology has been used extensively in scientific research for studying the structure and dynamics of material at the atomic level and quantifying minute quantities of various elements. Examples of peaceful nuclear explosions are large-scale excavations to create reservoirs and canals, cavities for underground oil, gas, and waste storage, and enhanced oil recovery.

Nuclear Power and Public Opinion

The debate over nuclear energy dates back over 60 years that marked the golden era of nuclear energy when it was supposed to produce unlimited amounts of energy, too cheap to be metered. Although the dream of "almost free" electricity never materialized, the oil embargo of the 1970s provided new ammunition for nuclear enthusiasts and nuclear energy became, once more, the cornerstone of U.S. energy policy. The nuclear accidents at TMI in 1979, and Chernobyl in 1986, along with the coincidental and simultaneous release of the movie *The China Syndrome*, dampened public enthusiasm, and nuclear power became a "dirty" name; seemingly, nobody wanted to be a part of it. In the U.S., the public reaction forced the government to stop licensing new construction since 1976 – a ban that was in effect until recently, when Congress lifted the ban and approved loan guarantees for new nuclear reactors.

In light of the new surge in the price of petroleum, the desire for greater independence from foreign oil, and the rising awareness of the threats of CO_2 emissions and global warming, U.S. public opinion regarding nuclear energy remains mostly positive. According to a poll conducted by the Nuclear Energy Institute in February 2011 just prior to the Fukushima accident, three out of four Americans supported nuclear energy and wanted to keep the nuclear option open and part of the overall U.S. energy policy -- a marked increase from 49% in 1983 when the question was first raised. Only 10% strongly opposed.

The Fukushima disaster reignited the strong protests against nuclear generation and renewed the decades-old debate about the safety of nuclear reactors. Environmental activists launched a major public campaign against nuclear energy around the world. Reactions in Europe, particularly in France and Germany, were the strongest. The accident had, understandably, a devastating effect on Japanese public opinion. At the time of this update (August 2021), Switzerland and Spain have banned the construction of new nuclear power plants, and the German Parliament voted to phase out nuclear energy by 2022; Italians voted to extend the ban, which was in effect since early 1990. China and India are expanding their shares of electricity generation from nuclear fuel. What other nations ultimately will decide is still too early to answer. Not surprisingly, nuclear experts are rallying to defend the nuclear industry and cite the accident as proof of the industry's safety, saying that, despite the plant's age, inadequate safety features, major design flaws, plus a monstrous earthquake and tsunami, no one was killed.

What role nuclear power will play in meeting the world's electricity demand, in the future, is not clear. What is clear is that despite the drawbacks, until major innovations provide clean and inexpensive sources of energy, nuclear energy will be here to stay. Many people, voluntarily or involuntarily, will accept some risks associated with energy-intensive modern living. When burned, fossil fuels release vast amounts of carbon dioxide, nitric and sulfur oxides, and other harmful greenhouse and toxic gases. Even renewable energy sources have undesirable environmental impacts. Nuclear energy emits no greenhouse gases, requires less mining, has a relatively abundant source of fuel, and costs less to operate. In fact, while nuclear produces 8 tons of carbon dioxide per gigawatt-hour, the figure for coal is 850, oil, 750, natural gas, 500, wind, 7, and hydro, 4. Furthermore, nuclear-generating stations occupy much less land space than solar or wind power plants of similar capacity and do not tax the environment in terms of water use, or substantial change to flora, fauna, and other ecological landscape. In smaller countries, such as France and Belgium, there is a great incentive to prefer nuclear power over fossil fuels and even renewable resources, such as solar and wind.

Nuclear plants are very expensive to build -- in excess of $12-14 billion each, license processing is cumbersome, and issues related to nuclear waste disposal, proliferation, and terrorism continue to plague the industry. Using a $14 billion estimate, electricity costs about $6,000 per kilowatt, much higher than electricity generated by wind at roughly $2,000-$2,500 per kilowatt and $1,000 for gas-fired power plants. Advocates argue that even at these higher

capital costs, the cost distributed over the life of the reactor at around 60 years is low and nuclear plants remain competitive. Furthermore, if the cost associated with carbon emission abatement is included, then nuclear energy will be hard to beat.

Since much of the cost of nuclear energy is associated with the risk associated with waste storage and safety, much of the research has been concentrated on the design of small modular reactors in the 40 MW-300 MW range, that are fabricated in factories and moved on sites (Figure 8-16). The modules can be securely buried underground, dug up only once every few years mainly for refueling, and routine maintenance. The new designs reduce the danger associated with such natural disasters as Japanese Tsunamis, keeps them out of reach of terrorists, and are small enough so the radiation leaks as a result of potential accidents are small and can be contained within small areas.

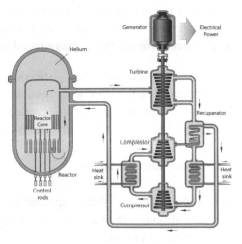

Figure 8-16
Basic schematics small modular gas-cooled nuclear reactor by General Atomics, San Diego.
Source: Wikipedia Commons.

Fusion

As concern about the long-term viability of nuclear fission mount, a new technology called "fusion" is rekindling interest in nuclear energy. Fusion is the same process that powers our sun (Figure 8-17). The enormous amount of energy released by the sun in the form of radiation is a result of the conversion of some of its mass to energy, as predicted by Einstein's famous equation $E = mc^2$. Unlike the process in fission reactions, nuclei are not split apart but, instead, are fused together, hence the name **nuclear fusion**. In the case of our sun (and all other stars), massive gravitational forces compress and heat hydrogen nuclei to form a plasma. Plasma is sometimes referred to as the fourth state of matter and is formed when gases are heated to a temperature that is high enough to cause ionization. This process knocks electrons out of the atom, leaving it with a positive charge. As the plasma is heated further, eventually a point will be reached where the positively charged atomic nuclei overcome their mutual electrostatic (coulomb) repulsion and fuse together. In the process, helium, neutrons, and a tremendous amount of energy are produced (See Digging Deeper: Physics of Fusion). Researchers inspired by such reactions are working feverishly to replicate these processes here on earth. If successful, fusion reactors have the potential of providing unlimited energy with fewer disadvantages than fission reactors.

Figure 8-17
Fusion is responsible for the energy released by all stars (including our Sun).
Source: ITER Organization

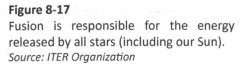

Worth Remembering – A gallon of water has enough deuterium that, when fused, gives as much energy as 300 gallons of gasoline, enough to power an average car for one year.

Fusion Challenge

The basic challenges facing the commercial development of fusion reactors are (a) to achieve ignition with a net gain in energy, beyond the break-even point; and (b) to find a method that supports a fusion chain reaction in a sustained manner. The break-even point occurs when the amount of energy released by the nuclear reaction exceeds the amount of energy required to raise the temperature (and pressure) of the reactants to the level needed to initiate fusion (namely, Q of 1). These requirements can be reduced to three tasks of acquisition:

1. *Very high temperatures* -- needed to overcome the repulsive forces of the positively charged nuclei.
2. *Long residence times* -- needed to keep the reactants in proximity long enough to sustain the reaction;
3. *Very high densities* -- needed to increase the collision frequency and the rate of reaction.

To achieve fusion, three approaches have been investigated: (a) gravitational confinement, (b) inertial confinement, and (c) magnetic confinement.

Gravitational confinement is what happens in the sun, where gases are compressed and heated by gravitational forces. Gravitational confinement cannot be duplicated on Earth.

Inertial confinement mimics a short-lived microminiature star; a spherical capsule containing a deuterium-tritium (D-T) mixture is heated and compressed by an array of powerful lasers directed toward the pellet for a few nanoseconds. Several designs have been tried at Lawrence Livermore National Laboratory (LLNL) in California. *Shiva Reactor*, completed in 1977, deployed the world's most powerful laser available at the time (Figure 8-18).[‡‡] Strong laser pulses strike and uniformly heat the deuterium-tritium pellet placed inside a vacuum sphere. The laser beams blast and incinerate the pellet and compress the gas to very high temperatures and pressures that are required to initiate fusion. Shiva lasers were later replaced by *Nova* lasers, which were 10 times more powerful. The National Ignition Facility (NIF), completed in February 2009, was the next generation of lasers, ten times more powerful than Nova, believed to be capable of delivering extraordinarily high temperatures and pressures needed to initiate and maintain the fusion chain reaction. Critics doubted that even NIF was sufficiently powerful enough to achieve ignition and break-even. The concern appeared to be justified. NIF officially ended on September 30, 2012 without achieving ignition.

Magnetic confinement is a process in which hot hydrogen plasma is circulated inside a huge coil of wire (magnetic bottle). If a current flows through this coil, it creates a magnetic field that confines the plasma within the torus-shaped cavity. The plasma is continuously heated as it circulates through the coil. Once it reaches the temperature of 150 million degrees Celsius , deuterium and tritium fuse to form helium. In the process, some neutrons are released. The magnetic confinement approach has been used in a number of facilities throughout the world [JT-60 in Japan, Tokamak Fusion

Figure 8-18
Shiva fusion inertial research facilities in Livermore, California.
Source: Lawrence Livermore National Lab.

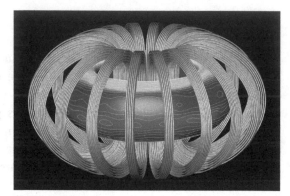

Figure 8-19
Magnetically confined plasma
Source: Oakridge National Lab

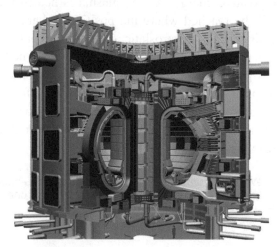

Figure 8-20
The ITER device.
Source: ITER Organization

‡‡ "Shiva," often called the Destroyer or The Lord of the Dance, is the Hindu God of many hands and is attributed with great power and physical prowess.

Test Reactor (TFTR) at Princeton (Figure 8-19), and EU's Joint European Torus (JET) located in England].

The 500 MW *International Thermonuclear Experimental Reactor* (ITER, "the way" in Latin, and pronounced "eater"), based on the Tokamak design, is a joint cooperative effort between 35 member countries jointly share the design, the research, and in its funding. The ITER, dubbed "the world's largest science project," is being built in Cadarache, France, for initial demonstration of its functionality, after numerous schedule delays, in or near 2025 (Figure 8-20). The initial goal is to sustain a deuterium-tritium chain reaction and generate ten times as much energy as was put into it, to a Q of 10. Furthermore, research will be conducted to test critical issues of fusion safety that must be resolved before full-scale commercial reactors can be built.

Magnetized Target Fusion combines features of magnetic confinement and inertial confinement fusions. Like the magnetic approach, the fusion fuel is confined by magnetic fields; as with the inertial approach, fusion is initiated by squeezing the target to very high pressures and temperatures. Hot plasma is injected into a ball of liquid metal inside a steel sphere, which then is compressed simultaneously by pistons from many directions until it is fused, and releases energy The energy heats up the surrounding liquid metal that is used to boil water, make steam and generate electricity.

Cold Fusion

When people talk about fusion, they are mostly referring to "hot fusion." There has been much talk about the possibility of "cold fusion" in the last couple of decades. In 1989, Stanley Pons of the University of Utah, and Martin Fleischmann from the University of Southampton in the United Kingdom claimed that they had achieved nuclear fusion in a simple photochemical cell.[§§] The reaction that was claimed to have occurred involved fusion nuclei of two deuterium atoms at room temperature and the release of a huge amount of gamma-ray radiation. These experiments generated enormous publicity around the world but were later denounced by leading experts who could not verify and reproduce the results. Although there are still some who believe that cold fusion is possible, most scientists view cold fusion as a farce and a pipe dream, not in the domain of scientific investigation!

Summary

Nuclear fission is the source of much of the energy available to us. The decay from nuclear radioactive fuels is what powers our nuclear reactors, and is also, the main engine fueling the earth. Heat diffusing from the earth's interiors is available to us in the form of steam and hot water reservoirs, volcanic lava, and hot bedrocks, cumulatively known as geothermal energy.

Compared to coal and natural gas plants, it produces a tremendous amount of energy per unit mass. Unlike fossil fuel combustion that produces toxic air pollutants, carbon dioxide, and other greenhouse gases, nuclear energy is clean and produces no such contaminants. Nuclear energy, however, generates other products that pose far greater threats to the environment if not handled properly. The radiation released during the Three Mile Island nuclear accident in 1979, the Chernobyl accident in 1986, and Fukushima in 2011, catalyzed a major debate about the safety of nuclear reactors, which has prompted many to abandon or limit the use of nuclear in favor of renewable and other forms of energy.

Nuclear fusion is what powers our sun, and is our ultimate hope for the vast amount of affordable energy. Fusion energy is inherently safe – it cannot meltdown, does not produce long-lived, highly radioactive waste, and cannot be easily weaponized, but it has yet to overcome major obstacles. Because of its complexity and cost, fusion research requires not only cooperation between private industries, utility companies, and the government, but also a high degree of international collaboration.

[§§] *The New York Times*, March 28, 1989, pp. C1

Unlike the claims of its proponents, fusion is not entirely clean and involves the production of neutrons. Neutrons carry no charge and thus can penetrate magnetic fields unnoticed. As they collide with reactor walls, they strike atoms, causing their ionization, and materials to become radioactive. Depending on what materials are used, the remains may stay radioactive for a very long time, creating a similar waste-disposal dilemma as fission. New research is required to develop newer, more exotic materials that can withstand neutron bombardment.

The optimistic view for the commercial operation of fusion power plants is sometime around the years 2045-2060. It appears that cold fusion and other tabletop devices will remain on the fringe of science.

ⓐ Digging Deeper: Nuclear Radiation

All forms of radiation can be categorized into two types: ionizing and non-ionizing. **Ionizing radiation** has enough energy to eject electrons from atoms and produce positively charged ions. Materials capable of emitting ionizing radiation are radioactive. Cosmic rays, gamma rays, x-rays, and high-energy ultraviolet (UV) lights are examples of ionizing radiation. Visible, infrared (heat), microwave, and radio waves do not have sufficient energy to cause ionization and, thus, are called **non-ionizing radiation**. Non-ionizing radiation was covered earlier and will not be discussed any further. Our bodies are largely transparent to both low-energy radar and high-energy x-rays and gamma radiation, but readily absorb visible and infrared. Although visible and infrared absorptions are quite safe, even small amounts of x-ray and gamma-ray absorption can harm our bodies.

Ionizing radiation can come from both natural and man-made sources. **Natural (background)** sources of radiation are cosmic radiation and terrestrial radiation. Cosmic radiation is due to interactions between the earth's magnetic field and charged particles coming from the sun and other distant stars. Cosmic radiation is stronger at higher elevations. Sources of terrestrial radiation are uranium and products of its decay, such as thorium, radium, and radon. Our bodies also contain radioactive materials such as potassium-40, carbon-14, and lead-210, when we are born.

Man-made (anthropogenic) sources of radiation come from nuclear reactors, consumer products, irradiated food, medical checkups, and radiation therapy. Precluded from this list is possible exposure to accidental release of nuclear radiation from nuclear reactors, testing of nuclear bombs, or nuclear wars. It is, therefore, reasonable to assume that the geographical location we live in, our lifestyles, and the state of our health all affect the amount of radiation to which we are exposed. Because the earth itself contains radioactive materials, the food and water we consume also may be affected. Even the materials from which our houses are made contribute. For example, stone and bricks are more radioactive than wood and aluminum. Consumer products such as televisions and computer screens, luminous watches and dials, smoke detectors, and airport x-ray machines (See Box "X-Ray Vision") also contribute to the radiation doses we regularly receive.

X-Ray Vision

Soon after the discovery of x-rays in 1895 by German physicist Wilhelm Röntgen, scientists constructed devices that looked into broken bones and located bullets in patients' bodies.[i] Critics, however, envisioned this device as a threat to privacy, fearing some might design instruments that could see through walls of houses and peek through women's clothing. The New Jersey legislature even tried to pass a law banning x-rays from use in opera glasses to protect the stars' modesty. Although the quality of x-ray images was rather poor at the time, new scanners now are being developed that reveal much more than meets the eye. Backscatter x-ray machines are being considered at airport security checkpoints. The woman in the figure appears to be carrying a gun and a grenade.

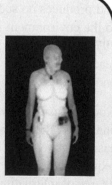

i The discovery of the x-ray by Roentgen brought excitement and public interest, along with much speculation on its possible applications. For example, one proposal suggested making an invisible ink that only can be read by x-rays. Another claimed to have taken photographs of his thoughts; one company marketed anti x-ray underpants, while others sent the hollow eyepieces of their opera glasses to be fitted with x-rays. One customer was even seeking to buy one kilogram of x-rays.

Source: Photonics, (http://www.photonics.com/Article.aspx?AID=51614). [Accessed July 5, 2012]

Ionizing Radiation

The energetic charged particles from radioactive decay lose energy as they pass through matter, in process, forming new and more stable radionuclides. The unstable nucleus undergoing decay is called a **parent**, and the resulting, more stable nucleus is called a **daughter**. The major emissions associated with nuclear reactions are alpha and beta particles, neutrons, and gamma and x-ray radiation. The penetrating powers of these particles are given in Figure 8-21.

Alpha particles are charged particles made up of two protons and two neutrons (the same as the nucleus of a He-4 atom). Due to their charge and mass, alpha particles interact strongly with matter, and only travel a few millimeters in the air, and are easily stopped by a sheet of paper. Although alpha particles cannot penetrate human skin, they can do serious damage if swallowed.

Beta particles are high-energy electrons ejected from the nucleus of a decaying atom when a neutron is converted to a proton. Since the number of protons in the nucleus of an atom determines the element, the conversion of a neutron to a proton actually changes the radionuclide to a different element.¶ Beta particles cannot be stopped by a sheet of paper or human skin but can be stopped by a thicker shield, like wood, aluminum, or a thick cloth.

Gamma and x-rays are high-energy electromagnetic radiation produced by radioactive decay of unstable nuclei; Gamma rays have no charge or mass and can travel thousands of meters in the air, easily

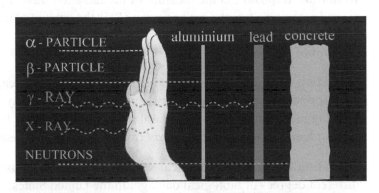

Type	Symbol	Charge	Composition	Penetrating
Alpha	α	+2	Helium nucleus	Low (1)
Beta	β	-1	Electron/Positron	Medium (100)
Gamma	γ	0	Photon	High (1000)
X-ray	X	0	--	--
Neutron	n	0	Neutron	High (1000)

Figure 8-21
Effect of radiation shield for different radionuclide. The numbers in parantheses indicate the relative penetrating powers.

penetrating the human body or even lead. X-rays are similar to gamma rays except that they are 10-100 times less energetic; they can penetrate the soft tissues but are stopped by bones.

Neutrons are heavy uncharged particles resulting from nuclear fission. Neutrons can travel great distances in air and require a thick layer of hydrogen-rich material, such as concrete or water to block them. Because they possess no charges, they cannot ionize a material. They can, however, be absorbed by other materials, making them radioactive, indirectly, emitting ionizing radiation.

Units of Ionizing Radiation

Depending on whether we refer to the strength of radiation emitted by a source **(activity)**, the amount of energy arriving at an object **(exposure)**, the amount absorbed or deposited **(dose)**, or the biological damage it causes **(quality)**, different units of measurement are used.

Radiation levels at the source: When radiation is first emanating from its source, physicists refer to its rate of emission (strength) in curies or becquerels. One becquerel (Bq) is defined as one disintegration per second irrespective of the source of radiation. One curie (Ci) is a huge amount of radioactivity equaling 37 billion becquerels. Both curies and becquerels are measured by an appropriate radiation detection device, such as a Geiger counter, and are used when the amount of radiation emitted from a source is of interest (Figure 8-22). They say nothing about the radiation dose that actually is absorbed by objects or the damage caused to organic or inorganic matters.

¶ There are two kinds of beta decay. When a neutron is converted to a proton, an electron is emitted from the nucleus and when a proton is converted to a neutron, a positron is emitted from the nucleus.

The **energy of ionizing radiation** is measured in *electron-volts* (eV), defined as the energy needed to move one electron across an electrical field potential of one volt. One electron-volt is an extremely small amount of energy. Commonly used multiple units are kilo-electron-volt (keV) and mega-electron-volt (MeV).

Radiation Exposure is the measure of the radiation traveling in the air and reaching a target. One *roentgen (R)* is the amount of radiation deposited in one cubic centimeter of dry air by an ionization equal to one unit of charge.

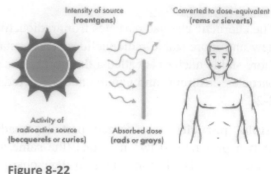

Figure 8-22
Radiation units.

Radiation deposits in the matter: Different materials are capable of absorbing different levels of radiation energy. One **gray** (Gy) is the SI unit for the absorption of one joule of ionizing radiation by one kilogram of matter — be it bone, fat, muscle, or concrete -- irrespective of the effects this deposit has on the material. One *rad* (radiation absorbed dose), equivalent to 0.01 Gy, is the unit commonly used.

Radiation damage to biological systems (equivalent dose): Equal doses of different types of radiation cause different degrees of biological damage. In the United States, radiation exposure is measured in rems. *Rem* (roentgen equivalent man) is a measure of the damage caused by one rad of radiation in the human body. It takes into account the effectiveness of both the source and the living tissue. Since one rem of radiation is a large quantity, the unit most often used is the millirem (**mrem**), which is one-thousandth of rem. One mrem is roughly equivalent to the radiation received during one coast-to-coast airline flight or three days of background radiation in Atlanta.

The SI unit of radiation damage is the sievert. One *sievert* (Sv) of radiation is the amount that causes acute radiation sickness and possibly death. Similarly, because the sievert is a large amount of radiation, microsieverts are more common.

$$1 \text{ Sv} = 100 \text{ rem}$$
$$1 \text{ } \mu\text{Sv} = 0.1 \text{ mrem}$$

Radiation Dosimetry

Individuals receive radiation from natural sources and various activities over their lifetimes. The exposure can be either chronic or acute. ***Chronic exposure*** refers to relatively low doses of radiation for periods of months and years. This typically is experienced in normal daily activities, such as handling nuclear materials and living next to a nuclear waste dump, or is accumulated as a result of years of radiation therapy and routine medical checkups. ***Acute exposure*** resulting from a high dose of penetrating radiation in a very short period during the radiation therapy, a nuclear accident, or a nuclear war.

Although people cannot sense radiation directly, sensitive instruments called dosimeters can measure the amount of radiation they receive. Dosimeters are small sensors that a person can carry to measure the total dose of radiation received over a period of time. Geiger counters are normally used to detect the presence of radiation.

The U.S. Environmental Protection Agency (EPA) is responsible for setting limits on the amount of radiation humans can safely receive. According to these guidelines, the maximum annual permissible dosage is 500 mrem for the public. Furthermore, it has set a limit of 5,000 mrem per year, not to exceed 1,250 mrem in any given three-month period, as the safety limit for adults working with radioactive materials from man-made radiation sources. The highest recommended limit for radiation exposures is for astronauts-25,000 millirems per Space Shuttle mission, principally from cosmic rays. The EPA guideline for the maximum, one-time radiation dose for emergency workers volunteering for life-saving work is 75 rem.

Worldwide, each of us receives roughly 0.34 μSv/h (about 3000 μSv or 300 mrem per year) of background radiation. During a routine chest x-ray, one receives about 10 to 100 μSv of radiation; exposure from a whole-body computerized

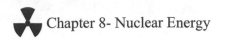

tomography (CT) scan is about 100 times more; mammograms expose one to about four chest x-rays. For those who receive radiation therapy or work in nuclear power plants, radiology units, and some research laboratories, the amount can be significantly higher.

To calculate the total effect of ionization radiation a body receives, it is common to define the effective dose – the sum of weighted equivalent doses in all the organs and tissues. The higher the effective dose, the higher will be the possibility of damage from radiation and the possibility of developing cancer.

Effective dose = Sum of [organ doses × tissue weighting factor]

Tissue-weighting factors for various organs are given in Table 8-3. The tissue-weighting factors, however, are not the same for all people and vary somewhat with age, and between males and females.

Table 8-3 Tissue weighing factors for Individual tissues and organs	
Tissue or organ	*Tissue Weighing Factor*
Testes or Ovaries	0.20
Red Bone Marrow, Colon, Lung	0.12
Bladder, Breast, Liver, Kidney, Uterus, Spleen, Thyroid Gland, Esophagus, Muscle, Pancreas	0.05
Skin	0.01

Radiation and Cancer

When molecules of living organisms are exposed to ionizing radiation, they become unstable and break down. DNA (deoxyribonucleic acid) is a double-helix polymer of millions of nucleotides strung along sugar-phosphate-linked struts that contain all the information needed to produce and control living cells and tissues. Each DNA is organized in a protein-coated structure known as a ***chromosome***. There are 46 chromosomes in the nucleus of human cells. These information-coding segments are known as ***genes***. There are about 20,000 distinct genes in humans.

Ionizing radiation may cause damage by changing the atomic structure of a gene - a process known as a mutation - leading to the loss of some cellular characteristics and functions. When a mutation occurs in reproductive cells (egg or sperm), the changes can be passed to subsequent generations, which may lead to a whole cast of inherited anomalies. Effects of ionizing radiation on human health are hard to assess and depend on the dose, the duration of exposure, and the type of cells involved. Three types of damage to organisms are possible as a result of radiation exposure:

1. *Acute somatic damage* results if a body receives a massive amount of radiation in a short time, such as what might occur following a nuclear accident or an atomic blast – and the effects are immediate. This normally causes fatal damage to a large number of cells – usually resulting in radiation sickness and possibly death. The symptoms of radiation sickness are nausea, vomiting, and severe headache. It is difficult to quote a number for the threshold at which death by radiation exposure is a certainty. Most nuclear scientists, however, agree that a single radiation dose of 500 rem and higher will almost certainly result in death within hours or days. If exposed to radiation doses of 100-250 rem, many may eventually die. No death is expected with a radiation dose of 100 rem or smaller, although, it significantly increases the risk of developing cancer, leukemia, cataracts, or sterility in future years.

2. *Genetic damage* is damage as a result of a non-lethal radiation dose to a reproductive cell such as sperm or egg. If the dose is sufficiently high, it kills the reproductive organ but does not cause long-term harm to the rest of the body. It may also give rise to genetically defective offspring.

3. *Delayed somatic damage* results from chronic exposure to low-level radiation, when damage may not be observed for many years. Rapidly growing cells like bone marrow and soft tissues such as ovaries, testes, and lenses of the eyes are most susceptible to destruction by radiation. Some scientists believe that genetic damage is probably independent of the dose rate since all doses cause non-reversible mutations. This is called the **linear no-threshold (LNT)** hypothesis, which implies that damage is determined by cumulative dose, no matter how it is administered. A one-time radiation exposure of 50 rem will increase the probability of acquiring cancer by the same amount as 50 exposures of one rem each. Looking at in another way, if one-time exposure to 50 rem of radiation raises the chances of getting cancer -- say by 10% -- then a one-time exposure to one rem of ionizing

269

radiation will result in increased cancer risk by only 0.2%. Current radiation protection standards are based upon the application of the LNT hypothesis, which considers that even very low doses of ionizing radiation can cause cancer.

Example 8-5: The current U.S. death rate from cancer is 20%, i.e., one out of every five people in the United States eventually dies of cancer. How many more die of disease if a Chernobyl-type nuclear accident occurs in the United States? An initial estimate was that the total dose received by the world population at large was 60 million rem. According to the Biological Effects of Ionizing Radiation Committee (BEIR V and VII), the risk of cancer death is 0.08% per rem for doses received in a short time (acute) and about 0.04% per rem for doses received over a long time (chronic).·

Solution: For a U.S. population of 300,000,000, a Chernobyl-type accident will cause every citizen to receive, on average, 0.2 rem of radiation (60 million divided by 300 million). Assuming the linear hypothesis, the cancer risk will increase by 0.2 x 0.08 = 0.016% (from 20% to 20.016%). The eventual number of additional deaths from the nuclear accident is 300,000,000 x 0.016% = 48,000 persons. Note that, because of the linear hypothesis assumption, it makes no difference how this radiation is distributed, so the number of expected cancers is independent of the total population. (*Check:* 60,000,000 rems x 0.0008 cancers/rem = 48,000 cancers.)

Question: The radiation from the damaged Fukushima nuclear reactors in Japan has created increasing anxiety among many, especially those living in the plant's vicinity. Using the conservative, linear no-threshold risk model (i.e., all radiations, no matter how small the dose, are dangerous), estimate the number of cancers that are expected from the incident.

Answer: The impact of radiation on health is not fully understood, but it is widely believed to depend on both total accumulated dose and dose rate. The linear no-threshold hypothesis, however, ignores the dose-rate effect. The preliminary studies show that residents of Iitate Village, 20 miles from the site of the accident, received the maximum accumulated dose of ~7600 μSv radiation, in the first three weeks following the earthquake, when the dose rate dropped to a steady rate of 6 μSv/h. Assuming a residual radiation level of 4 μSv/h (14 times normal background level of 0.3 μSv/h), we expect a person to receive 7,600 + 4 x 24 x 365 x 30 ~ 10^6 μSv ~ 1 sievert (100 rem) over 30 years. Assuming the LNT hypothesis is valid, an average resident can expect an additional 4-8% risk of acquiring cancer over his or her lifetime.

It should be noted that not all scientists believe that the LNT theory is completely valid and depending on the general state of an individual's health, the same amount of radiation may or may not lead to cancer. For example, when a dose is spread over hours and weeks, the effect may be an order of magnitude lower than an acute delivery.*** What is certain is that more accumulated doses of radiation give a higher probability of contracting cancer, or shortening life expectancy. They argue that the somatic effects of several smaller doses must be less because time allows for some repair between incidents. Some studies of Hiroshima survivors suggest that there is evidence for "threshold" doses below which no negative effects occur.††† A small number of studies even suggest that very low doses of ionizing radiation may actually have some health benefits due to the stimulation of certain enzymes. This phenomenon is termed radiation hormesis (See Box "Healthy Radiation")·

Figure 8-23 shows the radiation effect versus dose for threshold/no-threshold hypotheses. Most data on high-level radiation doses are available from the survivors of the two nuclear bombs dropped on Japan and the nuclear accident in Chernobyl. Over 200,000 people perished in a few days following the Hiroshima and Nagasaki bombings, and numerous others suffered from cancer, miscarriages, birth defects, and stillbirths in the years thereafter. Data from

---

*** This can be clearly shown for non-radioactive doses. For example, the data shows that half of all persons taking 30 aspirin tablets die of an overdose. The linear hypothesis cannot be extended to conclude that there is a 50% chance that one of every 30 people who take one aspirin tablet will die.

††† Strictly speaking, dose rate may have a significant effect on the cancer rate. According to studies by the National Council on Radiation Protection and Measurement [NCRP Report No. 64, April 1, 1980], lengthening the time over which a large dose of radiation is administered lessens cancer mortality rates by as much as a factor of 10. It should be noted that studies were limited to Hiroshima's A-Bomb survivors and only those who received cumulative doses of 250 millisieverts or larger. The applicability of the model for extrapolating to low-dose radiations is not warranted.

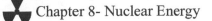

the Chernobyl accident point to similar catastrophes.[‡‡‡] More than 28,000 square kilometers of prime farmland were contaminated and another 200,000 people were forced to leave their homes as a result. According to the WHO, rates of thyroid cancer have climbed five to thirty-fold, depending on the individual's distance from the power plant. There also has been a considerably higher rate of spontaneous miscarriages. The effect of low-level radiation is much harder to assess, as factors that can affect one's health increase with time. However, it has been established that low-level radiation is responsible for increased rates of several types of cancer. Iodine-131 accumulates in victims' thyroid glands and ovaries very fast and, thus, is of prime concern in times immediately after its release into the atmosphere.

Fortunately, it has a very short half-life and practically disappears after a few weeks or months. This is why, when a person is unexpectedly exposed to an external source of ionizing radiation (such as in a nuclear accident), doctors prescribe normal (nonradioactive) iodine pills to saturate the body before the radioactive isotope has a chance to be absorbed. This, of course, gives no protection against other types of radioactive materials.

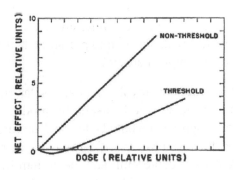

Figure 8-23
Radiation effect versus dose.

Others, such as radioactive isotopes like strontium-90 and cesium-137, with half-lives of about 30 years, enter the body by inhalation or by ingestion of contaminated foods and slowly decay by the continuous emission of beta and gamma radiation. Cesium-137 is mostly absorbed by the liver, kidneys, and sexual organs; strontium-90 attacks bone marrow. Chemically, cesium behaves like potassium found in all of our cells and is readily picked up by our bodies. Because of its long half-life, cesium-137 presents the most significant long-term hazard of a contaminated environment. Plutonium-239 is one of the most toxic substances known, and if inhaled, even one-thousandth of a gram can cause massive fibrosis of the lungs.

Useful Radiation

Radiation is not always associated with ills and disasters. Radiation can be used in numerous research and diagnostic tools, such as x-rays, MRI, and CAT scanners. Radioactive solutions can be ingested by patients as tracers to allow mapping of the bloodstream for the detection of tumors and restricted blood vessels, as well as photography of particular internal organs. Radiation therapy also can be used in the treatment of disease, primarily to kill cancerous cells. Other applications include crop improvement and protection, the manufacturing of consumer products, such as watches and ionization smoke detectors, and the sterilization of such products as cosmetics and medical supplies. Foods also are irradiated to kill germs and other microorganisms to aid in the preservation and to increase shelf life. Radiation is a convenient tool for dating arts and antiques and even such things as the age of Earth or meteorites. Industrial uses of radiation include process monitoring, desalination, welding, detection of cracks and seams, and numerous others.

Worth Remembering – According to the linear hypothesis, every 1250 to 2500 rem of radiation causes one additional cancer.

Question: Radiation therapy involves irradiating and killing cancerous cells without damaging healthy cells. How does radiation distinguish normal cells from cancerous cells?

‡‡‡ The most compelling evidence supporting radiation hormesis comes from the Ramsar region in Iran, near the Caspian Sea, where background radiation levels are up to 135 mSv -- 200 times normal background radiation -- is found [Ghiassi-nejad, et al; "Very High Background Radiation Areas of Ramsar, Iran: Preliminary Biological Studies." *Health Physics*, 82(1): 87-93, 2002.] The source of radiation is believed to be Ra-226 and its decay products, which have been brought to the surface by the waters of nearby hot springs. The blood samples of residents showed significantly less genetic damage than those exposed to normal levels of radiation. The results suggest that prolonged exposure to very high levels of natural radiation may have led to the induction of radiation resistance among exposed individuals. It has been suggested that when the concentration of certain enzymes reaches a certain level, the production of repair enzymes is triggered and chromosome aberrations are decreased [S.M.J. Mortazavi, et al., "Cancer Incidence in Areas with Elevated Levels of Natural Radiation," *International Journal of Low Radiation*, Vol. 2, No.1/2 pp. 20 - 27, 2006.

Answer: Patients will be subjected to crossed beams of radiation that pass through the cancerous region. Alternatively, the patient can be rotated as he is radiated by a single beam of radiation. This way, the normal, non-cancerous cells are exposed to much less radiation than damaged cells that receive continuous exposure.

ⓐ *Digging Deeper: Physics of Fusion*

The thermonuclear fusion in the sun involves a series of reactions, starting with the fusion of two nuclei of hydrogen (protons) to produce deuterium and a positron. This process is called beta decay, in which a proton loses its charge to become a neutron, releasing a positron that carries the charge of the lost proton). The deuterium subsequently interacts with a proton to produce a helium-3 isotope. Finally, two He-3 atoms are fused together to produce a He-4 nucleus (alpha particle).

The reactions involved in the solar thermonuclear process are far too slow to be useful for producing energy on earth. A better approach would be to use deuterium or tritium to initiate the fusion. Two specific reactions of particular interest are deuterium-deuterium and deuterium-tritium. Unfortunately, these isotopes will not fuse with each other at ordinary temperatures and pressures because they are all positively charged. The attractive forces exist only over very short distances; the repulsive forces between the positive nuclei are too strong to allow these nuclei to bring them close enough unless their average speeds (ignition temperature) are raised -- 100 million degrees for a D-D reaction, and 45 million degrees for a D-T reaction. Ignition temperature refers to the point at

> **Healthy Radiation**
>
> A small but growing number of studies suggest that very low doses of ionizing radiation may actually have some health benefits due to the stimulation of certain enzymes.[i] Radon is believed by its proponents to have analgesic and anti-inflammatory properties, and have been used in treating severe pain in joints and rheumatic arthritis. This phenomenon is termed radiation hormesis. There is no consensus on the efficacy and safety of radon therapy among the scientific community, however.
>
> [i] *Luckey, T.D., "Hormesis with Ionizing Radiation," CRC Press, Baca Raton, 1980.*

which plasma heats itself, without the need for any external energy. If normal hydrogen is used as the fuel for fusion, the required temperature would be even greater.

$$^2D + {}^2D \xrightarrow{\text{100 million degree}} {}^3He + {}^1n + 3.3\ MeV$$

$$^2D + {}^3T \xrightarrow{\text{45 million degree}} {}^4He + {}^1n + 17.6\ MeV$$

The D-T reaction is currently the reaction of choice (Figure 8-24).

Deuterium is naturally present in seawater, but at a very low concentration – one atom for every 7,000 atoms of hydrogen. Tritium has a half-life of only 14 years; it was destroyed long ago and, does not exist naturally and must be manufactured. One possible source of tritium is lithium, which is plentiful both in the earth's crust and in seawater. Indeed, one gallon of seawater contains enough hydrogen isotopes for fusion to equal the energy that would be released by burning 300 gallons of gasoline. The best method for manufacturing tritium is by the bombardment of an isotope of lithium (Li-6) by neutrons in a reactor.

$$^6Li + {}^1n \rightarrow {}^4He + {}^3T$$

lithium + neutron → helium + tritium

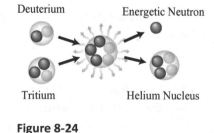

Figure 8-24
Fusion.
Photo credit: ITER Organization

An alternative method of acquiring fusion involves using boron. Instead of a tritium-deuterium (T-D) combination, a few scientists aim to fuse protons (hydrogen nuclei) and boron-11. The fusion requires five times more energy than T-D, but the reaction is also safer, as the end product is pure helium.

Because only a very small fraction of the energy release is carried by neutrons, there is little concern about nuclear radiation, allowing direct conversion of charged particles into electricity.

Example 8-6: Calculate the energy released from the fusion of two nuclei of deuterium (nuclei mass of 2.01410178 amu) and tritium (nuclei mass of 3.0160492 amu), forming an alpha particle and freeing a neutron. What is the binding energy per nucleon of deuterium?

Solution: The reaction equation follows: $^2D + ^3T \rightarrow\ ^4He + ^1n$

Mass defect is calculated as Δm = (2.01410178 + 3.0160492) - (4.002602 + 1.008665) = 0.0189 amu; energy released is: 0.0189 × 931.46 = 17.6 MeV. This is the amount of energy released for every nucleus of deuterium that undergoes fusion. The nucleus of deuterium consists of two nucleons, so energy released per nucleon is half as much or 8.8 eV/nucleon -- significantly larger than that released from the fission of U-235 (7.59 eV/nucleon). In fact, it takes a little more than a pound of hydrogen to generate the power equivalent of a one-gigawatt traditional nuclear reactor. ⓐ

ⓐ *Digging Deeper: Nuclear Weapons*

Only two things are infinite, the universe and human stupidity, and I'm not sure about the former.
~ Albert Einstein (1879-1955)

Alarmed by the military advances of Hitler's army, and fearing that Germany was developing its own nuclear weapon, Einstein wrote a letter to President Franklin D. Roosevelt, in 1939, informing him that the possibility existed to "set up a nuclear chain reaction in a large mass of uranium, by which vast amounts of power and large quantities of new radium-like elements would be generated."[§§§] In response to Einstein's letter, Roosevelt ordered a team of physicists to initiate research on uranium fission and discover if such a bomb could be built in a short time. The task proved to be difficult, as researchers soon found that uranium-238 could not sustain a chain reaction; uranium-235 was a possibility, but only if it were enriched to very high concentrations; separating the two isotopes was extremely difficult, since they were chemically identical, and their masses differed by a mere 1%. Roosevelt died on April 12, 1945, and Harry S. Truman became president.

As the work continued, a second possible path to building the bomb was suggested by scientists at Lawrence Radiation Laboratory. They had produced a new, man-made element (first identified as element-94 and later named plutonium), that "fissioned" more readily and could be produced easily in large quantities. On December 2, 1942, researchers, headed by Italian-émigré, Enrico Fermi, of the University of Chicago, achieved the first self-sustaining chain reaction in a graphite and uranium pile. Soon after that, Robert Oppenheimer, a professor of physics at the University of California at Berkeley, led a team of nuclear physicists (in what came to be known as the "Manhattan Project") to develop the atomic bomb. The effort eventually succeeded in the first nuclear explosion test, named *Trinity*, at the Alamogordo Bombing range near Los Alamos, New Mexico. The test conducted on July 16, 1945, used plutonium and had a yield of 21 kilotons of TNT[¶¶¶] (Figure 8-25).

Less than a month later, at 8:15 on the morning of August 6, 1945, the United States detonated the first atomic bomb on Hiroshima, Japan, which leveled the city and killed 140,000 people instantly. Germany was not a target, as it had surrendered earlier in May. In addition, many tens of thousands of people died from cancer in the years that followed. That bomb, nicknamed *"The Little Boy"* (allegedly named after U.S. President Roosevelt), used uranium-235 and had the destructive power of 13 kilotons of TNT.[****] Three days later, a bigger bomb (20 kilotons), nicknamed *"The Fat Man"* (allegedly named after British Prime Minister, Winston Churchill), was dropped over Nagasaki, Japan, killing another

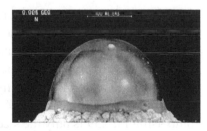

Figure 8-25
The "Trinity."

§§§ Later in his life, Einstein admitted that signing the letter to Mr. Roosevelt was the most tragic mistake in his life, and that he had never believed that the president would ever use the atomic weapon.

¶¶¶ Tri-nitro-toluene (TNT) is a chemical compound used commonly in road construction and for demolition. It is non-radioactive and its explosion does not result in the release of any nuclear products. Nuclear destructive power is often expressed in terms of kilograms or tons of TNT.

**** In comparison, the destructive power of the planes that flew into and destroyed New York's Twin Towers in 2001 was equivalent to only 1 kiloton of TNT.

75,000. The bomb was similar to Trinity and had comparable destructive power. Shortly thereafter, Japan surrendered, and WWII officially ended.

Following the Trinity test and the bombing of Hiroshima and Nagasaki, the U.S. conducted a number of other tests over the Marshall Islands in the Pacific, and underwater. In 1946, U.S. President Truman suggested the establishment of an international agency that oversaw all nuclear activity. Not surprisingly, the Soviet Union, a non-nuclear power, objected, arguing that all atomic weapons must be abolished before such an agency would have legitimacy. Three years later, in August 1949, the Soviets tested their first fission bomb. The Cold War had begun.

As the Cold War intensified, so did the demand for bigger and deadlier nuclear bombs. The advent of the Soviet bomb had reduced absolute U.S. superiority to only a numerical advantage. The Soviet scientist, Andrei Sakharov, first proposed a new idea in 1948, but it was the Hungarian émigré physicist Edward Teller, who promoted the development of the thermonuclear (hydrogen) bomb. In 1950, Truman ordered the accelerated development of the bomb. On November 1, 1952, the U.S. detonated "Mike," the first H-bomb, at Eniwetok in the Pacific. The bomb used liquid deuterium as fuel and had a yield of 10.4 MT, about 700 times more powerful than the A-bomb dropped on Hiroshima. A second 15-MT bomb, code-named Bravo, was tested on the island of Bikini, near the Marshall Islands in 1954. The Soviet Union conducted tests in 1953 and 1961; the British detonated an H-bomb in 1957. France conducted a test in 1960, as did China in 1964. Fortunately, hydrogen bombs never have been used in a military conflict.

Currently, nine countries belong to the nuclear club: the United States, Russia, the UK, France, China, India, Pakistan, N. Korea, and Israel. Since the dissolution of the USSR (Union of Soviet Socialist Republics or the Soviet Union), the former Soviet states -- Belarus, Kazakhstan, and Ukraine -- have abandoned their nuclear weapons and signed the Non-Proliferation Treaty (NPT).

Uncontrolled Nuclear Fission: The A-Bomb

As we discussed before, the difference between a nuclear explosion and a nuclear reactor is in the ability to control the chain reaction in the fission process. Unlike a nuclear reactor, in which the rate of neutron production must be controlled carefully, there is no such effort in a nuclear bomb.

Critical Mass

A small mass of pure fissile material, such as uranium-235 or plutonium-239, would not sustain a chain reaction. Too many neutrons leak out through the large, empty volume surrounding nuclei. A large enough mass of these materials is needed to ensure that enough neutrons are generated to compensate for the loss through the void. This mass is dependent upon the size, shape, and purity of the isotopes being used.

The minimum amount of fissile material (of a given shape) required for maintaining a chain reaction is known as the **critical mass**. In an atomic bomb, a mass of fissile material greater than the critical mass must be assembled and held together for about a millionth of a second to permit the chain reaction to propagate and the bomb to explode. Plutonium has a very small critical mass, whereas uranium must be substantially enriched before it can serve as weapons-grade material. Naturally occurring uranium has only 0.7% of the fissile uranium-235 isotope and must be enriched to a minimum of 90% before it qualifies as weapons-grade. The critical mass necessary to construct a bomb using Pu-239 is only the size of a baseball. For this reason, plutonium is favored over highly enriched uranium (HEU). Building weapons with HEU is, however, easier, since no reprocessing facility to separate plutonium from spent reactor fuel is needed (Figure 8-26a).

In addition to the A-bomb, which is a result of fission reactions, radioactive materials can be used in conventional bombs and warheads. Two examples are dirty bombs and depleted uranium warheads.

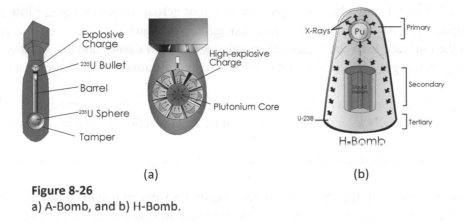

Figure 8-26
a) A-Bomb, and b) H-Bomb.

Dirty Bombs

The term *"dirty bomb"* usually refers to any device that generates a significant amount of radioactive waste without actually undergoing a fission reaction.[††††] These may include conventional weapons which upon explosion, spread radioactive materials, and may be delivered as aerosols or by wrapping the nuclear materials around dynamite. These devices do not necessarily require weapons-grade materials; even the relatively common materials used in radiological medical equipment would be enough to cause catastrophic results and extensive loss of life.

Depleted Uranium

Depleted uranium (DU) is the byproduct of the reprocessing of spent nuclear fuel that has been enriched for use in nuclear reactors or weapons - essentially, pure uranium-238. Much like natural uranium, depleted uranium is both toxic and radioactive. DU is 1.7 times denser than lead and has been used in the development of armor-piercing shells. The use of this material in ammunitions has remained highly controversial; when a DU round hits its target, as much as 70% of the uranium may be picked up and spread by the wind, eventually becoming part of the food chain. DU may be linked to a chronic and multi-symptomatic disorder that is affecting U.S. veterans of the 1991 Gulf War, and an increase in the rate of cancer among Iraqi children.

Uncontrolled Nuclear Fusion: The H-Bomb

An H-bomb is essentially a three-stage weapon (Figure 8-26b). In the first stage, a small amount of plutonium is detonated, as in a conventional A-bomb. In the second stage, the immense energy, in the form of x-ray radiation, compresses and heats up a solid mixture of lithium deuteride (a source of tritium) and deuterium, located in the center of the bomb, to millions of degrees, triggering the thermonuclear reaction. The fusion reaction produces an ample supply of neutrons so powerful they can initiate fission of the otherwise unfissionable casing of depleted uranium (third stage).

Neutron Bombs

Neutron bombs are small thermonuclear (<1 kiloton) bombs designed to produce a high-intensity burst of neutrons over a relatively small area. Since heat and blast effects are minimal, they work primarily on biological systems and are dubbed "anti-personnel" bombs. Because of that, many consider these weapons highly immoral and worry that they could be used prematurely in regional conflicts, which could lead to full-scale nuclear war.

Effects of Nuclear War

Nuclear bombs can result in a wide range of destruction in any of the following ways:

1. **Blast**: Right after the bomb detonates, a shock initiates at the center and moves outward at a rate several times

---

[††††] The term "dirty bomb" sometimes refers to biological or chemical weapons.

faster than the speed of sound, and a large overpressure develops across the shock wave. Most buildings suffer moderate to severe damage. As for humans, the most damage occurs in junctions between materials of different densities, such as the interface between bones and muscles or between tissues and air. Most eardrums rupture and lungs are damaged. Roughly 50% of the energy of the low-altitude atmospheric detonation is released in the initial shock wave.

2. **Heat**: Depending on yield, fireballs as large as one mile in diameter, with temperatures of several thousand degrees, are possible immediately after the explosion. Such fireballs practically vaporize everything near ground zero and cause extensive, rapidly spreading fires. The brilliant flash of light following the explosion causing severe eye injuries, including blindness. Thirty-five percent of the energy of a nuclear blast is in the form of heat and visible radiation.

3. **Radiation**: Shortly after the blast, the heat of the fireball vaporizes weapon residue into small particles that are quickly drawn up into, and are carried by the stratospheric wind around the globe, eventually showing up as radioactive fallout; larger particles settle and contaminate the earth. If detonation occurs over water, sea salts will act as condensation nuclei to seed the clouds, causing highly radioactive rain out. In turn, these radioactive materials release gamma and beta radiation over an extended period of time.

4. **Electromagnetic pulse**: In addition to various radioactive isotopes, nuclear blasts emit a significant amount of x-rays into the atmosphere. X-rays can ionize the air at high altitudes and produce large numbers of fast-moving electrons. The moving electric charge produces a pulse so powerful that long metal objects would act as antennae and electrify all electronic devices in its path. The resulting voltage and the associated high current could destroy unshielded electronics and interfere with electric signals, resulting in failures of critical medical and transportation equipment. The ionized air also disrupts radio traffic that would normally bounce from the ionosphere. Ionizing radiation and EMP account for the remaining 15% of the detonation energy.

Nuclear Arms Treaties and International Conflicts

Following WWII and the explosion of the two powerful nuclear bombs on Hiroshima and Nagasaki, the Allies, mainly the United States and the Soviet Union, engaged in a rapid buildup of nuclear weapons. So many weapons were amassed that if one country decided to use its nuclear option, the entire planet could have been destroyed many times over, in a matter of hours. At the peak of the nuclear weapons stockpile in 1967, the U.S. and the USSR maintained over 40,000 active warheads. The rapid proliferation of the nuclear arsenal and, with it, the escalation of Cold War rhetoric, required a new way of thinking and bold initiatives to save the world by preventing an accidental nuclear war.

In 1970, the five great nuclear powers (the U.S., the USSR, the UK, France, and China) signed a non-proliferation treaty which mandated that those countries would "pursue negotiations in good faith on effective measures relating to the cessation of the nuclear arms race at an early date and nuclear disarmament." In exchange, nations without nuclear weapons pledged never to acquire them and, as signatories, open their nuclear facilities to the Vienna-based International Atomic Energy Agency (IAEA), to monitor nuclear program activities and assure that no nuclear weapons are being developed. In the years that followed, the U.S. and the Soviet Union negotiated the Strategic Arms Limitation Treaty (SALT-I, 1971 and SALT-II, 1979). These treaties aimed at limiting the number of strategic offensive weapons on each side. Furthermore, the Anti-Ballistic Missile Treaty (ABM) constrained the number of launchers and interceptors available to each country. The underlying assumption prevalent during this time was that if each country had enough nuclear power to survive an enemy's first strike and was still able to retaliate with an overwhelming nuclear response, then neither country would undertake such madness. The policy, commonly referred to as Mutually Assured Destruction (MAD) left no doubt that both countries would be destroyed in the event of any nuclear attack. ‡‡‡‡

---

‡‡‡‡ Nuclear arsenals can be divided into either strategic or tactical categories. Strategic nuclear weapons are weapons designed to target cities and other large areas. Tactical nuclear weapons are smaller weapons used to destroy specific military targets. Depending on the delivery method, weapons are classified as bombs, ballistic missiles, cruise missiles, artillery shells, or hand-held. Ballistic missiles are long-range missiles that use ballistic orbital trajectories, whereas cruise missiles use low-altitude trajectories and are suitable for short-range and smaller payloads. Artillery shells and hand-held devices are purely for tactical use.

In 1983, U.S. President Ronald Reagan announced his intention to initiate a program for research and development of a space-based system to defend the nation from attack by strategic ballistic missiles. The **Strategic Defense Initiative** (SDI), popularly referred to as "Star Wars," would supposedly eliminate the threat of a nuclear arms confrontation by installing lasers and other space-based defensive systems that detected and destroyed all incoming missiles. The critics charged that this would be in violation of the ABM treaty and would encourage the militarization of space and destabilize the nuclear balance of power. Furthermore, SDI was based on untested technologies and was unable to defend against cruise missiles, airplanes, and several other possible delivery systems. Following the dissolution of the Soviet Union in 1991 and the end of the cold war, the SDI program has been put on hold.

The reality of the new world order and the demise of communism provided a unique opportunity not only to limit the nuclear arsenal but also actually to reduce it. The **Strategic Arms Reduction Treaties** (START-I, II, and III) are the first comprehensive arms-control agreements that require a reduction of offensive nuclear weapons. Under these treaties, the United States, the former Soviet Union, and its successor states (Russia, Ukraine, Belarus, and Kazakhstan) had to cut down their nuclear warheads and delivery systems that included intercontinental bombers and land-based and submarine-launched ballistic missiles. In 2010, U.S. and Russia signed a new treaty that sets a ceiling for the maximum number of nuclear warheads held by each country to 1,550 and delivery vehicles to 700 ballistic missiles and heavy bombers.

Terrorism

The end of the Cold War and the resulting reduction in tensions between the former Soviet Union and the United States brought about a new spirit of cooperation that has resulted in reducing the number of nuclear warheads and the threat of nuclear war but also has raised a new threat: terrorism. As nuclear warheads are dismantled, an abundant supply of plutonium and other weapons-grade nuclear fuels and accessories must be eliminated. Less than eight kg of plutonium is all that is needed to make a Nagasaki-sized bomb. The possibility exists that terrorist groups, with no access to reprocessing plants, could steal or buy enriched uranium and plutonium fuels on the black market and use them for making crude and dirty bombs. Equally important is the danger of attack on, or accidental spillage of, nuclear waste en route to a yet-to-be-determined permanent repository. Nuclear reactors themselves also could be the subject of sabotage and, therefore, must be designed with many layers of safety. The key defense against large radioactive leaks is to keep the radioactive materials contained. The containment dome is shaped such that it can withstand internal stress resulting from the buildup of gas pressure, but may not be able to withstand major rocket attacks or car bombs. In light of September 11, 2001, terrorist attacks on New York and Washington D.C., nuclear reactors may be particularly vulnerable.§§§§ ⓘ

Endnotes

1   World Nuclear Association, (2019). Retrieved from https://www.world-nuclear.org/information-library/nuclear-fuel-cycle/uranium-resources/supply-of-uranium.aspx.

2   Villani, S., & Becker, E. (1979) Uranium enrichment. New York: Springer.

3   European Nuclear Society, (2021). Retrieved from http://www.euronuclear.org/info/encyclopedia/n/nuclear-power-plant-world-wide.htm

4   Matzke, H. (2003). Development Status of Metallic, Dispersion and Non-Oxide Advanced and Alternative Fuels for Power and Research Reactors, IAEA-TECDOC-1374, September 2003.

5   Farber, D. & Weeks, J. (2001). A Graceful Exit? Decommissioning Nuclear Power Reactors, *Environment, 43*(6) July/August 2001.

6   Tuttle, R. & Becker, D. (2000). The Chernobyl accident and its consequences: Update at the millennium. Seminars , in *Nuclear Medicine, 30*(2), 133-140, **doi: 10.1053/nm.2000.5412**

7   Damage Situation and Police Countermeasures, (2016). *National Police Agency of Japan*, 10 February.

§§§§ Early on the morning of September 11, 2001, Al Qaeda terrorists hijacked four commercial jets and crashed three of them into the World Trade Center in New York and the Pentagon in Washington, D.C. The fourth aircraft was heading toward the White House but crashed in Pennsylvania after passengers overpowered the terrorists who had commandeered the plane. Over 3,000 innocent lives were lost, 265 aboard the airplanes and the rest in the buildings that collapsed as a result of the tragic incident. Canadian Centre for Occupational Health & Safety, http://www.ccohs.ca.

8   Rosa, et al. (2010). Nuclear Waste: Knowledge Waste?, *Science*, August 2010, pp. 762-763.

9   Department of Energy, (2013). Strategy for the Management and Disposal of Used Nuclear Fuel and High-Level Radioactive Waste, 2013, http://tinyurl.com/aun2g9h

10   Rossin, A. D. (2015). US Policy on Spent Fuel, PBS Frontline, https://www.pbs.org/wgbh/pages/frontline/shows/reaction/readings/rossin.html

11   IAEA. (2006) Global Public Opinion on Nuclear Issues and the IAEA, *Nuclear Technology Review*, pp. 7, IAEA GC(50)/INF/3.

12   https://en.wikipedia.org/wiki/Nuclear_energy_policy_by_country

13   Monbiot, G. (2011). Why Fukushima Made me Stop Worrying and Love Nuclear Powe, *Guardian*, Monday 21 March 2011, http://www.guardian.co.uk/commentisfree/2011/mar/21/pro-nuclear-japan-fukushima

14   Nevins, W. M. (1998). A Review of Confinement Requirements for Advanced Fuels, *Journal of Fusion Energy*, 17(1), 25–32.

15   Maniscalco, J. (1980). Inertial Confinement Fusion, *Annual Review of Energy*, vol. 5, pp. 33-60.

16   Yamanaka, C. (1999), Inertial Confinement Fusion: The Quest for Ignition and Energy Gain Using Indirect Drive, *Nuclear Fusion, 39*, pp. 825.

17   Baumer, M. (2015). Why Has the National Ignition Facility Failed to Live Up to Its Name?, http://large.stanford.edu/courses/2015/ph241/baumer1/

18   Seife, C. (2000). Will NIF Live Up to Its Name?, *Science, 289*(18), 1128, August 2000, http://large.stanford.edu/courses/2015/ph241/baumer1/

19   International Thermonuclear Experimental Reactor, Retrieved from http://www.iter.org

20   For a good discussion of the difficulties associated with nuclear fusion, see: *Sun in a Bottle*, by Charles Seife, Penguin Books, 2008.

21   General Fusion, Retrieved from https://generalfusion.com/

22   Rafelski, H. et al. (1991). Cold Fusion: Muon-Catalyzed Fusion, *J. Phys.* vol. 9: At. Mol. Opt. Phys. vol. 24, pp. 1469-1516.

23   The Utah Fusion Circus, (1989). *The New York Times*, Editorial, April 30.

24   MIT News, (1994). Radiation, how much is considered safe for humans?, https://news.mit.edu/1994/safe-0105

25   Canadian Centre for Occupational Health & Safety, http://www.ccohs.ca

26   Dietze, G. et al. (2009) .Effective Dose: A Flawed Concept That Could and Should Be Replaced. Comments on a paper by D. J. Brenner (Br J Radiol 2008;81:521–3), *British Journal of Radiology* vol. 82, pp. 348-351.

27   Thorndike, E. (1976). *Energy and Environment,* Addison Wesley, pp. 130.

28   BEIR V, (1990). Committee on the Biological Effects of Ionizing Radiations), Health Effects of Exposure to Low Levels of Ionizing Radiation, Washington, D.C.: *National Academy Press*.

29   BEIRVII, (2005). Committee on the Biological Effects of Ionizing Radiations): Health Risks from Exposure to Low Levels of Ionizing Radiation, *National Academy of Science*.

30   Yanch, J., Comments on the radiation levels resulting from the damaged nuclear power plants in Fukushima and the impact of these levels on human health, http://web.mit.edu/nse/newsandmedia/news.html

31   See for example, C. L. Sanders, *Radiation Hormesis and the Linear-No-Threshold Assumption*, Springer, 2009.

32   The Atomic Bombings of Hiroshima and Nagasaki: The Manhattan Engineer District, 1946, The World Wide School, 1997, http://worldwideschool.org/library/books/hst/northamerican/TheAtomicBombingsofHiroshimaandNagasaki/legalese.html.

33   Catalinotto, J. (1995). *Metal of Dishonor -- Depleted Uranium: How the Pentagon Radiates Soldiers & Civilians with DU Weapons*, 2nd ed., Independent Publishers Group, Chicago.

34   Hastings, D. (2006). "Is an Armament Sickening U.S. Soldiers?" *Associated Press*, August 12.

35   Peterson, S. (2003). Remains of Toxic Bullets Litter Iraq, *Christian Science Monitor*, May 15.

36   Glasstone, S. & Dolan, P. (1977). *The Effects of Nuclear Weapons,* 3rd ed. Federal Emergency Management Agency.

37   For information on nuclear weapon effects is the Federation of American Scientists is http://www.fas.org/nuke/intro/nuke/effects.htm

38   A good reference on the history of nuclear arms treaties can be found at http://www.icanw.org/history

39   For an excellent overview of nuclear terrorism risks see: P. L. Leventhal & M. M. Hoenig, 'Nuclear Terrorism: Reactor Sabtage and Weapons Proliferation Risks', *Contemporary Policy Issues*, 8(3), 106-121, July 1990.

☝ Exercises

I. Consult the periodic table to determine

1. The atomic numbers of the following elements:
   a. Helium
   b. Iodine
   c. Chlorine
   d. Lead
   e. Barium

2. The atomic structures of gold and mercury are represented as $^{196}_{79}Au$ and $^{200}_{80}Hg$. For each of these atoms, determine:
   a. The atomic number
   b. The atomic mass
   c. The number of protons
   d. The number of neutrons
   e. The number of electrons

II. Name the term that best fits the definitions given below:

a. The nuclear reaction involving the splitting of atoms.
b. The elementary particles differ in number between different isotopes of an atom.
c. The elementary particles in number equal to the number of protons in a nucleus.
d. The sequence of steps that release neutrons that cause additional atoms to fission.
e. The material commonly used to slow down neutrons and improve their chance of capture by nuclear fuel.
f. The component of the reactor core responsible for absorbing excess neutrons and prevent runaway reactions.
g. The process of concentrating uranium-235 to make it suitable for nuclear fuel.
h. The process of turning acid-washed uranium into a gas.
i. The type of reactor that uses uranium-238 as its fuel.
j. The type of reactor that uses graphite as the moderator and helium as the coolant.
k. The minimum amount of nuclear material required to sustain a chain reaction.
l. The force that binds neutrons and protons into a nucleus.
m. Type of reactor using deuterium as its fuel.

III. Discussion Questions

1. What is the difference between chemical and nuclear reactions? In each case, which of the following are conserved?
   a. Total number of nucleons
   b. Total number of protons
   c. Atoms
   d. Molecules
   e. Mass

2. What is a half-life? How many half-lives does it take for the activity of a radioactive isotope to drop by a thousand times? By a million times? By a billion times?

3. What were the causes of the TMI and Chernobyl accidents? What are the differences in the design of the two reactors?

4. What is a chain reaction? How can a chain reaction be stopped? What will happen if a chain reaction continues indefinitely?

5. A radioactive substance with a half-life of five years contains 8,000 radioactive atoms. How many atoms in the sample are expected to remain radioactive after 15 years? after 25 years?

6. Where is the nearest nuclear power plant to you?
   a. When did it start operating?
   b. What type is it?
   c. What is its electric generating capacity?
   d. Are there any controversies regarding its operation?

7. What are the main obstacles to the development of fusion reactors?

8. Name three approaches proposed as possible alternatives to storing nuclear wastes. What are the advantages and disadvantages of each?

9. Name three sources of natural (background) and three sources of man-made ionizing radiation.

10. What is depleted uranium, what is it used for, and why is it dangerous?

11. What are the differences between a dirty bomb, an A-bomb, and an H-bomb?

12. What is transmutation? What are its applications?

IV. Internet Research

1. Search the Internet for various radioactive materials in our bodies. What are the sources of these isotopes, and how much remains in our bodies? How do the

concentrations of these isotopes change as we age? Do these radioactive isotopes serve a purpose in our bodies?

2. Look up "neutron activation" and find out how it is used in forensic applications? In the search for rare atoms?

3. What is the status of fusion research at this time? Which of the obstacles have been overcome, and which one(s) remain(s)?

4. A new design called the Pebble Bed Modular Reactor (PBMR) has received favorable reviews. Do a survey and answer the following questions:

   a. How is this design different from conventional nuclear reactors?

   b. What are the advantages and disadvantages of this design?

   c. What is the status of this technology?

5. What was the contribution of each of the following scientists in the development of nuclear weapons and nuclear electric generating reactors? Search the Internet and write a few paragraphs on the roles of the following individuals and their contributions in the field.

   a. Albert Einstein

   b. Enrico Fermi

   c. Robert J. Oppenheimer

   d. Edward Teller

6. At the end of WWII, the United States and the Soviet Union were furiously engaged in nuclear weapons research and development. Edward Teller, a prominent nuclear physicist (Director of Lawrence Livermore Laboratory and commonly known as the father of the U.S. hydrogen bomb) was advocating the development of the hydrogen bomb, while J. Robert Oppenheimer (director of the Manhattan Project) thought such weapons would only accelerate the race, could heighten global instability, and increase the danger of full-scale nuclear war. Because of the rivalry between Teller and Oppenheimer, and Teller's subsequent testimony against Oppenheimer during Congressional hearings, Teller, was ostracized by much of the scientific community, but remained popular in government and military circles. A tremendous number of articles are written on the Teller-Oppenheimer controversy. You are asked to review a few of these articles and comment on the validity of their arguments. In your opinion:

   a. Did the development of the H-bomb help

maintain a balance and prevent further escalation of hostilities among nations?

   b. Was Teller right to testify against his colleague, which subsequently resulted in Oppenheimer's arrest and the revocation of his security credentials?

   c. Do you see Oppenheimer as a traitor and a communist sympathizer, or as a patriot advocating the cause of peace?

V. ⓐ Problems

1. A quantity of radioactive substance has lost 94% of its radioactivity after one minute. What is its half-life?

2. Calculate the energy released from the fission of 1 kg of U-235 in tons of TNT? How does it compare to the bomb dropped during WWII on Nagasaki?

3. Find the mass defect for the oxygen-18 isotope. ^{18}O has an atomic mass of 17.99916 amu, and a nuclei mass of 17.995 amu.

4. What is the mass-energy equivalent? Express the mass in kilograms, and energy in joules. How much mass must be annihilated* to meet all the world's primary energy needs for one year (382 quads in 2014)?

5. What is the nuclear mass of helium-3, of which atomic mass is 3.016030 amu?

6. How much U-238 must be removed from uranium oxide (UO_2) ore for enriching the U-235 concentration to 3.5%?

7. Two deuterium nuclei fuse forming a tritium nucleus and a proton. What is the energy released per nucleon? Compare the energy from 1 kg of deuterium with that of one kilogram of gasoline.

8. Calculate the BE/nucleon of Fe-56, the most stable nucleus. The atomic mass of Fe-56 is 55.9349 amu.

9. Calculate the mass defect for lithium-7. The mass of lithium-7 is 7.016003 amu.

10. How long does it take for the activity of cesium-137 ($T_{1/2}$ = 30 years) to diminish to 1% of its initial value?

11. What is the binding energy of helium (in MeV and joules), if it has a defect mass of 0.030377 amu? What is the energy equivalent of one gram of graphite, that is, the energy available if all its mass were annihilated?

12. The concentration of an isotope is 1/500 of its initial

---

* Strictly speaking mass is not destroyed, but changes entirely into energy.

280

value after one day. What is the rate of decay?

13. What is the total mass that needs to be entirely converted to meet the entire U.S. annual energy demand? How much uranium ore do we need to meet this demand?

14. How many centrifuge stages do we need to enrich uranium from its natural 0.7% to 3.5%? To weapon-grade 90%? Assume each stage enriches the U-235 by 1%.

15. How much uranium do we need to generate one GWh of electrical energy?

VI. Multiple Choice Questions

1. The nucleus of _____ is fissile, while that of _____ is fertile.
   a. ^{235}U, ^{238}U
   b. ^{239}Pu, ^{235}U
   c. ^{238}U, ^{235}U
   d. ^{239}U, ^{235}U
   e. ^{238}U, ^{239}Pu

2. Isotopes of the same element have the
   a. Same number of electrons but a different number of protons.
   b. Same number of neutrons but a different number of protons.
   c. Same number of protons but a different number of neutrons.
   d. Same atomic mass but a different atomic number.
   e. Same atomic mass and same atomic number.

3. The energy released in a nuclear reaction (fission or fusion) is proportional to
   a. The mass which disappears
   b. The mass which is created
   c. The mass of protons
   d. The number of neutrons being released
   e. The atomic mass

4. The reason that alchemists could not convert copper or mercury to gold was that
   a. They did not use the right chemicals.
   b. They did not know how the chemicals reacted.
   c. They did not know about the structure of the atom.
   d. They did not pick the right elements.
   e. They were not persistent enough.

5. The atomic number is
   a. Mass of an atom.
   b. The number of protons in a nucleus.
   c. The number of neutrons in a nucleus.

d. The number of electrons orbiting the nucleus.
e. The total number of protons and neutrons in a nucleus.

6. The chemical properties of the elements are mainly determined by their
   a. Atomic mass.
   b. Number and distribution of the outer electrons.
   c. Number and distribution of the inner electrons.
   d. Number and distribution of the neutrons.
   e. All of the above.

7. The main advantage of plutonium breeder reactors over conventional hot-water reactor is
   a. Reduction in the operational cost of the reactor.
   b. Reduction in the amount of thermal pollution.
   c. Extension of the lifetime of uranium reserves.
   d. Reduction in the amount of plutonium produced.
   e. Reduction in the threat of nuclear weapons proliferation.

8. Which of the following reactions could describe the fission of U-235?
   a. $^{235}_{92}U + ^{1}_{0}n \rightarrow ^{137}_{52}Te + ^{97}_{40}Zr + 2\left(^{1}_{0}n\right)$
   b. $^{235}_{92}U + ^{1}_{0}n \rightarrow ^{140}_{55}Cs + ^{93}_{37}Rb + 3\left(^{1}_{0}n\right)$
   c. $^{235}_{92}U + ^{1}_{0}n \rightarrow ^{143}_{56}Ba + ^{90}_{36}Kr + 3\left(^{1}_{0}n\right)$
   d. All of the above
   e. None of the above

9. Which of these reactors use ordinary water as the moderator and a coolant?
   a. High-temperature gas-cooled reactors
   b. Light-water reactors
   c. Heavy-water reactors
   d. Fast breeder reactors
   e. Graphite reactors

10. The largest reserves of uranium lie in
    a. The United States.
    b. Kazakhstan.
    c. Russia.
    d. South Africa.
    e. Australia.

11. In the equation $E = mc^2$, m represents
    a. The mass of an object undergoing a chemical reaction.
    b. The mass of an object undergoing a nuclear reaction.
    c. The mass disappearing during a nuclear reaction.
    d. The mass added to nuclei as it turns to energy.
    e. None of the above.

12. How long would it take for the strength of a 10,000-curie iodine-131 (with a half-life of 8.04 days) source to drop to one-millionth of its initial strength?
    a. Around 80 days
    b. Around 5-6 months
    c. Around 5-6 years
    d. Around 1,250 years
    e. Millions of years

13. Which of the following statements applies to commercial nuclear reactors?
    a. A neutron smashes the nucleus of a uranium atom with no neutrons produced.
    b. A neutron smashes the nucleus of a uranium atom with 2-3 additional neutrons released on average. Each neutron goes on to smash additional nuclei.
    c. A neutron smashes the nucleus of a uranium atom with 2-3 additional neutrons released on average. Practically all except one neutron are captured.
    d. Is essentially the same as an A-bomb.
    e. Differs from a nuclear bomb only in the amount of energy that it releases.

14. Which of the following statements is correct?
    a. The moderator slows down the neutrons so they can be captured by the fuel rods.
    b. Both moderator and control rods absorb excess neutrons.
    c. Both moderator and control rods slow the neutrons down.
    d. Control rods slow the neutrons down, whereas the moderator captures the excess neutrons.
    e. Depending on the reactor type, either moderator or control rods are used.

15. Which of the following is a principal disadvantage of nuclear reactors?
    a. They produce long-lasting dangerous wastes.
    b. They produce more greenhouse gases than non-nuclear plants.
    c. They are not safe to operate.
    d. They promote the proliferation of nuclear weapons.
    e. All of the above.

16. The current cost of a modern nuclear reactor is estimated to be in the order of
    a. $10-15 million.
    b. $100-150 million.
    c. $1-1.5 billion.
    d. $10-15 billion.
    e. $100-150 billion.

17. A suitable fuel for a heavy-water reactor is
    a. Natural uranium containing 0.7% ^{235}U.
    b. Uranium enriched to contain at least 3% ^{235}U.
    c. Uranium enriched to contain at least 90% ^{235}U.
    d. Uranium enriched to contain 99% ^{235}U.
    e. Pure ^{235}U.

18. A suitable fuel for a fast-breeder reactor is
    a. Enriched uranium.
    b. Thorium.
    c. A mixture of plutonium and natural uranium.
    d. A mixture of deuterium and tritium.
    e. Hydrogen.

19. A nuclear reaction has become critical when
    a. It generates power to rated capacity.
    b. It is generating more power than it was designed for.
    c. The reactor is about to melt down.
    d. The chain reaction has accelerated to a level such that it causes automatic splitting of the fuel.
    e. It generated no heat.

20. The coolant most suitable in a fast breeder reactor is
    a. Water.
    b. Graphite.
    c. Liquid sodium.
    d. Carbon dioxide.
    e. Helium.

21. Most commercial nuclear reactors use fuel enriched to
    a. About 0.7% uranium-235.
    b. 3% or greater in uranium-235.
    c. 90% or greater uranium-235.
    d. 3% or greater in uranium-238.
    e. 3% or greater in plutonium-239.

22. If both the atomic mass and atomic number changes, then
    a. The weight is essentially unchanged.
    b. The number of neutrons has changed.
    c. The number of neutrons has changed.
    d. A different element is produced.
    e. All of the above are correct statements.

23. What is the force that keeps the nucleus together?
    a. The gravitational force
    b. The weak force
    c. The strong force
    d. The electromagnetic force
    e. All are equally important

24. In the nuclear reaction $_{80}Hg^{197} + X \rightarrow {}_{79}Au^{197} + {}_1H^1$, X stands for:
    a. Proton
    b. Electron
    c. Neutron
    d. Positron
    e. Gamma radiation

25. Most nuclear reactors in operation today are of this type
    a. Fission
    b. Fast breeder
    c. Hot fusion
    d. Cold fusion
    e. Modular compact

26. What is currently being done with waste generated by the U.S. nuclear power plants?
    a. It is reused as nuclear fuel
    b. It is enriched to make more atomic bombs
    c. It is disposed of in nuclear landfills
    d. It is sold
    e. It is held in temporary storage facilities

27. In nuclear reactions
    a. Mass is conserved,
    b. The number of atoms is conserved.
    c. The number of molecules is conserved.
    d. The number of elementary particles (neutrons plus protons) is conserved.
    e. All of the above.

28. Different isotopes of a nucleus
    a. Have the same Z, but a different A.
    b. Have the same A, but a different Z.
    c. Have the same Z, and A, but a different number of electrons.
    d. Could be either a or b.
    e. Cannot tell.

29. How many protons are in $_{92}^{238}U$
    a. 92
    b. 143
    c. 146
    d. 238
    e. Cannot tell

30. Two radioactive sources A and B, have the same number of active nuclei at a given instance. When the measurement is repeated ten days later, it was found that the number of active nuclei in B is twice that of A. Which of the following statements is correct?
    a. The mass of A is larger than B.
    b. The mass of B is larger than A.

c. The half-life of B is longer than A.
d. The half-life of A is longer than B.
e. No conclusions can be made from these observations.

31. The nucleons in a nucleus are attracted by
    a. Strong nuclear force
    b. Weak nuclear force
    c. Magnetic force
    d. Gravitational force
    e. Electrostatic force

32. The number of electrons in a neutral charge atom is
    a. Equal to the number of protons.
    b. Greater than the number of protons.
    c. Smaller than the number of protons.
    d. Equal to the mass number.
    e. Equal to neutron number.

33. Which organization is in charge of inspecting and ensuring the safety of nuclear facilities around the world?
    a. U.S. Atomic Energy Commission
    b. International Atomic Energy Agency
    c. World Association of Nuclear Operators
    d. U.S. Department of Energy
    e. U.S. Defense Nuclear Agency

34. Which of the following statements is correct?
    a. Currently, fusion provides only a small fraction of world electricity needs.
    b. Although theoretically possible, achieving a sustainable fusion reaction is many decades away.
    c. Fusion is a pipe dream, not in the domain of scientific investigation.
    d. It is easier to achieve cold fusion before an attempt to harness the hot fusion is made.
    e. None of the above.

35. Which of the following is considered to be ionizing radiation?
    a. Microwaves
    b. Radiofrequency
    c. Visible
    d. Infrared
    e. High-frequency ultraviolet

36. The negative beta particle is
    a. The same as the proton.
    b. The same as the electron.
    c. The same as the positron.
    d. The same as the neutron.
    e. None of the above.

37. The amount of radiation damage to living tissue is

expressed in

a. Roentgen.
b. Rad.
c. Curie.
d. Rem.
e. Becquerel.

38. What is a rad?

a. The unit of radiation level at the source
b. The unit of absorbed dose
c. The unit of exposure to ionizing radiation
d. The unit of radiation damage to biological systems
e. None of the above

39. What is rem?

a. The unit of radiation level at the source
b. The unit of absorbed dose
c. The unit of exposure to ionizing radiation
d. The unit of radiation damage to biological systems
e. None of the above

40. The maximum permissible occupational dose for the general public in the U.S. is _____ per year.

a. 500 mrem
b. 5,000 mrem
c. 500 rads
d. 5,000 rads
e. 5,000 curies

41. What was the name of the project charged to develop nuclear weapons?

a. The Little Boy
b. The Fat Man
c. Manhattan
d. Trinity
e. Mike

42. Who was the U.S. president who ordered the dropping of the nuclear bomb on Japan?

a. Harry Truman
b. Franklin Roosevelt
c. Dwight Eisenhower
d. John F. Kennedy
e. Winston Churchill

43. In what form is the energy from a nuclear blast released into the atmosphere?

a. Shock
b. Heat
c. Prompt radiation
d. Radioactive fallout
e. All of the above

44. An electromagnetic pulse generated by nuclear explosions is most effective in

a. Killing people.
b. Destroying other nuclear weapons.
c. Damaging building.
d. Harming the environment.
e. Damaging electrical equipment and communication devices.

45. The fuel used in the nuclear bomb dropped on Hiroshima was

a. TNT.
b. Hydrogen.
c. Uranium.
d. Plutonium.
e. None of the above.

46. What was the name of the bomb dropped on Nagasaki?

a. The Little Boy
b. The Fat Man
c. The Trinity
d. The Peacemaker
e. The Dirty Bomb

47. Who was the scientist in charge of the design and fabrication of the atomic bomb dropped on Japan?

a. Albert Einstein
b. Enrico Fermi
c. Robert J. Oppenheimer
d. Glean Seaborg
e. Edward Teller

48. START nonproliferation treaty stands for

a. START arms reduction now.
b. STrategic Arms Reduction Treaty.
c. STop Arm Restructuring Treaty.
d. STop ARming the Terrorists.
e. None of the above.

49. Alpha particles are

a. The same as the nuclei of helium.
b. The same as electrons.
c. Electromagnetic radiation with no electric charge and no mass.
d. The same as protons.
e. None of the above.

50. The agency responsible for setting the standards for safe radioactive exposure in the United States is

a. The Nuclear Regulatory Commission.
b. The Department of Energy.
c. The Environmental Protection Agency.
d. The International Atomic Energy Agency.
e. The White House.

VII. True or False?

1. All the atoms in a material have the same number of neutrons in their nuclei.
2. The only difference between various isotopes of an atom is in the number of neutrons in their nuclei.
3. The nucleus of a normal hydrogen atom is called a proton.
4. All nuclear materials remain highly toxic for thousands of years.
5. About half of all electricity in the world is generated by nuclear reactors.
6. The function of a control rod is to slow down fast neutrons to thermal neutrons.
7. The easiest way to shut down a reactor is to remove the fuel rods.
8. One of the main concerns of nuclear power plants is that they can explode like an atomic bomb.
9. The electricity produced by one pound of uranium is equivalent to the power generated by roughly 2-3 million pounds of coal
10. The first cold fusion experiment was successfully concluded in 1989.
11. It is easier to achieve fusion by fusing atoms of D-T than D-D.
12. Rad is an abbreviation for radiation.
13. Relative to the surrounding areas, coal mines have elevated levels of radiation.
14. Because of their enormous destructive powers, atomic weapons are commonly referred to as dirty bombs.
15. Depleted uranium is uranium depleted of all its harmful radiation.
16. Strategic nuclear weapons refer to weapons designed to target cities and other large installations.
17. The key issue triggering the crisis at the Fukushima Daiichi plant following March 11, 2011, earthquake and tsunami in Japan was the loss of the cooling system to control the radioactive fuel and spent fuel.
18. Infrared and visible radiations are the primary sources of ionizing radiation.
19. Gamma radiation is high-energy neutrons.
20. The human body is naturally radioactive.

VIII. Fill in the Blanks

1. Isotopes of an element that can be split through fission are called _____.
2. The process in which high-temperature liquid waste is dried is called _____.
3. After the uranium ore is cleaned and acid washed, it is dried to what is commonly referred to as the _____.
4. The principal causes of major nuclear accidents are the production of an excessive number of _____ and the loss of coolants.
5. All U.S. commercial reactors are of the _____ reactor type.
6. A breeder reactor produces more _____ than it uses.
7. The agency responsible for granting operating licenses and overseeing the safe operation of nuclear reactors in the United States is _____.
8. Compared to fossil power plants, nuclear plants produce _____ amount of greenhouse gas emissions.
9. The fuel made of recycled uranium and plutonium oxides from spent fuel is called _____.
10. The best method of determining the age of volcanic rocks is by measuring the concentration of isotope _____.
11. Any accumulated radiation dose less than _____ millirem is considered an acceptable level for the general public.
12. A radiation exposure of over _____ rem will certainly cause death.
13. A _____ is used to detect radiation.
14. Uncontrolled nuclear fusion is the basis for manufacturing the _____ bomb.
15. Neutron bombs are small _____ bombs designed to produce a locally intense burst of radiation.
16. The most penetrating type of radiation is _____.
17. The radiation emitted from a source is measured in _____ or _____.
18. Electromagnetic radiation in the frequency range just higher than x-rays is called _____.
19. The three types of radiation in order of _____ penetrating power are alpha, beta, and gamma.
20. _____ are produced when a target is bombarded with an electron beam.

PROJECT I - Half-Life of Pennies

In this experiment, you will use a statistical approach to gain a better understanding of the concept of half-life. For this experiment, you need 100 pennies (or other coins), a large tray, a pencil, and a piece of paper.
Procedure:
1. Lay all pennies heads up in the tray.
2. Shake the tray for a few seconds; remove all the coins that have turned tails up. Count the number

of the remaining pennies in the tray (those which stayed heads up). Enter the data in a table similar to Table 1.

3. Shake the tray some more; remove all the coins that have turned tails up. Enter the number of heads in the table.

4. Repeat this procedure until no pennies are left on the tray.

5. Now repeat the whole experiment two more times.

Data reduction:

6. Plot the number of pennies remaining in the tray versus the trial #. Make the y-axis represent the number of heads and the x-axis the trial #.

7. On the same graph, repeat the procedure for the second and third attempts. Use different symbols or colors to distinguish between different attempts.

8. Take the average number of heads for each trial; plot this graph, superimposed on top of the earlier graphs.

Now answer these questions:

a. How reproducible were your data?

b. How does this experiment simulate the behavior of radioactive isotopes? Which set of results represents the best model of half-life?

c. How many trials does it take for the population of pennies to reduce by 50 percent? By 75 percent?

d. What is the rate of decay of pennies in the tray?

e. Compare your results with those of three other classmates. What do you conclude?

Table 1 Half-Life of Pennies			
	1	**2**	**3**
Trial #	No. of Heads	No. of Heads	No. of Heads
0			
1			
2			
3			

PROJECT II - Radiation Dose Estimator

In this project, you are asked to estimate the annual radiation dose your body receives. Fill up the EPA dosimeter chart given below, and answer the following questions:

a. What is the annual radiation dose you receive?

b. Do you receive considerably more radiation during any particular season? If so, why?

c. Do you meet the radiation exposure limit set by the regulatory agencies in your country of residence? Explain.

d. Are there reasonable ways that you can reduce your harmful radiation exposure?

Radiation Dosimetry Estimator		
1	Where do you live? _____ Cosmic radiation at Sea level Elevation Elevation (meters) _____ x 0.015	28 mrem _____
2	If you live within 10 km of a nuclear or coal power plant, add 0.03 for coal, 0.09 for nuclear	_____
3	If your house is made of brick or concrete (Add 7) If you have a smoke detector in your home (add 0.008)	_____ _____
4	Ground radiation (U.S. average) Radon (consult EPA sources) Water, food, and air (U.S. average)	26 mrem _____ 28 mrem
5	Number of miles you fly every year____x.001 or Numbers of hours of flying _____x 0.5	_____ _____
6	Number of chest x-rays _____ x 40 Number of dental x-rays _____ x 5 Number of mammograms _____ x 30 Others (chemotherapy, varies)	_____ _____ _____ _____
	Total	

Source: http://www.epa.gov/radiation/understand/calculate. html

The Los Alamos National Laboratory maintains a website that provides information on radiation health physics and a radiation exposure calculator *(http://newnet.lanl.gov/ dosecalc.htm)*. Estimate your exposure and compare data with EPA results.

CHAPTER **9**

Grand Prismatic Spring, Yellowstone National Park ~ Wikipedia Commons

*All these reckonings of the history of underground heat,
the details of which I am sure you do not wish me to
put before you at present, are founded on the very sure
assumption that the material of our present solid earth
all round its surface was at one time a white-hot liquid.*

~ Lord Kelvin (1824-1907)

Geothermal energy is heat energy from magma (molten rock) deep within the earth, brought to the surface naturally by geysers and springs, by tapping into hot reservoirs, or by exploiting the thermal mass of soil and groundwater. Geothermal energy has been used since ancient times when the Romans, Greeks, and Japanese, among others, used naturally heated mineral water for bathing, heating, and medical applications. It wasn't until 1904 that Prince Piero Ginori Conti used a dynamo powered by geothermal steam in Larderello, Italy, and lighted five light bulbs. Today, geothermal energy is used not only for heating, cooking, and electricity production but also for industrial applications; hot springs and spas* are still some of the most attractive spots for recreation and therapeutic bathing.

The temperature of the geothermal reservoir is an important factor in determining its end-use. Lower temperatures are most applicable for recreational use and domestic heating. They are scattered throughout the continent with their largest in Iceland. Higher temperatures are best for electrical power generation, predominately found in volcanic ranges and island chains. As of 2019, worldwide, geothermal energy provides about 14 gigawatts of electricity and 107 gigawatts of direct-use thermal energy.

Table 9-1 Countries with the highest installed geothermal capacity, 2019*		
Country	Installed (MW)	Installed (%)
United States	3,676	24%
Indonesia	2,133	14%
Philippines	1,918	12%
Turkey	1,526	10%
New Zealand	1,005	7%
Mexico	963	6%
Iceland	755	5%
Rest of the world	3,431	22%
World Total	15,406	100%
Source: BThink Geothermal (2020).		

Although only 10% of the earth's surface is at temperatures hot enough to be used as a practical energy source, the earth's geothermal resources are large enough to provide many times the energy needs of the entire population. Iceland uses the largest fraction of its energy needs from geothermal energy. In fact, its capital city, Reykjavik, is heated entirely by geothermal energy. The U.S., with 3.7 GW of installed electrical capacity, ranks first, followed by Indonesia, the Philippines, Turkey, and New Zealand (Table 9-1). The largest dry steam field in the world is the Geysers in California, generating 750 MW, enough to supply electricity to a city the size of San Francisco (Figure 9-1). Western parts of the continental United States, Hawaii, and Alaska are also rich in geothermal energy.

Geothermal energy can be considered renewable as long as the rate of heat extraction from a reservoir does not exceed the rate at which it is recharged by the earth's heat, which, depending on its temperature, may last from a few to many hundreds of years. Geothermal energy is distributed, to various extents, across the globe. It can be used to provide base-load electricity, requires no storage, has a relatively small footprint, and compare to many other sources, produces little pollution. In the past few decades, researchers have found new ways to trap natural thermal gradients in dry rocks; when this technology matures, geothermal energy promises to become an important source of renewable energy, available virtually anywhere on the planet.

Figure 9-1
Geysers near San Francisco account for a quarter of all U.S. installed geothermal capacity.
Source: NREL photo library.

The Earth

Earth is the third planet from the sun, with an average radius of 6,400 kilometers. Its internal structure includes five distinct concentric spheres -- an inner core, an outer core, lower and upper mantles, and a crust (Figure 9-2); the deeper you go, the hotter it gets. The ***inner core*** – the center of the earth – is a sphere 2,600 kilometers in diameter

---

* Named after the town of Spa in Belgium, famed for healing hot mineral springs since the 14th century.

and may reach temperatures as high as 5,000-7,000°C; it consists mainly of iron, nickel, uranium, thorium, and various heavy metals. Because of the extreme pressures in the center, the inner core remains solid. The ultimate source of geothermal energy is the radioactive decay of the isotopes of these materials and the original heat produced by gravitational collapse as the earth was being formed.

The *outer core* is 2,100 kilometers thick and composed of hot liquid molten metals. The temperature of the outer core is relatively uniform and varies from 5,000°C to about 4,000°C at the outer edges. The outer core, along with the earth's rotation, is believed to be responsible for the earth's magnetic field.

Surrounding the core are the lower and upper mantles. The combined mantles constitute 80% of the earth's volume and about 2/3 of its mass. The *lower mantle* is 2,300 kilometers thick and is made of highly viscous fluids forming circular patterns, called *convection cells*, bringing hot magma toward the earth's surface. The *upper mantle* is solid, has a thickness of about 600 kilometers, made mostly of silicates and iron, and may contain pockets of high-temperature volcanic reservoirs. Magmas reside near the top of the mantles at depths of 5-10 kilometers beneath the crust and range in temperature from about 650°C to 1,300°C, depending on chemical composition. Magma that reaches the surface is called *lava*.

Moving toward the surface, rock cools at a rate of 20-30°C/km and gradually solidifies to form the crust. The *crust* is not a continuous sheet of rock but broken into solid plates that float on top of the hot mantle; its thickness varies between 20-65 kilometers in continental areas, and 5 to 6 kilometers in oceanic zones, making up only 1% of the earth's total mass and 2% of the volume. Crust and a portion of the mantle that contain the tectonic plates are called the *lithosphere*. This heat is transferred by *conduction* to nonporous hot dry rocks and porous rocks that become saturated with water and form reservoirs of water and steam. Such reservoirs eventually find their way toward the surface through faults and cracks, providing what we call **geothermal energy**. Figure 9-3 shows the subsurface temperature maps at depths of 3.5, 6.5, and 10 kilometers for the United States. At present, there is no technology to dig deeper than 10 kilometers.[†]

Question: Considering that our best drills can barely cut through a minimal depth of the earth's surface, how can we know anything about the earth's interior structure?

Answer: We know that the average density of earth (as measured by dividing its volume by mass determined from its gravitational force field) is higher than the measured surface density, which implies that the earth's interior must be denser than its surface. Furthermore, detailed analyses of the seismic waves following earthquakes give us information about the internal structure. The speed of the propagation of the waves is a function of the density of materials through which they travel.

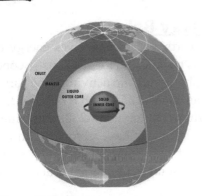

Figure 9-2
Earth's internal structure.

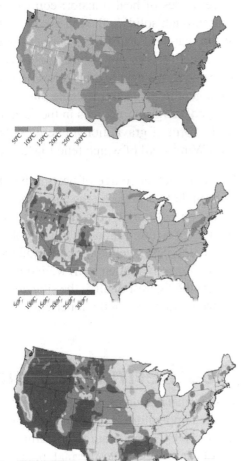

Figure 9-3
Geothermal surface heat flux map of the conterminous United States in sedimentary and basement rocks to 10 km depth, the limit possible to reach with today's drilling technologies.
Source: Blackwell, D.D., et al., SMU Geothermal Laboratory, 2011. Available at http://www.smu.edu/geothermal.

[†]   Because of its relatively smaller size and lower internal heat, moon is devoid of these activities..

Energy Balance

The earth's surface receives energy both from the sun above and from the internal heat within. *The heat from the sun* is responsible for all climatic conditions, cloud formation, wind patterns, and ocean waves. It is also responsible for photosynthetic activities, the formation of forests, rivers, and lakes, and the soil erosion that shapes the surface of our planet. *The source of the internal heat* is the radioactive decay of isotopes of various elements, principally thorium-232, uranium-238, potassium-40, and uranium-235, with half-lives of between 0.7 to 14 billion years. All other elements have isotopes with half-lives considerably shorter and, thus, have already decayed to such a great extent that they do not account for any significant heating of the earth. This suggests that as these fuels are used, the earth's sources of internal heat are also reduced.

Both the energy received from the sun and generated within the earth must be eventually discarded. The solar energy budget was already discussed in Chapter 4. The mechanisms responsible for rejecting terrestrial heat involve all three modes of heat transfer: conduction, convection, and radiation. Conduction is responsible for the transfer of heat through solids -- the inner core and the crust. Convection helps moving heat upward from the liquid outer core to the mantle. Part of this energy is used to move the lithosphere's tectonic plates (continental drift). When these plates collide, the rim of one rides over the other, pushing it down (subduction), in the process pushing some of the volcanic fluids up, creating zones rich with minerals and geothermal fluids. It is, therefore, reasonable to expect that most geothermal activities take place at the boundaries where tectonic plates meet. The earth's surface gives off the trapped energy, sometimes in the form of short spectacular bursts -- earthquakes and volcanic eruptions -- but often in the form of gravitational energy -- building mountains -- and always as infrared terrestrial energy at the rate of 0.08 W/m^2 -- all of which tend to slowly cool the planet.

There is another source of heating besides radioactivity -- the heat liberated when moving bodies are slowed down or brought to a stop. As the earth and other planets were forming, giant clouds of dust and gas were drawn together by the pull of gravity, creating protoplanets (planets the size of the moon, or smaller). Protoplanets attracted a large number of asteroids and other heavenly objects. In the process, nearly all of their kinetic energy was turned into heat and, in our case, melted the earth and gave its spin. As the gravity pulled the liquid soup inside, the heavier materials (predominantly molten iron) were pulled toward the center, forming the core. The lighter materials floated to various layers; the lightest of all -- the silicate -- migrated to the surface, forming the crust. As the earth cooled, the iron core turned solid, forming the inner core -- a process that continues even today, turning more of the gravitational energy into heat.

Geothermal Resources

Geothermal resources typically lie from a few hundred to a few thousand meters below the earth's surface. Depending on the temperature, geothermal resources can be classified as very low temperature (below 30°C), low temperature (30°C-100°C), moderate temperature (100°C-200°C), and high temperature (greater than 200°C). These resources are of four types: hydrothermal, pressurized, magma, and hot dry rock.

Hydrothermal resources, referred to as underground reservoirs containing hot water or steam, are the most common source of geothermal energy. As water seeps underground, it heats and eventually turns into steam. Depending on how the geothermal eruption appears, a hydrothermal resource can be classified as a hot spring, a warm spring, a fumarole, or a geyser. ***Hot springs*** refer to the continuous upwelling of groundwater with temperatures above that of the human body. It is called a ***warm spring*** when the temperature is lower than body temperature but higher than the surrounding atmosphere. When a reservoir does not contain adequate water to seep through, it eventually turns into steam, and the geothermal resource is referred to as a ***fumarole***. ***Geysers*** are intermittent hot springs that, depending on geological conditions, erupt in regular intervals, ranging from a few minutes to hours or months apart (See Box "Old Faithful"). Both hot springs and geysers contain significant amounts of minerals in solution which become deposited, often as colorful structures around the vent. Active geysers are limited in numbers but provide much hotter water or steam. Sixty percent of all geysers in the world are in Yellowstone National Park in Wyoming;

others are scattered in California, Italy, New Zealand, Iceland, and elsewhere. Almost all geothermal sources currently being utilized are hydrothermal, residing in depths below three kilometers.

Pressurized resources are high-temperature, high-pressure brines trapped in porous rocks. Depending on temperature and pressure, water may boil and accumulate as steam or water.

Aside from their high heat contents, pressurized resources are associated with substantial amounts of methane, which can be separated, collected, and used. Because of their great depth, drilling costs are quite high, and tapping into these resources is considered uneconomical. Hydrofracturing techniques, widely used in oil and gas exploration, also are used to enhance the utilities of deep geothermal resources.

Magma is the hot, molten rock in volcanic formations that resides within the 5 km beneath the surface.

Old Faithful

A geyser is like a periodically erupting pressure cooker. The one known as "Old Faithful" has been a popular attraction in Wyoming's Yellowstone National Park for many years. Geysers work the same way a coffee percolator works; a long, narrow column of water is heated from below. In the case of geysers, the source of this heat is volcanic activity and magma. Because of its weight, water reaches temperatures well above its boiling temperature under atmospheric conditions. As pressure reaches a critical level, the lower layer of water turns into steam and expands, pushing out the upper layer and lifting the column of water above it. As the eruption continues, the weight of the column of water (and with it, the pressure at the bottom) decreases and water turns liquid again. After the water begins to reenter the channel, the whole process repeats in 50-70 minutes.

Depending on its depth, magma can reach temperatures up to 1,300°C. Thermal energy from magma can be recovered by drilling holes and injecting cold water through magma. The magma heats the water into steam, which rises buoyantly through a second pipe. Magma is, however, highly corrosive and, when solidified, creates a layer of insulation that limits the operability of such systems. Finding materials that can withstand hot corrosive magma for an extended time is a major obstacle to the commercial development of this technology.

Hot dry rock (HDR) refers to heat stored in the impermeable solid slabs of hot rocks a few kilometers below the surface. Granite usually contains trace amounts of radioactive uranium and thorium and is, therefore, substantially hotter than surrounding nonradioactive rocks. Observed thermal gradients vary widely from one location to another, from a low of 10°C/km in non-thermal regions to 30-70°C/km in regions considered to be prime candidates for hot dry rock exploitation. The thermal gradients in some areas of the earth are much higher, reaching as much as 800°C/km in Larderello, Italy. Such gradients are rare and considered to be the exception rather than the rule, however. In principle, the natural gradients present in hot dry rocks can potentially deliver an unlimited amount of heat, far exceeding all other forms of geothermal energy -- if the technology to exploit them becomes available. With current technologies, only reservoirs within roughly four kilometers from the surface are considered to be economically viable sources of geothermal energy. Deeper reservoirs are generally higher in temperature and of higher efficiencies if used to produce electricity; drilling costs rise exponentially with depth, significantly increasing the overall cost of extracting energy from deeper mines.

It should be pointed out that high thermal gradients do not necessarily mean high heat flow. As we saw in Chapter 4, the rate of heat flow at any point within a solid slab is proportional to the product of the thermal conductivity and the local temperature gradient. Thus, the high thermal gradient across a rock with poor thermal conductivity may not guarantee a large flow of heat.

Question: Is geothermal energy sustainable?
Answer: Whether geothermal energy can be considered renewable or non-renewable depends on the rate at which geothermal fluid is extracted. Many natural hot water springs and steam sources are considered renewable since the resource is being utilized on the same time scale as production from the source. Hot dry rocks and some hot water aquifers in sedimentary basins are recharged only by thermal conduction at a slow rate and, therefore,

must be considered finite energy sources.

Earth, like sun, has an immense amount of stored energy, which will, by all accounts, last billions of years into the future. Unlike solar energy, which is readily available, geothermal resources must be tapped -- i.e., "mined" rather than "harvested." It is estimated that energy is extracted from many geothermal sources 10 to 100 times faster than the natural rate of replenishment, i.e., depending on their locations, they recharge and become operational in years or decades. For example, the power-generating capacity of the Geysers has dropped by 50% from the peak of 1.6 GW_e in 1987, to 750-800 MW_e, today. To curtail depletion, it has, therefore, been suggested that, plant operate only during peak times, rather than, as a base-load operation. With optimum production strategies and methods, geothermal energy resources can be prolonged or sustained for many, many years.

Depending on the temperature, geothermal resources can be used in many applications -- the two most common uses are electricity generation and direct use.

Electricity Generation

Geothermal resources can be used to generate electricity in the same fashion that coal or oil is used; there is no need for a boiler; however, as steam is already available. Conventional geothermal power plants operate with efficiencies of 5-20%, depending on the source and temperature of the reservoir. Dry steam plants are, by far, the most common at temperatures above 200°C, as flash steam between 170-200°C. Binary systems are utilized with water in the 100-170°C temperature range. Lower temperature sources are not very effective for the production of electricity and are mostly of value in direct use and as hot springs.

A. Dry-Steam (Vapor-Dominated) Systems

This is the simplest, oldest, and cheapest method of extracting power, but can only be deployed for power generation in a few regions in the world. Dry superheated steam reservoirs are highly efficient but rare. When dry steam is available, it is extracted through a production borehole and its solid particles are removed before it is expanded through a turbine. Exhaust steam is then condensed and re-injected back into the earth. Because of their higher temperatures, vapor-dominated systems are most efficient. Furthermore, unlike liquids, steam does not have to be pumped but moves up naturally through the borehole. The largest plants of this type are the Geysers in California and Larderello, Italy.

The vapor-dominated systems are the preferred systems, but as the geothermal heat becomes more utilized, their availability may become limited, and at some point, we will be forced to tap more and more into hot water systems.

B. Flash-Steam (Liquid-Dominated) Systems

For hot water reservoirs under high pressure, the geothermal fluid consisting of a mixture of steam, and the salt-water solution is brought to the surface and sprayed into a tank. As the pressure drops, some of the water flashes into steam. The steam is subsequently cleaned and piped directly into the steam turbines, which drive electric generators. A *single-flash* system uses a single chamber at high pressure, while in a *dual-flash* system, a portion of the high-pressure steam from the first separator is flashed into a second separator which runs a second lower-pressure turbine. The remaining water is either used in a direct-use application, as heat input to a binary system (see below) or re-injected back into the reservoir to help maintain its high temperature and pressure.

C. Binary Systems

Using *moderate- and low- temperature steam* to generate electricity is not practical because it condenses through the turbine and corrodes the blades before it has appreciably expanded. Under such circumstances, binary-cycle power plants are more applicable. In a **binary plant**, the geothermal water at high pressure is pumped through a heat exchanger where it passes its internal heat to a secondary fluid such as alcohol, isopropanol, or any refrigerants with lower vapor pressure than water, causing it to boil. The vapor is then used in a closed-loop cycle to drive a turbine/generator assembly. Because binary plants do not use steam or hot water directly, the fluids can be re-injected into the reservoir. This maintains the pressure and prevents any toxic or noxious gases from entering the atmosphere.

Binary plants are most suitable for small modular units of a few hundred kilowatts to a few megawatts. Furthermore, the overall efficiency of binary systems is higher. One such plant is the binary power plant near Mammoth Lakes in California; this system transfers heat from steam at 170°C to isobutene, which vaporizes and drives the turbines for a net generating capacity of 37 megawatts.

Figure 9-4 illustrates the vapor-dominated, liquid-dominated, and binary geothermal systems.

D. Enhanced Geothermal System (EGS)

Hydrothermal reservoirs are useful only when they are in the geographical areas where rocks are sufficiently

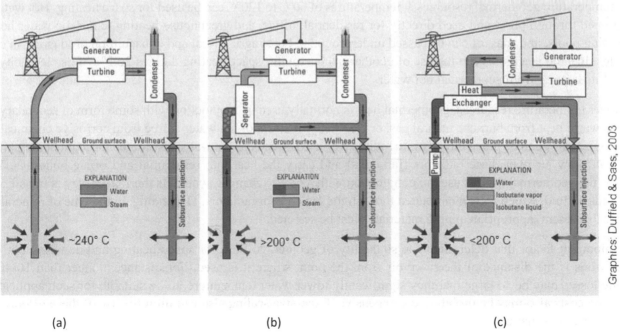

(a)   (b)   (c)

Figure 9-4
Geothermal systems: (a) vapor-dominated; (b) liquid-dominated; and (c) binary
Source: Wikimedia Creative Commons.

permeable to allow easy flow of fluid. In areas with solid bedrock, fractures are induced in surrounding rocks to increase permeability, allowing geothermal exploration in areas that otherwise were deemed inoperable. Cold water or some supercritical fluid is injected into a well 5,000 meters deep and pressurized until rocks crack, conducting its heat to the water as it moves toward nearby production wells where it is extracted. Since the pressure is high, water remains liquid, even at temperatures of 200°C or more (See Table 9-2).[‡] When electricity generation is of interest, a binary system is used, where refrigerant steam drives a turbine-generator assembly, before returning to the well for reheat -- closing the loop. An experimental plant of this type was constructed by the Los Alamos National Laboratory in New Mexico in the early 1980s and operated until 1995 when it was shut down. As it stands today, EGS technology is not mature and the cost is too high for commercialization, but it is expected to be able to provide 100 GW or more of cost-competitive generating capacity in the next 50 years. A schematic of an EGS system is shown in Figure 9-5.

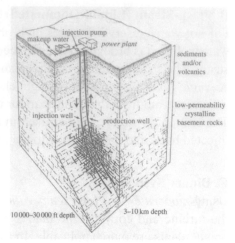

Figure 9-5
Schematic of a conceptual two-well geothermal hot dry rock.
Image courtesy of International Geothermal Association.

Direct Use

Geothermal direct use is the main advantage of this resource over all other competitors, as the efficiency is quite high, at around 50-70%. At temperatures below 100°C, geothermal sources are available in the form of liquid water, that can be used directly for space heating and cooling. In addition, geothermal energy is most convenient in raising exotic aquatic species (tropical fish, trout, and prawns among others), in the processing of agricultural products (such as vegetable dehydration, grain and lumber drying, pulp and paper processing), and wastewater treatment. Refrigeration cooling is possible using absorption refrigeration machines; geothermal heat pumps are available for air conditioning when both heating and cooling are desired.

Space and District Heating

Low-temperature geothermal resources at temperatures of 60°C to 120°C can be used for space heating. Hot water can be pumped through pipes and used directly for residential, office, and greenhouse heating, domestic water heaters, swimming pools, and spas, or can be passed underground to boost agricultural and aquacultural production in colder climates. Iceland is a pioneer in the use of geothermal energy for space heating derives 26.2% of its electricity[§] and 90% of its heating from geothermal hot water.

For lower temperature resources, geothermal heat is normally used in conjunction with some form of secondary fuel, such as waste heat from burners, natural gas, or electricity. If steam or hot water is free from corrosive chemicals and other toxins, they can be piped directly into radiators or used directly as tap water distributed throughout the building. Fans can blow air over these radiators (fan coils) and carry the heat into residential and office buildings. When impure, the geothermal fluid is used in conjunction with a heat exchanger, where its thermal energy is transferred to a secondary fluid, which is then circulated through the fan coils or radiators. Depending on the type of minerals and chemicals present, appropriate piping materials must be selected.

One important factor that determines the suitability of geothermal fluid for space heating and domestic hot water applications is the distance of the reservoir from the point where it is used. For distances longer than 10-40 km, the line losses may be so large that they significantly lower water temperature, to be suitable for such applications; insulation costs also may be prohibitively expensive. Excessive scaling also can limit the use of these resources for long-distance destinations.

---

‡ A supercritical fluid is a liquid that has been raised beyond a temperature and pressure at which the liquid and gas densities are equal -- its critical temperature and pressure. For carbon dioxide, the supercritical conditions are a pressure of 72.8 atmospheres and 31 degrees Celsius.

§ Hydro accounts for the remaining 73.7%; a mere 0.1% comes from fossil fuels.

Geothermal Heat Pumps

Heat pumps, as the name implies, are devices that move heat from one place to another, up the temperature gradient, i.e., removing heat from cold outside air, and dump it into the room in the winter. In reality, a heat pump is nothing more than a refrigeration unit. The only difference between a heat pump and a refrigerator is the desired effect-- cooling for the refrigerator and heating for the heat pump. Another distinguishing feature is that heat pumps can work in reverse -- remove heat from inside and dump it outside, thus provide cooling during summers.

Geothermal (ground-source) heat pumps (GHPs) take advantage of the relatively constant temperature of underground soil or water, from one season to another, by exploiting the earth (or underground wells and water pond surfaces) as a source by transferring heat to a house in winter, and as a sink by transferring heat from a house in summer. Because rocks and soil are good insulators, they are rather insensitive to variations in ambient air temperature. They are warmer than the ambient air temperature in the winter and colder than the ambient air temperature during the summer. Below a depth of approximately two meters, the temperature of the soil in most of the world's regions remains stable, between 7°C and 20°C.

The operation is simple: in the simplest form, a mixture of water and ethylene glycol solution (antifreeze) circulating in underground pipes or loops is used as a medium for transferring heat into or out of a building. In the heating mode (during winter), the mixture is colder than the surrounding ground; thus, it absorbs heat from the ground and warms up. The heated liquid is pumped into the building where it transfers its heat through a heat exchanger, into the room. In the cooling mode (during summer), the process is reversed. Here, the water/glycol mixture is hotter than the surrounding soil, and, thus, it releases its energy to the ground and cools. A blower heats or cools the air by forcing it across the refrigerant coil (See Figure 9-6).

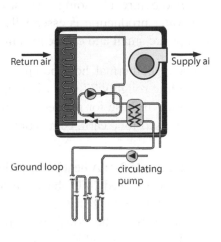

Figure 9-6
Geothermal heat pump.

Question: What are the advantages and disadvantages of a ground-source heat pump over an air-source heat pump?

Answer: Just a few meters below the surface, the ground temperature is rather uniform throughout the day, and even during the entire year. This is not the case for the air, which can change dramatically between day and night, and summer and winter. Heat pumps work best when the temperature difference between the source and the sink is not very high. Because there are smaller temperature differences that heat must be pumped using the ground as the sink, instead of the outside air, geothermal heat pumps have higher efficiencies than air-source heat pumps. On the other hand, the ground is not an infinite source of heat; if we suck heat out of the ground too fast, the ground becomes too cold and a heat pump will stop functioning. This may become a problem if all houses in the neighborhood deploy ground-based heat pumps at the same time.

Just like conventional heat pumps, geothermal heat pumps can operate in a closed- or an open- loop cycle. In closed-loop systems, a small pump is used to circulate the fluid. In open-loop systems, water from an underground aquifer is piped directly from a well into a building, where it transfers its heat. The water then is returned to the aquifer through a second well, some distance away. Open-loop systems are simpler and less costly but can be used only when there is an abundant supply of groundwater.

Depending on the location and the availability of ground space, loops can be installed either horizontally or vertically and in linear or loop configurations (See Figure 9-7). *Horizontal* installation is the most cost-effective for residential sites and in new constructions where sufficient land is available. It requires trenches between one and two meters deep. *Vertical* installations are used in large commercial buildings, in places where land area is limited, where land is too rocky to dig trenches, or where digging causes major disturbances to the existing landscape. To save space, the pipe may be coiled or looped into a *spiral*. When there is an adequate body of water, submerging the loop into the water may be the most cost-effective strategy. In such instances, the supply line is run underground from the building to the water and coiled into circles a few meters below the surface to assure that it is not susceptible to winter freezing.

Geothermal heat pumps are rated in two ways: The heating performance is typically reduced to dimensionless units as the *Coefficient of Performance* (COP) while cooling performance is typically expressed as the cooling effect produced by the unit (in Btu/hr) divided by the electrical input (in watt) resulting in units of Btu/watt.hr as the *energy efficiency rating* (EER).[¶] [**]Residential ground-source heat pumps on the market today have standard COPs ranging from 2.4 to 5.0 and EERs ranging from 10.6 to 30. Geothermal heat pumps can be installed practically anywhere and, when compared to conventional cooling and heating systems, use 30-50% less electricity. If a geothermal system is planned before a building is constructed, installation is easy, and the cost is relatively small. Furthermore, domestic hot water production is essentially free during the summer. Unlike conventional rooftop models, geothermal heat pumps are small and can be installed indoors, typically in a basement or attic.

Today, geothermal heat pumps are one of the fastest-growing applications of renewable energy in the world, providing roughly 77 GW of thermal energy. In the USA alone, over 50,000 GHP units are sold each year, with a majority of these for residential applications. Worldwide, it is estimated that a half-million units are installed, with 85% closed-loop earth connections (46% vertical, 38% horizontal) and 15% open-loop systems.

Example 9-1: A heat pump is designed to heat a building using a ground source at 7°C. If the building temperature is to be raised 24°C above the cold outside ambient, what is the coefficient of performance of the best heat pump to achieve this task?

Solution: The ideal heat pump is a Carnot heat pump operating between the ground temperature $T_c = 273+7 = 280$ K and desired temperature $T_h = 273 + 24 = 297$ K, i.e.,

$$COP_{Heating, ideal} = T_h/(T_h - T_c) = 297/(297-280) = 17.4$$

Example 9-2: What is the minimum power (kW) required to heat a room from 7°C to 24°C? The room is losing heat at a rate of 30,000 Btu/hr.

Solution: Minimum power can be achieved only when the heat pump is ideal. Such heat pumps have a COP of 17.4. Noting that COP is the ratio of heating load to the required work, the power input is:

$$W_{min} = \frac{Q_h}{COP_{ideal}} = \frac{30,000}{17.4} = 1,724 \text{ Btu/h} \times \frac{1 \text{ kWh}}{3,413 \text{ Btu}} = 0.5 \text{ kW}$$

Greenhouse Heating

Geothermal energy can be used to heat greenhouses. Traditional greenhouses use a transparent material like common glass or plastic to allow the solar heat in. Because these materials are opaque to low-temperature infrared emissions, the heat cannot escape, providing an environment conducive to the growth of certain plants and a variety of other species. Solar heating, however, may not be enough to provide sufficient heating. Geothermal heating can supplement solar heating during periods of low solar intensity and at night. The level of sophistication depends on the season, plant type, and cost. In the simplest form, hot water from a geothermal source is circulated through a coil buried under the ground surface, heating the soil and plant roots. By properly routing the pipe, various degrees of heating can be achieved that benefit plants with different temperature requirements. Other variations include the use of fans, air-water heat exchangers, and aerial installations. Similar systems can be designed to provide heating in **aquacultural** farms designed to operate at controlled temperatures suitable for raising species such as carp, salmon, shrimp, and other marine organisms. Certain fish species are very sensitive to water temperature and flourish best if water is controlled to a specific, narrow temperature range. The same goes for raising farm animals such as chickens,

---

[¶] EER = COP (cooling) × 3.413.
[**] See Chapter 4, pp. 118-119.

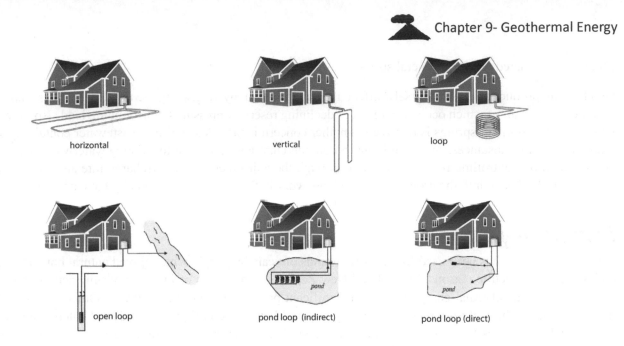

Figure 9-7
Geothermal heat pumps. Depending on geographical limitation and availability
of water, different GHP designs may be envisioned.
Adapted from Rafferty, K., "An Application Survival Kit For the Prospective Geothrmal Heatpump Owner," U. S. DoE, February 2001.

pigs, and cattle.

Industrial Applications

Among potential applications that can benefit from geothermal energy are vegetable and fruit dehydration, grain, pulp, and lumber drying, and paper processing. Geothermal energy also can be used for leaching precious metals, such as gold and silver, making pottery and bricks, and for therapeutic purposes.

Economics of Geothermal Energy

Costs associated with geothermal power plant varies widely depending on the type of plants, the geological conditions, flow rate and temperature of the hydrothermal source, and the depth of drilling. Dry steam is superior as it can be used directly to turn a turbine, and cycle efficiency is higher. The economics of EGS systems vary considerably depending on the type, porosity, and permeability of the rock, and vertical temperature gradients, but are substantially more expensive, as technology is still in its infancy. As the price of petroleum and other fossil fuels increases, geothermal sources become more competitively priced or may even prove to be cheaper than fossil fuel plants.

Like most renewable energies, direct-use geothermal energy systems require a larger capital investment, compared to traditional systems, but the absence of fuel costs and lower operating expenses offset the initial investment in a few years.

Environmental Concerns

Compared to fossil fuels, geothermal energy produces much less pollution -- 60% less carbon dioxide than natural gas, with none of the nitric oxide (NOx) gases and with much lower sulfur compounds than coal and oil power plants.[††] Geothermal plants do, however, produce some hydrogen sulfide -- a gas that smells like rotten eggs and

††   Combustion of bituminous coal emits about 900 kg of carbon dioxide per MWh; the corresponding numbers for natural gas and geothermal plants are 300 and 120 kg per MWh.

usually is associated with hot mineral springs.

Geothermal production can adversely affect the environment by degrading geological features and increasing seismic activity, all of which occur as a result of declining reservoir pressures. Surrounding land also may subside or sink, as water from hot springs is removed. Another concern is the release of hot wastewater containing significant amounts of toxic substances, such as lithium, boron, mercury, and arsenic, into existing waterways. This impact can be mitigated by controlling reservoir pressure through the adjustment of the discharge rate and by re-injecting the geothermal fluid back into the ground. Binary plants work in this fashion and typically have no releases. ⓐ

Summary

Geothermal energy has been used for many thousands of years by people who enjoyed natural hot water springs for bathing and therapeutic reasons. Iceland and New Zealand, two islands of intense volcanic activity and numerous hot springs use geothermal energy to meet a significant portion of their energy needs. Other countries increasing their share of geothermal resources include Italy, Japan, Mexico, the Philippines, and the United States. Up to now, geothermal energy has been used extensively in industrialized countries, but future growth is expected to be only moderate, unlikely to provide more than 1% of total electrical capacity. The rate of growth in many developing countries is expected to be much higher, giving geothermal energy a significant role in meeting the electricity needs of these countries.

Unlike wind, solar, or tidal plants, geothermal power plants can deliver power continuously and provide base-load electricity. Furthermore, geothermal plants are not vulnerable to weather changes, no storage is needed, and distribution is simple. Geothermal reservoirs are, however, limited to specific geographical areas. Geothermal fluid cannot be transported to large distances from the geothermal site, as the cost of insulation becomes excessive.

Depending on the resources and on power demand, geothermal plants can be constructed in any size -- as small as 100 kW (convenient for local grid applications and rural electrification) to many hundreds of megawatts for base-load applications, and national grids. Modular plants can be built so that capacity can be added as the need for power increases. Geothermal systems have a small footprint with minimal visual and environmental impacts, and unlike other forms of renewable resources, they require no storage. Currently, most geothermal resources are limited to steam and hot water reservoirs. Innovative technologies are being developed that enable us to exploit the temperature gradients in hot dry rocks, allowing electricity generation, anywhere in the world. This requires the ability to drill approximately 5 to 20 kilometers into the earth's surface and at a reasonable cost -- a technology that is not yet available. The exploitation of energy from volcanic eruptions and magma flow remains in the distant future.

ⓐ *Digging Deeper: Phases of Matter*

Depending on the pressure and temperature, underground pockets of geothermal fluid can be present in the form of superheated vapor, pure liquid, or a mixture of liquid and vapor.

Let's consider a kettle of liquid water placed on top of a gas stove (alternatively, you may consider a frictionless piston-cylinder assembly, containing water and heated from below). When water is a liquid, we normally refer to its phase as a **compressed** or a **subcooled liquid**. The kettle lid has a small port that opens to the atmosphere, keeping the pressure constant at one atmosphere. As heat is added and temperature increases, water expands slowly, until it reaches 100°C. At this point, water is still a liquid, about to boil, a state commonly known as a **saturated liquid**. Further heating does not result in any temperature rise, while more and more liquid turns to vapor. The kettle (cylinder) contains a mixture of saturated liquid and vapor (**wet steam**). The process continues until all the water has turned into vapor (**saturated steam**). Any heat loss will cause some of the saturated vapor, at least partially, to re-condense. When the vapor is heated beyond its boiling point, no liquid will be present, and we have **dry (superheated) vapor**. The process is best represented on a temperature/volume diagram as a broken line 1-2-3-4-5, where a substance changes from compressed liquid to saturated liquid, transforms to a mixture of liquid and vapor, to saturated vapor, and finally, change phase to superheated vapor (See Figure 9-8). The pressure remains constant throughout this process (one atmosphere or 100 kPa, in this example). The curve line (called saturation line) represents all points where water is saturated, either as a liquid or vapor.

If the experiment is repeated on top of a mountain, the pressure is lower and water boils at a lower temperature. For example, water boils at 81.3°C, if pressure is reduced to 50 kPa. Similarly, if pressure is increased to 1 MPa (about 10 atmospheres), as is the case in pressure cookers, water's boiling point is raised to 179.9°C.

Question: Why water boils faster on top of Mt. Everest?

Answer: At higher altitudes, the pressure is reduced and the air is thinner. The lower the pressure, the lower is the boiling temperature and less heat is required to raise the temperature to its boiling temperature. Similarly, the lower the pressure, the higher the melting temperature; the ice caps will be less likely to melt.

Example 9- 3: Saturated steam at 1 MPa enters a rigid container. Heat is now removed as pressure drops to 100 kPa, What are the initial and final temperatures of the steam? Is the steam wet or dry?

Solution: Since the container is rigid, the volume remains constant and the process takes place along the dashed line 7-8 in Figure 9-8. The initial temperature is that of saturated temperature at 1 MPa, i.e., 179.9°C. The final state is a wet state (saturated mixture), at a temperature of 100°C.

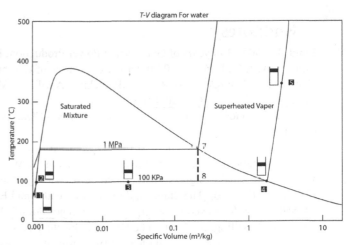

Figure 9-8

The saturated lines for water at pressures of 100 kPa and 1 MPa. As the graph shows, at pressure of 101 kPa (1 atm), and temperatures below i100°C, water is a compressed liquid (Point 1). As temperature rises to 100°C, it boils (point 2). Any additional heat causes water to turn from liquid to vapor. Both temperature and pressure remain constant, and we have a mixture of saturated liquid and vapor (point 3); volume increases rapidly, until all liquids turns to vapor (point 4). Heating further, results in vapor to become superheated, both volume and temperature rise (point 5).

Table 9-2 Boiling Point of Water at various Pressures			
Pressure (kPa)	Pressure (psia)	Temperature (°C)	Temperature (°F)
50	7.3	81.3	178.3
75	10.9	91.8	197.2
101.3	14.7	100.0	212.0
500	72.6	151.8	305.2
1,000	145.1	179.9	355.8
5,000	725.6	263.9	507.0

Example 9- 4: An underground geothermal reservoir is found to have a temperature of 120°C and a pressure of 1,000 kPa (1 MPa). In what form do you expect to find the water? What if the temperature was 200°C?

Solution: According to Table 9-2, the saturated temperature (boiling point) of water at 1000 kPa is 145.1°C. At temperatures below this, water is in the liquid phase, whereas any temperature above the saturated temperature is indicative of the presence of water in a superheated vapor form. *@*

Endnotes

1   Lund, J. (2004). 100 years of Geothermal Power Production, Renewable Energy World, 7(4), July-August.

2   Lund, J. W. & Toth, A. N. (2020). Direct Utilization of Geothermal Energy 2020 Worldwide Review, Proceedings World Geothermal Congress 2020, Reykjavik, Iceland, April 26 – May 2, 2020, Retrieved from https://www.geothermal-energy.org/pdf/IGAstandard/WGC/2020/01018.pdf

3   Norton, G. & Goat, C. (2003). Geothermal Energy – Clean Power from.the earth's Heat. U.S. Geological Survey, U.S.G.S., Circular 1249.

4   Holm, A. et al. (2010). Geothermal Energy: International Market Update, International Geothermal Association, May 2010.

5   Bertani, R. (2008). Geothermal Power Generation in the World 2005-2010 Update Report. Bali, Indonesia: Proceedings of the World Geothermal Congress. Available at: http://www.geothermal-energy.org/pdf/IGAstandard/WGC/2010/0008.pdf.

6   Kutscher, CF. (2000). The Status and Future of Geothermal Electric Power, National Renewable Energy laboratory. NREL/CP-550-28204. Retrieved from https://www.nrel.gov/docs/fy00osti/28204.pdf

7   Kious, W. & Tilling, R. (2001). The Dynamic Earth: The Story of Plate Tectonics, U.S. Geological Survey. The electronic version of this book can be downloaded from http://pubs.usgs.gov/publications/text/dynamic.html

8   Pielou, E. (2001). The Energy of Nature, The University of Chicago Press. Chicago, pp. 155.

9   Stephenson, V. (2000). The Renewability of Geothermal Energy, Proc. Kyushu- Tohoku, Japan: World Geothermal Energy Congress 2000, pp. 879-883.

10   Dobson, P. et al. (2020). Analysis of curtailment at The Geysers geothermal Field, California., Geothermics, Vol. 87, September 2020, https://doi.org/10.1016/j.geothermics. 2020.101871

11   Thorndike, E. (1976). Energy and Environment: A Primer for Scientists and Engineers, Addison-Wesley Publishing Company.

12   Gawell, K. & Greenberg. G. (2007). Interim Report: Update on World Geothermal Development, U.S. Geothermal Energy Association, May 2007.

13   Hooper, G. & Duchane, D. (2019). Hot Dry Rock: An Untapped Sustainable Energy Resource', U.S. Dept. of Energy. http://www.ees11.lanl.gov/EES11/Programs/HDR/documents/HDREnergy.pdf

14   Garnish, J. ed. (1987). Proceedings of the First EEC/US Workshop on Geothermal Hot Dry Rock Technology, Geothermics, vol. 16, pp. 323-461.

15   Dateline Los Alamos, Monthly publication NO. W-7405-ENG-36, Los Alamos National Laboratory, 1995.

16   Tester, G. et al. (2006). The Future of Geothermal Energy: Impact of Enhanced Geothermal Systems on the United States in the 21st Century, Idaho National Laboratory, http://www1.eere.energy.gov/geothermal/egs_technology.html

17   Lund, J. & Freestone, D. (2001). Worldwide Direct Uses of Geothermal Energy, Geothermics, vol. 30, pp. 29-68.

18   Dickson, M. & Fanelli, M. (2003). Geothermal Energy: Utilization and Technology, United Nations Educational, Scientific, and Cultural Organization (UNESCO).

19   Rafferty, K. (2001). An Information Survival Kit for the Prospective Residential Geothermal Heat Pump Owner. Geo-Heat Centre Quarterly Bulletin (Klamath Falls, Oregon: Oregon Institute of Technology), 18(2), 1–11. ISSN 0276-1084, http://geo-heat.oit.edu/ghp/survival.pdf

20   Lund, J. et al. (2004). Geothermal (Ground-Source) Heat Pumps – A World Overview. (2004). Edited and updated version of the article from Renewable Energy World (July-Aug, 2003, vol. 6, no. 4, Geo-Heat Center (GHC) Quarterly Bulletin, 25(3), 10, ISSN 0276-1084, September 2004.

✌ Exercises

I. Discussion Questions

1. Can geothermal energy be considered a renewable energy? Explain.
2. What are the geothermal resources available to us? Which ones are technologically and economically viable?
3. What are the uses for low-temperature geothermal resources? What type of power plant is most suitable for these reservoirs?
4. What are the differences between vapor-dominated and liquid-dominated systems? What are the advantages and disadvantages of each?
5. How do geothermal heat pumps work? What is the advantage of GHPs over conventional heat pumps?

ⓐ II. Problems

1. A geothermal heat pump with a coefficient of performance of 4.2 is capable of removing 500,000 Btu of heat over a 24-hour period. What is the electrical power input to this heat pump? What is heat pump's Energy Efficiency Ratio?
2. A GHP system utilizes the thermal mass of the underground soil to cool/heat the building during summer/winter months. What are the maximum theoretical coefficients of performance for cooling and heating? Assume coldest and warmest outside air temperatures of -10°C, and 42°C, and that underground soil temperature remain essentially constant at 10°C throughout the year.
3. In the previous example,
   a. What is the electrical power required, if the house gains heat at the rate of 20,000 Btu/hr during summer months, and loses heat at the rate of 28,000 Btu/hr during winter months?
   b. What is the energy efficiency rating for the cooling load?
4. A dry-steam power plant operates between the temperature limits of 12°C and 300°C. What is the minimum amount of heat that must be rejected by the condenser, if the electrical power generated by this plant is 4 MW?
5. [Challenging] A pressure cooker contains superheated steam at the temperature of 300°C and 1 MPa. Heat is removed from the cooker at constant pressure until steam starts to condense. Refer to Figure 9-8 and answer the following questions:
   a. Show the process by indicating the path steam

takes to go from its initial to final states.
   b. What is the temperature at which steam condenses?
   c. What is the specific volume and density?
   d. Assuming cooling continues until the specific volume is 0.1 m³/kg. What is the final temperature and phase?

[Hint: Note the graph is a semi-logarithmic, so results are only an approximate]

III. Multiple Choice Questions

1. The United States has about _____ percent of the world's total geothermal electrical capacity.
   a. 0.35
   b. 29
   c. 50
   d. 90
   e. Cannot tell
2. Which country takes the most advantage of its geothermal resources for meeting its domestic space heating needs?
   a. The United States
   b. Philippines
   c. Italy
   d. Iceland
   e. New Zealand
3. The largest geothermal power plant in the world is _____, in _____.
   a. Larderello, Italy
   b. Reykjavik, Iceland
   c. Old Faithful, Wyoming- the USA
   d. Geysers, San Francisco- the USA
   e. None of the above
4. What distinguishes the earth's inner and outer cores?
   a. Because of its extreme temperatures, the inner core is a gas. The outer core is cooler and remains liquid.
   b. Both the inner and outer cores are liquid. The only difference is their temperatures.
   c. Both the inner and outer cores are solid. The only difference is their temperatures.
   d. The inner core is solid. The outer core is liquid.
   e. The inner core is liquid. It solidifies gradually as temperature drops toward the surface.
5. What does it mean when we say that geothermal energy is 'sustainable'?
   a. That it will never be completely used up
   b. That it is economical to produce
   c. That it can be used anywhere on earth

d. That there is a limited supply

e. That technology is mature enough to extract an unlimited supply

6. The central region of earth's core is solid because

a. The composition at the center of the core is mostly iron.

b. The pressure at the center raises the melting point.

c. The magnetic field cannot penetrate into the center of the core.

d. Convection does not extend all the way to the center of the core.

e. Earth initially formed from solid particles in the solar nebula.

7. The average thickness of the crust is

a. Less than 1 km.

b. 5-65 km.

c. 100-200 km.

d. 200-1000 km.

e. More than 1000 km.

8. What method of using geothermal energy involves piping steam directly to a generator?

a. Direct use

b. Geothermal heat pump

c. Flash steam power plant

d. Dry steam power plants

e. All of the above

9. The earth's surface gives off energy at an average rate of about

a. 1000 W/m^2

b. 80 W/m^2

c. 0.08 W/m^2

d. 0.08 W

e. 0.80 Btu/ft^2

10. What is the approximate distance from the surface to the center of the earth?

a. 1,000 miles

b. 2,000 miles

c. 4,000 miles

d. 10,000 miles

e. 20,000 miles

11. What region of the earth is molten?

a. Crust

b. Lower mantle and outer core

c. Lower mantle and upper mantle

d. Inner core and outer core

e. None are molten

12. The molten material mixed with gases in the mantle of the earth is called _____.

a. Core

b. Lava

c. Geyser

d. Magma

e. Steam

13. In deep mines, for every kilometer deeper we go, temperature increases by about

a. 0.3°C.

b. 3°C.

c. 30°C.

d. 300°C.

e. 3,000°C.

14. In which region of the earth is heat transfer mainly by conduction?

a. Crust

b. Mantle

c. Inner core

d. Outer core

e. None of them

15. On average, the energy available from geothermal resources

a. Is much greater than the solar influx.

b. Is about the same as the solar influx.

c. Is much less than the solar influx.

d. Depending on location, could be much smaller or much larger than the solar influx.

e. Not known.

16. The source of geothermal energy is

a. Radioactive decay of elements below the earth's crust.

b. Heat still left from the time when the earth was formed.

c. Chemical reactions among gases trapped below the earth's surface.

d. Underground nuclear explosions.

e. Both a and b.

17. Moving toward the surface, the temperature in the upper mantle and crust falls at the rate of

a. 1°C/m.

b. 1°C/km.

c. 5-10°C/km.

d. 20-30°C/km.

e. More than 100°C/km.

18. Of the following choices, which best describes or defines geothermal energy?

a. Heat energy from rocks on the earth's surface

b. Heat energy from hot springs

c. Heat energy from the earth's interior

d. Heat energy from the sun reflected by the

earth's surface
  e. All of the above
19. Which layer of the earth's interior has the least thickness?
  a. Crust
  b. Lower mantle
  c. Upper mantle
  d. Inner core
  e. Outer core
20. Most of the geothermal energy that can be economically exploited today is from
  a. Volcanoes.
  b. Hot water springs and geysers.
  c. Hot dry rocks.
  d. Desert surfaces.
  e. All of the above.
21. Binary-cycle power plants are most often used
  a. When the geothermal source is at a temperature below the boiling point of water.
  b. When the geothermal source is at a moderate temperature, between 100-200°C.
  c. Only when steam is available at temperatures above 300°C.
  d. Only when they are in association with hybrid design plants.
  e. Only when underground sources contain large fractions of alcohol and other refrigerants.
22. Depending on their size, geothermal plants can be
  a. Used for base-load electricity production.
  b. Designed to follow daily load demands.
  c. Used for mini-grids and rural electrification.
  d. Used for direct thermal use.
  e. Used for all of the above.
23. The largest geothermal power plant in the United States is located near
  a. San Francisco.
  b. The Rocky Mountains.
  c. Hawaii.
  d. The Yellowstone.
  e. New York.
24. Geothermal energy
  a. Is essentially a zero-emission source of energy.
  b. Produces some pollution, but not as much as fossil fuels.
  c. Produces some radioactive waste, but with a short half-life.
  d. Produces more pollution than fossil fuels, but with no radioactive waste.
  e. None of the above.

25. The central regions of earth's core are solid because
  a. The core is made entirely of iron.
  b. The pressure is extremely high,
  c. The magnetic field cannot penetrate into the center of the core.
  d. Convection does not extend all the way to the center of the core.
  e. Earth initially formed from solid particles in the solar nebula.
26. Which of the following statements is not true?
  a. Geothermal energy is heat from within the earth.
  b. Geothermal energy is mostly renewable because heat is continuously produced inside the earth.
  c. The U.S. is the largest producer of geothermal energy.
  d. Most geothermal reservoirs lie close to the surface of the earth.
  e. All are correct.
27. The most active geothermal resources are usually found
  a. Off the Atlantic coast.
  b. Along major plate boundaries where earthquakes and volcanoes are concentrated.
  c. In the Southern Hemisphere.
  d. Along the coasts of the Indian Ocean.
  e. Spread around the world.
28. Which statement describes the best use of geothermal energy?
  a. Using hot water from springs or reservoirs for bathing and recreation.
  b. Generating electricity from steam.
  c. Using stable ground or water temperatures near the earth's surface to control building temperatures above ground.
  d. Using hot water or steam for domestic heating.
  e. All of the above.
29. Geothermal power plants have low-emission levels because
  a. They are renewable sources of energy.
  b. They get most of their energy directly from the sun.
  c. They use steam to generate electricity.
  d. They burn a low-emission fuel to produce electricity.
  e. None of the above is true.
30. At what temperature does water boil on top of a very tall mountain, where pressure is 75 kPa?
  a. 10.9°C

b. 91.8°C
c. Higher than 91.8°C but lower than 100°C
d. 100°C
e. Higher than 100°C

IV. True or False?

1. As of 2015, the Philippines has the highest installed geothermal capacity in the world.
2. Geothermal heat pumps are highly efficient because they utilize the relatively constant temperature of underground soil or water.
3. HDR is an innovative technology that can possibly meet many of the energy needs of the 21st century.
4. Geysers are considered renewable only if they are used at a sustainable rate.
5. Binary plants are advantageous over non-binary plants because they can be designed virtually pollution-free.
6. Water in a 3-cm deep pan is observed to boil at 98°C. Water in a 30-cm deep pan will boil at a temperature higher than 98°C.
7. Enhanced Geothermal Systems use geothermal energy aided by gas turbines running on fossil fuels.
8. A heat pump is a device used to circulate water stored in a hot water storage tank inside a building.
9. Compared to natural-gas-fueled power plants, geothermal plants produce little carbon dioxide.
10. High heat flux from rocks requires high thermal gradients within the rocks.

V. Fill-in the Blanks

1. Geothermal resources can be categorized as hydrothermal, _____, _____, and _____.
2. Geothermal plants produce trace amounts of _____, a gas that smells like rotten eggs.
3. _____ installation of heat pumps is most cost-effective for residential sites and new construction where sufficient land is available.
4. Upwelling of groundwater with temperatures above surrounding atmospheric temperature but lower than body temperature is called _____.
5. The water spewing out of hot springs has temperatures _____ that of the human body.
6. Geothermal energy is considered _____ if it is used faster than it is replenished by nature.
7. The only emission of geothermal systems is trace amount of _____.
8. Dry steam geothermal systems are used only if reservoirs of superheated steam at temperatures above _____ °C are available.
9. The United States accounts for slightly more than _____ of the total world installed geothermal capacity.
10. _____ installations are most suitable in places where land is too rocky to dig trenches.

CHAPTER 10

Solar Energy

Nellis Solar Plant in Nevada ~ Wikipedia Commons

Give me the splendid silent sun with all his beams full-dazzling.
~ Walt Whitman (1819-1892)

I'd put my money on the Sun and solar energy. What a source of power! I hope we don't have to wait 'til oil and coal run out before we tackle that. ~ Thomas Edison (1847-1931)

Since ancient times, humans have demonstrated a basic understanding of solar energy by designing weapons of war that killed their enemies, and shelters that protected them from the cold of winter and the heat of summer. According to legends, during the siege of Syracuse (214 - 212 BCE), Archimedes used mirrors to focus the sun's rays to set fire on approaching enemy ships.[*] Socrates suggested that houses should be built facing south in order to maximize the heat of the winter sun. Anasazi Indians designed their dwellings under cliff overhangs, maximizing the solar gain in winter and providing shade in summer. The sheltering overhangs also reduced radiant heat loss at night and protected against cold winds. Furthermore, some houses were built with thick stone and clay walls and had small windows to retain heat during the day and release it gradually at night.

Today, solar power has been proven to be highly effective not only in providing heat to buildings and swimming pools but also in cooling applications and for the generation of electricity. As with many other sources of energy, there are limitations on where this energy source can be used. The amount and intensity of solar energy available vary depending on geographical location, the position of the sun in the sky, weather conditions, and the orientation of the collector and surrounding objects.

The market growth of photovoltaic cells has been particularly impressive -- doubling every two years between 2000 to 2015. By the end of 2018, the global solar PV exceeded 505 GW_e, accounting for 2.4% of the world's total electricity demand. An additional 5.5 GW_e was supplied by concentrating solar thermal power (CSP). The accumulated global solar water heating collector capacity was estimated at 480 GW_{th}.

In this chapter, we start by looking at the sun, itself, and the amount of radiation that can potentially be intercepted by a collector on earth. We then discuss how thermal and photovoltaic systems utilize solar energy for heating, cooling, and producing electricity.

The Sun

The sun is a 1.4-million-kilometer diameter sphere of extremely dense, hot gas that resides approximately 150 million kilometers from earth (Figure 10-1). Composed predominately of hydrogen (75%) and helium (25%), its core temperature and pressure are estimated to reach 15 million degrees Celsius and 250 billion atmospheres – conditions suitable for nuclear fusion to take place. The core is surrounded by radiation and convection layers. At its outer layer (called the photosphere), ionized gases both absorb and emit a continuous spectrum of radiation, causing this layer to be, essentially, opaque. Temperatures drop to about 5,800 K at the surface of the sun.

Figure 10-1
The sun.
Source: NASA Photo Archives

The process of fusion was discussed in some detail in Chapter 8. Briefly, under extreme pressures and temperatures, atoms of hydrogen are fused into a helium nucleus. In this process, sun loses mass at a rate of about 4.3 billion kilograms every second, while producing an enormous amount of energy that supports life, propels the wind, and provides energy contained in ocean waves.[†] The energy received by earth in only one hour is enough to satisfy the energy needs of the entire world for the entire year.

As solar radiation passes through the earth's atmosphere, it is absorbed, reflected, scattered, and transmitted. To calculate the amount of solar radiation received at the ground we need to know the day of the year, the local time, position, as well as the orientation of the collector plate, the amount of shading by neighboring trees and buildings, and such meteorological factors as cloud cover, humidity, dust concentration, etc. Of the amount reaching the surface, a certain amount is absorbed and used for heating, or utilized to provide cooling and electricity.

---

[*] The legend has been tested many times with some conflicting results. See for example, Archimedes Death Ray: Testing with MythBusters," *Massachusetts Institute of Technology.* (http://web.mit.edu/2.009/www//experiments/deathray/10_Mythbusters.html)

[†] This loss of mass is nothing to worry about! By some estimates, the sun will have enough energy to support life on earth for another five billion years.

Solar Position

The geometric position of the sun as seen from a particular place on the surface of the earth varies from day to day, and hour to hour. At any given instant, the sun's position can be fixed by two angles, altitude (θ) and azimuth (ϕ) (Figure 10-2).

Altitude measures the sun's height above the horizon. When the sun is on the horizon (at sunrise and sunset), this angle is zero. At an altitude angle of 90°, the sun would be directly overhead (solar noon). The complement of solar altitude, or the angle of the sun from a vertical line directly overhead, is called the *zenith*.

Azimuth describes the sun's position from east to west. It is the angle between a north-south line on the earth's surface and the horizontal projection of the Sun's rays. It is measured from true south.[‡,§] By convention, solar azimuth is negative before noon and positive after noon. At the equinoxes, the sun rises directly east and sets directly west regardless of the latitude, thus making the azimuth angles 90° at sunrise and 270° at sunset.

To calculate the sun's incident angle we need to know not only the relative position of the sun but also the **geographical location of the observer on earth**. Two angles that define the position of any point on the surface of the earth are latitude (λ) and longitude (γ) (Figure 10-3).

Latitude is the angular distance along a parallel north or south of the equator, measured from the center of the earth. All points on the equator have a latitude of zero; the north and south poles have latitudes of +90° (90°N) and -90° (90°S). Greenwich has a latitude of 51.5°N, and New Orleans is located at latitude 29.9° N.

Longitude specifies the east-west position of a point on the earth's surface, measured as the angular distance east or west from the Prime (International) Meridian -- an imaginary meridian passing through Greenwich, England. Since the period of rotation of earth about its axis is 24 hours, each hour covers 360/24 = 15° longitude. All the points along a given meridian have the same time. Greenwich has a longitude of zero; New Orleans has a longitude of 90.1°W. Calculating the relative position of the sun in the sky from earth at different locations and times is outside the scope of this book, but readers are encouraged to refer to more advanced texts.

> **Example 10-1:** What are the local solar time differences between Los Angeles and San Francisco with longitudes of 118°15'W and 122°25'W, respectively.
>
> **Solution:** The difference between the two latitudes is 4°10' or 4.157°. Earth is rotating about its axis 15 degrees in one hour. i.e. local time

difference between the two cities is (4.157/15) x 60 = 16.63 minutes, even though we have adopted the same time zone for both cities.

Figure 10-2
The position of the sun in the sky can be determined by knowing the solar altitude (θ) and azimuth (ϕ) angles.

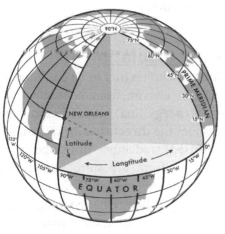

Figure 10-3
Meridians and parallels; longitude and latitude of New Orleans, IL (30°N, 90°W) is shown on the map.

---

‡ Historically, astronomers have measured azimuth from the south, and plane surveyors have measured from north.

§ True north is different from magnetic north in that true north lies along earth's axis, whereas magnetic north changes with earth's magnetic field.

Earth-Sun Position

Earth is orbiting the sun every 365.25 days, in an elliptical path, while rotating once every 24 hours about its axis, which is tilted at 23.5° (Figure 10-4). If the earth's axis of rotation were perpendicular to the **ecliptic plane** (plane of the earth's orbital path around the sun), it always would receive the same amount of solar radiation and we would have no seasons.¶ The inclination means that different locations on the earth are tilted toward the sun at different times. In the Northern Hemisphere, the angle of the earth's rotation tilts toward the sun in the summer and away from it in the winter. In the Southern Hemisphere, the earth's tilt is in the other direction and the seasons are reversed. What is interesting to note is that, in the Northern Hemisphere, *the earth is actually farther away from the sun in the summer, than in the winter* -- closest on January 3, and farthest away on July 4. Once a year, on around June 21, the sun's rays strike earth directly overhead at latitude 23.5° (Tropic of Cancer). This day is called the **Summer Solstice**. The Summer Solstice marks the onset of summer (June 21 in the northern hemisphere) when earth's pole has its maximum tilt toward sun. On this day, every location north of the Arctic Circle (the Land of the Midnight Sun) is illuminated for the entire 24 hours; the sun never rises or sets here, but circles around, above the horizon (Figure 10-5a). On the other side of the globe, all the points within 23.5° of the South Pole (Antarctic Circle), miss out on the sun entirely, and we have 24 hours of night time. At the intermediate intervals, around March 21 and September 21 (**Spring and Fall Equinoxes**)**, the sun shines directly on the equator (Figure 10-5b). The circle of illumination passes through the poles, and the sun's rays strike every part of the world for approximately 12 hours. Days and nights are equal in duration, and the sun sets roughly 12 hours after sunrise. As days progress, earth's tilt is away from the sun, and the days get shorter and shorter, until they reach their minimum, around December 21 *(Winter Solstice)*.†† Winter solstice is the first day of winter, with the shortest number of daylight hours (and the longest night) when earth's northern pole has its maximum tilt away from the sun. It occurs on December 21st in the northern hemisphere (Figure 10-5c).

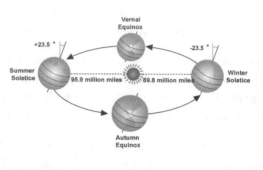

Figure 10-4
Earth's orbit around the Sun.

Solar Insolation

Solar insolation (not to be confused with insulation) is the amount of radiation arriving from the sun that collides with a flat surface per unit time **(energy flux)**, usually expressed in W/m², or kWh/m²/day. This includes the **direct (beam)** radiation directly on a surface, **scattered (diffused)** radiation from the sky, and **reflected (reradiated)** radiation from the surroundings. Direct radiation is predominant radiation when the sky is clear, and when the sun is high in the sky in mid-day. Diffuse radiation is significant during overcast skies, in high altitudes, and during early morning and late afternoons. The shadow cast by an opaque object is the result of blocking the direct radiation, the light available during overcast is from the scattered radiation.

Of all the radiation emitted by the sun, only a very small fraction is intercepted by the earth's atmosphere. This amount is called the solar

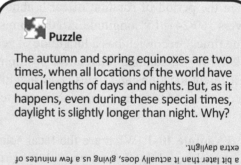

Puzzle

The autumn and spring equinoxes are two times, when all locations of the world have equal lengths of days and nights. But, as it happens, even during these special times, daylight is slightly longer than night. Why?

Answer: This would certainly be true if Earth did not have any atmosphere. However, because of atmospheric refraction, the Sun will appear to rise a bit sooner, and sets a bit later than it actually does, giving us a few minutes of extra daylight.

¶   Mercury is the only planet in our solar system without tilt, so technically lacks seasons. But because of its highly elliptical orbit, creates a version of summer and winter

**   Also referred to as Vernal and Autumn Equinoxes.

††   The seasonal variation of the lengths of days and nights can be explained by noting the relative position of the sun with respect to the earth. Twice a year on the Vernal (first day of spring) and Autumnal (first day of fall) Equinoxes, day and night become equal in length. The Vernal Equinox has been celebrated throughout history as the time of rejuvenation and rebirth, thus marking the start of a New Year on the Zodiac calendar. The summer solstice occurs around June 21 and represents the longest day of the year. The shortest day of the year falls on the winter solstice, at or around December 21 in the Northern Hemisphere.

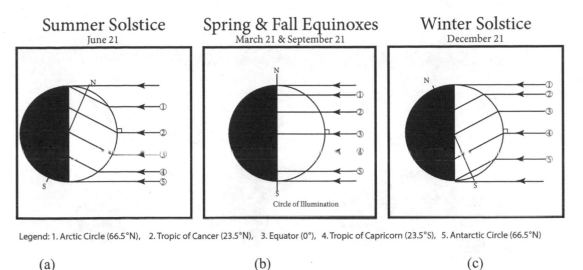

Legend: 1. Arctic Circle (66.5°N),   2. Tropic of Cancer (23.5°N),   3. Equator (0°),   4. Tropic of Capricorn (23.5°S),   5. Antarctic Circle (66.5°N)

(a)   (b)   (c)

Figure 10-5
(a) summer solstice, (b) spring and fall equinoxes, and (c) winter solstice

constant and represents the energy from the sun, per second, that falls on a surface perpendicular to the sun's rays and just outside the earth's atmosphere. The solar constant is not truly "constant," however. Because the actual orbit of the earth around the sun is elliptical, the average distance differs by about 3.4% during the year and the solar constant varies between 1,300-1,400 W/m². The actual energy flux received by the earth's surface is somewhat smaller -- roughly 1,000 W/m² (for a surface perpendicular to sunlight on a clear day), a value we call "one sun."

$$\textbf{1 sun} = \textbf{1 kW/m}^2$$

Like the sun, the earth is also emitting radiation, but at a much lower rate. The earth's terrestrial emission is in the infrared region of the spectrum and averages at around 172 W/m².

World Distribution of Solar Radiation

Solar radiation is not distributed evenly everywhere on the earth but depends on the location, season, cloud cover, and other atmospheric conditions. In general, the radiation received by the earth can be divided into three regions:

1. The most favorable places lie between 15-35°N, covering landmasses of many developing countries of Northern Africa and Southern Asia. They receive, on average, 3,000 hours of mostly direct sunshine and limited cloud cover.
2. The moderately favorable belt (0-15°N), or equatorial belt, has high atmospheric humidity and cloudiness that favors scattered radiation, reducing annual direct sunshine to about 2,500 hours. The intensity is almost uniform throughout the year since the seasonal variations are slight.
3. As we move further north past the tropic of cancer (or further south in the Southern Hemisphere), there is a greater percentage of cloud cover, which sharply reduces solar radiation intensity.

Figure 10-6 shows the annual average daily solar insolation map for various locations in the world.

Radiation Reaching the Surface

To calculate the amount of solar energy reaching a surface, not only do we need to know the position of the collector plate, but also its tilt – the angle that the collector makes with a horizontal plane. It is obvious that the highest amount of solar energy will be received by a collector that is perpendicular to the sun's rays when it is at its highest point

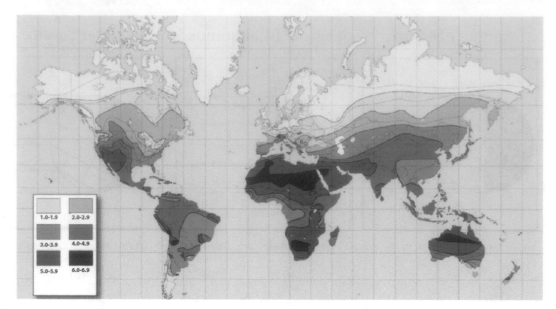

Figure 10-6

Annual average daily solar insolation [kWh/m²/day] in different parts of the world; the insolation values represent the resource available to a flat plate collector, such as a photovoltaic panel, oriented due south at an angle from horizontal, to equal to the latitude of the collector location. The greatest potential is in geographical regions falling between the tropics of Capricorn and Cancer.

Source: NREL Dynamic solar maps, (http://www.nrel.gov/gis/solar.html).

in the sky (solar noon). The sun is, however, rarely directly overhead, and its position changes throughout the day, limiting the solar power averaged over a 24-hour period to only 342 watts of energy enters the earth's atmosphere. Of this, 30% is reflected back to the sky, and under clear dry conditions, the remaining 70% of incident radiation reaches the ground (See Figure 4-4). The range varies widely, at about 270 W/m² for a spot in the Sahara (always sunny, near the equator), to only 75 W/m² for a spot in Alaska (often cloudy and at high latitude) Reflected radiation depends on the topography of the surrounding area, the amount of shade, and the reflectivity (*albedo*) of the earth. Albedo varies significantly with the type of material and whether the surface is exposed or covered by water, snow, or vegetation.

Example 10-2: According to EIA data, the U.S.'s electrical energy consumption was 4,120 terawatt-hours in 2008. How much land was required if all electricity was generated by solar means in California?

Solution: From figure 10-6, it can be seen on average, about 6 kWh/m²/day of sunlight is available in the Western United States. With cells at 10% efficiency, electrical power density is 0.6 kWh electric per day per square meter. The land area necessary to meet U.S. demand is

$$\left(\frac{4{,}120\dfrac{TWh}{y}}{0.6\dfrac{kWh}{m^2.day}}\right) \times \left(\frac{10^9\ kWh}{1\ TWh}\right) \times \left(\frac{1y}{365\ day}\right) \times \left(\frac{1\ km^2}{10^6\ m^2}\right) = 18{,}810\ km^2$$

A solar collector area of approximately 137 km by 137 km (about one-third size of the Mojave Desert) should be sufficient to satisfy the entire electricity needs of the United States.

It is a common experience that in the Northern Hemisphere, the sun rises higher in the sky in summer than in winter. Also, it appears that the sun rises south of due east in winter and north of due east in summer. As winter proceeds into spring and summer, the sun rises earlier in the morning, moves higher in the sky, reaches its highest point at noon,

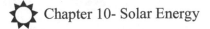

and sets later in the afternoon (See Figure 10-7). The opposite is true in the Southern Hemisphere.[‡‡]

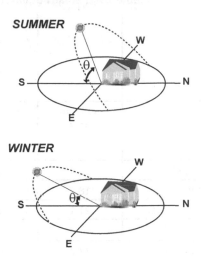

Of note is the possibility that total solar energy incident on a south-facing window is greater during the winter than in the summer, in spite of the fact that days are longer in the summer. Two factors contribute to this:

1. Although the sun rises earlier in the summer, it remains north of the window before it sets in the afternoon. In winter, the opposite is true – the sun rises and sets south of the window; therefore, south-facing windows are subject to incident sunlight for the entire length of the solar day. For example, a house in Long Beach, California, located at latitude 33° 48', experiences about 14 hours of daylight (5:30 am to 7:30 pm) on Summer Solstice (June 21) and 10 hours of daylight (7:30 am to 5:30 pm) on Winter Solstice (December 21). The south-facing windows in this house receive sunshine for only seven hours (8:30 am to 3:30 pm) during summer and receive the full 10 hours of sunshine during the winter.

2. The summer sun is higher in the sky than the winter sun. In the winter, the lower sun strikes the windows more directly than in the summer, when the sun is higher. For example, every square meter of the window of a house in Long Beach receives, on average, 220 watts of solar energy per hour of daylight in the winter, whereas the same window receives 40% less energy in the summer. Furthermore, because of the higher angle of incidence in summer, more of the sunlight is reflected off the glass than would be during the winter.

Figure 10-7
Summer and winter sun paths in the Northern Hemisphere.

Effect of the Collector's Tilt Angle

The solar radiation arriving at the surface depends not only on the meteorological conditions, and position of the sun relative to the earth, but also, on the angle of the tilt of the collector, and whether sunlight is concentrated or not). Ideally, collector plates should be perpendicular to the sun's rays at all times. This requires a tracking device that is able to follow the sun's change in elevation during the course of the year, and turn to follow the sun's apparent path from east to west during the day. Because of the high cost and complexity of the tracking device, fixed flat-plate collectors are often used instead. For optimal efficiency, collectors are placed on rooftops or in open areas facing south (north if in the Southern Hemisphere) and tilted at an angle equal to the latitude of their location. This allows an equal amount of energy before and after noon, maximizing radiation collected during an entire day. On certain occasions when power is needed most during the early hours of the day, the collector may be rotated and fixed to face the east. Table 10-1 shows the solar flux reaching flat and parabolic collectors at various tilt angles for Los Angeles.

Example 10-3: An average household in Los Angeles requires about 50 MJ of energy for a hot water system (~ 300 L storage tank). An owner intends to install a solar panel to meet his heating needs. How big must the flat plate solar collector be? What is the best orientation? Because of the reflection of the light by double-pane cover glass, radiation losses through the glass, and conduction losses from the backplate, flat panels have collection efficiencies of roughly 50%. Recall: 1 kWh = 3.6 MJ.

Solution: The required heating is 50/3.6 = 13.89 kWh. The area of the panel can be calculated by dividing this number by the solar insolation data given in Table 10-1. For the collection efficiency of 50%, we require the total surface area to be twice as large The table to the right shows the result for a fixed flat-plate collector positioned horizontally and tilted at an angle of the local latitude. As is expected, a collector installed on a flat

	Horizontal plate, m²	Tilted Plate, m²
March	5.4	4.5
June	3.5	4.0
September	4.9	4.2
December	9.9	5.7

[‡‡] From now on, we will limit our discussions to the Northern Hemisphere.

	Average Temperature (°C)	Flat plate, Horizontal	Flat plate, tilt = Latitude	Flat plate, Vertical	Flat plate, tilt = Latitude, 1-axis (N-S) tracking	Flat plate, 2-axis tracking,	Parabolic trough, 1-axis (N-S) tracking
Table 10-1. Solar Radiation for Flat and Parabolic Collectors Facing South (kWh/m²/d) in Los Angeles							
March	14.4	4.8	5.7	3.8	7.1	7.1	7.1
June	18.7	6.6	6.0	2.2	7.7	8.2	7.7
September	21.1	5.3	6.0	3.6	7.4	7.4	7.4
December	13.8	2.6	4.2	4.1	4.9	5.3	4.9
Annual	**17.2**	**4.9**	**5.6**	**3.5**	**7.0**	**7.2**	**7.0**

Source: NREL (http://www.nrel.gov/docs/legosti/old/5607.pdf)

roof works best for the summer; for winter months, a tilted collector is preferable.

Solar Heating and Cooling

The heating and cooling of space are needed when the temperature falls below or rises above the desired value. To determine how much heating or cooling is necessary, we must determine how much heat enters or leaks out of a building. The load increases with the temperature difference between the inside and the outside and depends on several factors such as design, season, time of the day, atmospheric parameters, and type of building materials. The detailed calculation is outside the scope of this book, but the interested reader is referred to heating, ventilating, and air conditioning (HVAC) trade journals and texts dedicated to this topic.

Passive Heating

Passive heating refers to the collection of solar energy without the use of electrical or mechanical power. The passive solar design takes advantage of the local climate using a building's windows, walls, and floors to collect, store, and distribute solar energy in the form of heat in the winter, and reject solar heat in the summer (Figure 10-8a). Because they have fewer (if any) moving parts, passive designs are simpler, more reliable, more durable, and cost less than active systems.

The simplest form of passive heating is the **direct gain** of solar energy as it passes through the window glass. **Indirect gain** is the process by which the sun warms a heat storage element, to distribute later to the interior space by convection, conduction, and radiation.

Solar rooms are south-facing rooms (north-facing in the Southern Hemisphere) with large windows, thick walls, and well-insulated roofs. Large windows allow maximum gain of direct solar radiation. Double and triple glazing of windows can significantly decrease heat losses from the room, with only a moderate reduction in the solar gains. Thick walls have large masses and high thermal storage capacity. The use of overhangs reduces incident solar heat, preventing excessive heating during the

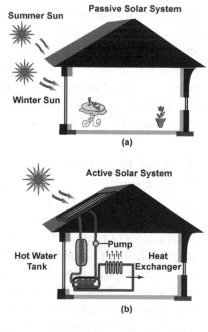

Figure 10-8
(a) passive, and (b) active solar systems.

312

Window Glass

Window glass is a simple and economical way of getting both light and heat conveniently into a living room or an office building. However, in many instances, such as during the hot summer days, we would like to block the Sun's heat, while still allowing the light into the room. This is traditionally done by laminating window glass with ultra-thin layers of silver, or by adding infrared-absorbing dyes that are broken down by strong sunlight and scatter light, thus giving the glass a smoky haze look.

A new technique has recently been developed that blocks the infrared by an order of magnitude and, at the same time, allows visible light to pass through.[i] The key is to sandwich small particles of lanthanum hexaboride in the glass. These particles strongly absorb the near-infrared radiation, but are so small in size (smaller than the wavelength of the visible light) that cannot scatter sunlight, leaving the glass highly transparent.

[i] Schelm, S. & Smith, G. B. Dilute LaB6, "nanoparticles in polymer as optimized clear solar control glazing," Applied Physics Letters, 82, 4346 - 4348, (2003).

---

summer months.

Trombe walls are thick walls designed to absorb and hold sunlight during the day and release it during the night. They usually consist of walls with the addition of a glass pane or plastic glazing installed next to them. A gap is placed between the two, in effect allowing solar radiation to enter through the glass and absorbed by the wall, and then reemitted in the form of long-wavelength radiation that heats the house interior. Modern Trombe walls incorporate openings at the top and bottom, allowing warm air to naturally circulate into the building. At night, vents are closed off, allowing heat retained in the concrete wall to be released to the interior.

Active Heating

The main component of most active systems is a rooftop solar collector, in which solar energy heats a working fluid and either store it in a hot water reservoir or distributes it directly to interior spaces through pipes or ducts (Figure 10-8b). For most low-temperature applications (up to 125°C) collectors are the most convenient. Furthermore, flat-plate collectors have the advantage of absorbing not only the energy coming directly from the sun (beam radiation) but also the scattered solar energy (diffused radiation) and that which is reflected from the ground. For applications that require higher temperatures, solar concentrators such as lenses and mirrors are necessary.

Flat-plate collectors consist of many tubes through which a working fluid, either water or a water-glycol antifreeze mixture, is heated by solar energy. Tubes are arranged in parallel inside an airtight collector (absorber plate) covered by a sheet of glass or plastic and insulated on the back. To absorb the maximum amount of energy possible, the back-plate is painted black.[§§] A glass or plastic covering permits most radiation in the visible range in, but allows only small losses during the night.

Solar water heaters are characterized as either open-loop (direct) or closed-loop (indirect). In an open-loop system, water circulates through the collector; a closed-loop system uses a heat-transfer fluid (usually diluted antifreeze) and a heat exchanger to collect heat and transfer it to the household water. Subsequently, a fan can blow air across the hot, circulating fluid and provide heating to rooms.

The most common uses of flat-plate collectors are for domestic hot water systems, pools, spas, and space heating. Usually, gas or an electric-powered heater is added as a backup for periods when sufficient solar energy is not available. A typical domestic hot water system is shown in Figure 10-9.

---

§§ Solar water heaters, sometimes called domestic hot water systems, can be either passive or active and either open- or closed-loop. Passive systems rely on the principle that water in the collector becomes lighter and rises as it heats while cooler water in the tank sinks, causing circulation by natural convection (thermosiphon). No pump is needed for water circulation through the collectors, making the systems simpler and less expensive. For passive systems to work, tanks must be above the collectors. Active systems use pumps to assist circulation. Open-loop systems are popular in mild climates where there is no danger of freezing. These systems require a circulation pump and are, therefore, inherently active. Closed-loop systems use a mixture of water-glycol antifreeze mixture and, thus, can be used in areas where freezing is a possibility.

Although most domestic hot water systems use pumps to circulate the fluid, there are some that do not. **Thermosiphon Systems** instead rely on the buoyancy of the warm water. As the water in the collector heats, it becomes lighter and rises naturally into the tank above. Meanwhile, cooler water in the tank flows toward the bottom causing circulation throughout the system.

Evacuated-tube collectors are similar to flat-plate collectors except that the glass tubes are replaced with two concentric tubes. Fluid flows inside the inner tube, while the outer tube is evacuated. This arrangement eliminates conduction and convection losses, which results in increased collection efficiency. Evacuated-tube solar collectors can be used under cloudy conditions, so their year-round efficiency is higher, but they are considerably more expensive and maintenance costs are higher.

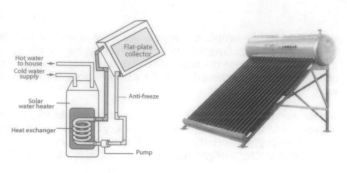

Figure 10-9
Schematics of a typical domestic hot water system.

Passive Cooling

To keep a building cool, we must keep heat out. This is possible by insulating the walls, making walls thicker, reducing the surface area of south-facing windows, and plugging all the leaks. Fewer windows, of course, reduce the cooling load, but also diminish the solar advantages during winter, when solar heating is most desirable. One possible solution is the use of overhangs. Recall that the sun is high in the sky in summer; a small **overhang** can effectively block most, if not all, of the solar radiation. During the winter, the sun angle is low and, therefore, nearly all the radiation strikes the window.

Natural Ventilation

Natural ventilation in a building relies on the wind or buoyancy without the use of any mechanical systems. Wind-driven devices rely on pressure differences induced intentionally by building design which forces air to flow into or out of the building. In buoyancy-driven systems, pressure differences are created as a result of differences in temperature or humidity. Openings on opposite sides of the building are used for enhancing the cross-ventilation driven by breezes, The wind-catchers found throughout the Middle East are all examples of passive air-conditioning (Figure 10-10). Iranian architectures effectively utilize underground water reservoirs (*qanats*) to humidify and cool air before returning it into the buildings (Figure 10-11). In dry climates, **evaporative cooling** by springs and fountains has been tried since ancient times; roof ponds allow evaporative cooling to be used in more temperate climates.

Cool roofs

Cool roofs apply to roofs that have surfaces that reflect sunlight while emitting heat more efficiently, substantially decreasing the cooling load. Dark roofs absorb 90% or more of the incoming solar energy causing them to reach temperatures exceeding 150°F (66°C) in the sun. In contrast, light-colored roofs absorb less than 50% of the solar energy, reducing their

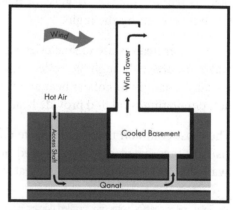

Figure 10-10
Persian wind catcher (*badgir*), Yazd, Iran.

Figure 10-11
Qanats help raise humidity and cool the air supplied to the interiors of old Persian buildings.

314

temperatures to about 110°F (44°C).

To have a cool roof, the surface has to have both high "solar reflectance" (ability to reflect sunlight), and high "thermal emittance" (ability to emit thermal radiation). Nearly all nonmetallic surfaces have high thermal emittance, which helps them cool down. Bare and shiny metal surfaces, like aluminum foil, have low thermal emittance, which helps them stay warm.

Examples of cool roofs are roofs painted white, roofs having special reflective pigments that reflect sunlight, and shingled roofs consisting of overlapping panels made from wood, polymers, or metals coated with reflective materials. Lawrence Berkeley National Laboratory has an extensive program in developing concepts and materials for more effective cool roofs.

Active Cooling

There are two approaches to solar cooling: vapor compression and absorption. In Chapter 9, we reviewed the principle of operation of both systems. In vapor compression systems, cooling occurs as a result of a refrigerant removing heat from the refrigerated (air-conditioned) space and becomes vaporized (step 1). The vapor then is heated to a high temperature and pressure by a compressor (step 2); it then enters a condenser where it is condensed and becomes liquid (step 3). Finally, the liquid is expanded in an expansion valve, allowing the refrigerant to cool to the evaporator temperature (step 4). The refrigerant is now ready to remove additional heat and repeat the cycle. The point to remember is that some energy, in the form of electricity or heat, is needed to carry out step 2. The source of this energy can be natural gas, oil, or in this case, solar energy.

Absorption cooling is the most commonly used method of solar cooling. It works differently from a compressor refrigerator, in that it replaces the compressor with an absorption-regeneration system powered by solar energy. There have been several proposed solid-state absorption systems also, using thermally driven static sorption beds. These systems take advantage of the ability of certain materials, such as activated carbon or "charcoal," to sorb (soak up) a relatively large quantity of refrigerant vapor (ammonia) at low temperature and pressure. The refrigerant is subsequently released at a higher pressure, simply by applying heat.

For detailed operation see Digging Deeper: Air Conditioning and Refrigeration in Chapter 9.

Solar Thermal: Heat to Electricity

Solar energy can be exploited to generate electricity by one of the two methods: 1) by concentrating light to boil water to steam, or 2) by direct conversion to electricity through photovoltaics. Both methods have been tried and both offer attractive alternatives to fossil fuel combustion. In addition to these, a temperature gradient resulting from non-uniform heating of land and water masses has been exploited to produce power.

Solar thermal systems work very much like conventional coal, oil, or nuclear power plants except that their source of energy comes from concentrated sunlight. They can be designed in any size capable of producing from 10s to 100s of megawatts of power. They can work with different working fluids (water, oil, salts, air, helium, etc.) and in different types of engines (steam engines, gas turbines, Stirling engines, etc.). Because it utilizes heat, its maximum conversion efficiency is set by the Carnot limit, at around 30 to 40 percent. Furthermore, they are more adaptable to a sudden drop in insolation, as they can be complemented by burning fossil fuels. Heat storage is much easier, making solar thermal more attractive (and economical) for large-scale energy production. In addition to generating electricity, a byproduct of thermal plants -- waste heat -- can be used to desalinate seawater, used for thermal cooling, or used directly in industrial applications.

Photovoltaics (PV), on the other hand, convert the sun's light into electricity directly. Depending on the technology, either direct or diffuse lights are collected. Because electricity cannot be stored effectively (as is for the heat), PV solar panels are most effective during daylight hours. Photovoltaic projects can be constructed in modular form for applications requiring from a few milliwatts (call boxes, solar lights) to many megawatts (distributed power).

> **Example 10-4:** What is the total area of land required to satisfy the world's electricity needs? Assume 20% conversion efficiency and a 2,000 hours per year of natural sunshine of 1,000 W/m² striking the surface. According to BP, the total global electrical capacity in 2014 was estimated at 23,536 TWh. What would be the total land area required in 2030, if electricity demand increases to 36 terawatt-hours?
>
> **Solution:** On average, every square meter of land receives 2,000 h x 1 kW = 2,000 kWh of solar energy, and has the potential to produce 2,000 x 0.20 = 400 kWh of electrical power. Total land required is 23,536x10¹² /400x10³) = 5.884 x10¹⁰ m² = 58,840 km², roughly the size of Egypt's Sinai Peninsula, or 0.04% of the total landmasses of earth). Following the same procedure, the area needed in 2030 would be 90,000 km² (a square parcel of land 300 km by 300 km).

Concentrated Solar Power (CSP)

Concentration can be achieved through reflective surfaces in the forms of parabolic troughs, dishes, Fresnel lenses, or an array of mirrors forming a heliostat. Concentrated Solar Power (CSP) is generally proven to be advantageous in areas with high direct solar gain and access to large plots of land. Unlike the flat-plate thermal and photovoltaic collectors that absorb all beam and diffuse incident radiation, concentrating collectors collect only beam (direct) normal solar irradiation, and therefore must be able to track the sun.

The potential for CSP is enormous, but challenges are also plenty. The prices for mirror materials must be lowered substantially, novel materials and heat transfer fluids must be developed, better thermal storage materials are needed, and collection efficiencies must be increased. The latter requires higher operating temperatures and higher concentration ratios. Global installed CSP capacity has been increasing steadily from 355 MW in 2005 to more than 6.2 GW in 2015 and expected to reach 22 GW by 2025.·

Solar Concentrator

When temperatures higher than 100°C are demanded, solar energy must be concentrated. The degree to which solar energy is concentrated by a given collector is called the geometric concentration ratio (concentrator efficiency)[¶¶] and is defined as:

$$C.R. = \frac{Aperture\ area\ of\ collector}{Surface\ area\ of\ receiver}$$

i.e., a 1-cm² solar cell under 1000-sun concentration produces the same electricity as 1,000 cm² normal incidence with no concentration. Depending on the type, concentrators can boost solar intensity to 200-1000 suns (20 to 100 W/cm²). Concentration ratios lower than 100 are considered low concentration; those above 100 are high concentration. Figure 10-12 shows several concentration techniques tried for boosting the efficiency of solar thermal electric generating stations.

Depending on the application, different types of concentrators are desired (Table 10-2). Towers and troughs are best suited for large, grid-connected power systems in the 30- to 300-MW range, whereas dish/engine systems are modular and can be used singly in remote applications or be grouped together to power a small community, and can be expanded as more power is needed.

A single flat mirror does not concentrate, but concentration can be obtained by superimposing the reflections of many mirrors. Towers (heliostats) work by spreading flat (or curved) mirrors in a two-dimensional array. A central

---

[¶¶] Do not confuse with optical concentration ratio (collector efficiency) which is the ratio of useful thermal or electrical energy to the solar energy falling on the collector aperture area. Both optical and geometric concentration ratios are equal when irradiance is uniform over the entire aperture and absorber surface areas.

processor controls each mirror, individually, in order to track and, at all times, focus[***] the sun's rays toward a receiver located at the top of the tower. A fluid (liquid or gas) circulates through the receiver and takes the heat away to run a gas turbine, or generate steam that is subsequently expanded in a steam turbine and produces electricity. Using this concept, two demonstration plants, called Solar One and Solar Two were designed by the Sandia National Laboratory and operated by Southern California Edison in Daggett, California. Solar One was a 10-MW plant in which water was heated directly in the solar receiver. In Solar Two, water was replaced with a mixture of molten nitrate salt as the working fluid. The advantage of molten salt is that it remains liquid to a higher temperature, and thermal efficiency is increased.[†††] The Solar Two plant operated from 1996 to 1999, after which it was decommissioned. Based on lessons learned, Spain adopted the technology and constructed two power plants, the Abengoa PS-10 and PS-20, in Seville, with capacities of 11 and 20 megawatts, respectively. The U.S. has also intensified the effort, and now operates the Ivanpah Solar Electric Generating System, the largest solar thermal power plant in the world. The facility consists of three separate plants deploying 350,000 mirrors with a gross capacity of 392 megawatts, in the California Mojave Desert, providing clean electricity to 140,000 Southern California homes.

The solar furnace in Odeillo, France, uses a similar setup, focusing light from about 2,000 square meters of a mirrored surface onto a spot 60 cm on each side and produces temperatures as high as 3,800°C, enough to drill a hole in a sheet of steel (Figure 10-13). At the present, the facility is being used as a high-temperature research lab for testing materials under extreme environments such as inside nuclear reactors or during space vehicle atmospheric reentry.

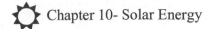

Parabolic Trough

Concentric Dish

Fresnel Lens

Central Receiver

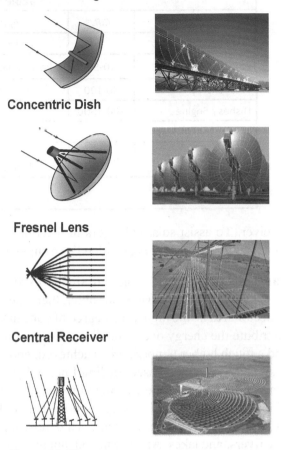

Figure 10-12

From top: Parabolic trough, parabolic dish, Fresnel lens, and tower heliostat.
Image sources: SEGS solar field in Mojave Desert (SunLabs, U.S. Dept. of Energy), middle), SunCatcher (Stirling Energy Systems), bottom) , Kimberina Solar Plant (AREVA Solar), and Ivanpah Solar Power Plant (www.eere.energy.gov)

Parabolic troughs are parabolas stretched along an axis perpendicular to their surface. They are formed by long sheets of metal bent to concentrate sunlight on a tube (receiver) containing a liquid and placed along the focal line running the length of the trough. The trough must be tracked about one axis. Parabolic troughs are the easiest to construct and are used to collect sunlight with concentration ratios as high as 1000:1 allowing to heat water to superheated steam at 1,200°C.

Solar Electric Generating Stations (SEGS) in California's Mojave Desert are the world's largest parabolic trough facilities ranging in size from 14-80 megawatts for a combined electric generating capacity of 354 MW, enough to meet the needs of 500,000 people. Each plant consists of a collector field of many troughs aligned on a north-south axis, which reflect sunlight onto receiver pipes filled with oil. Each trough is mounted on a tracking device that follows the sun as it moves from east to west during the day, to ensure that the sunlight is continuously focused 30 to 60 times the normal intensity onto the

Figure 10-13
Solar furnace in Odeillo, France

[***] The word "focus" in Latin means "fireplace."

[†††] New advanced materials, such as special concretes or high-temperature phase-change materials are currently being developed.

Table 10-2 Solar Concentrators						
	C.R.	Applications	Tracking	T_{max}	$\eta_{theoretical}$ *	η_{actual} **
Flat Plate Collectors	1	Heating & Cooling	Fixed	100°C	20%	--
Parabolic Troughs	10-50	Power, Heating & Cooling	1-axis	400 °C	56%	21%
Fresnel Lens	50-100	Power	1-axis	1000°C	77%	
Dishes / Engines	100-1000	Power	2-axis	1200°C	80%	29%
Towers (Heliostats)	500-1500	Power	2-axis	2000°C	87%	23%
Combination	> 1500	Solar furnace, Space propulsion	2-axis	4000°C	93%	--

* Assume sink at 25°C.
** Peak efficiency

receiver. To assist solar collectors in meeting demand during the night, on rainy or cloudy days, or extreme cold, some gas-fired generators are added as a supplement.

Parabolic dishes (paraboloid) are similar except that light is focused on a receiver placed at its focal point. They are formed by rotating the parabolas about their axes. It is a matter of common sense that the bigger and more curved the collector area is, the higher the degree of concentration and better collection efficiency will be. Since parabolic dishes distribute the energy over a smaller collector surface, they have higher concentrating power than parabolic troughs, and a much higher temperature is achieved, enough to run a heat engine. One such system, called SunCatcher™, was designed by Arizona-based Stirling Energy Systems, Inc. (SES) and uses arrays of curved-glass mirror facets in the shape of parabolic dishes. To maximize efficiency, the assembly automatically tracks, collects and focuses the sun. The concentrated light heats up a working fluid that drives a closed-cycle, four-cylinder Stirling engine.[‡‡‡] SES uses a closed cooling system, and thus, is the most appropriate in desert climates and areas far from large bodies of waters like rivers, and lakes. Another big advantage of this system is its modularity. Each unit is about 12 m in diameter and generates 25 kilowatts of electricity. In 2012, the company filed for bankruptcy as the Stirling dish technology could not compete with the falling costs of solar photovoltaics. At this time, the viability of this technology for large-scale electricity production projects remains uncertain.

> **Question:** The most common approach to concentrating solar light is to use parabolic reflectors. What is the advantage of using parabolic reflectors over spherical reflectors?
> **Answer:** Parabolic reflectors are capable of concentrating parallel solar rays into a single focal point. Spherical reflectors disperse the light over a wider area (spherical aberration) causing temperature drops and efficiency suffers.

A **Fresnel lens** replaces the curved surface of a conventional lens with a series of concentric grooves, molded into the surface of a thin, lightweight plastic sheet. The design allows the construction of much thinner, lighter lenses of large aperture and short focal length that would be required by a lens of conventional design. It does so, by dividing the continuous surface of a standard lens into a set of surfaces of the same curvature (See Figure 10-12). Because light has to travel through shorter paths, it suffers smaller energy losses by absorption, and efficiency is higher. *Fresnel reflectors* are made of many thin mirror strips to concentrate sunlight onto the absorber tubes. *Fresnel lenses* use refracted light (light bent by a lens). Depending on the design, Fresnel collectors can be either line- or point-focusing.

[‡‡‡] Stirling or "Hot Air Engine" refers to a class of engines in which heat is provided from a non-combusting external source, such as nuclear or solar energy. Because the temperature of the heat source and sink can be controlled and kept uniform throughout the heat supply and heat rejection part of the cycle, the thermal energy of the Stirling cycle can reach that of the Carnot cycle.

Solar Energy Storage

Electricity cannot be stored in its form, but most be converted to other forms of energy before it can be converted back to electricity when needed again. In thermal power plants, the electricity generation is in two steps: producing heat from the primary source (in this case the sun), and converting the heat into electricity by running steam or a gas turbine. The other approach is to store thermal energy when there is excess heat, and convert it to electricity at night, during cloudy days, and during peak demands. We discussed methods of storing electricity in Chapter 5.

Thermal energy can be stored in three ways: by raising the temperature of a medium, by changing its phase, and by reversible thermochemical reactions. Sensible heat storage is done by raising the temperature of a liquid or solid, without changing its phase during the process. Water is one of the best mediums for storing heat at temperatures below 100°C; it has a high specific heat, is inexpensive, non-toxic, non-combustible, and widely available. The disadvantages are that it is corrosive and freezes at low temperatures. For temperature ranges from 100°C to 300°C, oil is used. Above 300°C, most organic fluids tend to decompose and, therefore, liquids such as inorganic molten salts, liquid metals, and solids like rocks, pebbles, and refractory materials are best. Sensible heat storage systems are simple in design, but are bulky, and cannot store or deliver energy at a set temperature.

A better approach is to store solar energy as latent heat by changing a material from one phase to another without changing its temperature -- such as evaporating a liquid or melting a salt. Water has a specific heat of only 4.2 kJ/kg for each degree rise in temperature. Oil is even less, at around 2.1 kJ/kg. Compare that to the heat of fusion of sodium hydroxide (NaOH) of 156 kJ/kg when it melts; one kilogram of magnesium chloride hexahydrate salt releases 167 kilojoules as it solidifies.

Reversible thermochemical reactions are an attractive method for high-temperature storage of solar energy -- use the energy to break the chemical bonds, and restore the bonds when energy is needed back. A familiar example is the dissociation of water to its elements hydrogen and oxygen at temperatures in excess of 2000°C. The reverse reaction, combining oxygen and hydrogen to form water, produces electricity as is done in fuel cells.

Direct Conversion: Photons to Electrons

Photovoltaic (PV) systems convert light energy directly into electricity by photoelectric effect. When sun is the source of light, the collectors are known as solar cells. The the photoelectric effect was discovered in 1887 by the German physicist Heinrich Hertz. In 1888, Russian physicist Aleksandr Stoletov made the first solar cell. In 1905, Albert Einstein explained how the photoelectric effect worked, for which he received the 1921 Nobel Prize in physics. In 1968, Peter Edward Glaser proposed placing a satellite solar power system in geosynchronous orbit that would collect sunlight and beam it to collectors, which then would generate electricity (See Box "Solar Power Satellites"). By the mid-1970s, solar cells were primarily used in space for powering the instruments aboard space stations and in satellites. As the technology matured and the cost of production decreased, solar cells found new applications in everyday appliances, from pocket calculators and wristwatches to highway call boxes, message boards, and traffic signals. Solar cells also have been used in a number of transportation demonstration projects, such as solar planes, solar cars, and even solar boats (Figure 10-14). Flat-plate photovoltaic cells used today consist of an array of individual cells encapsulated in glass or plastic. Like the flat-plate collectors, PV modules are mounted on roofs and other flat surfaces or tilted conveniently toward the sun. Both direct and diffused radiations are collected. Unlike flat-plate collectors that are designed to minimize heat losses from the backside, PV cells are not insulated, allowing heat to escape, as the performance of solar cells suffers at higher temperatures.

> **Example 10-5:** A solar car used 8 m² of solar cells with an efficiency of 15%. Assuming an average solar flux of 800 W, what is the total power generated by the solar panel? If the car and its driver had a total mass of 300 kg, how long would it take for the car to accelerate to the speed of 90 km/h on a flat road?
>
> **Solution:** The total power generated is 800 W/m² x 8 m² x 0.15 = 960 W (~1.3 hp). To accelerate the car from

0-90 km/h, we need to supply energy equal to the change in kinetic energy: $E_{kin} = 1/2\ mV^2 = 1/2 \times (300\ kg) \times (25\ m/s)^2 = 93{,}750\ J$. Time to accelerate to its final speed is $93{,}750\ J\ /\ 960\ W = 98\ s$, which is slow in comparison to modern passenger cars.

This example demonstrates why designing a regular passenger car using solar energy only is not practical. A solar panel installed on the car's roof is hardly enough to power such auxiliaries as radio, horn, or small electronic gadgets.

Types of Solar Cells

Commercially available cells often come in the form of either wafers or thin films. *Wafers* consist of several layers of materials, a cover glass, anti-reflective materials, p-type, and n-type semiconductors, and some backing material stacked on top of each other. Silicon is the substrate most widely used. In *thin films* thin layers of micron-size thickness semiconductor material are deposited on a substrate, thus use less materials and cost is lower. Because of their size, thin films can be built to be highly flexible -- manufactured in rolls, or sprayed onto surfaces. The most common thin-film technologies currently in the market are silicon, cadmium-telluride, and multi-junction tandem solar cells. The technology is rapidly improving as cost decreases while efficiency rises.

The advances in photovoltaic technology are often reflected in categorizing solar cells into three generations (Figure 10-15). Table 10-3 compares the current status of various solar cell technologies:

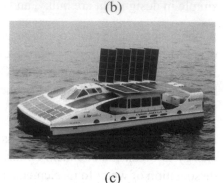

(a)

(b)

(c)

Figure 10-14
Solar transportation (a) NASA Helios, (b) GM Sunraycer, and (c) Solar Sailer.

First Generation Solar Cells relied on high-quality silicon wafers as the substrate. The efficiency of silicon cells (c-Si) depends on their purity -- the purer the silicon, the higher the efficiency. In monocrystalline cells, each of the four valence electrons of a silicon atom is linked to another silicon atom. Polycrystalline cells use an ingot made up of many smaller crystals. Monocrystalline cells have a uniform and continuous molecular structure without any resistance to obstruct their motions. In polycrystalline crystals, there are defects along grain boundaries.

Crystalline silicon solar panels are well-established and currently are dominating the current solar market, but it appears fast becoming obsolete as second and third-generation cell technologies are becoming more mature.

Second Generation Solar Cells use thin films to reduce the cost of single-crystal silicon technology, as they use less than 1% of the raw silicon material. Thin layers of nano- to micron-size thickness semiconductor material are deposited on a substrate. Thin films are manufactured in rolls or sprayed onto surfaces. The most common thin-film technologies currently on the market are amorphous silicon, cadmium telluride, and multi-junction tandem solar cells. One advantage of thin films is that they can grow on flexible substrates and large surface areas. These materials are simpler to process, less expensive and offer higher conversion efficiencies than silicon cells.

Amorphous Silicon (a-Si) lacks a crystalline structure and

Table 10-3 State-of-the-Art Solar Cell Efficiencies (2019)	
Monocrystalline silicon (mono-Si)	26.6%
Polycrystalline silicon (multi-Si)	22.3%
Amorphous silicon (a-Si)	10.2%
Monocrystalline gallium arsenide (GaAs)	29.3%
Cadmium telluride (CdTe)	22.1%
Copper indium gallium selenide (CIGS)	23.3%
Dye-sensitized (DSSC)	11.9%
Organic thin film (OPV)	16.4%
Perovskite thin film (PSC)	24.2%
Perovskite/Si	28.0%

is fabricated by vapor-depositing silane gas directly onto a plastic or metal substrate that has been coated with a layer of transparent conducting oxide. Amorphous cells are cheaper to produce and have found a wide range of applications such as calculators, call boxes and traffic signals. Amorphous solar cells can achieve efficiencies of about 13.6%.

Cadmium-Telluride (CdTe) uses rare-earth metals capturing energy at shorter wavelengths than is possible with silicon. The manufacturing cost is lower than silicon cells. Cadmium is, however, a toxic heavy metal, which might cause some environmental concern when cells are being discarded. Also, it is rare and not enough to meet global energy demands. Conversion efficiency of about 20% has been reported.

Multi-Junction (Tandem) solar cells consist of several very thin layers of light-absorbing materials sandwiched together. Each layer absorbs a different color light, increasing the overall efficiency. The layer with the highest bandgap lies on top. As photons of light impinge on this layer, the high-energy photons of the visible light are absorbed, leaving the lower energy infrared part of the spectrum to be collected by the low bandgap material underneath. The efficiency of tandem solar cells can vary somewhat depending on the choice of material and the manner various layers are packed. Tandem cells can be fabricated in a wide variety of shapes and sizes, make it possible to use this technology in building-integrated PV (BIPV) applications.

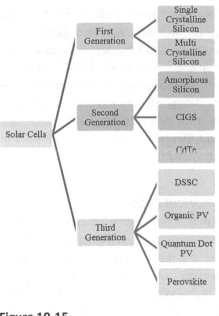

Figure 10-15
Three basic gewnerations of solar cells.

The technology has been implemented on the Mars Rover but remains too expensive for its wide use in commercial products. In one configuration, a triple-junction cell constructed of CIGS (a chemical compound of copper, indium, gallium, and selenium) was shown to achieve efficiencies as high as 41%. There are other technologies where light is split into six to eight colors, which then are dispersed to a cell made of a semiconductor that absorbs it; efficiencies as high as 50% are reported. In the extreme, with an infinite number of layers, tthe theoretically possible limit is 68% with unconcentrated light and 86% with concentrated light. In addition, thin-film Gallium-Arsenide (GaAs) solar cells are used in space vehicles and concentrated terrestrial applications. The larger efficiency, larger power to weight ratio, and lower launch cost make these cells particularly attractive.

Third Generation Solar Cells are state-of-the-art technologies using novel organic materials and nanostructured semiconductors. Technologies falling in this category include dye-sensitized, organic polymers, quantum dots, and perovskite solar cells.

Dye-Sensitized Solar Cells (DSSCs) use organic dyes to absorb light, much like chlorophyll in green leaves during photosynthesis, but unlike plants that convert light into sugar, these cells convert light into electricity. In brief, sunlight enters a cell through a transparent cover and strikes a dye on the surface of the TiO_2 material, causing an electron to be injected into its conduction band. These cells are less efficient than inorganic cells but have the potential to be much cheaper, more flexible, easier to manufacture, and the ability to operate in diffused light.

Organic Photovoltaics (OPVs) use organic semiconducting polymers or small molecules as photoactive materials. Compared to inorganic devices, OPVs have lower material costs, weigh less, are more flexible, and can be fabricated using roll-to-roll printing techniques. Their efficiencies are less compared to the second generation technologies, but materials used are more abundant and less harmful to the environment.

Quantum Dot Solar Cells use quantum dots – particles of semiconductors in the nanometer size range. By adjusting the particle size, the light of different frequencies is absorbed, which allows deploying multiple layers and take advantage of the entire solar wavelength.

Perovskite Solar Cells (PSCs) are the latest solid-state solar cell technology with a promise of higher efficiency, lighter weight, enhanced flexibility, semi-transparency, reduced processing cost, simpler manufacturing, more abundant and cheaper materials, and a broad absorption spectrum. The ability to fabricate perovskite solar cells at low temperatures (120-130°C) using roll-to-roll printing devices allows easier manufacturing processes. That compares to production process temperature as high as 600°C for CIGS and 900°C for CdTe thin-film PV cells. The latest experiments have shown efficiencies as high as 24.2%, making PSCs the fastest-improving solar technology. By stacking several layers of material in tandem, it is theoretically possible to achieve efficiencies higher than the SQ limit. Perovskite, however, is highly unstable and can degrade in a matter of days to months in a humid environment and sustained heat from the sunlight. This limitation has hindered their commercial potential, so far.

Spherical Cells

A major problem with flat-panel cells is that, once they are installed in a particular orientation, they collect the maximum sunlight if the sun is directly overhead. As the sun's incident angle changes, the light intensity drops, and less power is produced. The basic idea behind spherical cells is that a spherical receiver can collect light from all directions. This allows the capture of direct beams of light, as well as light diffused from clouds and reflected from buildings, resulting in efficiencies up to 50% greater than those of the flat cells. Spherical cells use single crystal silicon droplets of 0.5-2 mm in diameter to make the p-layer. (Figure 10-16). A thin layer of n-type film is diffused and, except for a small opening for electrodes, covers the surface of the microspheres. The microspheres are lined up along a fine copper string and connected in a series or a parallel configuration and mounted on a white resin reflection plate covered with a transparent layer. The spherical solar cell module is highly flexible and can be made to match the contours of buildings or cars, thus providing integrated power sources in windows, roofing materials, canopies, and other surfaces.

Figure 10-16
Spherical micro solar cells.
Image courtesy of Kyosemi Semiconductor Corp.,Japan, (http://www.kyosemi.co.jp).

Solar Thermophotovoltaics (STPV)

Solar Thermophotovoltaic Cells combines two common technologies, thermoelectric (TE) and photovoltaics (PV) to take advantage of the full spectrum of solar radiation. Conventional silicon solar cells mainly capture visible light. In solar thermophotovoltaics, an absorber-emitter device funnels solar light onto the cells, heating the absorber to temperatures as high as 1,000°C. Subsequently, the emitting layer radiates this energy as light is narrowed to bands that the photovoltaic cells can absorb. In a **hybrid system,** the sun's light is split at about 800 nm. The visible and ultraviolet part is directed to the PV cell; the infrared part to the TE cell (Figure 10-17). Not only the overall efficiency is increased, but also the waste heat is reduced, keeping the cell temperature low. With appropriate designs, concentration ratios of as much as 5,000 suns and a power density of 10-100 kW/m^2 is possible, a far better power density than solar cells, which only can deliver 1 kW/m^2 of power.

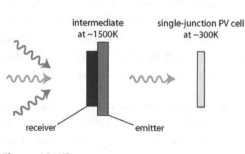

Figure 10-17
Thermophotovoltaics

The conversion efficiency for the first stage is determined by the blackbody radiation exchange between the sun and the absorber, and that of the second stage is limited by the Carnot efficiency between two heat reservoirs at emitter and cell temperatures. For an emitter at 1500 K and a cell at 300 K, the absolute maximum efficiency imaginable is 1 - (300/1500) = 80%. In reality, only photons of a certain frequency are participating and efficiency is much lower.

Solar Power Satellite

A solar panel facing the sun in near-earth space receives about 1,350 watts of sunlight per square meter. Because of the Sun's angle and the attenuation by the atmosphere, the radiation received on the earth's surface is considerably reduced. Furthermore, solar cells can work only during the day, so they can only receive sunlight half of the time. If solar collectors are placed in a geostationary orbit (36,000 kilometers high), they could collect sunlight that otherwise would not hit the earth, and convert it to electricity.[i] This electricity then can be beamed through the ionosphere, the outermost layer of the earth's atmosphere, received on the earth, as microwaves, which can pass unimpeded through clouds and rain, 24 hours a day, 365 days a year, and can be before they are converted back into electricity. This electricity is in the form of direct current, which then can be converted to the 50- or 60-cycle alternating current electricity used in homes. Because the panel always faces the sun, electricity would be generated 24 hours a day and there will be no need for storage.

Image courtesy of Space Science Institute.

Such a system has indeed been proposed by the U.S. Department of Energy and NASA. A preliminary design consisted of a 5-km x 10-km rectangular solar collector and a 1-km diameter circular transmitting antenna array. The SPS would weigh 30,000 to 50,000 tons and provide five billion watts of electricity, equivalent to ten 500 MW conventional coal or nuclear power plants.

Recently, the California-based Solaren Corporation™ announced that it has closed a deal with San Francisco PG&E to build a 200-megawatt space power station by 2016, and sell 1,700 gigawatt-hours of electricity for 15 years.[ii] Japanese Mitsubishi Electric and IHI Corporations also joined in a $21-billion project intended to build a 1-gigawatt solar station within three decades. The system will be fitted with four square kilometers of solar panels capable of powering 294,000 average Japanese homes.

i Alternatively, some have proposed placing the collectors on the surface of the moon.

ii Glaser, P.E., "Power from the Sun: Its Future," Science, Vol. 162, 1968, pp. 856-861. (http://www.solarenspace.com).

Luminescent Solar Concentrators (LSC)

A luminescent solar concentrator consists of a glass or plastic plate coated with a luminescent dye that absorbs sunlight and emits it at longer wavelengths. The approach mimics a photosynthesis process that converts sunlight to food. Unlike chlorophyll which absorbs mainly visible light, the dye absorbs both visible and infrared lights.

The fundamentals are similar to the light trapped in optical fibers (waveguides). The molecules deposited on the glass sheet absorb photons of light and re-emit them as infrared. With proper material, the re-emitted photons are trapped by total internal reflection and guided to the edges of the LSC plate, where they are absorbed by small-area PV cells installed at the plate boundaries. Efficiencies of 11% have been demonstrated.

Concentrated Photovoltaics (CPV)

We discussed how solar thermal systems can take advantage of CSP by concentrating the solar power and increasing the temperature of a fluid, and thus the thermal efficiency. The efficiency of photovoltaic systems can similarly be improved *if sunlight first is concentrated* before it falls on the solar cell. Because light is concentrated on a smaller area of the receiver, less semiconductor material is used and the cost is lower. In principle, light can be concentrated to any extent. The higher the concentration ratios, the higher is the flux of radiation on a cell area. The drawback is that at the very high concentration ratios the cell temperature rises and may damage the cell. As a result, most cells reach a maximum efficiency when light is concentrated to around 500 suns. Another disadvantage of CPV systems is their small accepting angles that necessitate 2-axis tracking. Because CPV cannot concentrate diffuse light, their applications for areas with low-intensity light and under overcast conditions are limited.

CPV systems are either refractive or reflective. Refractive types use a single lens or a Fresnel lens to focus light on the target. Fresnel lenses can be constructed in the shape of a circle to provide a point focus, or a cylinder to provide a line focus. Reflective types use planar or curved mirrors and work by reflecting incoming light onto a receiver. Refractive systems are more tolerant to misalignment but can suffer from chromatic aberrations.[§§§] Reflective systems have no such aberration but require accurate tracking. Figure 10-18 shows both types.

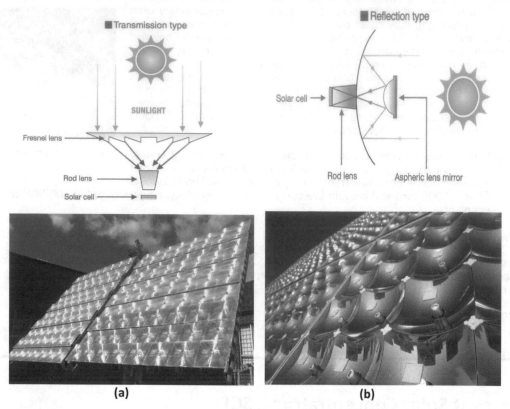

Figure 10-18
Concentrating PV, (a) Amonix refractive Fresnel lens, (b) Solfocus reflective system.

Solar Thermal vs. Photovoltaics

The two most common solar power plants are concentrated solar plants (CSP) and photovoltaics (PV). The main advantages of PV over CSP are:

a. PVs can collect both direct and diffuse radiation, so it works on even cloudy and rainy days.
b. PVs are easier and cheaper to construct, require less land, and unlike CSPs do not have to be constructed on flat surfaces.
c. PVs can be constructed in small modules of a few kilowatts each and expanded as need increases.
d. PVs are more suitable than CSP for off-grid applications. They have no moving parts and work quietly; maintenance cost is much less.
e. PVs are undergoing revolutionary evolution in terms of higher efficiencies, cheaper and lighter materials, and manufacturing techniques. As the production cost goes down, PV is proving itself more competitive with other renewable resources technologies.

The main advantages of CSP over PV technologies are:

---

§§§ Blue light has a shorter focal length than red light.

a.   CSP systems are capable of storing large amounts of energy as heat and use it to generate electric power on cloudy days for few hours after the sun goes down, and used on-demand and dispatched at the request of power grid operators when there is a market need. PV systems, on the other hand, generate electricity directly and are difficult to store.

b.   CSP systems produce AC, which is more convenient than DC produced in PV systems. Most electrical devices run on AC power.

c.   CSP system with thermal storage capability is a natural complementary solution to other renewable energy sources such as the wind, with large diurnal and unpredictable fluctuations.

Solar Chimney

The power plant consists of a large solar collector covered with a heat-absorbing material and a long chimney placed in the center of its base. Sunshine heats the transparent canopy open at the periphery, heating the air trapped underneath to 95°C above ambient temperature and guides it toward the base of the tall chimney in the middle. The air flows upward exiting the collar on top, in the process running many turbines at the base which then convert that flow into electricity and fed into a grid. At nights, the temperature gradient and direction of flow reverse, and more power is generated. The conversion efficiency of 2-3% has been achieved. To increase efficiency, a heat exchanger may be placed at the outlet of the turbine to capture the remaining thermal energy in the air column or preheat the incoming air.

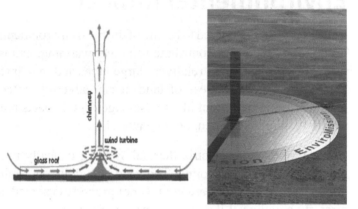

In addition to generating electricity, solar chimneys can be designed that collect cool ambient air into the bottom of a glass canopy which is subsequently heated by sunlight and rises to the top before released into a room. Solar chimneys are advantageous in that they can eliminate direct sunlight and glare and reduce heat losses during the night. The heat input can be adjusted by controlling the amount of air being circulated.

Figure 10-19
Solar Updraft Tower power plant prototype in Manzanares, Spain, seen from a point 8 km.
Source: Wikimedia Commons.

A 50-kW demonstration prototype was built in Manzanares, Spain in the 1980s and operated for seven years. Figure 10-19 shows the artist's rendition of the Spain prototype plant. Building on the success of the Spanish plant, a company called EnviroMission plans to construct a 200-MW plant in La Paz, Arizona. Because of the lack of sufficient financing, at the time of this writing, no construction has yet begun.

Solar Ponds

Solar ponds are shallow lakes of salty water where higher temperatures lie in the bottom and colder temperatures are near the top. As solar radiation penetrates shallow waters, it is absorbed in the bottom, raising its temperature. Surface water remains cool as it evaporates and convects heat to the air above. If the water is fresh, the buoyancy causes mixing of the water and the temperature will soon become uniform throughout the pond. If the water contains some salt, it becomes heavier than fresh water and sinks to the bottom, retaining the heat and temperature gradient. Temperatures as high as 95°C can be reached at the bottom layers.

Practical applications of solar ponds are many but direct use of thermal energy for heating is the most popular. Other applications include chemical and industrial heat processing, electricity production, and desalination. When power production is of primary interest, heat is extracted from the hot, salty fluid at the bottom of the pond and passed through heat exchangers to heat a working fluid, causing it to evaporate. The vapor is used to drive a turbine, similar to conventional steam power plants. Freshwater is produced as the by-product of these processes.

The key feature of a salt-water solar pond is the increase in the salinity of water with depth. As a result of convection, there is always some diffusion of salt from the bottom to top layers. By adding salt at the bottom and removing it at the top, the salt concentration gradient is maintained, Seas with high salt concentration are better candidates since they provide the natural salinity gradient necessary for the efficient operation of solar ponds. The largest solar ponds are in Israel, where the hot, dry climate is ideal for their operation. Figure 10-20 shows the schematic and aerial view of the solar pond in El Paso, Texas, the first-ever salt-gradient solar pond in the United States.

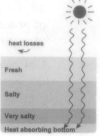

Figure 10-20
Solar pond in El Paso, Texas.
Source: http://wwwold.ece.utep.edu.

A similar design can be used to exploit the temperature differences between the warm surface and cold deep ocean waters. The technology is called Ocean Thermal Energy Conversion (OTEC) and will be discussed in Chapter 13.

Environmental Impact

Solar energy is considered to be one of the most environmentally friendly energy alternatives. Their operation produces no pollution, does not contribute to global warming, and is noise-free. Compared to other sources of energy, solar energy facilities require relatively large areas and may interfere with the existing land use. If construction requires the clearing of large areas of land, it can adversely affect native vegetation and wildlife by destroying habitats and interfering with rainfall and drainage. The impacts are exacerbated when the species affected are classified as sensitive, rare, threatened, or endangered.

Concentrating solar electric thermal systems typically use conventional steam plants, which require considerable amounts of water for cooling. This may put additional strain on available water resources, especially in arid regions, where most solar plants are built. If not properly designed, reflected light beams could blind pilots and interfere with aircraft operations. Like wind farms, solar farms can be aesthetically unpleasing to some, especially in areas of high population concentration.

Although PV operation is generally clean, its manufacturing (and disposal) is associated with the production of some of the most toxic materials, such as cadmium and arsenic. In addition, mining silicon produces fine dust that also can be considered a health problem. Furthermore, some fossil or other non-renewable energy sources are normally used during their production. With proper safety precautions, the total emission is, however, small, compared to fossil-fuel burning.

Summary

Solar energy provides the world with an unlimited supply of virtually carbon-free electricity. Solar technology can be used for space heating and cooling, or in various industrial and scientific applications, such as drying, desalination, and manufacturing. It also can provide power to operate electrical appliances, and for telecommunication and lighting in remote areas. So far, solar energy satisfies only 2.2% of the total U.S. electricity production, but as newer and cheaper technologies emerge, this is expected to change.

Unlike solar concentrating technologies that rely on direct radiation, photovoltaic cells rely mainly on indirect radiation and can be used in areas with few hours of sunlight. Compared to current PV technologies with typical efficiencies of 5-17%, solar thermals are more efficient and can reach efficiencies of up to 30%. If the light is concentrated, efficiencies of 40% or higher are also possible.

Solar Sail

Did you know that solar light can exert a gentle pressure just like water squirting out of a nozzle onto a plate? A team of Russian and American scientists has proposed to exploit the impact of light particles or photons off of a reflecting surface to propel and boost a spacecraft without heavy and expensive onboard fuel sources. Sunlight pressure is enough to accelerate the sail made of a sheet of aluminum-coated Mylar, at the rate of 100 mph a day. That doesn't sound like much, but it can quickly add up over time. The effort opens a new chapter in space travel, offering hope for future interplanetary missions. The sails can be as large as football fields, but only 5 microns in thickness, 100 times thinner than a sheet of paper. The virtually limitless energy source could eliminate the reliance on fuel-based propulsion systems for deep space travel. It also can stop satellites from falling back into geosynchronous orbit filled with thousands of pieces of space junk. Solar sails lose their effectiveness, beyond Mars, however, as the sun's radiation intensity falls off, too faint to push the solar sail.

The solar sails on some satellites have been used in the past to help in accelerating the spaceship, but no one has been able to deploy the sail as the only mode of propulsion. Cosmos-1 was launched in 2005 from a Russian submarine in the Arctic Barents Sea but was lost shortly after launch. The first successful launch of solar sail -- Ikaros, short for Interplanetary Kite Accelerated by Radiation of the sun, took place in May 2010.[i] According to legend, Ikaros (Icarus), the son of Daedalus, fell to his death, after flying too close to the sun, on wings made of wax. Unlike Icarus, the Ikaros craft is set to travel deeper and deeper into space, uncovering ever more mysteries of the universe.

[i] Cass, S., "Solar Power Will Make a Difference – Eventually," MIT Technology Review, September/October 2009, pp. 93.
Source: Universe Today, (http://www.universetoday.com/66225/japanese-solar-sail-deploys-successfully/).

A major impediment to large-scale use of solar energy is its intermittency -- available only during daylight and under favorable atmospheric conditions. PV cells are capable of generating electricity when the sun shines, solar thermal can store energy in an insulated vessel and be used to produce electricity (and heat) at any time of the day and whether the sun shines or not. If electricity is not used directly, or cannot be put on the electric grid, it must be stored. Storage is not easy, however. One way is to store the energy in large, bulky, and expensive batteries, or use it to produce hydrogen, either by electrolysis or by stripping hydrogen from liquid and gaseous fuels. Other storage methods have been discussed in this and previous chapters, such as to design a storage pumping facility, or compress air in underground caverns.

For solar energy to capture a major utility market share, large power plants with capacities comparable to coal or nuclear plants in the range of 500-1000 MW must be developed. Compared to fossil fuels, electricity generated by solar energy is still more expensive. Photovoltaics don't last forever, so they must be replaced periodically; most manufacturers guarantee a lifetime of around 20 years. Thermal systems are cheaper but require more land area.

ⓐ *Digging Deeper: Physics of Solar Cells*

To understand the photoelectric effect, it is best to visualize sunlight as small packets (quanta) of light called photons. The other, equally valid, view considers light as a wave. Photons are emitted at different frequencies and, therefore, have different wavelengths and energies. When photons strike a thin layer of materials, some are absorbed, some are reflected, and some pass through. The minimum energy required to dislodge electrons off a substrate is called the *bandgap*. In insulators, the bandgap is relatively large making the electronic transition from the valence band to the conduction band difficult. For metals, conduction and valence bands overlap and so no additional energy is needed; electrons are essentially free to migrate to the conduction band.

Semiconductors have relatively small bandgaps. For silicon, the bonding energy is 1.1 electron-volts corresponding to a photon in the near-infrared. Photons with energy less than 1.1 electron-volts do not have enough energy to interact with a bond in the silicon crystal and will necessarily pass right through the crystal or be reflected from the top without dislodging any electrons. Photons of energy higher than the energy gap participate in energy conversion; the excess energy goes into heating the cell. Bandgaps of GaAs and CdTe are 1.43 and 1.50 eV, respectively. The bandgap of CGIS varies between 1.1-1.7 depending on concentrations of various constituents. Materials with lower bandgaps have a higher capacity to absorb solar energy and efficiencies are higher.

Though pure silicon is a bad conductor of electricity, it can be doped with material like phosphorous and boron, Phosphorus is a substance belonging to group V of the periodic table, having one extra electron than silicon, making silicon negatively charged. Doping silicon with boron, a substance of group III of the periodic table results in silicon being positively charged.

When two layers of silicon, one doped with phosphorus and another doped with boron are pressed against each other a p-n junction is formed which facilitates electrons migration from an n-type to p-type material. Alternatively, we can say holes are migrating from the p-type material to the n-type material. When solar energy of the right frequency hits the n-layer, it knocks out some of the free electrons and breaks them loose. The electrons wander around and eventually fall into the holes in the p-layer and get absorbed. However, if a wire connects two layers across a load (for example, a light bulb or an electric motor), electrons follow the path of the lowest resistance and flow into the wire and create an electric field. As long as the light falls on the cell, the current is established (Figure 10-21).

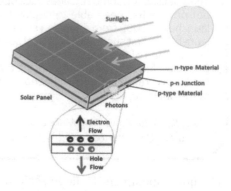

Figure 10-21
Schematic representation of a solar cell.

The most common type of cells is made from a single semiconducting material, usually silicon. Silicon absorbs light only in a narrow band around the red part of the solar spectrum; the rest is lost as heat, so it is rare that more than 20% of the incident solar light converts to electricity. Coating the cell with an anti-reflection material allows more photons to be absorbed and the current increases. A typical cell is 10 cm × 10 cm and produces about 1.5 watts (0.5 volts at about 3 amperes) of electric power when exposed to strong sunlight. Normally, cells are wafers encapsulated in a weather-proof package to form a module or a panel. Depending on the voltage desired several panels are connected in a series configuration. The current can be adjusted by connecting several such modules in parallel. The output of photovoltaic cells is in the form of DC (direct current) that can be stored in batteries or used for powering various devices. The output must be converted to AC (alternating current) and amplified by transformers to high voltages before being transmitted through commercial electrical grids.

Maximum Theoretical Cell Efficiency

Solar cells are often characterized by the percentage of the incident power that is converted into electric power called conversion efficiency. The efficiency is highest at a certain frequency -- low frequencies do not have sufficient energy to expel the electrons and are reflected off the front surface; higher frequencies have more energy than required and must be dissipated as heat. Solar cells come in the form of wafers or thin films. The maximum theoretical solar conversion efficiency from a single p-n junction with a bandgap of 1.34 eV under one sun illumination and assuming sun emits as a blackbody at 6000 K was calculated by William Shockley and Hans-Joachim Queisser (The Shockley-Queisser limit) at 33.7%.

📚 Endnotes

1   REN21(2019). Renewables 2019 Global Status Report, ISBN 978-3-9818911-7-1.
2   See for example, Duffie, J. & Beckman, W. (1991). *Solar Engineering of Thermal Processes*, 2nd. ed., John Wiley and Sons.
3   Arca, A., et al. (1984). Solar Disinfection of Drinking Water, Regional Office for the Middle East and North Africa, UNICEF. Retrieved from http://almashriq.hiof.no/lebanon/600/610/614/solar-water/unesco/24-26.html

4   Electric Power (2008) Annual Report, DOE/EIA-0348. Retrieved from http://www.eia.doe.gov/cneaf/electricity/epa/epa.pdf

5   See for example *ASHRAE Journal of Heating, Ventilating, and Air Conditioning.*

6   Hoagland, W. (1995). Solar Energy, *Scientific American*, vol. 273, pp. 170-173.

7   Anderson, B. & Wells, M. (1981) . Passive Solar Energy, New Hampshire: Brick House Publishing.

8   Bahadori, M. (1978). Passive Cooling Systems in Iranian Architecture. *Scientific American, 238*(2), 144-154, doi: 10.1038/scientificamerican0278-144

9   Urban, B., & Roth, K. (2010). *Guidelines for Selecting Cool Roofs.* Available at: http://heatisland.lbl.gov/sites/heatisland.lbl.gov/files/coolroofguide_0.pdf

10   Levinson, R. (2009). *Cool Roofs Q &A*, Lawrence Berkeley National Laboratories. Aailable at: http://coolcolors.lbl.gov/assets/dooo/faot oheeto/Cool roof Q%2BA.pdf

11   Christy, C. Fusco. D. & R. Toossi. (2004). *Adsorption Air-Conditioning for Containerships and Vehicles*, METRANS contract number 65A0047.

12   Readers interested in detailed designs of solar concentrators should refer to *Solar Energy Systems Design* by Stine W. & Harrigan, W. (1985). John Wiley and Sons. An updated copy of the text is available from http://www.powerfromthesun.net

13   REN21 (2020) Renewables Global Status Report

14   Kalogirou, S. (2004). Solar thermal collectors and applications. *Progress In Energy And Combustion Science, 30*(3), 231-295). doi: 10.1016/j.pecs.2004.02.001

15   Manchini, T. et al., (1997). Solar Thermal Power, Advances in Solar Energy, *Solar Energy,* p. 11.

16   Odeio Solar Furnace, http://www.atlasobscura.com/places/worlds-largest-solar-furnace.

17   Kearny, D. (1989). Solar Electric Generating Stations (SEGS), *IEEE Power Engineering Review*, Aug 4-8. doi: 10.1109/MPER.1989.4310850, http://www.anglophone-direct.com/Mont-Louis-Font-Romeu-Odeillo-Via

18   Stirling Energy Inc., http://www.stirlingenergy.com

19   Fresnel Technologies, Inc., http://www.fresneltech.com/pdf/FresnelLenses.pdf

20   APS, Challenges of Electric Energy Storage Technologies: A Report from the APS Panel on Public Affairs Committee on Energy and Environment (2007) Retrieved from http://www.aps.org/policy/reports/popa-reports/upload/Energy_2007_Report_ElectricityStor ageReport.pdf

21   Stein, W. & Geyer, M. (2001). *Power from the Sun: Chapter 11,* http://powerfromthesun.net

22   Glaser, P. (1968). Power from the Sun: Its Future. *Science, 162*(3856), 857-861. doi: 10.1126/science.162.3856.857

23   Mah Oilvia. (1998). *Fundamental of photovoltaic materials,* National Solar Power Research Institute, Inc. pp. 4-5.

24   Applied Energy Mater, (2019). *ACS Appl. Energy Material.* vol. 2, pp. 4609–4617, https://pubs.acs.org/doi/pdf/10.1021/acsaem.8b02149

25   Green, M. et al., (2013). Solar cell efficiency tables (version 42), *Progress in Photovoltaics: Research and Applications, 21*(5), 827–837.

26   Press Release, World Record: 41.1% efficiency reached for multi-junction solar cells at Fraunhofer ISE. (2019). Aailable at: http://www.ise.fraunhofer.de/press-and-media/press-releases/press-releases-2009

27   Higgens, N. (2020). Solar and Wind Power Could Ignite a Hydrogen Energy Comeback, *Scientific American*, February 1, 2020.

28   Grandidier, J., et al. (2013). Solar cell efficiency enhancement via light trapping in printable resonant dielectric nanosphere arrays (Phys. Status Solidi A 2/2013). Physica Status Solidi (A) 210(2), n/a-n/a. doi: 10.1002/pssa.201390004

29   Vos, A. (1980). Detailed balance limit of the efficiency of tandem solar cells. *Journal Of Physics D: Applied Physics,* vol. 13, no. 5, pp. 839-846. doi: 10.1088/0022-3727/13/5/018

30   Andreev, V. Khvostikov, V. Khvostikov, and O. (2014). Solar Thermophotovoltaic Converters: Efficiency Potentialities Presented at 6th Conference on Thermo-photovoltaic Generation of Electricity, Freiburg, June 2004.

31   Kyoto Semiconductor Corp., Japan, http://www.kyosemi.co.jp

32   Wang, Y., Liu, H., & Zhu, J. (2019). Solar thermophotovoltaics: Progress, challenges, and opportunities, APL Mater. 7, 080906 (2019), https://doi.org/10.1063/1.5114829

33   Taylor, C., et al. (2001). Concentrating Solar Power in 2001, SolarPaces Corp.

34   Brutting, W. (2005). *Physics of Organic Semiconductors*, Wiley-VCH, Weinheim.

35   Schlaich, J., et. al. (2005). Design of Commercial Solar Updraft Tower Systems—Utilization of Solar Induced Convective Flows for Power Generation. *Journal Of Solar Energy Engineering, 127*(1), 117-124. doi: 10.1115/1.1823493

36   Schlaich, J. (1995). *The Solar Chimney: Electricity from the Sun*, C. Maurer, Geislingen, Germany.

37   von Backstro¨m, T., and Gannon, A. (2000). Compressible Flow Through Solar Power Plant Chimneys. *Journal Of Solar Energy Engineering, 122*(3), pp. 138-145. doi: 10.1115/1.1313528

38   Boyce, F. (1980). On the possibilities of thermal energy conversion in lakes, *Atmosphere-Ocean, 18*(3), pp. 195-206. doi: 10.1080/07055900.1980.9649087

39   Golding, P., Sandoval, J., and York, T., editors (1993). *Proceedings of the 3rd International Conference: Progress in Solar Ponds*, May 23-27, p. 379.

ⓐ Exercises

I. Discussion Questions

1. What information is needed to locate the position of the sun from a point in space? From a point on the surface of the earth?
2. What is the best orientation for a solar collector assembly installed on a house on the equator? In the north pole?
3. What is a sun? How much is it, and what does it represent?
4. What is the difference between beam, diffuse, and re-radiated radiations?
5. What is the difference between passive and active solar cooling? Give examples of each.
6. Explain how a solar chimney works? What is the status of each technology?
7. Explain the operation of a solar power satellite. What is its status?
8. Explain how does a solar pond work? What is the status of each technology?
9. What is a reflective and a refractive optical system? What are the advantages and disadvantages of each system?
10. How does a qanat work? What kind of environments are best served by qanats?

II. Problems

1. Find the solar insolation data for your hometown. Determine the minimum solar collector area that is needed to meet the hot water heating requirement of 80 MJ year-round. Make calculations for three scenarios:
   a. The solar collector is placed flat on a roof.
   b. The solar collector is mounted on a base with a tilt angle equal to the latitude of your city.
   c. The solar collector is mounted on a 2-tracking system.
2. What is the average solar power available in the Mojave Desert in California? Assuming electricity costs of 8 cents per kilowatt-hour, what are the savings in annual electricity bills for every square meter of an installed solar panel, with an efficiency of 10%, oriented toward the Sun? Use Figure 10-6 to estimate average solar insolation for various geographical areas around the globe.
3. A designer proposes to use a circular reflector (a section of a long cylinder), instead of a parabolic reflector to heat water to produce steam to generate electricity. Assuming both have the same aperture diameter, which one would provide a larger concentration ratio? Draw a diagram comparing the way light rays are concentrated. Comment on the merit of this design.
4. A solar utility company decides to change its array of parabolic concentrators to parabolic dishes. What improvement in efficiency should the company expect to achieve? The maximum temperatures achieved by the trough and dish are 300°C and 1000°C.
5. The 392 MW Ivanpah Solar Generating System delivers electricity with a capacity factor of 31.4 percent and a remarkably intense electrical output of 2,717 kWh/m²/y. Calculate the plant's footprint and compare it with the data presented in this chapter.

III. Multiple Choice Questions

1. The sun core is a sphere consisting mainly of
   a. A mixture of molten liquid and hot gases.
   b. A mixture of hydrogen and helium gases.
   c. A mixture of hot helium and hydrogen gases.
   d. A mixture of noxious ammonia and sulfur gases.
   e. The same material that makes the core of planet earth.
2. Energy generation in the sun results from
   a. Gravitational contraction.
   b. Fission of uranium.
   c. Fission of hydrogen.
   d. Fusion of hydrogen.
   e. The sun has stopped generating energy; it is just cooling now.
3. Seasons are primarily a result of
   a. The rotation of the earth.
   b. The rotation of the sun.
   c. Varying distances of earth from the sun.
   d. The tilt of the earth's axis.
   e. The orbiting of the earth around the sun.
4. Which of the following is not a form of solar energy?
   a. Biomass
   b. Wind
   c. Wave
   d. Hydropower
   e. Geothermal
5. The angular location of a point on earth relative to the equator is called the
   a. Latitude.
   b. Altitude.

  c. Zenith.

  d. Meridian.

  e. Azimuth.

6. The angle between a north-south line on the earth's surface and the horizontal projection of the sun's rays is

  a. Latitude.

  b. Altitude.

  c. Zenith.

  d. Meridian.

  e. Azimuth.

7. The sun's location relative to an observer on the ground can be determined by its

  a. Azimuth and altitude.

  b. Latitude and altitude.

  c. Azimuth and latitude.

  d. Latitude and longitude.

  e. All four angles.

8. Albedo is

  a. The fraction of incident light that is absorbed by the earth.

  b. The fraction of incident light that is reflected by the earth.

  c. The fraction of incident light that is transmitted through the atmosphere and reaches earth.

  d. An organism exhibiting deficient pigmentation.

  e. Unnaturally strong sexual drive in humans.

9. The average solar power incident on the earth's surface is about

  a. 1,368 W/m^2

  b. 1,000 W/m^2

  c. 340 W/m^2

  d. 270 W/m^2

  e. Depends on the location and time of the year

10. Insolation refers to

  a. A layer of material added to reduce heat losses from a building.

  b. Another name for solar constant.

  c. Radiation flux leaving a surface.

  d. The amount of incoming radiation.

  e. No such words, a spelling error.

11. Solar insolation at a point on the earth depends strongly on

  a. The day of the month, the time of the day, and the weather.

  b. The topography of the area and the amount of shade.

  c. The albedo of the earth.

  d. The type of clothing we wear.

  e. All of the above.

12. During the winter in the Northern Hemisphere, the "land of the midnight sun" would be found

  a. At high latitudes, north of the Arctic Circle.

  b. At middle latitudes.

  c. Near the equator.

  d. In the desert southwest.

  e. Only at the North Pole.

13. Where are the days and nights of equal length all year long?

  a. At 66.5° latitude.

  b. At 23.5° latitude.

  c. At the equator.

  d. At the poles.

  e. Nowhere.

14. When it is January and winter in the Northern Hemisphere, it is _____ and _____ in the Southern Hemisphere

  a. January, summer

  b. January, winter

  c. July, winter.

  d. July, summer.

  e. Cannot tell.

15. The best orientation for installing fixed-flat plate collectors is

  a. Parallel to the ground surface, because maximum radiation occurs when the Sun is directly overhead.

  b. Tilted at an angle roughly equal to the latitude of the location where they are going to be installed.

  c. Tilted at an angle roughly equal to the complement of the latitude of the location where they are going to be installed.

  d. Perpendicular to the ground surface to occupy the least space.

  e. It does not make any difference, because the Sun is traveling across the sky.

16. Flat-plate collectors

  a. Are large flat arrays of photovoltaic cells.

  b. Work by using sunlight to electrolyze water to its components hydrogen and oxygen.

  c. Are faced toward the wind to catch the most wind.

  d. Are useful for heating domestic water heating systems.

  e. None of the above.

17. A liquid flat plate collector is usually held tilted in a fixed position, facing _____ if located in the

Southern Hemisphere.
a. North
b. South
c. East
d. West
e. Cannot tell

18. An overhang on a southern-facing window is useful because
a. It blocks the mid-day summer sun.
b. It prevents rain from hitting the side of the house.
c. It prevents squirrels from looking in.
d. It makes for more space in the ceiling for insulation.
e. It allows rain to drain efficiently.

19. For maximum efficiency, flat-plate solar panels
a. Must be horizontal.
b. Must face south and vertically.
c. Must be painted white.
d. Must face north.
e. Must be perpendicular to the Sun's rays at all times.

20. The best solar system for producing process steam at temperatures of 300°C-400°C is a.
a. Flat-plate collector.
b. Parabolic trough.
c. Parabolic dish.
d. Heliostat with flat mirrors.
e. Photovoltaic.

21. A solar cell converts
a. Thermal energy into electrical energy
b. Light energy into electrical energy
c. Heat energy into light energy
d. Solar energy into heat
e. Electrical energy into light

22. The primary drawback of electricity produced by solar energy is that it is
a. Intermittent.
b. In the wrong frequency.
c. Unpredictable.
d. Dispersed.
e. All of the above.

23. The main advantage of solar cells over other methods of electricity generation is that
a. They are clean sources of energy with no adverse environmental impact.
b. Their power correlates with the utilities' daily load patterns when it is needed most – during daylight hours.

c. Their cost is coming down, making it competitive to the power produced from coal power plants.
d. There are plenty of sunny areas that are suitable for installing solar power plants.
e. All of the above.

24. Which one of the following ways of harnessing solar energy does not involve the movement of thermal energy?
a. Active heating
b. Passive heating
c. Indirect generation of electricity
d. Direct generation of electricity
e. Passive cooling

25. The main attraction of the concentrating photovoltaic system is that
a. It increases efficiency by raising the cell operating temperature.
b. It reduces the amount of semiconductor materials used to manufacture the cells.
c. By allowing radiation to infiltrate deeper and deeper layers.
d. By eliminating the need to track the Sun.
e. All the above.

26. What does the word photovoltaic mean?
a. Sun-powered
b. Light-cells
c. Light-electricity
d. Solar-energy
e. Picture-electricity

27. Who discovered the photovoltaic effect?
a. American physicist Enrico Fermi
b. Italian physicist Alessandro Volta
c. German physicist Heinrich Hertz
d. French physicist Edmond Becquerel
e. American physicist Peter Edward Glaser

28. What are the most common photovoltaic cells used today?
a. Cadmium-Telluride
b. Organic photovoltaics
c. Quantum-dot photovoltaics
d. Crystalline silicon cells
e. Polymer cells

29. One factor responsible for the strength of gravitational attraction between a planet and the sun is the
a. Degree of tilt of the planet's axis
b. Planet's period of rotation
c. Mass of the planet

d. Distance between the planet and the sun

e. Both c and d

30. Which of the following is <u>not</u> deployed in concentrating solar power?

   a. Linear Fresnel lens

   b. Power tower

   c. Parabolic trough

   d. Parabolic dish

   e. Spherical cells

IV. True or False?

1. Since dishes have a smaller aperture than trough reflectors, these systems are best suited for small-scale power production or as a stand-alone unit in remote areas away from power grids.

2. The higher the wavelength of photons, the more energy, and the higher efficiency solar cells will have.

3. Since the output of solar cells is in the form of direct current, they cannot be directly fed into electrical grids.

4. Aphelion (point farthest away from the Sun) occurs on July 4th, which is summer in the northern, and winter in the Northern Hemisphere.

5. At the equator, days and nights are approximately 12 hours every day of the year.

6. During summer and winter solstices, days and nights are of equal length.

7. Solar sails are designed to take advantage of solar energy to increase the speeds of sailboats.

8. Photons, like material particles of fluids, exert pressure on a surface they impinge.

9. Solar ponds exploit the salinity gradient of a shallow pond of water to drive a heat engine.

10. The efficiency of photovoltaics is limited by the Carnot efficiency.

V. Fill in the Blanks

1. The angular distance measured east or west from the Prime Meridian is called the _____ .

2. _____ are thick south-facing walls designed to absorb and hold sunlight during day, and release it during the night.

3. An effective passive method of cooling a room against intense summer heat is by using an _____ .

4. _____ heat is the quantity of heat absorbed or released by a substance changing of state at a constant temperature.

5. Removing heat from a surface by spraying it with cold water is called _____ cooling.

6. One square meter of a solar panel facing the sun in the space receives about _____ kilowatts.

7. The electricity produced by the solar power satellites is beamed in form of _____ energy toward receivers on earth.

8. Solar thermal plants can reach efficiencies of up to _____ percent, far exceeding _____ common in photovoltaics.

9. Two types of concentrated photovoltaics are _____ and _____ .

10. To improve efficiencies, several layers of thin light-absorbing materials are sandwiched together in a _____ configuration.

PROJECT I - Solar Photovoltaics for Homes

You are asked to evaluate the economics and the environmental merits of building a solar electric system for your home, instead of buying electricity from your local utility. Obtain a copy of your electric bill (desirably for a peak month) and note the following:

1. The monthly electric bill ($).

2. The total electric consumption for the month (kWh). Calculate:

   a. The average cost of unit electricity ($/kWh).

   b. Average power (kW).

   c. Average solar insolation for your area. Insolation maps and tables are generated from historical data and are readily available for many cities. U.S. data can be found from the National Renewable Energy Laboratory website at *http://rredc.nrel. gov/solar/pubs/redbook*.

   d. Pick a commercial manufacturer and determine the cost, peak and average power delivered, and efficiency. How many solar cells do you need? What is the cost?

   e. Peak power available from your solar system.

   f. Estimate the total cost by adding the cost of the cell, the inverter, and other control devices you may need. Add 50% for the cost of installation

   g. What is the payback period?

   h. Assuming utility company uses natural gas to produce electricity, how much less carbon dioxide are you producing annually (tons/year) when you choose the solar option?

Hint: Recall that efficiency is the ratio of work delivered per heat input, and that conservation of energy requires that the part of energy not converted to work must be disposed into the atmospheric sink.

PROJECT II - Passive and Active Solar Heating

A homeowner residing in Long Beach, CA (or the city of your residence) is exploring the feasibility of replacing her existing gas-fired air and water heating unit with a solar system. According to her calculations, the solar system must provide about 600,000 Btu during winter days for space heating, and an additional 200,000 Btu if she is to replace her water heater. She is considering fitting her south-facing walls with large glass windows. For her water heating application, she is planning to install a flat-plate collector placed on her roof. Evaluate whether such a system can supply her energy needs.

The house has a 50'x50' footprint, with 500 square feet of a south-facing wall. Consider two conditions: a) a flat roof, and b) a slanted roof, with half the roof surface is tilted toward the south at an angle equal to the latitude.

PROJECT III - U.S. Solar Potential

How much land is needed to satisfy all the energy needs of the United States? To answer this question, you need to estimate the following set of data:

a. Annual energy consumption (can be found in Department of Energy, Energy Information Agency (http://eia.doe.gov).

b. The average daily solar insolation across the continent of the U.S. Use solar maps provided by the National Renewable Energy Laboratory (http://www.nrel.gov/gis/solar.html).

c. The area of the U.S. (9.4 million square kilometers)

d. U.S. population (consult U.S. census for the latest update)

You are to answer the following questions:

1. What percentage of the U.S. land area is needed to satisfy all its energy needs, if solar cells with 15% efficiency are used? How much land area per person?

2. How would this number change if solar cells are placed in the California Mojave Desert? In the state of your residence?

3. Comment on the total cost of power production using solar photovoltaics. How does it compare to the cost of the imported oil? Use the OPEC website for the latest price per barrel of oil (http://www.opec.org).

CHAPTER 11

Bioenergy

The Earth laughs in flowers. ~ Ralph Waldo Emerson (1803-1882)

The lifetime of a carbohydrate molecule, starts with its "birth," energized by sunlight, and ends with its "death" by bacterial composition or fire; its lifetime maybe a few seconds or millions of years. ~ E. C. Pielou (1924-2016)

Bioenergy or biomass energy refers to the energy of all products derived from living organisms, including plants, animals, and microorganisms. Just like fossil fuels, biomass is formed by the sun, which through photosynthesis, converts carbon dioxide and water into organic matter. However, unlike fossil fuels that take millions of years to form, biomass can be produced in a short time. Sources of biomass are crops (sugarcane, maize, and soybeans), agricultural residues (husks, fibers, straws, and shells), forestry crops (trees and woods), forestry residues (sawdust, bark, and wood chips), animal waste (manure from pigs, chicken, and cattle), industrial waste (fruit peelings and pulp), and municipal solid waste (household trash).

Earlier engines by Henry Ford used ethanol instead of gasoline in his Model-T cars; Rudolf Diesel used peanut oil to propel his first engine. Today, millions of cars run on bioethanol and biodiesel either in pure form or blended with gasoline and diesel fuels. The main factors that determine the viability of a particular form of biomass as a fuel source are the type and annual yield of the plant, conversion efficiency, production cost, and environmental impact. As for the U.S., about 4% of energy demand is supplied by biomass, mostly for residential heating and cooking in the form of firewood, but also indirectly as feedstock for the production of liquid and gaseous biofuels. However, if the energy contained in food is included, biomass provides about 15% of all the energy consumed, making it our fourth largest energy resource after oil, coal, and natural gas. It is estimated that the U.S. has the necessary agricultural and forestry resources, which by 2030, could produce 60 billion gallons of ethanol per year, displacing about 30% of current domestic gasoline consumption. Biomass resources can be classified as primary, secondary, or tertiary.

Primary biomass is produced directly by photosynthesis and taken directly from the surrounding environment, in a wide variety of forms from giant sequoia trees to single-cell water plants (microalgae). *Secondary biomass* results from the processing of primary biomass by physical means (e.g., sawdust in mills), by chemical means (e.g., black liquor from pulping processes), or by biological means (e.g., manure production by animals). *Tertiary biomass* includes post-consumption residue streams, such as animal fats and greases, used vegetable oils, packaging wastes, and organic construction and demolition debris.

Biomass can be burned directly or converted into liquid fuels such as ethanol, methanol, biodiesel, and vegetable oil, and gaseous fuels like biogas, producer gas, and synthetic gas. Its use in the production of biofuel is, however, highly controversial and could be either a sensible way to establish energy security and to combat global warming, or compete with other natural resources such as water and land. Assessing its potential as a climate solution requires a look at its lifecycle carbon emissions —which vary according to the type of feedstock, how it is developed and harvested, the scale at which it is used, and the technology used to convert biomass into electricity.

Although bioenergy is renewable, it is not clean, and when burned, like other conventional fuels, it pollutes. The emissions are lower, however, and the carbon dioxide produced from the combustion of biomass offsets that used up during its formation, maintaining zero net production of this greenhouse gas.

Photosynthesis

When the earth was formed about five billion years ago, it was nothing more than a collection of extremely hot cosmic dust, with no atmosphere. With time, these particles were lumped together by the force of gravity, forming an early atmosphere of mostly hydrogen and helium. This was followed by volcanic eruptions and collisions with other bodies, mainly meteorites, that brought water, nitrogen, methane, sulfur, and a few other gases present in today's atmosphere. No free oxygen was yet present. As the earth cooled and the crust was formed, water vapor turned into liquid, filling up the oceans. Small amounts of oxygen gas appeared only after the sun's ultraviolet radiation broke up the water molecules. The condition was now just right for carbon dioxide and water to react through the process called photosynthesis, making simple organic compounds. As byproducts, more oxygen and ozone were formed. As the atmosphere thickened, dinosaurs, birds, more complex animals, and eventually, the primary form of a man appeared.

Photosynthesis (*photo* = light; *synthesis* = build) is the crucial link between the sun and the chemical energy stored in all living organisms. It involves the removal of carbon dioxide from the atmosphere by plants and its combination with water and other nutrients, in the presence of sunlight, to form carbohydrates (CH_2O). Carbohydrates are molecules that contain carbon (*carbo-*), hydrogen (*hydr-*), and oxygen (*ate*). Oxygen is released into the atmosphere, in process. The overall reaction can be written as:

$$6\,CO_2 + 6\,H_2O \xrightarrow{\text{light}} C_6H_{12}O_6 + 6\,O_2$$

carbon dioxide + water + sunlight $\rightarrow$ glucose + oxygen

In these reactions, two important tasks are accomplished. First, carbon is "fixed," that is, converted from its inorganic form (carbon dioxide) to its organic form (carbohydrates). Second, the sun's dispersed light energy is transformed into concentrated chemical energy. Once glucose is formed, it can be converted to sucrose (table sugar), oils, fats, starch, or combined with other nutrients such as nitrogen, phosphorus, and sulfur to create more complex molecules such as proteins (meat, eggs, and milk). In the reverse reaction, called respiration, carbohydrates, and oxygen are converted to carbon dioxide and water, releasing a large amount of energy in the process (Figure 11-1). Unlike photosynthesis, which relies on sunlight to occur, respiration occurs continuously, regardless of the presence or absence of light.

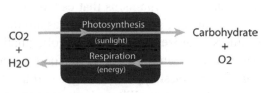

Figure 11-1
Photosynthesis and respiration. Carbon dioxide and water, through the process of photosynthesis, are turned into organic carbon. During respiration, the reverse happens and plants' and animals' organic carbon is broken down into carbon dioxide and water.

For photosynthesis to occur, light must be of the right frequency. To capture light, plants have special pigments, called chlorophyll, that absorb only the red and blue portions of sunlight, reflecting the green, giving leaves their natural green color. Lower-frequency light does not have sufficient energy, so plants do not absorb it. Higher-frequency light is too strong and the excess energy is wasted. The result is that photosynthetic efficiency is at a maximum for the red light, drops abruptly to zero for the light of lower energy infrared, but slowly for higher energy blue and green. The net effect is that only about one-third of the solar energy absorbed by plants participates in photosynthesis. The overall efficiency, defined as the ratio of energy absorbed in the produced biomass to the total solar energy arriving at the leaf, is about 6.7%. This maximum efficiency corresponds to C_4 plants (mainly corn and sugar cane) -- named so because their primary products contain four carbon atoms. C_3 plants, with their primary products containing three carbon atoms (such as wheat, rice, and other grains), are even less efficient, at around 3%. In addition to chlorophyll, plants have two other pigments to trap light in regions that chlorophyll misses. *Carotenes* absorb blue and blue-green light and *anthocyanins* absorb green and yellow light and are responsible for the leaves' yellow, orange, brown, or red colors common during the fall season.[*]

Photosynthesis can be aerobic or anaerobic. **Aerobic** photosynthesis occurs in plants, and algae[†], in which carbon dioxide and water react catalytically, releasing oxygen as a waste product. In **anaerobic** photosynthesis, certain bacteria use light energy to create organic compounds without producing oxygen. These bacteria have photosynthetic pigments that are similar to the chlorophyll used by higher plants. Anaerobic fermentation occurs naturally in marine sediments, marshes, gastrointestinal tracts, and geothermal habitats.

Photosynthesis in water: Photosynthesis is not responsible for the production of food on land only, but also for manufacturing microscopic, single-celled plants called *phytoplankton* in the oceans. All forms of marine life except for hydrothermal vent organisms (See Box "Living Without Sunlight") -- depend on phytoplankton for energy and minerals. The rate of photosynthesis is the highest -- not at the surface, but at a depth of about 10-20 meters, where

---

[*] Sunlight not only provides the energy for photosynthesis, but also causes chlorophyll to break down. In fact, plants continuously have to work to produce new chlorophyll to replace that which was destroyed. In autumn, in preparation for winter, trees absorb as much nutrients as they can before their leaves fall. As chlorophyll disappears, another pigment called carotene, which holds up better in sunlight, remains. Since carotene absorbs blue and blue-green, the leaves appear yellow.

[†] Coming from *Alga*, meaning seaweed in Latin.

light intensity is not too high. As we go deeper, the rate of photosynthesis slows and eventually stops.

Food Chain and Food Web

A **food chain** is a path through which animals find their food. The simple food chain starts from plants **(producers)** and passes on to other animals **(consumers)** through three or more nutritional stages called *trophic levels.* At the base of the food pyramid are autotrophs, which are responsible for primary food production. *Autotrophs* (self-feeders) are those organisms, such as green plants, algae, and certain bacteria, that are able to produce organic molecules from inorganic raw material, mostly by photosynthesis.[‡] Trees and most other plants are autotrophs. *Heterotrophs* (other-feeders) are those organisms that cannot produce their own food, but rather feed on other organisms. All animals, including humans, are heterotrophs, as are many microscopic organisms. Heterotrophs can be divided into primary consumers or grazers *(herbivores)*, colloquially referred to as vegetarians, and secondary consumers or meat-eaters *(carnivores)*. A simple three-level food chain is grass → sheep → wolf. Weed → mouse → snake → hawk and grass → grasshopper → frog → trout → man, are examples of four- and five-level food chains. *Omnivores* (meaning " devouring all") eat both plants and other animals as their primary food source. Humans, most bears, pigs, and ravens are omnivores.

Things are not always that simple in nature since there are multiple types of prey for a single predator. Each step in the food chain can be linked with many other food chains, making a complex set of feeding relationships that is more accurately called the **food web**. Food webs show how plants and animals are interconnected by different paths and provide mechanisms that collectively help animals to survive. If a part of this web is broken, the entire population of species is being affected.

In addition to herbivores, carnivores, and omnivores, there is another group of animals or insects called detritivores. *Detritivores* obtain nutrients by consuming detritus. As animals and plants die, some are consumed by other animals, or burned in forest fires. The rest, called detritus, are partially decomposed by bacteria and mold and used as a source of energy. Eventually, all end up as fossil fuels. Common detritivores are beetles that feed on wood, maggots that feed on rotten meat, aquatic insects that feed on leaves at the bottom of still water, and clams that feed on suspended particles in saltwater. Other common detritivores are earthworms, slugs, and sea stars.

Energy Flow Through the Biosphere

As was discussed previously, photosynthesis is not only responsible for providing energy for a plant's own growth, but also must provide food for other consumers, as it is passed from one trophic level to the next. The **photosynthetic capacity**, i.e., the rate at which a plant fixes solar energy, varies with temperature, rainfall, and the biochemistry of

---

Living Without Sunlight

Until only a few decades ago, biologists thought that organisms in the deep ocean lived only on the debris of marine plants and dead animals falling from the surface to the bottom. Because of the high concentration of deep-sea plants near hydrothermal (volcanic) vents, it is presumed that another mechanism called **chemosynthesis** is differentiated from photosynthesis in that they can occur in the dark and during nights, and get the chemical energy necessary for growth and reproduction directly from inorganic molecules – mainly oxides of sulfur, nitrogen, or iron.[i] According to this hypothesis, these organisms utilize chemicals to metabolize carbon dioxide from air and carbonate in the water to form carbohydrates. Examples of vent animals include snails, crabs, limpets, mussels, and tubeworms. Although chemosynthesis is not an important source of energy on earth, it may be the primary source in other planets not being constantly showered by their sun.

[i] *Little, C. S., and Vrijenhoek, R. C. (2003). Are hydrothermal vent animals living fossils? TRENDS in Ecology and Evolution, V. 18, No. 11, November 2003.*

---

‡ The study of algae growth in the euphotic zone shows that maximum photosynthetic activity occurs at a depth of only 10-20 m beneath the surface of water. Warmer surface temperatures limit the amount of carbon dioxide that can be dissolved. Below this point, photosynthesis becomes light-limited, and so, decreases with depth.

the plant. The rate of **gross primary production** (GPP) is, therefore, dependent not only on the amount of sunlight and the nutrient supply but also on geography. Overall, it is estimated that a mere 1% of incident solar energy is responsible for the production of all plants estimated at around 243 billion tons of dry mass per year. A small portion of this energy is used for a plant's own respiration and growth. The rest, referred to as the **net production,** is the total available energy in the ecosystem in the form of dry biomass to be used by consumers and decomposers. Additional losses cause efficiency to drop at each level of consumption, beginning with plants, only 10% of the energy is converted from one trophic level to the next (See Box "Rule of 10"). For example,

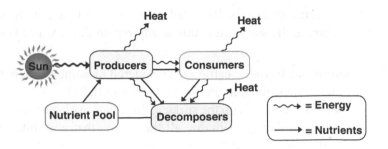

Figure 11-2
The flow of nutrients and energy through biological systems. Note that while nutrients are recycled over and over again, the sun must continuously supply energy.

Adapted from Masters, G. M., (1974). Introduction to Environmental Science and Technology, John Wiley & Sons.

only 10% of the energy contained in plants is used to warm a herbivore and make it grow. Similarly, our bodies use only 10% of the energy we take in as food (plants or meat) to keep us warm and for various other bodily functions. The rest is excreted as waste.

It should be noted that although nutrients continuously undergo cyclic processes, energy does not. As it was explained in Chapter 4, living organisms are heat engines, taking energy as fuel to help their movement and growth. In the

---

Rule of Ten

Humans extract about 95 % of the potential (chemical) energy available in food, but convert only about 10% of this energy into useful work, such as lifting weights and building muscle tissue. The rest is turned into heat and dispersed into the environment. Every time an organism eats another, some of the energy stored in the prey is released to the predator. Each of these storage steps along a food chain is called a **trophic level**. Estimates of energy loss between trophic levels vary widely, but on average, only about 10% of the energy fixed (captured and stored) by plants is ultimately stored by herbivores. Only about 10% of the energy that herbivores accumulate ends up being stored in the living tissues of the carnivores that eat them, and only 10% of that energy is successfully converted into living tissue by carnivores on the third trophic level. In other words, at every step of the food chain, only 10% of the energy devoured by the prey remains in the body of the predator.[i] This pattern of energy loss is known as the **Ecological Rule of 10**.

Inefficient energy chains create the so-called ecological pyramid, in which each trophic level contains only one-tenth as much living tissue as the level beneath it. For instance, consider a person who decides to eat only red meat to gain one pound in weight. That person must then eat 10 pounds of beef. The cattle that produced the 10 pounds of flesh must have originally eaten about 100 pounds of fodder. That's why it makes good ecological sense that larger animals, such as elephants, are vegetarians. By feeding at, or near, the base of the ecological pyramid, larger animals make much more efficient use of energy, and the given ecosystem can support many more of them.

Of course, the ultimate source of energy on earth is the sun. Through photosynthesis, plants use most of the energy they get from sunlight to grow roots, pump water, and so on. As a result, they convert only about 1% of the sun's energy into chemical energy, which is then stored in their molecules. Evidently, this is enough to provide for the whole planet and even keeps gardeners busy.

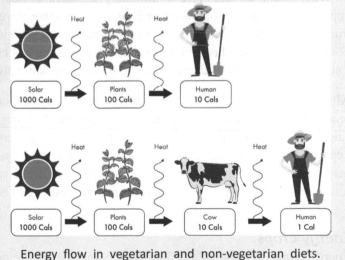

Energy flow in vegetarian and non-vegetarian diets.
Adapted from http://Humboldt.earthsave.org.

[i] *Miller, G. Tyler, (1971). Energetics, Kinetics, and Life: An Ecological Approach, Wadsworth Pub. Co., Belmont, CA, , pp.233.*

process, some energy is discarded as waste heat that cannot be restored to help the growth process. To keep the system going, the sun must continuously replenish the wasted energy (See Figure 11-2).

Question: In India, cattle are considered by some as sacred and cannot be slaughtered for food. How does this practice contribute to the food shortage in India?

Answer: Although on the surface, this practice may appear unjustifiable, it actually is an effective way to combat hunger. In fact, considering all the energy that goes into food production, affluent diets enriched with animal fat, meat, dairy, and eggs use up as much as three times more biomass than vegetarian diets. Domestication of animals and livestock such as cows, sheep, goats, pigs, horses, and camels was a major factor that led to the development of ancient societies. Not only did they provide food for their habitats, but also fertilizer and plowing power needed to grow various plants. In fact, these mammals yielded several times more energy over their lifetimes than if they were slaughtered and consumed as meat. Raising livestock for meat is a very inefficient way of producing food. For example, it takes far more resources (fuel, water, etc.) to produce a kilogram of meat than a kilogram of corn. Adding all the energy used for transportation, feedlots, and storage, it takes the equivalent of one gallon of gasoline to produce one pound of grain-fed beef. In general, depending on whether the principal goal is for producing food or fuel, crops are divided into food crops and energy crops. The distinction is not clear; however, as many times, one kind of crop is used for the application mainly intended for the other.

Food Crops

Food crops are crops that are grown for consumption. There is a wide variety of food crops, although only a relatively small number of crops, rice, wheat, and corn (maize) supply the great bulk of world's food, covering about 60 percent of the harvested land of the world. Depending on the region, staple foods may also include sorghum, olive oil, coconut oil, and sugar.

The rate of food production varies widely among developed and developing countries. Modern agricultural machinery, better fertilizers, and more complex irrigation techniques have allowed developed countries to produce food at a rate exceeding the rate of their population increase. Unfortunately, the same cannot be said for developing and underdeveloped countries. In these countries, although yearly food production has remained relatively constant, their populations have been steadily increasing. As a result, the amount of food per capita has been decreasing dramatically, and many countries have faced severe food shortages and even famine. Furthermore, the food surplus in richer countries that were traditionally exported to poorer countries is now used, either to feed the increasing appetites of the local population or is exported to other developed countries. To make the matter worse, at the same time, much of the high-quality food produced in less-developed countries is being exported to industrial countries. For example, for the last few years, the United States has been the world's largest importer of beef and fish, while Latin America has been the major exporter of these same products.

Although technology has helped to increase the volume of food, replacing traditional, pre-industrial, non-mechanized practices with modern agricultural techniques and farming practices has demanded higher energy input for every calorie of food grown. Furthermore, much of the commercial production and delivery of our food, at all stages, depends heavily on oil as the primary source of energy. Fossil fuel is essential in cultivating the land, planting seeds, manufacturing fertilizers and pesticides, irrigating, and harvesting, processing, packaging, and distribution. As a result, only 1 in every 7 to 11 calories of energy expended is available through food.

Energy Crops

Energy crops (also called agrofuels) are plants that are being cultivated specifically to be used later as fuel. Energy crops are those burned directly for heating or to produce high-pressure steam or used as transportation fuel. Examples are wood logs, short rotation crops, and waste from forests, yards, or farms. In the liquid form, biomass plays an important role as a transportation fuel.

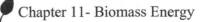

Municipal Solid Waste (MSW)

Municipal solid waste (trash) consists of everyday items such as product packaging, paint, yard waste, newspaper, rubber, leather, textiles, bottles, cans, and many other household items. Not included are construction and demolition materials, municipal wastewater treatment sludges, and non-hazardous industrial wastes. In 2013, the U.S. produced 254 million tons of waste, divided among residential, commercial, and construction sectors. This represented a 2.8-fold increase since 1960, equivalent to 2.25 kg per person, per day. Of all the garbage collected, roughly 60% is biodegradable (biogenic) and can be considered biomass (Figure 11-3). Over 54% of this is buried in landfills, about 12% is incinerated, and the rest is recycled, composted, or reused. Compare this with Denmark where 69% of the waste is recycled, 24% is sent to waste-to-energy plants, and only 7% is landfilled. Serious efforts must be taken to decrease the volume of the waste and to dispose of it more efficiently with minimal environmental impacts. This can be accomplished through the reuse of products, recycling, composting of food and yard trimmings, and more efficient combustion. Of interest to this discussion is how biomass can be used in providing heat and produce electric power.

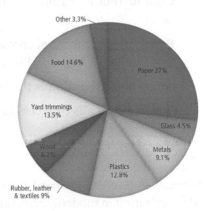

Figure 11-3
Composition of municipal solid waste in the U.S. by type, 2015. RLT refers to rubber, leather, and textiles.

Power Generation by Biomass

Biomass is not only the source of our food, but also plays an important role in meeting our energy needs; it can be burned directly, incinerated in specially designed furnaces, or converted by thermochemical and biological methods to gaseous and liquid fuels, before being burned as a source of heat. Depending on the source, when burned, biomass can produce between 15-25 MJ/kg, compared to 20-30 MJ/kg for coal, and 55 MJ/kg for methane. The calorific values for several biomass fuels are given in Table 11-1.

The United States has the potential to grow a wide variety of plants that can be used to satisfy its demand for food, but also as fuel for transportation, and electrical and heating needs. Some of the leading candidates that could be grown on these lands specifically for biofuel production are hybrid poplar, eucalyptus, loblolly pine, willow, and silver maple.

In 2005, a joint study by the U.S. Departments of Agriculture and Energy concluded that the available land resources of the U.S. are sufficient to produce enough fuel to displace 30% or more of the country's petroleum consumption. The report was updated in 2011 to consider the environmental impact of biomass and concluded that growing crops for biofuel production is likely to have a significant adverse impact on water resources, and there is a need for the development of traditional and cellulosic crops that required less water and fertilizer and are optimized for fuel production.

To be a good candidate as a biofuel, the organism must have the ability to meet the need of a small community or that of the whole nation *(scalability)* and must have a high growth efficiency. i.e., regenerate in a short time, and at a large amount measured as megatons per acres of cultivated land *(productivity)*. and it must grow in nonarable land, using nonpotable water, so as not to compete with the food and water resources *(sustainability)*.

Depending on the type of biomass, many different technologies are deployed:

Table 11-1 Calorific Values For Several Biomass Fuels	
Source Heating	**Heating Value* (MJ/kg)**
MSW	13.0
Newspaper	19.7
Hardwood	20.4
Grass	18.5
Sugar cane	21.5
Pinewood	21.3
Methanol	20.0
Ethanol	27.0
* Lower heating value	

Combustion is burning the feedstock using excess air or oxygen. The process is highly exothermic (releases heat).

Pyrolysis is the thermal conversion of a feedstock in the absence of any air. The process is endothermic (requires heat) and must be carried in air-tight reaction chambers.

Anaerobic Digestion is the biochemical conversion of a feedstock in the absence of oxygen to generate biogas.

Gasification falls between the two and involves partial oxidation of the organic content in the MSW.

Direct Burning (Incineration)

This is the oldest and the traditional method of burning biomass in furnaces or wood stoves for heating and cooking. Materials used in modern incinerators are scrapped wood and sawdust, solid wastes, garbage, and landfill gases (Figure 11-4). Biomass is first converted into a low- to medium- Btu gas mixture called **producer gas**, which is then burned inside gas turbines. In some instances -- in what is commonly referred to as combined heat and power units (See Chapter 5) -- the exhaust heat from the gas turbine may be used to drive a secondary steam turbine, converting more of the fuel energy into electricity. The waste heat from the secondary plants is hot enough for hot water and space heating, which would otherwise be lost to the atmosphere.

Figure 11-4
Map of potential feedstock for conversion into biofuel that could be grown in different regions of the United States.

Source: DOE Oak Ridge National Laboratory.

Some newer technologies burn these materials at much higher plasma temperatures. *Plasma* is gas heated (usually by passing a strong electric current through it) to temperatures around 10,000°C, causing electrons to be stripped off the atoms. At these temperatures, hydrocarbons, PCBs, and other toxins break down, allowing them to be burned completely. This has the advantage of producing both electricity and heat, and also reducing the volume of trash, toxic metals, detergents, solvents, and other household products released into the atmosphere. The residues are mixed with soil and hardened into inert and harmless rocks suitable for road gravel. Incineration uses 10-15% of all garbage generated in the U.S. but accounts for only a tiny one-tenth of 1% of all electricity supplies.

Another approach that has been tried out with some success is mixing the biomass with coal – a process known as **co-firing**. Up to 20% of the coal used in boilers can be substituted with biomass. Because coal burns at higher temperatures than biomass, *co-fired power plants* operate at higher efficiencies than *direct-fired power plants* using only biomass. Currently, the U.S. has 10 GW of installed biomass electricity generating capacity, 25% of that from MSW, and another 5% from landfill gases. In addition, many utilities using mixtures of switchgrass and coal.

Biomass has the additional advantage that it can be processed and used in small, distributed biofuel refineries, and draw from many varied feedstocks available locally, and at a small fraction of the cost of building large fossil-fuel-based refineries. By utilizing various energy crops, a bio-refinery can optimize output by producing low-value, high-volume liquid transportation fuels, or high-value, low-volume specialty chemicals and, at the same time, producing electricity and processing heat.

Thermochemical Conversion

In thermochemical conversion, dry biomass is decomposed into simpler molecules. The process takes place under high temperatures and pressures and a suitable catalyst, with little or no oxygen. In **pyrolysis**, no oxygen is used and no chemical reactions or combustion is involved; **gasification** involves the addition of some oxygen or air during the process, enough to turn solid biomass into a gaseous fuel. No matter what the process, the final product is a gaseous mixture of carbon monoxide and hydrogen, which can be burned directly for cooking and heating, expanded in gas turbines, or converted to methanol. Methanol is of great interest in reformers, to produce hydrogen for fuel cells, and as an alternative fuel for vehicles. Another byproduct is *biochar,* which has properties similar to coke and may be used for steel production.

Gasification for producing synthetic fuel is not new, having been used extensively for producing liquid fuel from coal during WWII. The process is called Fischer-Tropsch and was discussed in Chapter 6.

Biochemical Conversion

Biochemical conversion is what happens in nature. It is similar to thermochemical conversion, except the process is taking place at much lower temperatures. Here, instead of heat doing the work of decomposition, the decay is done by microorganisms and enzymes that break cellulose and hemicellulose down into sugar and lignin.

Biochemical conversion processes include anaerobic digestion and anaerobic fermentation. In **anaerobic digestion**, the feedstock is cooked in biochemical digesters and exposed to bacteria in an oxygen-free environment to form *biogas* and a nutrient-rich *digestate*. Biogas is a mixture of methane and other synthetic fuels; digestate is the leftover fibrous material composed of lignin and cellulose that is usually used as a fertilizer. The overall reaction is

$$C_6H_{12}O_6 \rightarrow 3\ CH_4 + 3\ CO_2$$

Anaerobic fermentation involves the conversion of sugar to alcohol. The oldest form is the *fermentation* of grapes, corn, and barley by yeast or other microorganisms to produce wine, beer, and other alcoholic beverages. For example, in the production of ethanol from glucose, the chemical reaction is

$$C_6H_{12}O_6 \rightarrow 2\ C_2H_5OH + 2\ CO_2$$

Depending on the fermentation temperature, different products are expected. At temperatures below 200°C, sugar can be fermented into ethanol and other fuels in much the same way that corn or sugarcane is. At medium temperatures of 300-600°C, the product is a biocrude that can be directly refined into gasoline or biodiesel. At very high temperatures over 700°C, products are gaseous hydrocarbons that can be cooled into liquid fuel. Preliminary studies suggest that low-temperature processes are best suited for lighter materials such as grasses. In contrast, higher temperatures work best for harder lignin-type materials, such as wood chips, roots, and tree trunks.

First-generation biofuels refer to the production of bioethanol and biodiesel utilizing traditional technologies for making alcohol and liquors. The choice of fuel for bioethanol is *sugar* or *starchy* crops -- corn starch in the United States and sugarcane in Brazil. The main source of biomass for biodiesel is fats in plants and animals. *Oilseeds* having a high concentration of extractable lipids, ranging from 20% in soybeans to 40-50% or more in sunflower and oil palm, are most favored. Much home-brewed biodiesel use recycled oil and grease from fryers. Algae is still in the developmental stage but has a huge promise. Almost all gasoline sold in the United States contains 10% bioethanol (E10); biodiesel can be used in pure form (B100) or blended with diesel fuel. Blended gasoline is superior to regular gasoline, since the octane number is raised (See Chapter 6), and there is lower carbon dioxide emission. Biodiesel is superior to fossil diesel fuel as it improves piston lubrication reduces friction, and there is little sulfur dioxide emission.

Sugarcane and sweet sorghum stems are easiest to ferment, as they are high in sucrose that readily is convertible to ethanol. Using corn as a feedstock is a bit more difficult, as enzymes must first break down corn starch into glucose before yeast can start the fermentation process. Cold-season starchy cereals such as barley and wheat may also find applications when cultivating other plants is difficult. The main objection to first-generation biofuel production is that these plants have been traditionally used as food, they must be replanted every year, require much more fertilizer and care, and the conversion efficiency is relatively low. As more and more of these grains are diverted from food consumption to biofuels production, their prices increase, making them less attractive as energy crops.

Biodiesel can undergo a chemical process called transesterification to remove water and free the fatty acid. The byproduct of the process is glycerin that is separately sold to make soap and other products. Any oily plant will work. Palm, however, has a much better yield than other oil seeds. The problem is that palm grows only in a narrow region around the tropics, so growing palm trees means more rainforests must be cleared. Like corn, the palm is also considered a food source.

Second-generation biofuels are *cellulosic* biofuels. Cellulosic biomass is derived from non-food sources, such as trees and grasses. The sugar in these feedstocks is locked in cellulose, lignin, and complex starches, and thus, more difficult to extract. These plants are richer in energy and include woody perennial and herbaceous species and forestry and agricultural residues such as wood chips, treetops, and branches, sawdust, wheat, and rice straws, corn stalks and cobs, hay, and dead or dying trees.

The most suitable perennial plants -- poplar, maple, and willow -- grow in cooler and wetter climates; others, like sycamore, sweetgum, and eucalyptus are the best choices for warmer climates with plenty of sunshine. Switchgrass, miscanthus, and jatropha are also among several perennial herbaceous species most favored for their cellulosic biomass production potential. These plants are resistant to floods, droughts, and pests, and grow in almost any climate and any type of soil – even soil with poor nutrients and with little fertilizer. Most fertilizers are synthesized from fossil fuels. Other possibilities are aquatic plants, such as seaweed and algae, that grow naturally in lakes, and also are ideal sinks for carbon dioxide.

Producing ethanol from cellulose is a harder process than producing it from corn and other starchy biomass. Cellulose is made of molecules involving large numbers of carbon and hydrogen atoms. It is much richer in oxygen and must be broken down into simpler molecules consist of only carbon and hydrogen. This step normally requires enzymes or bacteria that ferment sugar into ethanol. Enzymes must endure the harsh environmental conditions necessary for the reactions to take place, and are normally very expensive. Termites and wood-boring beetles have shown promise because their digestive systems contain enzymes that break down woody biomass and allow access to the sugar stored within the cells, converting 95% of what they eat into methane and hydrogen. Because microorganisms found in nature do not survive in this hostile environment, much effort is put into creating "super-bugs" that can thrive under these conditions. The goal of much current research in the field is to find enzymes that break down cellulose cheaper, more efficiently, and at a faster rate. Research is also being conducted to develop genetically modified crops that produce similar enzymes.

According to one estimate, the U.S. can produce enough cellulosic biofuel to substitute half of all the gasoline used. Because they are not food, they do not compete with it, can be grown on marginal lands, and are considered a more sensible approach to the production of biofuels, both from the economic and the environmental points of view.

> **Example 11-1:** American farmlands can produce up to 2,700 kg of soybeans per hectare per year. Estimate the land area needed if the entire U.S. liquid petroleum demand is to be met by soybean ethanol. Assume ethanol has a density of 0.86 kg/L, and 20% conversion efficiency. The U.S. petroleum consumption is estimated at 20 million barrels a day. 1 ha = 10,000 m^2; and 1 bbl = 159.1 L
>
> **Solution:** At 20% conversion, production is 540 kg/ha. At 0.86 kg/L, that translates into 540/0.86 = 628 L/ha or 0.0628 L/m^2. The total land required is (20,000,000 bbl) x (159.1 L/bbl) / 0.0628 (L/m^2) = 5.07×10^{10} m^2 = 5.07×10^4 km^2 (19,600 sq. mi), equal to one-third of the land area of North Dakota, the largest producer of soybeans in the United States.

Ecological Impacts

One of the major attractions of biomass is that it is carbon neutral. The carbon dioxide produced during consumption just balances carbon dioxide removed from the atmosphere during photosynthesis. The choice of biomass depends on whether it is used for electrical production, or producing liquid fuels, and whether it competes for food production. The carbon footprint, calculated using Life Cycle Analysis (LCA)[§], determines the amount of greenhouse gas emissions throughout its life, from planting the seeds, to harvest, to the production of biofuel, to burning in a vehicle or a power plant. Studies abound but the scientific community has largely reached a consensus that starch ethanol (e.g., from corn) may not reduce GHG emissions at all, and may not warrant harvesting corn for the sole purpose of fermenting it into ethanol. By contrast, cellulosic ethanol reduces GHG by 85% over reformulated gasoline.

Fossil Fuel Replacement Ratio

The ratio of the amount of energy produced when biofuel is burned to the amount of fossil energy used to make the biofuel is called the **fossil energy replacement ratio** (FER), and can be used to indicate the relative merits of various biofuels. Corn ethanol contains roughly 1.3-1.7 times the energy of the fossil fuel energy required to produce it; sugarcane is found to yield eight times more energy; for cellulosic ethanol, the ratio is as high as 10 or more. Figure 11-5 shows fossil fuel replacement ratios for several feedstocks. The data confirm that Brazilian sugarcane and cellulosic ethanol could achieve positive energy balances and substantial greenhouse gas offsets, while American and Chinese maize offers modest or no offsets.

Recently, there has been a push to grow genetically engineered microorganisms in transparent bioreactors that use energy from the sun to convert carbon dioxide and water directly into ethanol or other biofuels. The laboratory-scaled plants manufacture biofuel at a cost-competitive to fossil fuel. If scaled to industrial levels, the cost would be much lower.

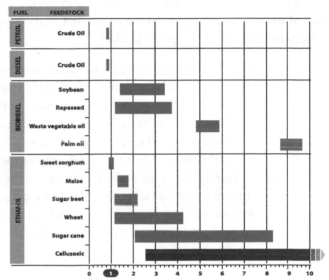

Figure 11-5
Fossil energy replacement ratio for selected biofuels. *[Ref. 24]*

Impact on Energy, Water, and Land

The choice of crops most suitable for efficient production of biofuel depends, to a large degree, on how the plant is grown, how much energy and land it requires, and how big carbon and water footprints are. Sugarbeets and sugarcane have low water and land footprints, soy, and rapeseed have very high footprints, and that of jatropha is medium. Maize's water and land footprints are among the lowest, but it has a low yield (FER) -- a major criticism levied against its use as a biofuel. The overall yield is about 428 gallons of ethanol per acre; that can be translated into roughly 10 MJ of energy delivered for every square meter of land under cultivation.

No detailed studies of algae footprints have been made, but algae may prove to be among the best choices. Algae is easily scalable, and productivity is quite high. It is estimated that algae can produce up to 5,000 gallons per acre per year -- compared to 50, 200, and 600 gal/acre/yr for soy, jatropha, and palm. The results vary widely, however.

Impact on Food Production

It is projected that, by 2030, the world population will reach eight billion, with the majority of growth occurring in the poorer tropical regions where food insecurity is most pronounced. Furthermore, as many developing countries strive for better economic conditions, their incomes, and so, their consumption of dairy and meat products and better

---

§   Also referred to as, "well-to-wheels", or "cradle-to-grave."

nutritious foods, will rise. Thus, world food production must increase by 50% to satisfy these demands. Energy and water demands also will increase accordingly. Any reallocation of agricultural land to biofuel use will necessitate greater food-transport distances, which will incur additional labor and energy costs. Today, every bite of food consumed in the United States travels an average of 1,300 miles; this number exceeds 5,000 in Canada.

Figure 11-6 compares global hectares per ton, as well as the land-use and carbon-footprint intensities for various foods. Meat products and cold cuts (salami and ham) have the highest footprints, so the consumption of these foods has the highest environmental impact. They also require an extensive amount of land and energy in agricultural production. Dairy products, bread, and bakery come next; vegan and vegetarian diets have the lowest.

The degree to which biofuel production impacts the availability of food resources depends on three factors: a) the use of existing arable land; b) the expansion of the agricultural frontier; and c) the use of marginal land that is not otherwise suitable for crop production.

a. *Biofuel cultivation on existing arable land* -- Small farmers may use the land, water, and labor resources by growing both food and biofuel crops with resource demands that peak at different times of the growing season. This increases their cash flow, but also makes them vulnerable to high food-price fluctuations that result from changes in the price of energy. Large-scale production of biofuel, controlled by a few agribusiness giants, also will impact small farmers by limiting their choices in determining the type of crops that they can grow, and the prices they can charge.

b. *Extending the agricultural frontier* -- Forests and savannahs are home to a wide variety of trees and animal inhabitants. As these lands are converted to agricultural lands, there are risks associated with the loss of biodiversity and a net loss to the carbon dioxide sink.

c. *Biofuel cultivation on degraded or arid land* -- Certain crops are suited for growing on degraded lands

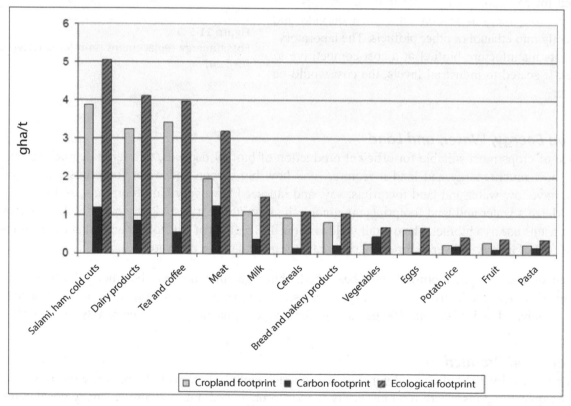

Figure 11-6
Ecological footprints of various food categories.

and require little water, fertilizers, or nutrients, and may have the potential to improve soil properties. Two often-quoted crops are jatropha (which is native to Central America), and pongamia (which is native to India). Other feedstock crops suitable for bioethanol production that can be grown on marginal land include sweet cassavas and sweet potatoes. This approach is probably the least risky and is the method of choice, when possible.

Impact on Food Prices

The link between food and energy is an obvious one. It takes energy to grow food before it is converted back as a source of energy. The vast increase in our food resources, is a result of using modern tractors and other farm machinery, better chemical fertilizers (herbicides, insecticides, and fungicides), and more efficient transportation systems, all directly connected with higher use of energy resources. The link becomes more apparent when corn and other crops are used to produce biofuels, and by noting that the prices of both food and fuel have risen and fallen in tandem in recent years (Figure 11-7).

Soaring food and fuel prices have a disproportionate impact on poorer less-developed countries and could threaten the affordable food supply. The current farming strategies are highly fuel-dependent, focused on large-scale mechanized production and transportation across long distances. Furthermore,

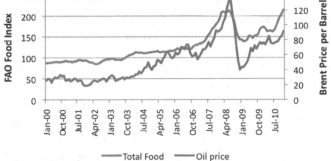

Figure 11-7
Correlation between the world food and sweet light crude (Brent oil) prices.
Sources: US Energy Information Administration and FAO

they encourage the production of often-subsidized cash crops at the expense of staples for local consumption. Poor farmers who cannot afford machinery and pay for the rising fuel costs find themselves at the mercy of industrial food-exporting countries that dump their surplus food onto developing countries. It is, therefore, reasonable to conclude that the agricultural policy must emphasize domestic food production and small farming that relies mostly on the local economy and human labor.

Summary

Biomass is a result of photosynthetic activities in which carbon dioxide and water, in the presence of sunlight, combine to form carbohydrates. The conversion efficiency is rather low, however; only 1% of incoming solar energy is converted to the chemical energy stored in plants; compare this to solar cells, which convert up to 40% of solar energy directly into electricity. Besides, biomass can be processed in small, distributed local biofuel refineries, and at a small fraction of the cost of building large refineries that use fossil fuels. By utilizing various energy crops, a bio-refinery can optimize output and produce low-value, high-volume liquid transportation fuels, or high-value, low-volume specialty chemicals and, at the same time, produce electricity and process heat. It is unlikely that any single species will prove to be the ideal form of biomass, and the choice will vary widely depending on climate, types of soil, the availability of water, and the frequency of harvest. It is expected that even in a single location, the diversity of multiple energy crops planted at different times is necessary to give the maximum yield.

Biomass is considered by many to be a renewable source of energy. Others point out that for biomass to be truly renewable, the rate of cultivation of new trees must be equal to or exceed that of biomass consumption. That is to say, for every tree that is cut and burned, another tree must be replanted somewhere else. Furthermore, even if biomass were entirely renewable, it's not clean. As is the case with fossil fuels, burning biomass creates major air pollutants, such as carbon monoxide and particulates. Also, biomass produces aldehydes, which although not carcinogenic, give off an unpleasant odor at high concentrations. No matter what species is used, there always will be some land diverted from food production. Also, some environmental damage due to water diversion and nutrient runoff is inevitable. Biomass, however, does not contribute to global warming and is relatively low in sulfur, and therefore, contributes little to the acidity of the environment.

Besides pollution, biomass, as a source of energy, has been controversial for other reasons. Harvesting forests for fuelwood and lumber ultimately will lead to deforestation. Crop farms will not be able to produce the same crop for a very long time, as soil erosion and massive use of herbicides and fertilizers will reduce their productivity. Furthermore, these farms are usually built on lands that, otherwise, could produce the food crops necessary to feed the world. Burning trees, dung, and other animal wastes deprives the soil of its essential nutrients, reduces yields, and makes the land less capable of supporting natural vegetation. It is, therefore, important to use only plants that are not suitable for food consumption, and are planted in marginal land unsuitable for food crops.

Trash and municipal solid wastes have become a major problem for many countries. Trash must be stored in landfills, shipped away to areas with lower population densities, or simply burned. Landfills are filling up fast, especially near towns. They are polluters; they may leak hazardous chemicals into the ground and water, and they are breeding grounds for rats, flies, and microbes that cause diseases, rotting food, and may react to produce other unwanted products. Hauling trash is not popular with potential recipients. Incinerators are appealing to some because they reduce trash volume significantly and produce energy at the same time. Incinerators, however, produce deadly smoke and ash, which require expensive scrubbers, filters, and other control equipment. Furthermore, many toxic metals, such as mercury, lead, and cadmium, cannot be effectively removed and will eventually find their way into the ground or are released into the atmosphere. Recycling seems to be a sensible solution to the problems of waste disposal. The problem with this approach is that it encourages waste, which ultimately increases energy use and generates more pollutants. In addition, recycling demands consuming additional energy -- as much as 25% of the energy used in manufacturing the original material. The only solution to our trash problem is to create less trash. Unfortunately, unless the price of fuel rises considerably above the current price or the government subsidizes biofuels, biomass will play a secondary role in meeting our long-term energy demand.

Endnotes

1   EPA website (2010). Monthly Energy Review. U.S. Department of Energy, Washington, D.C., May 2010. http://tonto.eia.doe.gov/FTPROOT/multifuel/mer/00351005.pdf

2   Perlack, R. D. and Stokes, B. J. (2011). *U.S. Billion-Ton Update: Biomass Supply for a Bioenergy and Bioproducts Industry.* Oak Ridge, TN: Oak Ridge National Laboratory.

3   Union of Concerned Scientists, (2015). http://www.ucsusa.org

4   Thorndike, E. (1976). *Energy and Environment* , p.33, Addison-Wesley Publishing.

5   Interaction, in *Encyclopedia of Life Support Systems* (EOLSS) Developed under the Auspices of the UNESCO, EOLSS Publishers, Oxford, UK., http://www.eolss.net

6   Smil, V. (2008). Energy in Nature and Society, p.90. *MIT Press*.

7   Pielou, E. (2001). *The Energy of Nature*, p.132, The University of Chicago.

8   Pidwirny, M. and Jones, S. (2010). *Physical Geography*, University of British Columbia Okanagan, http://www.physical-geography.net

9   Diamond, J. (1999). *Guns, Germs, and Steel: The Fate of Human Societies*, p.88, W. W. Norton and Company.

10 United Nations Food and Agricultural Organization website, http://www.hsus.org/ace/352

11 Green, B. (1978). *Eating Oil – Energy Use in Food Production*, Westview Press, Boulder, Colorado.

12 Günther, F. (2001). Fossil Energy and Food Security. *Energy and Environment, 12*(4), 253-273. doi: 10.1260/0958305011500779

13 U.S. EPA. (2010). Municipal Solid Waste in the United States: 2009 Facts and Figures, (5306P) EPA530-R-10-012 Environmental Protection Agency, Office of Solid Waste. December 2010) REtrieved from http://www.epa.gov/wastes/nonhaz/municipal/pubs/msw2009rpt.pdf

14 U.S. DoE, (2005). Biomass as Feedstock for a Bioenergy and Bioproducts Industry: The Technical Feasibility of a Billion-Ton Annual Supply (2005 BTS), Oakridge National Lab., ORNL/TM-2005/6. http://www1.eere.energy.gov/bioenergy/pdfs/

final_billionton_vision_report2.pdf.

15 U.S. DoE, (2011). *Billion-Ton Update: Biomass Supply for a Bioenergy and Bioproducts Industry*, Oakridge National Lab., DOE/EE-0363, August 2011, Retrieved from http://www1.eere.energy.gov/biomass/pdfs/billion_ton_update.pdf

16 Federal Energy Management Program (2004). Biomass Co-firing in Coal-fired Boilers, DOE/EE-0288, Washington, D. C: U.S. Department of Energy, http://www1.eere.energy.gov/biomass/pdfs/33811.pdf

17 Mayfield, S. (2007). The Next Generation in Biofuels -- A New Approach to the Production of Biofuels, in Biotechnology, [Eds. Horst W. Doelle, Stefan Rokem, Marin Berovic], in *Encyclopedia of Life Support Systems* (EOLSS) Developed under the Auspices of the UNESCO, Eolss Publishers, Oxford, UK, Pierce. http://www.eolss.netHuber, G. & Dale, B. (2009) Grassoline: Biofuel Beyond Corn, Scientific American, July.

18 Huber, G. & Dale, B. (2009). Grassoline: Biofuel Beyond Corn, Scientific American, July.

19 Sun, Y., & Cheng, J. (2002). Hydrolysis of lignocellulosic materials for ethanol production: a review. *Bioresource Technology, 83*(1), 1-11. doi: 10.1016/s0960-8524(01)00212-7

20 Parrish, D. and Fike, J. (2009). Growth and Production of Herbaceous Energy Crops, in Soils, Plant Growth and Crop Production, [Ed. Willy H. Verhey], in *Encyclopedia of Life Support Systems* (EOLSS), Developed under the Auspices of the UNESCO, Eolss Publishers, Oxford, UK, http://www.eolss.net

21 Krupp, F. and Horn, M., (2009). *The Sequel,* p. 95, W. W. Norton.

22 Wald, M. (2007). Is Ethanol for the Long Haul?, *Scientific American*, January 2007.

23 Transportation Briefing, (2009). *MIT Technology Review,* 112(6), 60, December 2009.

24 Tan, Y., and J. S. Amthor, Chapter 12: Bioenergy, Photosynthesis, (2013) http://www.intechopen.com/books/photosynthesis/bioenergy

25 U.S. Department of Agriculture, Retrieved from http://www.ers.usda.gov/statefacts/us.htm

26 Renewable Transport Fuel Obligation (2018). Dept. of Transportation, Gov. UK. https://www.gov.uk/government/collections/renewable-transport-fuels-obligation-rtfo-orders#group_31.

27 Vetöné Mózner, A. & Csutora, M. (2013). Designing lifestyle-specific food policies based on nutritional requirements and ecological footprints. *Sustainability: Science, Practice, & Policy 9*(2) 48-59.

28 Yang, H., Zhou, Y., and Liu, J. (2009). Land and water requirements of biofuel and implications for food supply and the environment in China. Energy Policy, 37(5), 1876-1885. doi: 10.1016/j.enpol.2009.01.035

29 Cortez, L. & Leite, R. (2008). Relation Between Biofuels Versus Fossil Fuels, in Petroleum Engineering - Downstream," [Ed. Pedro de Alcantara Pessoa Filho], in *Encyclopedia of Life Support Systems* (EOLSS) Developed under the Auspices of the UNESCO, EOLSS Publishers, Oxford, UK. http://www.eolss.net

30 Heinberg, R. (2011). How Oil Prices Affect the Price of Food, Post Carbon Institute, Dec. 21. Retrieved from http://oilprice.com/Energy/Oil-Prices/How-Oil-Prices-Affect-The-Price-Of-Food.html

31 Keating, J. (2014). A Revolution Marches on Its Stomach, *Slate,* April 8.

🌱 Exercises

I. Exploring the Internet

1. The research on energy production by biomass is very active and undergoing rapid transformation. Search the Internet to find new advances in various technologies discussed in this chapter. Have we found any new biomass resources that were overlooked in the past? Has there been any increase in the level of biomass consumption? Has there been any major technological or scientific breakthrough that reduces the cost of biofuel production?

2. The difficulty in accessing the sugar contained in woody biomass, coupled with criticism that the use of food crops for biofuel production has a detrimental effect on food supply, has prompted research into biofuels that can be made from cellulosic biomass, such as trees and grasses. Comment on the status of research and the latest progress made in this field.

II. Discussion Questions

1. Describe various methods that biomass can be used to produce useful energy?

2. Why are most plant leaves green? Why do they turn yellow in the fall?

3. What does it mean to "fix" carbon? How is this done through photosynthesis?

4. What is a hydrothermal vent? Why do deep-sea organisms mostly grow near these vents?

5. Describe the processes of aerobic and anaerobic conversion. Give examples of physical activities that involve these conversions.

6. What are the various trophic levels? How does energy transfer from one trophic level to another?

7. What are the differences between incineration, gasification, and pyrolysis? Between thermo-chemical and biochemical conversions? Between the processes of aerobic and anaerobic conversion?

8. Why did the U.S. decide on promoting corn ethanol, instead of sugar ethanol? Why is corn being subsidized? Which approach has a higher conversion efficiency? How does corn price change with the rise in the price of fossil fuels and food? What were the impacts on reducing our dependence on fossil fuels? on the emission of GHGs?

9. Describe the difference between gross and net production. What are the factors that limit production efficiency from one trophic level to the next?

10. Which has a higher metabolic rate, a hummingbird, or a human? How does the size of an animal affect its metabolic rate?

11. Describe what a food chain and a food web are. Give examples of each.

12. Describe different methods of producing liquid fuels from biomass. What is the difference between ethanol and biodiesel?

III. Multiple Choice Questions

1. Biomass
   a. Is a form of solar energy.
   b. Can be used to produce electricity.
   c. Refers principally to plants, food, wood, and animal and human waste.
   d. Use will likely increase because it is an abundant source of energy.
   e. All of the above.

2. Which mechanism fixes carbon in green plants as simple sugars?
   a. Carbonation
   b. Bacteria
   c. Photosynthesis
   d. Hydrolysis
   e. Chlorophyll

3. Biomass energy generally refers to
   a. Wood and agricultural products.
   b. Solid waste.
   c. Landfill gases.
   d. Alcohols.
   e. All of the above.

4. An organism that eats both plant and animal matter is called a
   a. Parasite.
   b. Carnivore.
   c. Herbivore.
   d. Omnivore.
   e. Detrivore.

5. A network of interrelated food sources in a given area is called a
   a. Food web.
   b. Food chain.
   c. Food court.
   d. Network.
   e. None of the above.

6. The process in which food is manufactured in deep-sea hydrothermal ecosystems is called
   a. Chemosynthesis.
   b. Photosynthesis.
   c. Biosynthesis.
   d. Anaerobic metabolism.
   e. Respiration.

7. If 0.1% of solar energy that falls on the earth is captured by plants, and 2% of that energy is involved in photosynthesis, what fraction of sunlight that hits the earth is converted to food?
   a. 0.2
   b. 0.02
   c. 0.002
   d. 0.0002
   e. 0.00002

8. What kind of organisms can produce their own food?
   a. Heterotrophs
   b. Autotrophs
   c. Herbivores
   d. Carnivores
   e. Detritivores

9. The sun is not the source of which of the following?
   a. Biogas
   b. Coal
   c. Wind
   d. Uranium
   e. Hydro

10. Organisms that depend on other organisms for their food are called
    a. Autotrophs.
    b. Herbivores.
    c. Heterotrophs.
    d. Carnivores.
    e. None of the above.

11. If you eat a frog that eats insects which, in turn, eat plants, you would be a
    a. Producer.

b. Primary consumer.
    c. Secondary consumer.
    d. Tertiary consumer.
    e. Trophic consumer.

12. Humans and bears are considered _____; lions and tigers are examples of group of animals referred to as _____.
    a. Herbivore, carnivore.
    b. Carnivore, omnivore.
    c. Omnivore, detritivore.
    d. Omnivore, carnivore.
    e. Omnivore, omnivore,

13. Sawdust from mills and manure production by animals are examples of
    a. Primary biomass.
    b. Second generation biomass.
    c. Third generation biomass.
    d. Detritivores biomass.
    e. Biowaste.

14. Respiration is
    a. An intermediate step in photosynthesis.
    b. Another name for photosynthesis.
    c. The reverse of photosynthesis.
    d. The same as sweating.
    e. Photosynthesis in water.

15. Incineration is
    a. Burning biomass at a very high temperature.
    b. The process of hydrogenation of biomass by adding steam.
    c. Breaking down the biomass matter by using heat in the absence of oxygen.
    d. Thermochemical conversion at room temperature.
    e. Disintegration by microscopic organisms in the absence of oxygen.

16. Incineration
    a. Is becoming the most popular way to produce energy at very low costs.
    b. Is the process of choice for making large volumes of biofuels from the garbage.
    c. Is not clean and may produce harmful byproducts that are highly toxic to humans and animals.
    d. Is best for disposing of metals and plastics.
    e. All of the above.

17. Pyrolysis is
    a. Burning biomass at a very high temperature.

b. The process of hydrogenation of biomass by adding steam.

c. The breaking down of biomass matter by using heat in the absence of oxygen.

d. Thermochemical conversion at room temperature.

e. Disintegration by microscopic organisms in the absence of oxygen.

18. Fermentation of grape into wine is an example of
    a. Anaerobic digestion.
    b. Anaerobic fermentation.
    c. Thermochemical conversion.
    d. Anaerobic photosynthesis.
    e. Aerobic photosynthesis.

19. The rate at which solar energy is fixed by a plant is called
    a. Gross primary production.
    b. Growth capacity.
    c. Net production.
    d. Photosynthetic capacity.
    e. Fixed capacity.

20. The best approach to deal with the huge volume of trash in America is to
    a. Build more landfills.
    b. Burn the trash to produce electricity.
    c. Ferment to produce biofuel.
    d. Produce less trash.
    e. Compact to reduce volume.

21. Which of the following is not considered a biofuel?
    a. Gasohol
    b. Hydrogen
    c. Algae
    d. Biodiesel
    e. Animal dung

22. First-generation biofuels are
    a. Mostly food crops.
    b. Cellulosic biofuels.
    c. Sugar, corn, and starchy materials
    d. Mostly agricultural residues such as wood chips, treetops, and branches.
    e. Could be any of the above.

23. The total energy used to produce a given amount of biomass is called
    a. Photosynthetic efficiency.
    b. Gross primary production.
    c. Net production.

d. Net energy.
e. Solar insolation.

24. Organisms in the ecosystem that are responsible for the recycling of plant and animal wastes are
    a. Decomposers.
    b. Predators.
    c. Preys.
    d. Competitors.
    e. Vultures.

25. Thermal treatment of biomass into a gaseous fuel in the presence of only a limited amount of oxygen is called
    a. Pyrolysis.
    b. Incineration.
    c. Gasification.
    d. Fermentation.
    e. Decomposition.

26. The best approach to reducing waste is
    a. Reducing consumption.
    b. Incineration.
    c. Recycling.
    d. Using disposable material.
    e. All are equally important.

27. In ecosystems, nutrients
    a. Are often wasted at higher trophic levels.
    b. Follow the same cycles as energy.
    c. Are recycled repeatedly and are never used up.
    d. Are used up and must be replenished each year.
    e. Are reduced by a factor of 10 from one trophic level to the next.

28. Wolves eat lambs, whereas lambs feed on grass as their food supply. This is an example of a
    a. Food web
    b. Food chain
    c. Food court
    d. Rule of 10
    e. Trophic

29. Second-generation biofuels refer to
    a. Sugar-containing plants.
    b. Corn starch.
    c. Cellulosic biofuel.
    d. Products of incineration of first-generation biofuel.
    e. Products of fermentation of first-generation biofuel.

30. Based on data presented in Figure 11-5, to produce the same volume of biofuel
    a. Soy and rape seeds require the least amount of fossil fuel.
    b. Soy and rape seeds require the most amount of fossil fuel.
    c. Sugarcane requires the least amount of fossil fuel.
    d. Sugarcane requires the most amount of fossil fuel.
    e. Maize has a higher conversion efficiency than sugarcane.

IV. True or False?

1. Plant material is made up of cellulose, hemicellulose, and lignin.

2. Ethanol is extracted by pressing the seeds of crops such as rape, sunflower, and olives.

3. Roughly two-thirds of garbage from American households are made of biomass.

4. Heterotrophs are organisms that cannot produce their own food but are fed by other organisms.

5. An organism that is fed by a producer is called a secondary consumer.

6. Autotrophs are placed at the base of the food pyramid and are responsible for primary food production.

7. Net productivity is gross productivity minus that which is metabolized by the producer.

8. Biomass is stored chemical energy in plants.

9. Burning biomass in the air at a very high temperature is called incineration.

10. The three different paths to using biomass as fuel are incineration, thermochemical conversion, and biochemical conversion

V. Fill in the Blanks

1. Some living organisms are found to survive without relying on sunlight as the source of their food, through the mechanism of _____.

2. The reverse process of photosynthesis, in which carbohydrates and oxygen react to produce carbon dioxide and water, is called _____.

3. _____ is the process where sugar is converted to alcohol.

4. Thermal conversion of organic material into combustion gas is called _____.

5. Each of the nutritional steps in which energy is passed from one living species to another is called _____ level.

6. Biogas is produced mainly by the process of _____ digestion.

7. Heating at high temperature in absence of oxygen is called _____.

8. The ratio of the amount of energy produced when the biofuel is burned to the amount of energy used to produce the biofuel is called _____ ratio.

9. Compared to protein diets, vegan and vegetarian diets have _____ carbon footprints.

10. There is a high correlation between prices of food and _____.

PROJECT I -- Creationism and Evolution

How the early form of life was formed, has been debated by scientists and theologians for a long time, without reaching a consensus. Scientists strongly favor the theory of evolution as laid out by the noted British biologist, Charles Darwin (1809-1882). Theologians, however, believe that the odds of amino acids combining to form the necessary proteins by undirected means is so minute that the proteins needed for life could never have come into existence by chance, or by any natural processes. In this project, you are asked to research arguments for and against each theory and answer the following questions:
   a. What constitutes life? How can we distinguish living from non-living organisms?
   b. How do different religions (Buddhism, Judaism, Native Americans, Christianity, Islam, etc.) view the origin of life? What are the common beliefs among them? Any discrepancies?
   c. Is there any contradiction between Christianity and the theory of evolution? Name a few.
   d. What are the main features distinguishing evolutionists and creationists regarding the origin of life?
   e. Is there a scientific basis for the creationists' point of view? What are they? Do these

arguments withstand the accepted methods of scientific inquiry?

f. How does the doctrine of "Intelligent Design" differ from traditional creationists?

g. Does science rule out divine intervention?

PROJECT II -- Origin of Life in the Universe

Life, as we know it, is made up of mainly four elements -- oxygen, carbon, hydrogen, and nitrogen. A few other elements, notably calcium, phosphorous, potassium, and sulfur, provide the bulk of nutrients we need to sustain life. Most oxygen is bound to hydrogen to form water, whereas carbon makes up a cellular structure. In this project, you are asked to research the internet to find whether other forms of life can, or cannot, be sustained on earth, or any other place in the universe. In particular, try to answer the following questions:

a. What is unique about carbon that makes it so suitable for forming much of the internal structure of living organisms on earth? (Hint: look at the molecular structure of carbon and how it binds with other molecules).

b. Why do some scientists (and science-fiction writers) propose other forms of life, especially those based on silicon, as a possibility? Why is carbon-based life more prevalent than silicon-based life? What makes silicon less favorable?

c. What other elements have been suggested and why?

d. Why is it highly unlikely to have any other form of life, such as nitrogen-based or iron-based life forms, in the universe?

PROJECT III - Crop Choice

You are being approached by a government official who is considering growing plants to meet a percentage of the electricity and transportation fuel demands by a community. You are to advise on the type of plants that are most suitable for incineration in a local electric generation station, and for producing liquid fuels for use in gasoline and diesel vehicles. What would be your recommendations if the community resides

a. in a region with cold winter and summer months?

b. in a region with cold winters, and hot and humid? summers.

c. in a moderate temperate zone year-round?

d. in a hot desert climate?

e. near a rainforest?

Justify your answers in terms of yields, fossil energy ratio (FER), environmental impact, cost, and availability of land and water.

CHAPTER 12

Wind Energy

The twin mills of Greetsiel, East Frisia, Germany, ~ Wikipedia Commons

*I hear the howl of the wind that brings the long drear
storm on its heavy wings.*
~ William Cullen Bryant (17912-1878)

In the last quarter of the century, wind energy technology has gone through revolutionary changes, making the wind the fastest-growing source of electricity in the world, averaging 24.4% a year on average (Figure 12-1). The cumulative capacity of installed wind power worldwide reached nearly 743 gigawatts in 2020.

The upward trend is expected to continue for the foreseeable future, increasing total wind installed capacity to 2,000 gigawatts, or 20% of total global electricity production by 2030. This is partly because of increased demand for green energy but, mainly, because of new technological innovations that have reduced production costs from $1.00 to around $0.04 for one kilowatt-hour. Currently. China, with more than 237 GW of installed capacity, is the leader in wind generation capacity. The U.S. with 105 GW or 7.3% of all electricity generated ranks the distant second, with Germany, India, and Spain following. Denmark, with 47.2% of its electricity portfolio from the wind, ranks first in terms of percent total power.

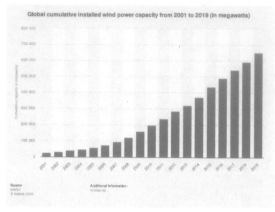

In the United States, only three states -- North Dakota, Kansas, and Texas -- have sufficient wind that, if harnessed, could satisfy national electricity needs. Though these states have the most wind, they are sparsely populated, and there are not many transmission lines. The U.S., however, has ambitious plans to increase the capacity to generate up to 20% of its electrical demand by 2030. That requires the construction of as many as 100,000 new turbines.

Figure 12-1
World accumulated electrical capacity from wind.
Image courtesy of Global Wind Energy Council.

Overview

Like waterwheels, windmills were among the original prime movers that replaced human beings as a source of power. Wind power had been used as early as 5,000 years ago by the Egyptians to sail ships on the Nile. The first windmills were invented by the Persians, as early as 500-900 A.D., to pump water from wells and to grind grain. They were constructed by fastening bundles of reeds onto wooden frames mounted on vertical shafts (hence called vertical windmills) housed in brick or clay walls. The wind entered through an opening at the side and was caught between the spokes radiating from the shaft (Figure 12-2). The technology was exported to China after Genghis Khan imprisoned Persian millers and forced them to build windmills to power irrigation systems in China.

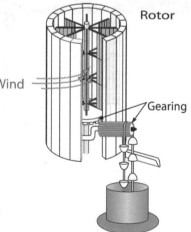

Figure 12-2
Persians invented the first practical windmills for grinding wheat and pumping water.
Image courtesy of Caroline Mawer.

It was not until the twelfth century that windmills found their way to Europe, where their use became increasingly widespread, until the early 19th century. These mills used vanes that looked like huge paddles mounted on horizontal poles (hence called horizontal windmills). The Dutch used windmills mainly for draining water from their low-lying land (hence the Netherlands), which was quite prone to flooding (Figure 12-3).

The first use of wind power to generate electricity was in 1888 by Charles Brush in Cleveland, Ohio. The Brush machine, shown in Figure 12-4, had a rotor 17 meters in diameter with 144 blades and generated 12 kW of electricity, enough to light 350 incandescent lamps. The device worked for 20 years until the advent of steam engines and the popularization of low-cost, seemingly inexhaustible fossil fuels, which made windmills less and less attractive. Later work by aerodynamicists showed that the most efficient number of blades is two to four (Figure 12-5), a far smaller number than those found in earlier windmills.

Figure 12-3
Dutch horizontal
windmill.

Figure 12-4
Brush windmill in
Cleveland, Ohio

Figure 12-5
Modern three-bladed
wind turbine.

During the late nineteenth and early twentieth centuries, attempts were made to design better and more efficient turbines, but the abundance of cheap fossil fuel made wind energy uneconomical. In the years after the oil crisis of 1973, there was another attempt for large-scale production of electricity from the wind -- mostly subsidized by various European and U.S. governments -- but once the price of oil stabilized and the crisis was over, the interest in wind energy diminished again. The recent awareness of the issues related to global warming and its catastrophic consequences, in addition to better manufacturing technology and increased dependence on Middle Eastern oil, once again, prompted a new interest in renewable energy resources -- wind in particular.

> **Question:** What is the difference between the operation of an electric fan and a wind turbine?
> **Answer:** A fan uses electricity to produce the wind, whereas a wind turbine uses the wind to make electricity.

Global and Local Wind Patterns

The wind is air in motion. We can't see it, but we can see its effect all around us. Winds are generated as a result of two factors: the non-uniform heating of earth by the sun; and the rotation of the earth. Equatorial regions receive the most radiation, whereas polar regions receive the least. The difference in ground temperatures between the equator and the poles induces a global circulation pattern where hotter (and lighter) air rises near the equator and colder (and heavier) air sinks at the poles. As a result, the overall wind flow direction is from the poles toward the equator, close to the surface, and from the equator toward the poles in the upper atmosphere. The detailed flow pattern, however, is much more complicated. The upper atmosphere wind (called **geostrophic wind**) is largely driven by the earth's rotation and temperature (and thus, pressure) differences. At regions below, we have **synoptic winds** that are associated with large-scale movements of warm and cold fronts. Hurricanes, tornadoes, and typhoons are of this kind. Close to the earth's surface, obstacles such as tall buildings, hills and valleys, earth's reflectivity or *albedo* (desert, forest, or snow) as well as proximity to the sea and heating by local sources (such as factories, power plants, and freeways) will determine the local wind pattern. The strongest winds are in mid-latitude between 40 and 60 degrees. The U.S.'s Pacific and Europe's Atlantic Coasts, and Western Australia are considered prime locations for exploiting wind energy.

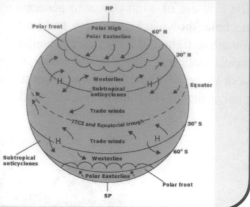
Sea breezes occur during the daytime when landmasses are heated more quickly than the sea. Sand has a lower heat capacity than water and cannot hold solar heat as effectively, resulting in its temperature rising above that of the water nearby. As the air rises above the hotter land, air from the cooler sea moves to replace it, resulting in a sea breeze. At night, the land gives off heat more quickly and its temperature drops faster than the surrounding sea, resulting in **land breezes**. At dusk, there often is a period of tranquility when the temperatures of land and sea are equal (Figure 12-6a).

Valley and mountain breezes result from a combination of both differential heating and local topography. As the sun rises, it hits the mountain tops first, and as the day progresses, the sun then hits the mountain slopes, causing differential heating between the two. As warmer air rises off the slopes, cold valley air moves up to fill the vacuum (valley breeze). In the afternoon, as the sun sets, the flow reverses, and we have mountain breezes (Figure 12-6b).

Wind Rose

The selection of a proper site for installing wind farms requires detailed meteorological data at all times. Wind data are routinely collected by wind anemometers installed on top of towers in the direction of the prevailing wind. Because speeds and directions are continually changing, 10- to 15-minute average values are recorded. Measurements are often normalized to the total period of observation to indicate frequencies. The data is plotted on a wind rose, which is a single, graphical representation of speed, direction, and frequency of occurrence. One simple way to graphically indicate both duration and direction is to drawbars extending radially from the center of the rose, in the direction

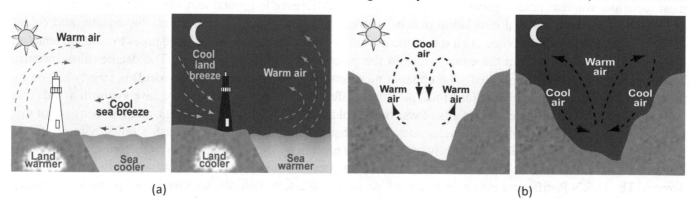

(a)   (b)

Figure 12-6
Wind formation along (a) the coastlines, and (b) mountain ranges

the wind is coming from; magnitude is represented proportionally to the time the wind blew in that direction. The colors (or thickness) of the bars indicate the range of speeds in a given direction. Each concentric circle represents a different frequency, and the length of each "spoke" indicates the frequency of the wind blowing from a particular direction. A typical wind rose is shown in Figure 12-7. The hourly data is represented in polar coordinates. As data shows, little wind blows from the east. North and northwest directions are most windy, however. Roughly 27% of the time wind blew directly from the north, the wind speed was greater than 22 mph (red) 9% of the time, 12% of the time in the range of 11-22 mph (orange), 4% of the times in the range of 6-11 mph (yellow); wind speed is smaller than 6 mph the rest of the time (green).

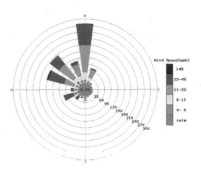

Figure 12-7
Typical wind rose; concentric circles represent the frequency, and different colors indicate ranges of wind velocity.

Wind Map

Depending on wind power density and speed, different geographical areas have been divided into seven classes. Class 1 regions are not suitable for wind energy development, and Class 2 regions may become only marginally acceptable. Class 3 areas will be suitable in the future, as technology matures. Class 4 and higher are considered suitable for wind power with existing technology. The United States compiles the wind map for various locations and different times of the year (Figure 12-8). Table 12-1 summarizes wind classes, along with available wind power density at 50 m height. The U.S. atlas of wind energy resources can be found at *http://rredc.nrel.gov/wind/pubs/atlas*. [Ref. 7]

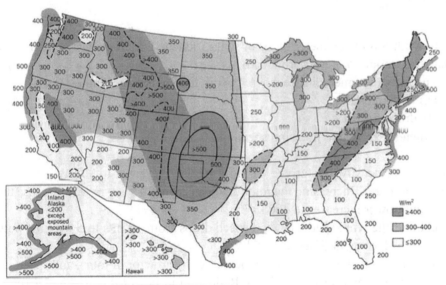

Figure 12-8
U.S. wind map at 50-m altitude. The darkest regions are areas with power density exceeding 400 W/m².
Source: National Renewable Laboratory.

Table 12-1 Wind Classes And Power Density At 50 m Height		
Wind Class	Wind Power Density (W/m²)	Average Wind Speed (m/s)
1	0-200	0-5.6
2	200-300	5.6-6.4
3	300-400	6.4-7.0
4	400-500	7.0-7.5
5	500-600	7.5-8.0
6	600-800	8.0-8.8
7	800-2,000	8.8-11.0

Maximum Theoretical Wind Power

The energy delivered by a wind turbine is proportional to the change in kinetic energy of the mass of air that is sweeping (sucked in) through its rotor. The mass itself increases with the air density, the size of the rotor, and the speed of the wind. Since kinetic energy is proportional to the mass and the square of velocity, it turns out that the total power available as it crosses the plane of the rotor increases with the air density, square of the rotor diameter, and the cube of the wind velocity. The final result is:

$$P = \frac{\pi}{8}\rho d^2 V_0^3 \qquad\qquad (12\text{-}1)$$

Where:

P = Maximum power that can be extracted from the wind energy (W)

ρ = Air density (~1.23 kg/m^3 at STP)

d = Rotor diameter (m)

V_0 = Wind velocity upstream of the wind turbine rotor (m/s)

Air density changes with both air temperature and elevation. So, it is understandable that more power is available in the winter and at lower elevations when air is heavier. In deserts and open areas, where most wind turbines are installed, a temperature change of about 40-55°C is normal between winter and summer months, so an additional 10% power surge is expected during the winter months. Most wind turbines are rated at standard atmosphere pressure (sea level and 25°C). A correction must be applied for warmer temperatures and higher elevations.

The most important parameter affecting power production is the velocity of the wind, perpendicular to the plane of the rotor. In the height of one km and above, wind velocity is barely affected by the surface of the earth. In the lower atmosphere, the wind is slowed as a result of friction, terrain contours, and other obstacles such as buildings and trees. As a result, velocity slows down, reaching zero at the surface. The profile is determined by the degree of roughness and the height above the ground. Since power increases with the cube of the velocity, a 10% increase in wind velocity will cause the power to increase by 33%.

> **Example 12-1:** A wind turbine with a rotor diameter of 20 m will produce 100 kW power when exposed to a wind speed of 10 m/s. Estimate the amount of power produced:
> a. When the same turbine is used in a warmer climate where the air density is 10% thinner.
> b. With a bigger turbine, 40 m in diameter.
> c. When wind speed suddenly drops to 5 m/s.
> d. With a turbine 10 m in diameter, exposed to the wind speed of 20 m/s.
> **Solution:**
> a. Since power is proportional to air density, the turbine will lose 10% of its power to 90 kW.
> b. Power is proportional to the rotor area. Increasing the rotor diameter from 20 to 40 m will increase the swept area by four times. The output power increases to 400 kW.
> c. Power changes with the cube of the wind speed. If wind speed drops from 10 m/s to 5 m/s, the power will decrease by a factor of two-cubed, or eight times to 12.5 kW.
> d. In this case, diameter decreases by a factor of two (power decreases by a factor of four), and speed increases by a factor of two (power increases by a factor of eight). Reduction in power due to smaller rotor size is more than compensated for by the increase in power due to higher wind speed, and net power increases by a factor of two to 200 kW.

Power Density

How much land do we need to dedicate to wind farms, if we are going to satisfy all electrical energy needs of the United States with wind power? The answer depends on two factors: power density, the power per unit area of the rotor; and, the number of wind turbines that can be installed over an area. **Power density** varies greatly, depending on local topography and prevailing wind speed. The **number of wind turbines** that can be installed without interfering with neighboring turbines, depends on the rotor diameter -- the bigger the diameter, the larger the mass flow rate through the rotor, and fewer is the number of turbines per square kilometer of the land area. It is interesting to note that -- working out the mathematics -- the power per unit of the land area will turn out to be independent of what size turbine is used. Figure 12-9 shows the wind-power potential for different swept areas and different land areas.

Example 12-2: Estimate a) the total available power in a square meter of wind blowing at 15 m/s, b) the diameter of a wind turbine capable of producing 1 MW of electric power, and c) the total electrical energy from one square kilometer of the wind farm over one year. Assume a capacity factor of 30% and a combined turbine-generator efficiency of 25%.

Solution: Referring to Figure 12-9 we find:

a. The total area of the wind stream capable of delivering one megawatt of wind power is 355 m² (2.8 kW/m² of rotor area);

b. The electric power generated from one square meter of sweep area is calculated by dividing the wind power by the efficiency; we need a turbine with a swept area of 355/0.25 = 1,420 m²;

c. One square kilometer of the wind farm has an equivalent of 36 MW of wind power, capable of producing 36 × 0.25 = 9 MW of electricity. For a capacity factor of 0.3, the annual electricity generation capacity is (365 d) × (24 h/d) × 9 MW × 0.3 = 23,600 MWh.

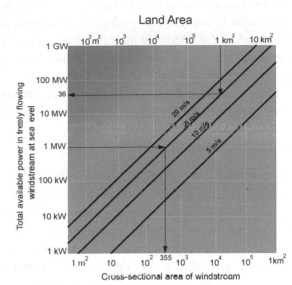

Figure 12-9

Maximum power in a wind stream and wind power that can be extracted from a given land area; the figures must be adjusted for turbine efficiencies.

Example 12-3: Estimate the average wind power potential per square meter of land area?

Solution A commercial 2.5 MW wind turbine has a diameter of 80 m (See Table 12-2). To prevent interferences, it is generally recommended that wind turbines be spaced about six to eight diameters apart. A 1-km² land area can house two to three such power plants, generating about 5-7 MW of electric power at the peak capacity. Assuming a capacity factor of one-third, roughly 2-3 MW is captured over a square kilometer of land area. The U.S. produced 1,400 GW of electrical power in 2019, of which 7.3% was from the wind. If the wind were to produce all electricity, we would need about 600,000 square kilometers (~150 million acres, or 6% on the U.S. land area) of wind farms.

In a study sponsored by the National Renewable Energy Laboratory (NREL), the land use data for 172 wind farms currently installed in the United States was collected. The land use was classified as that being directly impacted and the total area dedicated to the projects. Lands occupied by wind turbine pads, access roads, substations, and other infrastructure which physically occupies the land, are considered direct-impact. For development in forested areas, the additional land that had to be cleared around turbines also was included. Total land includes temporary construction access roads, storage, and lay-down, and also lands usually set aside for future development. According to this study, approximately 30 hectares of land are needed to produce one megawatt of electricity using wind energy.

> **Worth Remembering** – Wind can generate power roughly 30 ha/MW (~3 MW/km²) of land area. It should be noted, however, that the land between the turbines is still usable for its original purpose.

Wind Turbines

Wind turbines[*] are devices that convert the kinetic energy of wind into the mechanical energy of rotating blades. They range in size from very small machines that deliver only a few watts to very large turbines with the capacity

---

[*] The word windmill usually implies wind machine traditionally used for grinding flour, or pulling water from a well. We reserve the word wind turbine when it is used to generate electricity. We will use the same distinction when we discuss watermills and water turbines.

to produce many megawatts. Depending on which component of aerodynamic drag or lift drives the rotor (turbine hub and blades), wind turbines are classified as drag type or lift type. In **_drag-type turbines_**, the wind pushes blades that can be in the shape of paddles, cup-shaped, or s-shaped, to scoop the air. The wind turbine speed is limited by the speed of the paddle, which usually moves slower than the wind. Drag-type devices produce high torques and, therefore, were traditionally used for pumping water or grinding grains. Modern high-speed turbines are of **_lift types._** They are designed to maximize the lift -- i.e., divert the incoming wind so that air moves faster on one side of the surface than the other. Blades move because the pressure difference between the front and rear faces of the blades creates a torque that forces the rotor of a wind turbine to turn. The same principle is applied in the design of aircraft, where the difference between the top and bottom surfaces of the wings creates a lift and assures planes and helicopters to stay airborne.

Wind turbines are classified as a horizontal or vertical axis, depending on whether their axes of rotation are parallel or perpendicular to the ground. In horizontal turbines, the wind blows principally in the direction of the axis, so they are called *axial flow*. In vertical turbines, the wind blows perpendicular to the axis of the rotor, and so they are known as *cross-flow types*. **Vertical axis wind turbines** (VAWT) are designed to capture the wind from any direction and, therefore, no yawing mechanisms are needed. Furthermore, they have the advantage that the heavier components (the gearbox, generator, and controllers) can be placed near or on the ground, where the wind is weaker. The main disadvantages of VAWT are that they are not self-starting, torque is continuously varied as the blades move into and out of the wind, and efficiencies are relatively smaller. VAWTs could be of either a drag type or a lift type. Examples of drag-type VAWTs are cup anemometers and Savonius. Cup anemometers are normally used to measure wind velocity and are not suitable for extracting a lot of power. The Savonius blades are S-shaped, consisting of, basically, two half-cylinders mounted on a shaft; one faces the incoming wind, and the second positions its back toward the wind. Because one side is creating more drag than the other side, the device spins. Ancient windmills and other early vertical axis windmills were all of this type. The most advanced type, the Darrieus machine, looks like a giant eggbeater, having blades with a complex contour. They have the highest efficiency of all VAWTs, but manufacturing costs are high.

Figure 12-10

Vertical axis lift-type turbines such as Darrieus cannot start by themselves, and therefore are started electrically to reach their cut-in speeds. The assembly shows a novel approach where Darrieus turbine is combined with a drag-type (Savonius) turbine to eliminate the need for electric starting. In this design, Darrieus provides the initial torque and low-speed operation, whereas Savonius produces power at higher speed and windy conditions.

A compromise has been to build rotors with straight airfoils. Figure 12-10 shows a novel design combining two -- a Darrieus type and a Savonius type -- wind turbines that can operate over a wide range of wind speeds and directions.

Modern wind farms mostly use **horizontal axis wind turbines** (HAWT). Their operation is similar to that of the wings of an aircraft, or the propeller of a helicopter. Because of the shape of the cross-section, and angle of the airfoil (blade), the air changes direction as it approaches the airfoil. The change in airstream direction results in a change in its momentum. As we have learned from Newton's second law, a change in momentum requires a force. The force of the airfoil on the air is counteracted with an equal and opposite force on the airfoil (Newton's third law), which is called **the lift**. In airplanes, lift causes the plane to become airborne, whereas in wind turbines, lift forces the blades to rotate about the hub, which in turn, drives a generator. Perpendicular to the lift force, a drag force impedes rotor rotation.

High lift is essential in aircraft to prevent a stall. Stall refers to a condition at which the angle of attack is so steep that no lift is produced; even a small dent in the blade or airfoil can cause flow separation and trigger a stall. In wind turbine applications, some stalls are welcome in high wind conditions to slow the turbine down and prevent damage.

In new designs, the blade angles can be adjusted to change the lift-to-drag ratio and to optimize the turbine's power output for different wind speeds and directions. Unlike helicopter blades and aircraft wings, which are designed for the greatest lift, turbine blades are designed to reduce drag.

For maximum efficiency, horizontal axis turbines may be designed so that the rotor faces into the wind (upwind), or away from the wind (downwind). Named so, because of the location of the turbine relative to the tower. Most commercial turbines use an upwind design. The major advantage of upwind turbines is that there are no wake losses. The primary advantage of downwind machines is that they may be built without a yaw mechanism -- designed in a way that makes the nacelle follow the wind passively; the blades also can be made of lighter and more flexible materials; for large turbines, the proper orientation is guaranteed, by continuously measuring the yaw, and adjust the direction the turbine rotor is facing and ensure it is always positioned into the wind.

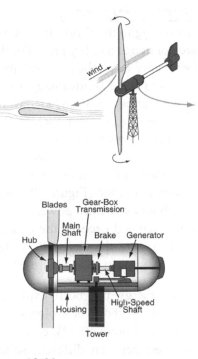

The major components of a wind power generator are the hub (on which rotor blades are attached), a gearbox, an electrical generator, and a controller with associated cooling units, and anemometers. Also, some turbines have built-in yaw mechanisms that tilt the rotor in the direction of the wind. The gearbox connects the low-speed and high-speed shafts to optimum rotational speeds of about 1,000 to 1,800 rpm. Anemometers measure wind speed, and vanes

Figure 12-11
Wind turbine operation.

measure wind direction. A typical wind vane has a pointer in front and fins in the back. When the wind is blowing, the wind vane points into the wind aligning itself with the direction of the wind. The simplest anemometers are cup anemometers in which the rate of rotation is directly proportional to the component of the wind speed normal to the surface of the cup. Sonic anemometers operate by measuring the time taken for a pulse of sound to travel between a pair of transducers, giving a fast and accurate measurement of wind speed in all directions. Except for the hub, the entire assembly is housed inside an enclosure called *a nacelle* that is mounted on top of a tower (Figure 12-11). The tower carries the weight and raises the turbine above trees, buildings, and other nearby obstructions, and face faster winds. Most turbines are equipped with automatic governors that protect rotors from spinning out of control in gusts and during high wind speeds.

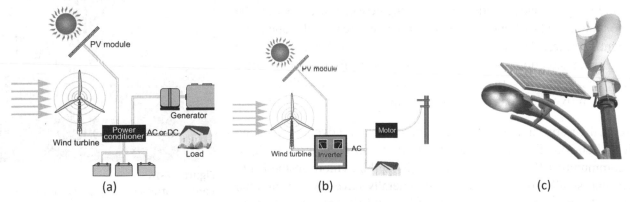

Figure 12-12
Hybrid systems involving a variety of energy sources can be used to power remote villages and generate income for their owners (a) battery-storage , (b) grid-connected, (c) stand-alone.

Adapted from Small Wind Electric Systems: A U.S. Customer's Guide, Office of Energy Efficiency, U.S. Department of Energy, DOE/GO-102001-1293, October 2002.

Hybrid Systems

According to the World Bank estimates, as many as two billion people, or 30% of all humanity, live in villages that are not tied to a utility grid. For these villages, a hybrid of energy sources, including wind, solar, and diesel-powered generators would be most suitable. In the United States, a typical stand-alone hybrid system involving photovoltaic cells and wind is advantageous over either system because it takes advantage of the longer and brighter sunlight in the summer when wind speeds are lower. In winter, the opposite is true; winds are strong when there is less sunlight. During periods of peak demand or when neither wind nor sunlight is sufficiently available, an auxiliary diesel can produce the additional energy required. In either case, to assure the availability of power at night or during periods of low winds, a battery storage system is needed (Figure 12-12a). When a grid connection is available, it is possible to sell extra power to the utility companies and buy back electricity when demand exceeds the capacity of the system. In this case, there is no need to store the electricity in batteries or have an auxiliary diesel power generating plant (See Figure 12-12b).

Figure 12-13
MS Beluga SkySail is the world's first cargo ship partially powered by a giant 600 square meter sail tethered to the ship. The kite is flown at an altitude between 100 and 500 meters, cutting fuel consumption by as much as 30%.
Image courtesy of SkySails.

Wind energy has been exploited to help power different transportation systems. Sailboats are obviously the first to come to mind. Solar Sailer boat (See Figure 10-14), combines the power from photovoltaics with wind captured between different solar panels to propel the boat. MV Beluga Skysails is the world's first cargo ship that uses a new wind propulsion system with a huge towing kite that provides additional thrust for the ship at sea – reducing fuel consumption by 20 to 30 percent (Figure 12-13).

Onshore and Offshore Wind Turbines

One of the important considerations in the design of any wind power generation station is its location. In general, wind generators must be installed in areas with open views and follow the altitude contours of the prevailing winds. The site must be chosen so that it is easily accessible, is near a high-voltage power grid, and so that its wind path is mostly clear of such obstacles as trees and tall buildings. Hilltops have the added advantage that they can pick updrafts, and wind speeds are generally higher. Valleys are also suitable because tunnel effects result in higher wind speeds than those found in open spaces. Pattern and spacing between turbines must be chosen so that the wake of one turbine does not interfere with the operation of adjacent turbines. The practical guideline is that turbines facing the prevailing wind direction should be spaced between five and nine rotor diameters apart; turbines that face perpendicular to prevailing winds should be from five to seven rotor diameters apart.

Figure 12-14
London Strata (razor) is one of the first buildings in the world to incorporate wind turbines as part of its structure.

Because of their appearance, noise, and their potential adverse effects on the price of surrounding properties, wind farms can be objectionable to nearby communities. Some consider large wind turbines more aesthetically pleasing than smaller ones because they generally have lower rotational velocities. Modern planning procedures and careful site selection can help to minimize visual impact. The selection of certain colors, turbine layouts also can help to minimize intrusiveness. Urban architects and city planners need to study these effects and design sites to match the local landscape or provide interesting additions to the nearby structures. Figure 12-14 shows the world's first skyscraper with wind turbines integrated directly within its building fabric.

Wind turbines do not always need to be placed on land and, if they are installed offshore, may benefit from the generally cooler and smoother lake and sea surfaces. Furthermore, because noise is not as much of a concern as with onshore facilities, turbines can be designed to operate at higher rotational speeds. As a result, up to 50%, greater efficiency is achieved at offshore wind farms. Offshore wind turbines are of two kinds, bottom-fixed and floating. Bottom-fixed types are most suitable in shallow waters (less than 30 m), and therefore could be the preferred close to the shores. Floating types are used in deeper waters away from the shoreline; they are not appropriate in rough waters, however. The main disadvantages of offshore wind farms are potential interference with shipping routes, the impact of noise on marine mammals, and the additional cost of the undersea cabling needed to connect the generators to the main electrical grids.

High-Altitude Wind Power

Ground-based energy systems have been growing steadily in the last couple of decades. These systems deploy wind turbines mounted on towers that extend hundreds of feet above the ground. Raising the towers to higher altitudes allows taking advantage of higher wind velocity and greater efficiency. The cost increases accordingly, however. To get the benefit of higher wind velocities of the upper atmosphere, many wind enthusiasts proposed airborne wind energy systems (AWES) be deployed at heights of 500-1000 m. At these altitudes, the wind has a power density many times that of ground-based systems. AWES replaces heavy and costly rigid towers with tethers, making it easier to adjust the height, or turn into the wind, giving a degree of flexibility not realizable in traditional wind turbine assemblies. The ideas are abundant, as different inventors have proposed harnessing energy by flying kites, tethered sailplanes, blimps, etc., all working by capturing the wind kinetic energy to turn a floating turbine that is coupled to a generator to produce electricity.

Summary

The wind is a potential source of an enormous amount of clean, renewable energy. Only 1% of the total wind energy available is enough to fulfill all global energy needs. As demand for energy and the environmental cost of burning fossil fuels increase, wind energy becomes more and more an attractive alternative. Wind turbine technology is undergoing rapid development: new, lighter and stronger composites have allowed making the construction of larger multi-megawatt turbines possible. Also, turbine noise is being continually reduced. Both shallow offshore (depth less than 30 m) and deep offshore wind farms are being considered; the costs are higher than land-based installations, however.

The average cost of electricity production from wind energy is now comparable to that from fossil fuel and is falling. At least, according to one study, the money spent on the 2001 Iraq War, to secure the flow of oil from the Middle East, including the cost of health care and rehabilitation of veterans, was enough to install enough wind turbines to meet U.S. entire electricity need.

Wind energy is not without its critics, however, as issues related to intermittency, noise, and look, have forced the licensing agencies to limit the sites only to remote areas, often at a considerable distance from the grid. Other disadvantages cited are the potential danger to birds, which may result in changes in migration patterns of some bird species, and shadow flicker – when moving blades cast shadows on nearby residences. Wind energy is expected to be a major energy source for most developing and island nations, as well as many developed European countries in the 21st century.

@ Digging Deeper: Design Considerations

Factors important in wind turbine design are the size of the rotor, the shape and number of blades, height of the tower, and the guidance and control mechanisms (gearbox, generator, controller, and brake) that are housed in a nacelle sitting atop the tower and holding the rotor.

Size

Depending on the application, wind turbines produce power from a few watts to many megawatts. Microturbines produce power in the range of 20-500 watts and are used in such applications as battery chargers and recreational vehicles. Turbines generating less than 50 kW are considered small, those producing between 50 kW and 1 MW are medium-sized, and turbines producing above 1 MW are large. Small turbines are used in applications such as pumping water, whereas medium and large wind turbines are used for producing electricity. With the current technology, turbines can be manufactured that under nominal design conditions can generate as high as 7-8 MW of electricity each (Figure 12-15). Table 12-2 shows the rotor diameter of wind turbines as a function of their maximum power (rated power).

Table 12-2 Rotor Diameters For Medium and Large Wind Turbines	
Power Rating (kW)	Rotor Diameter (m)
300	27-33
500	33-40
600	40-44
750	44-48
1000	48-54
1500	54-64
2000	54-72
2500	72-80

Figure 12-15
The world's largest wind turbine is now the Enercon E-126; this turbine has a rotor diameter of 126 meters (413 feet). The turbine will produce 7 megawatts (or 60 million kilowatt hours per year), enough to power about 5,000 German homes.
Image courtesy of Enercon Corporation.

For larger metropolitan areas, either a large number of small turbines or a few large turbines may be installed. The choice of using small or large rotors and generators depends on the application and the distribution of wind energy throughout the year. For the same total capacity, larger turbines occupy less space and are cheaper to install -- a 400-kW turbine costs considerably less than four 100-kW turbines. The cost of delivering electricity is also lower for larger turbines. Also, larger turbines can utilize the energy contained in high-speed winds and have greater efficiency. The drawback is that they cannot produce power at low speeds. The main advantage of small turbines is that they can produce continuous power for most of the year since they require only low to moderate wind speeds to operate. However, much of the energy in high-speed wind is wasted.

Airfoil

A rotor is comprised of the hub and the blades. Materials most often used are steel, wood laminate, and composites, such as fiberglass and carbon fiber. Steel and wood laminates are too heavy and are less attractive than composites. Aluminum is not suitable because of metal fatigue.

The *shape of the airfoil* is determined by the turbine-axis type -- horizontal or vertical -- and the load or stress that it encounters. The detailed aerodynamics of blades are rather difficult to explain and are outside the scope of this book. In brief, they are shaped like two lenses, placed back to back. The line that connects the two ends of these lenses is called the ***chord line***, and the angle that the chord line makes with the incoming wind velocity is called the ***angle of attack***. If the airfoil is symmetrical and the chord line is parallel to the wind direction, pressures on both sides of the surfaces are equal and no lift is produced.[†] As the angle of attack increases, or there is a greater curvature between the top and bottom surfaces, the pressure difference and the lift become greater. For horizontal-axis wind turbines operating at a given wind speed and direction, the angle of attack remains positive throughout their complete rotation. The blades are designed to maximize lift for a particular design point (rated velocity). For vertical-axis rotors, however, the angle of attack is constantly changing and remains positive during one-half of the rotation and negative during the second half. Blades use a symmetrical profile since there is no preferred direction.[16]

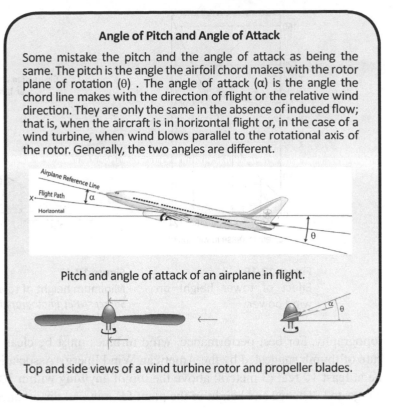

Angle of Pitch and Angle of Attack

Some mistake the pitch and the angle of attack as being the same. The pitch is the angle the airfoil chord makes with the rotor plane of rotation (θ) . The angle of attack (α) is the angle the chord line makes with the direction of flight or the relative wind direction. They are only the same in the absence of induced flow; that is, when the aircraft is in horizontal flight or, in the case of a wind turbine, when wind blows parallel to the rotational axis of the rotor. Generally, the two angles are different.

Pitch and angle of attack of an airplane in flight.

Top and side views of a wind turbine rotor and propeller blades.

Number of Blades

Theoretically, a wind turbine needs only one blade, some have two, and most have three, and a few have more. The greater the number of blades, the more stable the turbine -- but also, the heavier and more expensive. Single-, double, and to some extent, three-bladed turbines are cheaper but must operate at much higher speeds to capture the same amount of wind and are, therefore, noisier. They also have low to moderate starting torque, which makes their operation difficult at low wind speeds. One especially important factor in single- and two-bladed wind turbines is wind shear. Because air has a greater velocity farther from the ground, the wind puts greater force on the top blade than the bottom blade. To correct this, wind turbines are equipped with teetering mechanisms, which equalize the forces by allowing the blades to tilt slightly around their central pins. In some other designs, blades have a fixed pitch, so instead of pivoting at the hub, these turbines flex as wind speed picks up. To guard against over speeding, each blade has a small tip brake that, at high speeds, tips into the wind, stalling the turbine.

> **Question**: Windmills traditionally used for pumping water have small, solid rotors with many blades. What is the main advantage of these designs?
>
> **Answer:** The many blades assure operation at very slow wind speeds, allowing continuous operation all year. These windmills are, however, very inefficient at high speeds and must be shut down to prevent damage.

Tower Height

Wind speed increases with height above the ground, so the height of the tower on which the rotor is mounted indirectly influences power production; turbines installed on taller towers are more efficient than those on shorter towers. The cost of tower construction may not justify the extra gain in efficiency, however. Figure 12-16 shows the increase in power with the height of the tower. For example, it is possible to extract twice the power, if the wind turbine is mounted on a tower 120 ft (36 m) tall instead of a tower of only 30 ft (9 m) tall.

Another consideration for deciding on appropriate tower height is the surface roughness as well as the local

---

[†] Airplanes designed for aerial maneuvers and acrobatic exercises have symmetrical airfoils that enable them to fly upside down.

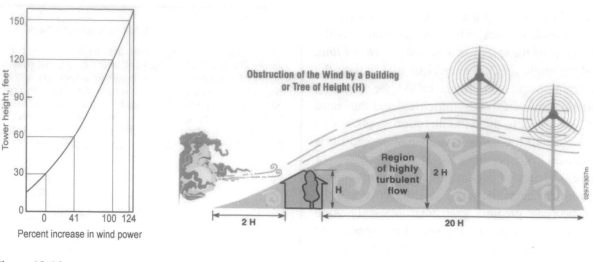

Figure 12-16
Effect of tower height on wind power.

Figure 12-17
Minimum height of tower to clear from obstacles.
Source: NREL Photographic Image Exchange.

topography. For best performance, wind turbines must be clear of all obstacles, such as trees, buildings, etc. The rule of thumb suggested by the American Wind Energy Association is that the bottom of the turbine's blades should be at least 10 feet (3 meters) above the top of anything within 300 feet (about 100 meters). Figure 12-17 shows the suggested distance and height of the plant for minimal disturbances from obstacles.

Power Train

To produce electricity, the power must be transferred to a generator. In **indirect grid connections**, wind turbines operate independently of the generator, and the system operates in a variable-speed mode determined instantaneously by wind speed. In this case, the voltage from the generator must be modified to match that of the neighboring electrical power grid. This must be done in several steps. First, the variable-frequency alternating current must be converted into a constant frequency alternating current. Next, the alternating current must be converted to direct current using a rectifier. Finally, using a DC-AC inverter, the direct current must be converted to an alternating current at a frequency matching the grid line. If the generator and turbine rotor are **connected directly**, then the rotor must turn with the same rotational speed as the generator. Normally, generators produce three-phase alternating currents at frequencies of 60 (for the U.S.) or 50 (for most other places in the world) hertz. The current is stepped down through transformers in order to increase the voltage to the 10-30 kV used in most local transmission lines. For a 60 Hz generator, this translates to 3,600 rpm (3,000 rpm for 50 Hz). Depending on the extent that the wind speed fluctuates, wind turbine speeds can vary over a wide range. The speed must match that of the generator that runs at a constant speed.

The first option is to use a slow-moving AC generator with a large number of poles. For example, if the number of magnets in the stator of a synchronized generator is doubled, the magnetic field must rotate only half a revolution before it changes direction (See Chapter 5). In theory, we can keep increasing the number of poles until the generator revolves at the same speed as the wind turbine rotor. The more practical approach is to use a **gearbox**. A gearbox is a device that converts low-speed, high-torque power from the turbine into the high-speed, low-torque power required to run the generator.

Safety and Control

To make wind energy economically viable, wind turbines must endure a wide range of hazardous conditions. Modern designs deploy various sensors that protect turbines, gearboxes, and generators against excess vibration, overheating, and high-speed wind gusts.

Temperature

One of the interesting features of electric motors and generators is that they require some electrical load to operate. If they overheat or if a load is removed, the rotors will accelerate out of control and the devices will fail. Furthermore, many electrical components are sensitive to changes in extreme atmospheric temperature. To avoid overheating, most generators are equipped with either air or water cooling systems.

Vibration

Depending on wind speed and direction, a wind turbine produces fluctuating torque and varying forces on the blades, causing the rotor and tower to swing back and forth. The frequency of oscillation depends on the height of the tower and on the material and weight of the rotor and nacelle. If the rotor spins at a synchronized speed with other vibrational frequencies, the oscillation can amplify and the tower could sway out of control. Wind turbines often are equipped with controllers that start the turbines when the wind reaches a certain velocity (around 3-6 m/s) and shut the machines off when wind velocity exceeds 20-30 m/s. Most wind turbines are designed to have a maximum output at wind speeds around 15 m/s; higher wind speeds are rare and lower wind speeds cannot produce sufficient power.

Noise

There are two sources of noise: aerodynamic and mechanical. The primary source of **aerodynamic noise** is the airflow from the trailing edges of the blades. Depending on the shape of the airfoil, rotation speed, and angle of attack, different regions of a blade produce noises of different frequencies, and so form a broadband noise. In addition, tip speeds of large-diameter rotors reach several times that of sound, causing unacceptable torsional load and deafening acoustic noise. **Mechanical noise** generally originates from the rotating components within the wind turbine, such as the generator and the gearbox. Mechanical noise tends to be tonal (narrow bandwidth) of a constant pitch, independent of the speeds of the wind and the rotor. Sources of mechanical noises can be easily identified and controlled.

Power Quality

The U.S. electric grid provides 110 volt AC power at a frequency of 60 hertz to U.S. households. European countries use 220 volts at 50 hertz. To connect generators to the grid, the electricity must be delivered at the same frequency as that of the electric network with almost no variation. It is, therefore, important to assure that the signal is of high quality with little contamination from other frequencies (flicker or noise). Furthermore, to prevent power surges and damage to the generator, the current must be in phase (in step) with the grid.

Danger to Birds

Wind turbines are known to interfere with birds' migration and are responsible for killing birds that fly in approaching air streams.[‡] Fatality rates vary widely regionally across wind resource areas. According to a study by the U.S. Fish and Wildlife Service, it is estimated that every year, 573,000 birds and 888,000 bats are killed by wind turbines. Bats are particularly vulnerable, as they fly in the mountain ridges where most wind turbines are installed. To protect bats, some researchers propose blasting ultrasounds that jam their sonars. Bats will intrinsically avoid areas where such waves are broadcast. This is, however, far fewer than birds who are killed by cats, buildings, or cars[§], according to a 2015 study published in the Annual Review of Ecology, Evolution, and Systematic.

[‡] It should be noted, however, that the highest rate of bird fatality is by far, the collision with building glasses and not flight into the wind turbines..

[§]

@ Digging Deeper: Performance

Wind turbine performance is measured by its efficiency, power coefficient, cut-in and cut-out wind velocities, and capacity factor.

Turbine Efficiency

The analysis given previously is the maximum power that can be generated under ideal conditions. Consider the flow passing through the wind turbine. If all the kinetic energy of the upstream airflow is to be utilized, no flow will pass through, and turbine efficiency is zero. If the wind velocity is zero, then again, no wind flows through the rotor, and no power is produced. So it is natural to conclude that not all the energy in the wind can be recovered, and there exists an optimum speed that gives the maximum efficiency.

Indeed, it can be shown that an ideal wind turbine would slow down the wind by 2/3 of its original speed and that the theoretical maximum power that can be utilized from a wind turbine is only 59.3% of this value.[¶] This is called the **Betz limit**, in honor of German Physicist Albert Betz, who calculated this limit in 1919. In practice, depending on the blade shape and its rotational speed, Up to a half of the wind spills over, reducing the overall efficiencies even lower. Another 10% is lost in the generator, reducing the electrical conversion efficiency to about 25-35%. Figure 12-18 compares the performance of several rotor designs at different wind speeds.

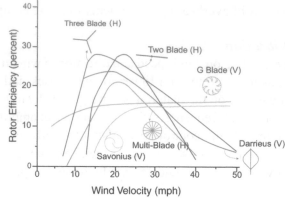

Figure 12-18
Effect of rotor design on performance.
Adapted from Wind Energy Systems, by G. L. Johnson, Prentice Hall, 1985.

Cut-in and Cut-out Velocities

In addition to the Betz limit, there are other factors that narrow the range of wind velocities for wind turbines to work. If the wind velocity is too low, the kinetic energy is not sufficient to overcome friction at the bearings. At high velocities, wind power is strong enough to knock the blades off, rendering the turbine inoperable.

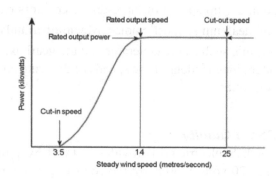

Figure 12-19
Power output for a typical wind turbine. No power is produced when wind speed is smaller than cut-in, or larger than cut-out velocities.

Modern wind turbines are equipped with mechanisms that automatically start the turbines when the wind reaches its *cut-in velocity*. Below this wind velocity turbine torque is not enough to overcome the mechanical losses and start the turbines (Figure 12-19). Turbines are designed to withstand extreme winds when they are not spinning. They are not intended for such speeds when they spin, and therefore, turbines must be stopped when the wind reaches speeds that may become unsafe for the turbines to operate (*cut-out velocity*). This can be done by controlling the blade angle (pitch-control), or by rotating the entire turbine in the horizontal axis (yaw-control).

Power Coefficient

Power Coefficient (C_p) is a measure of wind turbine efficiency often used by the wind power industry. C_p is the ratio

---

[¶] If air velocity remains the same before and after wind enters and exits the rotor, then no power can be transmitted to the blades and no power is extracted. If all the wind energy present in the streamline is to be transmitted to the wind turbine, then it has to slow down to a standstill and no air passes through. It turns out that the power is maximum when air velocity leaving the wind turbine is only 1/3 that of that entering it, which limits maximum efficiency only to 59.3%.

of actual electric power produced by a wind turbine divided by the total wind power flowing into the turbine blades at specific wind speeds. The power coefficient is specific to a particular design; it represents the combined efficiency of the various wind power system components, which include the turbine blades, the shaft bearings and gear train, the generator and power electronics, and therefore, can be directly used to compare the performance of different wind turbines.

As we may imagine, turbines do not always run at optimum wind speed and can capture only a fraction of the energy, and so the numbers must be adjusted for both the power coefficient (fraction of wind power captured and converted to electric power) and the capacity factor (fraction of the actual energy produced in a given period, to the hypothetical maximum possible, i.e., running full time at its rated power).

Pitch-Control -- The most common way to control the power is by changing the aerodynamic forces on blades. The pitch is the angle that the airfoil chord makes with the rotor plane of rotation. In pitch regulation, blades are mechanically turned out of the wind (turn blades around their own axis). When the wind speed becomes too high, rotor blades are turned along their longitudinal axes and out of the wind to allow some wind to pass by without increasing lift. At low wind speeds, blades are turned into the wind. The advantage of a pitch-controlled scheme is that relatively constant rotor speeds can be maintained within a large range of wind speeds. Most large wind turbines use this approach. In addition to the control mechanisms described above, wind turbines are normally equipped with disk brakes that are charged in case of emergencies, when rotors must suddenly come to a stop.

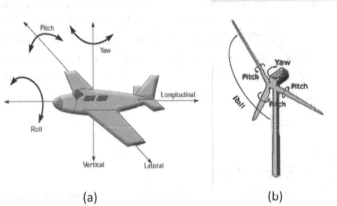

(a)   (b)

Figure 12-20
Principal degrees of freedom for a) aircraft; b) wind turbine.
Yaw – rotation of nacelle into/out of the wind
Pitch – rotation of blades about their lengthwise axis
Roll - rotation of rotor about its shaft

Yaw-control Another method of controlling rotor speed is to turn the rotor out of the wind by adjusting its yaw angle and tilting it either into or away from the direction of the wind. To optimize efficiency, turbine blades must face the wind at all times (they must be in a plane perpendicular to the direction of the wind). A large wheel called a yaw bearing turns the nacelle with the rotor into the wind. Yaw control ensures that the turbine is continuously facing into the wind to maximize the effective rotor area and, as a result, power. At very high speeds, the rotor is intentionally turned away from the direction of the trailing wind, reducing the total volume of air passing through the rotor and reducing the power. Figure 12-20 shows pitch and yaw angles for aircraft and wind turbines.

Power Rating

Wind turbine performance is determined by both its power and the total energy that can be extracted over an extended period, such as a month or a year. The first piece of data is furnished by the manufacturers that often characterize their turbines by their rated powers. **Rated power** is the maximum power delivered at the design condition -- often the point at which turbine efficiency is a maximum. However, turbines are not always operating at their optimum conditions and, depending on wind conditions, can have the power vary from zero (when wind speed is lower than the turbine's cut-in velocity) to a maximum at their optimal operating point. Efficiency also

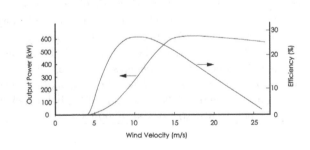

Figure 12-21
Power output and efficiency versus wind speed.

drops, somewhat, at higher speeds as it approaches the turbine's cut-out velocity. The power output follows a **wind speed-power curve** that depends on the type of turbine, size, the number of blades, and optimum tip-speed ratios (Figure 12-21).

The second factor affecting the performance is the **histogram** or wind speed frequency distribution -- the fraction of the time wind blows in the rotor direction, and at a given velocity. These data are normally available from published wind roses for a given geographic location, for a given month, and take into account the seasonal variation and year-to-year variations within a long period of observation. If such data are not available, it is customary to use the standard Weibull distribution.

This is important since average wind velocities cannot adequately give a good estimate of the total energy production. For example, let's assume two cities, both with an average wind velocity of 10 mph. City A experiences the wind at a steady rate of 10 mph, all the time, whereas, City B experiences wind speed of 8 mph, half the time, and 12 mph for the other half. The total energy generated by the wind turbine in City A is proportional to $10^3 = 1,000$ (don't worry about units, as we are interested in relative values), whereas an identical wind turbine in City B produces energy proportional to $0.5 \times (8^3 + 12^3) = 1,120$; i.e., given the same average wind velocity, the turbine exposed to gusts of the wind with variable wind speeds will be more efficient.

 **Endnotes**

1   World Wind Energy Association, http://www.gwec.net/global-figures/wind-in-numbers
2   Global Wind Energy Council, http://www.gwec.org
3   EIA (2016). Institute for Energy Research, http://instituteforenergyresearch.org
4   Woelfle, G., (1997). *The Wind at Work* (14), Chicago Review Press.
5   Hills, R. (1994). *Power from Wind: A History of Windmill Technology*, Cambridge University Press.
6   'Mr. Brush's Windmill Dynamo', (1890). *Scientific American*, December 20.
7   Wind Energy Resource Atlas of the United States can be found at http://rredc.nrel.gov/wind/pubs/atlas
8   NREL (2020). Land Use by System Technology, https://www.nrel.gov/analysis/tech-size.html
9   World Bank (2005). Rural energy and development for two billion people: meeting the challenge, Washington, D.C.
10 MS Beluga Skysail, http://www.skysails.info
11 Kwek, G. (2010). Wind-powered high-rise livin, *The Sydney Morning Herald*, July 30.
12 Canale, M., Fagiano, L., & Milanese, M. (2010). High Altitude Wind Energy Generation Using Controlled Power Kites. *IEEE Transactions On Control Systems Technology, 18*(2), 279-293, doi: 10.1109/tcst.2009.2017933
13 Archer, C., & Caldeira, K. (2009). Global Assessment of High-Altitude Wind Power, *Energetics, 2*(2), 307-319, doi: 10.3390/en20200307
14 Loyd, M. (1980). Crosswind kite power (for large-scale wind power production). *Journal Of Energy, 4*(3), 106-111, doi: 10.2514/3.48021
15 Bilmes, L., & Stiglitz, J. (2019). The Iraq War Will Cost us $3 Trillion, and much more. Washington Post, p. B01.
16 Kintisch, E. (2010). Out of Site. *Science, 329*(5993), 788-789, doi: 10.1126/science.329.5993.788
17 Ragheb, M. (2012). Wind shear, roughness classes and turbine energy production, Available at: http://mragheb.com
18 Smallwood, K. (2013). Comparing bird and bat fatality-rate estimates among North American wind-energy projects. *Wildlife Society Bulletin 37(1)*, 19-33, doi: 10.1002/wsb.260
19 Loss, S. R., Will, T., & Marra, P. P. (2015). Direct Mortality of Birds from Anthropogenic Causes, Annual Review of Ecology, *Evolution, and Systematics*, vol. 46, pp. 99-120.
20 Hau, E. (2006). *Wind Turbines: Fundamentals, Technologies, Applications, Economics* (2nd ed.). Springer.
21 Lun, I., & Lam, J. (2000). A study of Weibull parameters using long-term wind observations. *Renewable Energy, 20*(2), 145-153, doi: 10.1016/s0960-1481(99)00103-2

☝ Exercises

I. Essay Questions

1. Discuss the principles of wind turbine operation. Name the components of a modern wind power plant and describe their functions.
2. What are the advantages and disadvantages of upwind and downwind turbine configurations?
3. Define the pitch, and angle of attack. Under what conditions are they the same?
4. How does the height of a wind tower affect the operation of a wind turbine? What are the advantages and disadvantages of taller versus shorter towers?
5. What is the difference between a horizontal and a vertical wind turbine? How do they vary in shape? What is the advantage and disadvantage of an upwind design over a downwind design?
6. What is the power coefficient? Can a wind turbine extract all the power captured by a wind turbine rotor?
7. What are the rated speed and rated power? How are they related?
8. What is the function of a gearbox in a wind turbine? Under what conditions, they can be excluded?
9. What turbine efficiency of wind turbines cannot approach 100%. What is Betz limit?
10. Which factors limit the cut-in and cut-out speeds?

II. Problems

1. Refer to the wind rose plot of Figure 12-7, and answer the following questions:
   a. What fraction of time does wind blow in the south-eastern direction?
   b. What fraction of time does wind blow at a speed above 10 mph?
   c. What fraction of time does wind blow at speeds between 5 and 10 mph?
2. Calculate the power of wind moving with a velocity of 8 m/s incidents on a wind turbine 150 m in diameter. What is the maximum power that can be extracted from the turbine? How many such turbines are needed for a city requiring 500 MW of electricity?
3. Calculate the power output of a wind generator with propeller blades, each 40-m in length. Assume an efficiency of 10% and a wind speed of 10 m/s.
4. A farm has installed a windmill 18 m in diameter, with 35% efficiency. For a wind speed of 10 m/s:

   a. What is the power delivered?
   b. How much wind energy does it provide per year? Assume a capacity factor of 65%.
   c. What is the annual savings in electricity costs, if the utility charges 7 cents per kWh?
5. Referring to Figure 12-9, determine:
   a. The total available power in a square meter of wind blowing at 10 m/s;
   b. The diameter of a wind turbine capable of producing 1 MW of electric power, assuming a combined turbine and generator efficiency of 25%;
   c. The total electrical energy from one square kilometer of the wind farm over one year. Assume a capacity factor of 35%.
6. A 40-m diameter wind turbine delivers 500 kW of electric power when operating in summer and at a wind velocity of 10 m/s.
   a. How much power does a similar, 20-m diameter turbine deliver when it encounters a wind speed of 10 m/s?
   b. What is the power output during a gust of wind at 15 m/s? When does wind speed drop to 5 m/s?
   c. What is the power output of this turbine in winter, when air is about 15% denser?
7. Find the elevations for
   a. Long Beach, CA;
   b. Denver, CO;
   c. Brian Head, UT

   Calculate the air densities for these cities. What is the effect of elevation on the maximum power that can be extracted from the wind?
8. The graph below shows a manufacturer's data characterizing the performance of a 335 kW wind turbine. The rotor has a diameter of 33.5 m. What are cut-in, cut-out, and rated wind speeds for this turbine?

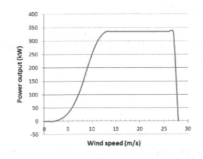

9. The wind map of Figure 12-8 shows that the

best regions for developing wind farms are in Central Plains and near the coastal U.S. continent. Assuming average wind speeds of 8 mph in Great Plane and 10 mph in coastal areas, what is the maximum theoretically possible amount of electric power that can be produced for every square meter of the blade area?

10. A Savonius wind turbine is constructed of four sheets of plates 4-m width and 12-m tall. Wind with a velocity of 12 m/s is blowing parallel to the ground. Assuming kinetic to the mechanical conversion efficiency of 25%, and generator efficiency of 90%, how much electric power can be generated?

11. Scandinavian countries can easily experience the temperature ranges of -20°C and +20°C between the winter and summer months. What is the impact of varying temperatures on electricity generation at a given wind speed?

III. Multiple Choice Questions

1. The wind is caused by
   a. Uneven heating of the earth
   b. Differences in atmospheric pressure between stratosphere and toposphere
   c. Earth's rotation
   d. Earth's tilt
   e. Both a and b

2. The direction of the global surface wind is from
   a. Polar to Equitorial region.
   b. Equitorial to Polar region.
   c. Equitorial to oceanic region.
   d. Oceanic to Equitorial region.
   e. Could be any of the above.

3. What accounts for forcing the global winds in a westerly direction?
   a. Gravitational force
   b. Coriolis force
   c. Centripetal force
   d. Centrifugal force
   e. Thermal force

4. Which country invented the first practical windmill?
   a. The U.S.
   b. Netherlands
   c. Egypt
   d. Persia
   e. China

5. Which country utilizes the greatest percentage of wind energy for producing electricity today?
   a. U.S.
   b. Germany
   c. Denmark
   d. China
   e. Iran

6. Which country has the highest total installed wind capacity?
   a. U.S.
   b. Germany
   c. Denmark
   d. China
   e. Iran

7. What fraction of the U.S.'s electrical capacity comes from wind?
   a. About 1-2%
   b. About 3-4%
   c. About 7-8%
   d. About 9-10%
   e. More than 10%

8. As early as 200 BCE, wind power was used in Egypt, China, and Persia. How were the first windmills that appeared in Europe in the Middle Ages different from those earlier turbines?
   a. They were used to generate electricity.
   b. They were used to grind grain.
   c. They turned on a horizontal axis.
   d. They turned on a vertical axis.
   e. They were similar, except used more blades.

9. Which states have the potential to generate the most amount of electricity from wind?
   a. Alaska, Montana, and California
   b. California, Texas, and Iowa
   c. North Dakota, Kansas, and Texas
   d. Illinois, California, and Alaska
   e. Alaska, Montana, and Hawaii

10. Which of the following is (are) true for horizontal-axis wind turbines?
   a. They are the most commonly used in the world.
   b. Their blades are designed for maximize lift.
   c. Traditional Dutch windmills are of this type.
   d. They normally have greater efficiencies.
   e. All are true.

11. Which of the following applies to a Savonius turbine?
   a. It is a vertical axis type.
   b. It is a drag type.
   c. It has blades shaped like an S.
   d. It is also known as the "egg-beater."
   e. a-c, but not d.

12. According to the U.S. Fish and Wildlife Service, what is responsible for the most bird deaths?
    a. Moving vehicles
    b. Cats, cars, and building window strikes
    c. Communications towers
    d. Wind turbines
    e. Hunting

13. Rated power is the maximum power delivered
    a. On a given day.
    b. Over one year.
    c. Under normal operating conditions
    d. Under design conditions
    e. At cut-in wind velocity

14. How much does the energy content of the wind change if wind speed suddenly doubles?
    a. About one-half
    b. About the same
    c. About twice as much
    d. About four times as much
    e. About eight times as much

15. How much does the energy content of wind change if we use rotors with twice the diameter?
    a. About one-half
    b. About the same
    c. About twice as much
    d. About four times as much
    e. About eight times as much

16. How much does the energy content of wind change if we use rotors with half the diameter, while at the same time, the wind speed increases by a factor of two?
    a. About one-half
    b. About the same
    c. About twice as much
    d. About four times as much
    e. About eight times as much

17. The rated power of a wind turbine is
    a. Often at a point at which turbine efficiency is a maximum.
    b. The average between maximum and minimum power.
    c. The average between powers produced at the highest and lowest possible speeds under which the wind turbine can operate.
    d. The average power a turbine produces in one day.
    e. The average power a turbine produces in one year.

18. Two wind turbines, 10 feet and 30 feet in diameter, are standing side-by-side against wind blowing at 5 knots. The smaller wind turbine produces 10 kW of electric power. The larger turbine is expected to produce
    a. 10 kW.
    b. 30 kW.
    c. 60 kW.
    d. 90 kW.
    e. 270 kW.

19. The angle between the blade's chord line and the direction of the incoming relative wind is called the
    a. Yaw.
    b. Pitch.
    c. Roll.
    d. The angle of attack.
    e. The angle of climb.

20. The pitch angle
    a. Is another name for the angle of attack.
    b. The angle the airfoil chord makes with the relative wind direction.
    c. Maximum when the wind blows parallel to the rotational axis of the rotor.
    d. The angle of rotation of the rotor about its shaft.
    e. The angle of rotation of the nacelle into the wind.

21. Rated wind velocity is
    a. The speed at which a turbine starts spinning.
    b. The maximum speed at which a turbine can operate.
    c. The speed at which maximum power is produced and the turbine is designed.
    d. The speed at which efficiency is maximum.
    e. All of the above.

22. Which of the following statements is not correct?
    a. Theoretically, wind turbines need only one blade.
    b. Generally, multi-bladed rotors are less efficient than rotors with only two to three blades.
    c. Two and three-bladed rotors have moderate starting torque, which makes them unsuitable at low wind speeds.
    d. Two-bladed rotors are lighter and run at faster speeds, which make their operation quieter, with considerably less vibration.
    e. The greater the number of blades, the more stable the turbines are, but also the heavier and more expensive.

23. Which of the following statements is correct?
    a. The power generated by a wind turbine varies

linearly with the kinetic energy of the mass of air passing through its rotor.

b. For the same wind velocity and rotor size, more power is generated in summer than in winter.

c. The total power generated by a wind turbine increases with the square of the rotor area.

d. The total power generated by a wind turbine increases with the square of the wind speed.

e. All of the above statements are correct.

24. Two cities, A and B, use the same number of identical wind turbines to generate power. City A has a steady wind speed of 10 knots. City B wind speed varies between 9 and 11 knots, roughly the same proportion of the time. Everything else being the same,

a. City A is producing more power.

b. City B is producing more power.

c. Both cities produce roughly the same amount of power.

d. Both cities produce roughly the same amount of energy.

e. Not enough information is given.

25. How many blades do most modern wind turbines have?

a. One

b. Two or three

c. Three or four

d. More than four

e. No standard number of blades.

26. The best location for installing a wind turbine

a. Is away from the population centers.

b. Is offshore.

c. Is near an electrical grid.

d. Is on top of the mountains.

e. Varies depending on the situation.

27. Among the main causes of aerodynamic noise are

a. The friction of the bearings of the rotor.

b. Background noise from aircraft.

c. The flow of air around turbine blades.

d. Gearbox.

e. All of the above.

28. Which wind turbine concept has the highest achievable efficiency?

a. Fast-running horizontal axis turbine

b. Multi-bladed slow-running horizontal axis turbine

c. Vertical axis Savonius turbine

d. Vertical axis Darrieus turbine

e. Old Persian-type windmill

29. Power train refers to

a. The same thing as maximum power

b. Power transmitted by a gearbox

c. Power put on a transmission grid

d. All the steps necessary to transmit power from the wind turbine to the end-users

e. The power needed by the train which carries a wind turbine to the final installation site

30. Most wind turbines have gearboxes because

a. The turning force (torque) of the wind turbine rotor is, otherwise, too weak to turn a generator.

b. The turning force (torque) of the wind turbine rotor is too high, so it would require a large and expensive generator to handle it.

c. The gearbox is needed to allow the turbine to run at variable speeds.

d. There would be, otherwise, no way to transfer power to the generator.

e. With a gearbox you convert between fast-rotating, low-torque power of the wind turbine rotor and low speed, high-torque power, you need to operate the generator.

IV. True or False?

1. Today, wind energy furnishes less than 3% of the total energy needs of the world.

2. The greater the number of blades, the higher the efficiency of the wind turbines.

3. Land breezes occur during the daytime when land warms up much faster than the surrounding water.

4. Valley and mountain breezes are affected strongly by local topography.

5. The wind rose is a mechanical device for measuring wind velocities.

6. Lift is the force perpendicular to the surfaces of the wind turbine blades.

7. Turbine efficiency is a measure of the fraction of wind energy extracted by a turbine.

8. Rated velocity is the velocity at which turbines must operate to avoid damage.

9. The best location for installing a wind farm is in wide-open fields, away from populated areas but close to the national power grid.

10. The main advantage of the VAWT is that it does not depend on which direction the wind blows.

11. Power density refers to the ratio of the number of wind turbines divided by the area of the rotor.

12. The main source of mechanical noise is the friction associated with the rotating parts of the wind

turbines.

13. The larger the number of blades, the greater is the efficiency of a wind turbine.
14. The amount of electrical power generated per unit land area is independent of the turbine size.
15. Maximum theoretical power extracted by a wind turbine is proportional to the rotor area squared.

V. Fill in the Blanks

1. _____ devices produce high torques and, therefore, were traditionally used for pumping water and grinding mills.
2. Modern large diameter wind turbines are usually of _____ type.
3. Winds are generated as a result of two factors, the non-uniform heating of Earth by Sun and the _____.
4. The power a turbine produces when it is run at its optimum operating condition is called _____ power.
5. The total power generated by a wind turbine is not constant and varies with wind speed and direction, rotor diameter, and air _____.
6. To modify torque from a wind turbine to run a generator, wind turbines are usually equipped with _____.
7. The best way to control the power is by changing the blades' _____ angle.
8. To capture wind independent of which direction is blowing from, _____ axis wind turbines are preferred.
9. The single largest diameter wind turbine operating today produces _____ of electrical power.
10. Raising the tower of a wind turbine from 30 to 60 feet results in the production of _____ more power.
11. The ratio of power captured by the wind turbine to the power available in the air stream is called the _____.
12. An example of a lift-type turbine is _____ turbine. The _____ is an example of a drag type turbine.
13. The first windmills specifically designed to grind flour and pulling water out of wells were designed in _____.
14. The ranges of wind speeds a wind turbine is designed to operate are called _____ and _____ velocities.
15. Rotation of wind turbine into or out of the wind is achieved by controlling then acelle's _____.

PROJECT I – Designing a Wind Farm

A small village is planning to install a wind farm to meet its energy demand. In this project, you are asked to evaluate various wind turbine technologies to meet the electricity needs of the community. The design options considered are the G-mill, two-blade, three-blade, multi-blade, Darrieus (egg-beater), and Savonius turbines. For comparison, assume that all wind designs must provide 60 kW of power when wind speed is around 33 mph.

a. Calculate the average wind speed and wind power factor for each speed range. Wind power factor is the ratio of power produced at a given wind speed to that at nominal speed (in this case, 33 mph).
b. Use data given in Figure 12-18 to estimate rotor efficiency. Calculate the power (kW) produced by each turbine when operated at a given wind velocity.
c. Find the total wind energy for each wind turbine by multiplying power times the number of hours of operation. Sum up capacities to find the annual cumulative value (kWh/year).
d. Assuming 50% conversion efficiency from mechanical to electrical power, determine electrical power for the most efficient turbine.
e. Assuming that the average cost of electricity generation is $0.12/kWh, determine the total annual cost.
f. Redo the problem if turbines are rated at points of their maximum efficiency. Which turbine do you choose? What is its power rating if we are to deliver 100 MWh of electricity annually? Comment!

The following wind data are available from local meteorological offices:

Wind Velocity	0-5	6-10	11-15	16-20	21-25	26-30	31-35	36-40	>40
Hours per Year	1200	1600	1950	1700	1480	960	280	50	10

Project Work Sheet											
Wind velocity (mph)		0-5	6-10	11-15	16-20	21-25	26-30	31-35	36-40	>40	kWh/year
Hours per year		1200	1600	1950	1700	1480	960	280	50	10	------
Average wind velocity					18			33			------
Wind factor					0.16*			1			------
G-Mill	η (%)										------
	kW							60			------
	kWh										
Two-Blade	η (%)										------
	kW							60			------
	kWh										
Three-Blade	η (%)				27%			18%			------
	kW				14.58**			60			------
	kWh				24,786						
Darrieus	η (%)										------
	kW							60			------
	kWh										
Multi-Blade	η (%)										------
	kW							60			------
	kWh										
Savonius	η (%)										------
	kW							60			------
	kWh										

The most efficient turbine: _____

Total mechanical energy available: _____ kWh

Total electricity generation capacity by one turbine: _____ kWh

Total annual operating cost of one turbine: US$ _____

* Wind factor = $(V/V_{nominal})^3 = (18/33)^3 = 0.162$

** Power calculated by scaling the nominal power (60 kW), corrected for wind velocity and efficiency.
   P (18 mph) = 60 kW x 0.162 x (0.27/0.18) = 14.58 kW

CHAPTER **13**

Hydro Energy

Water ~ Wikipedia Commons

Water is the driving force of all nature.
~ Leonardo da Vinci (1452-1519)

We never know the worth of water till the well is dry.
~ Thomas Fuller (1608 - 1661)

Oceans cover more than 70 percent of the earth's surface and are one of the oldest sources of energy. For thousands of years, watermills and paddle wheels have used water flowing in rivers to rotate millstones and grind wheat. The end of the 19th century saw the use of river dams to generate electricity. Today because much of the potential energy resources from rivers have already been exploited, there are increasing interests in harvesting energy from oceans. Oceans store a large amount of solar radiation that provides energy that drives the wind and forms waves and currents. Energy from the difference in elevation, from the rising and fall of ocean waves, from the motion of underwater currents, and from the gravitational energy of the moon-earth-sun system can be used to rotate hydraulic turbines that drive generators to produce electricity. Similarly, the temperature and salinity gradients between the surface and deep water can be exploited to operate a heat engine. Finally, oceans contain a huge amount of deuterium, the potential fuel for operating any future fusion reactor. The fusion reactor technology application is still far in the future and was briefly discussed in the previous chapters.

Hydro energy is the largest source of electricity generation from renewable sources, accounting for 17% of total electricity generation and 70% of all renewables in the world, estimated at 1,300 GW in 2019. With 320 GW installed capacity, China is the leader in the production of power using this resource. The United States, with 103 GW hydro capacity, is the third-largest behind Brazil. Norway with 98-99% of its electricity generated from hydroelectric plants, ranks as the cleanest country in the World.

Depending on which property of water we exploit, there are many ways to generate electric power. Table 13-1 shows various hydro technologies categorized based on location, sources of power, and availability.

Table 13-1 Hydroelectric Technologies			
Rivers and Lakes	*Tides*	*Waves*	*Density*
. Impounded plants . Pumped storage plants . Run-of-the-river plants	. Single pool . Multiple pool . Double basins . Divided bay . Alternating plants	. Fixed devices . Floating devices	. OTEC . Solar ponds . Salinity Gradients

Energy from Falling Waters and Running Rivers

The earliest known watermills were used by what is now eastern Iran in 947 CE to raise water for irrigating their gardens. The first European record dates back to the late twelfth century. These primitive devices allowed the force of falling water and kinetic energy of flowing rivers to act on waterwheels and provide rotational energy or shaft power. Through the centuries, mechanisms were designed to facilitate many other applications beyond simply grinding grain into flour. By the time of the Industrial Revolution, water power was driving tens of thousands of waterwheels in mining, metallurgy, and textiles. Today, hydropower is the most widely available renewable energy, exploited almost exclusively for generating electric power. Direct uses of hydropower are limited and constitute a very small fraction of the total capacity.

Hydroelectric developments exploit either the potential energy of water stored in a reservoir or kinetic energy of the natural flow of water in a river or stream. They range in scale from large falling water plants used in developed nations to small, river-runoff plants with no dams or water storage, used for rural electrification in less-developed countries. The potential for further expansion of hydroelectric plants is limited in most industrialized countries. Developing countries, specifically in Asia and Africa, have exploited very little of their hydro potential and maybe prime locations for developing small hydro projects. Figure 13-1 shows the potential for hydroelectric projects on various continents. The total amount of electricity that can be technically utilized is estimated annually at 14,000 TWh.

Depending on the total power generated, hydroelectric facilities can be classified as large, small, mini, micro, and pico. Obviously, such designations are rather arbitrary, but the commonly accepted definition considers hydro facilities in the range of gigawatt capacities as large, hundreds of megawatts as medium, tens of megawatts as small, and those in 1,000s and 100s of kilowatts as mini and micro. Pico hydro stations are those that generate less than 5 kW of electric power. Medium and large plants are designed to generate electricity directly fed into the grid. Small plants are usually stand-alone units designed to provide power to remote areas and large rural communities away from the grids. Smaller mini and micro units are suitable for small village-type communities and farms. Pico plants generate power to light up a few light bulbs for only a few homes.

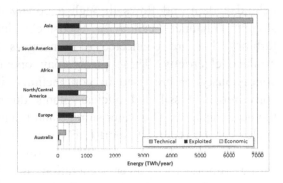

Figure 13-1
Hydroelectric potential by continent.

The largest hydroelectric development in the world is the Three Gorges plant built over the Yangtze River in China (Figure 13-2), producing 22,500 MW of electric power (equivalent to power output by twenty nuclear electricity generating stations).[*] The tallest waterfall in the world is Angel Falls in Venezuela, with a total drop of 980 m. The largest hydroelectric plant in the United States (and the fifth largest in the world) is the Grand Coulee on the Columbia River in Washington State. Its three power plants can collectively produce 6,800 MW (See Table 13-2). The power plants at Niagara Falls, at 2,700 MW, and Hoover at 1,350 MW capacity, are only of modest size.

Figure 13-2
Three Gorges dam in China.

Table 13-2 Largest Hydroelectric Developments in the World (2013)*						
Rank	*Plant*	*Location*	*Max. head (m)*	*Mean flow rate (m³/s)*	*Power (MW)*	*Annual electricity generation (TWh)*
1	Three Gorges	China	185	12,000	22,500	98
2	Itaipu	Brazil-Paraguay	127	6,200	12,600	98
3	Guri	Venezuela	146	4,750.	10,000	46
4	Tucurui	Brazil	78	11,100.	8,370	21
5	Grand Coulee	USA	108	3,100	6,800	21
For a list of references, see Wikipedia (http://en.wikipedia.org/wiki/Hydroelectricity).						

Worth Remembering – Norway relies on its vast hydropower resources for 99% of its electricity, making it the cleanest country in the world, in terms of energy use. Brazil with 86% is second, and Venezuela and Canada rank third and fourth.

Plant Types

The capacity to produce energy from falling waters is a function of both the available flow and the height from which it falls (head). Depending on these parameters, three kinds of hydropower plants are most suitable: impounded plants, pumped storage plants, and run-of-the-river plants.

Impounded Plants are the most common form of hydroelectric generating stations. Water is stored in a reservoir

---

[*] Note the difference between MW_e denoting the electrical power output and MW_t, which refers to thermal power output. As we saw in Chapter 5, only 30-35% of the thermal energy can be converted to electricity. For hydroelectric plants we can use kW and kW_e interchangeably.

behind a dam and flows through a downward sloping channel called a penstock into turbines that are connected to generators to produce electricity. These plants may operate continuously or are used in conjunction with conventional fossil and nuclear plants during the peak capacity. The water storage and release cycles can be relatively short (daily storage for peak-time power generation), or long (collecting spring runoff for power generation in the summer). The main drawback with these plants is that the water flow rate downstream from the dam can change greatly, causing a sudden power surge. A schematic of a typical hydroelectric generating plant is shown in Figure 13-3.

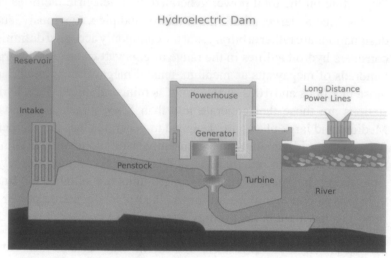

Figure 13-3
Schematics of hydroelectric power generating station.
Source: Wikipedia Commons

Pumped Storage Plants (PSP) take advantage of the excess capacity to store water in reservoirs for later use. This is accomplished by pumping water back into a storage tank at a higher elevation during off-peak hours when the need for electric power is low. During peak demands or when there is an unexpected spike in the electrical load, water is allowed to flow back into the lower reservoir to produce more electricity (Figure 13-4). Alternatively, instead of water being pumped to the storage reservoir at a higher elevation during peak hours, water can be allowed to fall in underground reservoirs dug out in the hard rocks. When demand falls, the baseload can pump the water back to the reservoir. Since there is a smaller fluctuation in the level of water in the main storage reservoir, the system is more stable.

In modern pumped storage plants, the same turbine-generator that generates electricity from falling water also can be used to pump the water back into the storage tank. In this case, the generator changes the direction of the electrical field, forcing the turbine to rotate in the reverse direction and act as a motor, which runs the pump. Since the available potential energy is a function of both the size of the reservoir and the head above the turbine, pumped storage facilities can be built with larger heads and smaller reservoirs. Efficiencies of 70-80% are common when water undergoes a full cycle -- pumped up to the reservoir and released back to generate electricity. In the United States, about one-quarter of all hydropower generated is from pumped storage plants. An important advantage of PSPs is the quick delivery of power during emergencies and power surges. Modern pumped hydroelectric plants use pumps and turbines that can change their speeds to automatically adjust the power output in less than a second. In

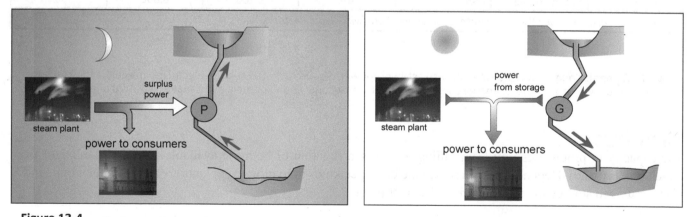

Figure 13-4
Pumped storage.
Adapted from Godfrey Boyle, Energy Systems and Stainability, Oxford University Press, 2003.

comparison, a lump of a typical coal- or natural gas- fired power plant takes many hours to start. Currently, there is more than 100 GW of pumped-storage hydroelectric plants operating worldwide.[†]

Run-of-the-River Plants rely on the natural flow of rivers and waterways. Depending on the slope and local geography, a hydro turbine can be placed in the stream in horizontal or vertical configurations. The horizontal configuration is easier to use as it can be directly connected to a millstone above; in a vertical configuration, the water wheel requires a right-angle gear to be connected to a horizontal millstone. Depending on the difference in water levels vertical watermills are classified as overshot, breastshot, or undershot (Figure 13-5). Undershot wheels exploit the kinetic energy of the flowing streams of rivers and canals. They work best in steady flows of fast streams and heads of up to 3 m. The overshot wheels utilize gravity in streams with heads of more than 5 m. The breastshot machines take advantage of both flow velocity and medium heads between 2 and 5 m.

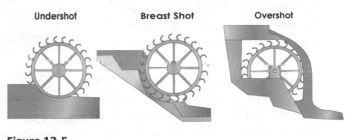

Figure 13-5
Waterwheels.

The power generated in run-of-the-river plants is generally smaller than in pumped storage plants and changes continuously with seasons and weather conditions. Run-of-the-river and small hydro projects are particularly attractive in rural areas with limited demand and away from electrical grids. Since these plants have small or no reservoir capacity and, therefore, do not impede water, their environmental impacts are minimal. According to a recent report by Oak Ridge National Laboratory, the U.S. has the potential to develop over 65 gigawatts of new hydropower development from rivers and streams.[‡]

Hydraulic Turbines

Turbines are devices designed to convert the kinetic energy of working fluids into the rotational energy of a shaft and produce work. Water is the working fluid in a hydraulic turbine. Earlier watermills were rather simple and constructed of many paddles constructed on a rim of a rotating wheel. For a hydraulic turbine to work efficiently, water must enter the turbine without producing any turbulence, and must leave it with little velocity. This assures that almost all the kinetic energy of the incoming water has been expended for driving the shaft. The type of turbine selected depends on the overall flow rate, available head, and whether the plant is in proximity to a grid.

Question: Two medieval varieties of waterwheels still used in many rural areas are undershot and overshot wheels[§]. An undershot watermill refers to a paddle wheel fixed to the bank of a river or hung from an overhead bridge. It is turned by the impulse of the water current. Overshot watermills work by bringing a stream of water through a pipe or canal and pouring it onto the wheel from above (Figure 13-6). Which of the designs seems to have a higher efficiency?

Answer: Overshot wheels. The weight of the water falling on the blades (gravity) forces the wheel to turn at a faster speed. Furthermore, undershot wheels require a steady current, so their operation could be interrupted due to flooding or when water levels drop during the summer months. On the other hand, overshot designs require a drop at least as high as the wheel diameters -- so they are not suitable for shallow river streams. The compromise between overshot and undershot wheels is a breastshot wheel, in which water enters through guidelines at roughly the same level as the wheel axis. Breastshot wheels have efficiencies somewhere between

---

† A closely related technology is lifting heavy blocks of cements, instead of water, to accomplish the task. The *Advanced Rail Energy Storage* (ARES)™ will consume electricity to move a series of rail cars up a hill to store energy. The electricity is reclaimed when it is needed by allowing the cars to go downhill. The concept could be superior to pump-storage, as no water is needed, and environmental impacts are fewer. The facilities are scalable in power and energy ranging from a small installation of 100 MW with 200 MWh of storage capacity up to large 2-3 GW power with 16-24 GWh of energy storage capacity.

‡ https://www.ornl.gov/waterpower.

§ In reality, the word "drop" should be replaced by *hydraulic head*. Hydraulic head is the energy per unit weight of water at a given point.

those of undershot and overshot wheels.

Question: Watermills come in vertical and horizontal configurations (Figure 13-7). What are the advantages and disadvantages of each configuration?

Answer: Most early watermills were used solely for grinding wheat, barley, and other seeds. Horizontal mills were easiest to operate since they could directly turn a shaft that was directly attached to the millstone above. The vertical designs required right-angle gears to transfer power to the stone mill and, thus, were not very convenient.

Figure 13-6
Left: Overshot waterwheel at Berry College in Rome, Georgia, USA
Right: Undershot watermill at at Braine-le-Château, Belgium.
Source: Wikipedia Commons.

Modern turbines are comprised of three elements -- a nozzle, a runner, and a draft tube. The nozzle is the mechanism that guides, which opens and closes depending upon demand. The heart of the turbine is the runner blades, which convert the hydraulic energy into kinetic energy by discharging water through jets of water that hit cups, paddles, or carefully shaped nozzles that direct flow over blades laid on the edge of large rotation wheels. Draft Tube is a diverging tube fitted at the exit of the runner.

Depending on how power is generated, turbines are classified as impulse or reaction types. ***Impulse turbines*** are characterized by several bucket-shaped blades bolted to the rim of the wheel. Jets of fast-moving water are aimed toward and strikes the turbine blades. The blades of an impulse turbine are usually bucket-shaped so they catch the fluid and change the direction of the flow. The change in momentum will result in a net force, imparting a torque that turns the runner. The most common impulse turbines are **Pelton** turbines. They are made in various sizes and are best suitable in mountainous regions at high heads and low flow rates. Because the turbine is not submerged, no housing is required and the pressure remains constant. Because the water head is constant, the power output is adjusted by the volumetric flow rate, which in turn requires the change in diameter of the nozzle impinging on the turbine blades.

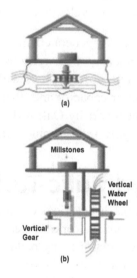

Figure 13-7
Waterwheel configurations:
(a) horizontal, and
(b) vertical.

(a) Pelton

(b) Kaplan

(c) Francis

Figure 13-8
Hydraulic turbines
Sources: a) Wikipedia Commons, b) Courtesy Voth Inc., c) Courtesy Hydrotu Co., Ltd.

Reaction turbines convert potential energy in the pressurized water to mechanical energy. The runner is submerged entirely in water, with the stream flowing over the blades. There is a large pressure drop across the turbine. A reaction turbine doesn't change the direction of the fluid flow as drastically as an impulse turbine; it simply spins as the fluid pushes through and past its blades. Wind turbines are perhaps the most familiar examples of reaction turbines. Their main advantage is that several runners can be placed in the same or separate housing, thus allowing greater flow with good flow control. **Kaplan** turbines are referred to as *axial flow turbines*, with shafts that rotate parallel to the direction of the flow and to which are attached adjustable blades, similar to a ship's propeller. They are best suited to relatively flat regions with low water heads and high flow rates. **Francis** turbines satisfy the intermediate ranges at medium water heads and medium flow rates. In this type, water enters into the runner housed in a spiral casing and exits axially through a diffuser and therefore called *radial flow turbines*. Run backward, it can operate as a pump, and therefore is most suitable for pumped storage power plants. Figure 13-8 shows runners for the three most popular hydraulic turbines.

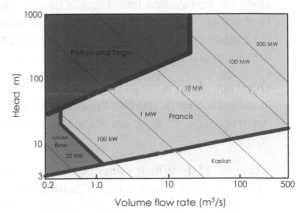

Figure 13-9
Turbine selection chart.

Figure 13-9 is a suggested map for optimum turbine types used in hydroelectric projects. Most low and medium-head power plants use reaction turbines, as they have the advantage that the blades can be adjusted to closely match the rotor speed to the generator speed. Impulse turbines are used at higher heads and low flow rates (See Table 13-3).

Table 13-3 Turbine Selection Guide						
	Applications	*Flow Direction*	*Flow rate (m³/s)*	*Head (m)*	*Type*	*Power*
Kaplan	Flat	axial	high	2-40	reaction	0.1 –100 MW
Francis	Pumped Storage	radial	medium	50-700	reaction	1–500 MW
Pelton	Mountainous	radial	low	50-1800	impulse	0.1-200 MW

Tidal Energy

Tides are the rhythmic up and down motion of the sea as a result of gravitational attraction between the earth, the moon, and to a lesser degree, the sun. Accompanying the vertical rise and fall of water, there also are horizontal or lateral movements, as the tides channel between islands or into bays and estuaries. To avoid confusion, the vertical rise and fall of the water are referred to as *tides*; whereas, the horizontal flow of water is referred to as a *tidal wave* or a *tidal current*. In other words:

The action of tides is best understood by examining the law of gravity as stated by **Newton's Law of Universal Gravitation**, discussed in Chapter 2.

At the same time that gravity is responsible for the near-spherical shapes of the planets, it also is the reason for their bulging along the lines connecting them with their neighboring celestial bodies. For example, as moon orbits earth, it is pulled by the earth's gravity. On the other hand, the moon is trying to escape by moving at a speed just enough to precisely balance gravitational attraction with centrifugal force – which keeps the moon in the earth's orbit.

Question: What explains the symmetrical bulging of water at opposite sides of the earth?

Answer: Gravity acts to pull both the earth and the ocean toward the moon. The pull of gravity becomes weaker at distances farther away from the moon. As the result of progressively declining gravity, the earth is stretched along the earth/moon line. Liquids have weaker internal bonds than solids, so ocean water stretches more than land masses, causing the water facing the moon to bulge. The result is that water is pulled on both sides, giving the earth the shape of a football. A little more than six hours later, the earth has rotated by 90 degrees, relative to the moon, and the situation reverses.

Question: What is the gravitational acceleration of an object on the surface of Jupiter? Jupiter is 300 times more massive than earth and has a diameter of 11.2 times the earth's radii.

Answer: We expect the gravitational acceleration on Jupiter to be $(318/11.2^2)$ or about 2.5 times that of an object on earth.

Example 13-1: Which system experiences a stronger attraction force, the earth/sun or the earth/moon? Sun, earth, and moon have masses of 2×10^{30}, 6×10^{24}, and 7.4×10^{22} kilograms, respectively. The mean distance between the earth and the sun is 1.5×10^{11} m, while the mean distance between the earth and the moon is 3.84×10^{8} m.

Solution: Substituting into Equation 2-1, the force of attraction between the earth and the moon is:

$$F_{E-M} = 6.67x10^{-11} \times \frac{(6x10^{24}) \times (7.4x10^{22})}{(3.84x10^8)^2} = 2x10^{20} \text{ N}$$

and that between the earth and the sun is:

$$F_{E-S} = 6.67x10^{-11} \times \frac{(6x10^{24}) \times (2x10^{30})}{(1.5x10^{11})^2} = 3.56x10^{22} \text{ N}$$

But what about the pull of the sun? Some erroneously attribute this to the much farther distance of the sun than the moon from the earth, i.e., since the denominator is much larger for the earth-sun than earth-moon interaction, the force of attraction is much smaller between the earth and the sun. This is not true, as we saw in Example 13-1, above -- the gravitational pull of the sun is about 178 times greater than that of the pull of the moon. It just so happens that, although the gravitational pull of the sun is much stronger than that of the moon because the sun is so much farther than the moon, its pull does not vary significantly from one side of the earth to the other, and its overall effect is only half that of the moon (Figure 13-10). The sun, however, gives a helping hand during the new and full moons, when it is inline with the earth and the moon. Under these conditions, we have very strong tides. The highest highs and the lowest lows are called **spring tides** (the name comes from the Saxon word *springen* meaning the swelling of water and has nothing to do with the spring season). Spring tides take place about twice a month, a few days after the full and the new moons, when the sun, moon, and earth are aligned and the gravitational pull of the moon and sun are combined.

When the sun-earth line is at a right angle to the earth-moon line (i.e., around the times of first and third quarters),

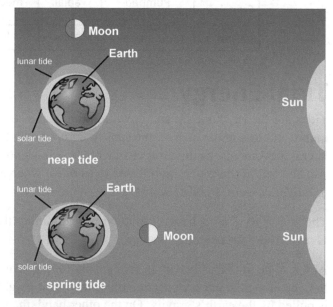

Figure 13-10
Neap and spring tides.

the gravitational effects of the sun and the moon tend to negate each other; tides are lower than the average range and we then have the **neap tides** (neap means scanty or lacking). Unlike a 24-hour solar day, a lunar day lasts a bit longer -- 24 hours and 50 minutes -- to "catch up" to the moon. As a result, we expect an interval of 12 hours and 25 minutes between two high or two low tides (called tidal intervals). Spring tides are roughly twice the height of neap tides. In addition to half-day and half-month cycles, there are minor effects due to the inclination of the moon's orbit that gives rise to semi-annual cycles between the highest spring tides in March and September. In general, most places experience two high and two low tides each day. Two different technologies can extract power from tidal barges and tidal streams:

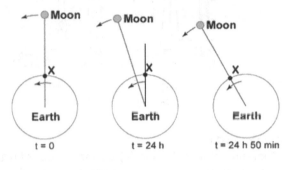

Tidal Barges

Using tides for power generation is not a new concept. Tidal mills operated off the western coasts of Europe for many centuries before being replaced by cheaper methods of producing energy. These mills took advantage of the natural rise and fall of coastal tides by allowing water to fill up a pond during flood tides and then emptying that water over a watermill during ebb tide. In the modern versions of tide mills, a barrier is built across an estuary and is allowed to be filled by water during the flood tide. The barrier is equipped with gates that are closed as the basin fills with water. As the tide recedes into the open sea during its ebb, the water empties and drives turbines, which in turn, drive generators and produce electricity. Upon emptying, the basin gates are closed to allow the water in the sea to rise. This creates a head against the basin during the flood, which can be emptied for a second time, turning the turbines in the opposite direction and generating more power (Figure 13-11).

Until recently, the largest tidal power station that has ever been constructed, was a 240-MW plant built-in 1966, and still operating today in La Rance Estuary in France (Figure 13-12). In 2011, a bigger plant, Sihwa Lake Tidal Power Station, with a capacity of 254 MW started operation in South Korea. Two other plants are operating commercially. The first, with an electrical generating capacity of 20 MW, is the Annapolis Royal Station in Nova Scotia, off the Bay of Fundy in Canada; the second is a small, 1.8-MW tidal plant in Kislaya Bay near Murmansk, in the Russian Arctic.

The potential energy of tidal power has been shown to increase linearly with the basin area and the square of the average range between the low and high tides (See Digging Deeper: Power Potential from Tides). Oceans having tidal ranges of 0.6 meters are typical; in narrow passages and estuaries, ranges as high as 15 m are common. To be practical, tidal ranges of at least 5 meters are recommended. Unfortunately, there is only a limited number of sites on the planet that meet this requirement. Russia has the largest potential to exploit tidal power – over 1,670 billion kWh annually. Canada and Argentina also are good candidates, but it is the United Kingdom that plans to build the largest tidal power plant -- a 16-km long barrage (dam) across the Bristol Channel (Severn Estuary). Once built, the Severn Tidal Plant would have the capacity to produce 8 GW of peak power (2 GW on average) producing in excess of 17 billion kWh of electricity annually and, at the same time, reducing carbon dioxide emissions by 16 million tons each year. The total tidal world potential energy has been estimated at 64 GW.

Using tidal energy in conjunction with the pumped storage approach has been discussed in the literature. Water can be pumped to an artificially built lagoon during high tides when plenty of power is available and the lagoon can be filled with very little head. The same water is let out during low tide, taking advantage of the much greater head available during this period. The energy generated is much larger than that used to pump water into the storage lagoon during high tides. This approach has the additional benefit of helping to distribute power, making it more accessible during periods of peak demand and low tides.

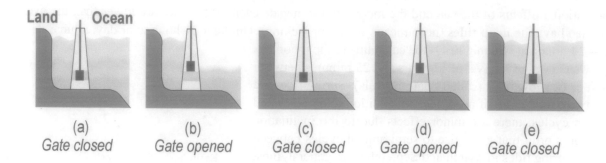

Land   Ocean

(a)
Gate closed

(b)
Gate opened

(c)
Gate closed

(d)
Gate opened

(e)
Gate closed

Figure 13-11
Operation of a tidal plant: (a) During periods of high-tides, water fills the basin. (b) At low tides, the gate is opened and water is allowed to empty into the open sea while turning a turbine. (c) Once all the potential energy is exhausted, the gates are closed again, allowing water to rise in the open sea. (d) The flow is from the open sea to the basin and the turbine runs in the opposite direction. (e) The gate is closed until water rises again and repeats the operation.

Tidal Currents

A **tidal current** is the horizontal back and forth flow of water near ocean floors as the tide rises and falls. Unlike water current through a river that is continuous, steady, and always in the same direction, tidal currents change speed and direction. Tide currents are easily set apart from wind waves in that they come roughly every 24 hours and 50 minutes -- their frequencies. Wavelengths are half the earth's circumference at the equator or about 20,000 km. When water enters estuaries or narrower channels, its wavelength becomes somewhat shorter, still in hundreds of kilometers. Amplitudes (heights) vary widely from day to day, depending on the distances of the earth to the moon and the sun, from less than a meter on ocean surfaces to a few meters in shallower estuaries. The ratio of wave height (crest to trough) to wavelength (two consecutive crests, or two consecutive troughs) gives the wave steepness. Tidal waves are, therefore, extremely flat and shallow. That's why, to an observer, tides seem to rise and fall like water in a tub with hardly any noticeable movements.[¶] Because tide waves are shallow waves, they maintain their back-and-forth motions even at ocean depth, result in what is normally referred to as ebb and flow tides. The strength of marine currents varies with the time of day and the shape of coastlines and the sea-bed. They are maximum at mid-tide, and slightly larger during ebb tides than at flow tides.

Figure 13-12
Tidal power plant at the Bay of Rance Estuary in France.

Figure 13-13
Underwater Turbines.
Image courtesy of SEAGEN.

Underwater turbines usually are of propeller types, similar to wind turbines, except that they are designed to capture the kinetic motion of the ebbing and surging of ocean tides to produce electricity. Speed is somewhat smaller and varies between 2-5 m/s. Because power is proportional to fluid density, for the same power output, water turbines can be made much smaller. There are no commercial tidal current plants yet, but many demonstration plants are under construction around the world. Figure 13-13 shows the 16-m rotor diameter SeaGen tidal turbine installed in a demonstration project in the Bay of Fundy in Canada. The 86 MW MeyGen Tidal Energy Project in Scotland is currently the world's biggest underwater tidal turbine power project under development.

> **Worth Remembering** – Tidal currents can generate roughly 4 W for every square meter of ocean floor.

¶ In addition to tidal and wind waves, there are some hydrothermal currents that are caused by heat from the earth's interior.

Wave Energy

As the wind blows across the ocean, some of its energy is transferred to the water, in the form of waves. The rougher the water, the larger the ripples, and the easier it is for the wind to transfer its energy. Since wind itself is a result of non-uniform heating of the earth's surface by the sun, waves can be considered a stored form of solar energy.

Per unit area, wave energy is small, less than 1% of the energy incident by solar radiation. However, as waves travel long distances of many hundreds of kilometers before they encounter wave power devices, they accumulate energy and intensify. So, it usually makes more sense to express the wave power in kW/m of the wavefront. The maximum power a wave can carry over deep waters is about 100 kW/m of the wavefront in the high seas, about 30-60 kW/m around the Atlantic coasts of Europe, and 20-30 kW/m off the West Coast of the United States (Table 13-4). Waves are strongest between 40°-60° latitudes, where the wind is the strongest, in both Northern and Southern Hemispheres and are, therefore, most suitable for power extraction. Surface currents flow clockwise in the Northern Hemisphere and counter-clockwise in the Southern Hemisphere.[**] The total theoretical energy that can be harvested from waves is estimated at 8×10^8 TWh, which is about 100 times the total annual hydroelectricity generated globally.

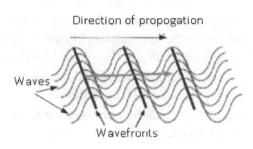

Figure 13-14
Wave front.

Surface waves result from the superposition of many waves of varying wavelengths and heights, from small ripples to monster or killer waves. They travel in groups, with the longest waves and faster speeds in front. Losses are larger in short waves than in long waves, causing short waves to fade away, while long ones survive, traveling many thousands of kilometers before they approach the shoreline. As waves get closer and closer, up to 70% of the energy is lost by friction to the ocean floors and slow down. Longer surface waves travel faster and farther than shorter ones, but the energy content of a wave is related solely to its height.

Table 13-4 Near-term Potential For Wave Energy In Several European Countries		
Country	Near shore (TWh/year)	Offshore (TWh/year)
UK	14-21	43-64
Ireland	7-11	21-32
Portugal	4-6	12-18
France	3-5	12-18
Spain	3-5	10-16

By far, the most common representation of a wave is the sine wave, normally associated with simple harmonic motion, and is mathematically represented by its *wavelength* (the distance between two consecutive crests or troughs), *wave height* (the vertical distance between crests and troughs), *frequency* (the number of waves that pass a particular point in one second), or *period* (the time for one complete cycle of a wave oscillation). *Amplitude* is the distance between the crest or trough to the still water line; i.e., one-half of the wave height. From these definitions, it appears that frequency and period are reciprocal to each other. The distance that a wave travels past a given point during one period is called wave velocity. Small ripples in the pond travel at less than 1 m/s, ocean waves travel at around 10 m/s, and sound propagates at about 1,500 m/s. Light has the highest speed of all. It moves at the incredible speed of 300,000 km/s, or about a million times faster than sound.

Ocean Waves

Depending on their origin, ocean waves can be classified as wind waves, tsunamis, tide waves, and currents. **Surface waves** are wind-generated waves occurring on the free surface of oceans, lakes, or rivers. They are produced when the wind blows across the surface of the ocean, in the same way as you see ripples when you blow on a cup of hot

[**] Tsunamis are special types of waves not caused by wind but by geological effects such as earthquakes, landslides, or nuclear explosions. In deep water, tsunamis are not visible because they have shallow heights and have very long wavelengths. As they get closer to the coast, their water depths reduce, their wavelengths decrease, and their height and energy amplify to devastating proportions.

tea. Their energy is, in effect, the wind energy that is temporarily locked in ocean waters. A wave is considered to be a **deep-water wave** when the water depth is greater than one-half of the wavelength. Water particles inside this type of wave move forward and back, up and down in a circular orbit, whose diameter decreases exponentially with depth, becoming weaker at the greater depth, until they eventually disappear at the bottom of oceans. Waves are said to be **shallow-water waves** when the depth is much smaller than their wavelength. At these depths, the particles have difficulty in completing their circular paths and are squeezed into more elliptical shapes (Figure 13-15). As water enters shallower and shallower depth, the particles closer to the bottom do not move, whereas the particles at the surface continue their motion; as the wave approaches the coastline, the crest eventually falls forward to form a *surf* (Figure 13-16). **Tidal waves** and **tidal currents** result from gravitational action between earth, moon, and sun, and were discussed above.

Tsunamis form when there is a sudden jolt, or a major disturbance in the ocean tectonic floor, such as an earthquake or underwater volcanic eruptions; the energy released travels in the form of concentric ripples that move away from the point of origin, similar to ripples emanating from a stone dropped into the water.[20]

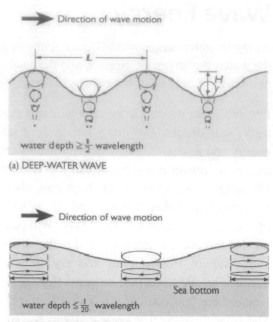

Figure 13-15
Deep water waves maintain their shape as eventually die out at a point referred to and wave bed. The shallow-water waves become more and more squeezed as they approach the sea bottom resulting in a constant current travelling toward or away from the shore.

Wave Energy Converters (WEC)

Wave power generation plants can be classified as onshore, nearshore, or offshore, and are either fixed type or floating type. Fixed generating devices are located along the shore or are fastened to the seabed and are generally simpler to maintain and operate. Floating devices are installed on floating platforms. The main advantages of onshore and nearshore plants are that they are much cheaper to construct and there is a shorter distance for electrical cables to be laid on the ocean floors. Their main disadvantage is that waves break up and lose much of their energy as they approach coastlines. Shore-based stations are mostly considered for small-scale electricity generation. Offshore devices have the advantage of being more efficient, they do not use up valuable beach property, and they are not as unsightly to the public as nearshore facilities. All of these devices work in a similar fashion; namely, they work directly by activating a generator or pushing a working fluid (water or air) to drive a turbine and generator. No matter which approach is used, there are always some navigational hazards to shipping and other marine transportation.

Just as wind is affected by local terrain, coastal waves are affected by underwater topography. Narrow channels between islands and around the coastal edges of oceans are best suited for power generation and can provide as much as one megawatt of power per square kilometer of the seabed. To increase the velocity of the water and, thus, its kinetic energy, some propose building barriers across channels and narrow straights. The best locations are near the shore at depths of between 20 to 30 meters, where wave velocities are approximately 2-3 meters per second.

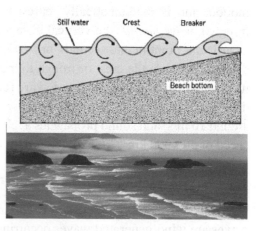

Figure 13-16
As waves approach the shoreline, they travel at slower velocities and shorter wavelengths, breaking, eventually.

> **Worth Remembering –** Waves are actually energy that travel across the ocean surface, not the water itself. Water particles only travel in small circles as a wave passes.

Design Requirements

Research on developing better wave power devices must focus not only on making them more efficient in extracting power from waves but also to devise cheaper and more elaborate schemes for converting mechanical energy into electricity. Volshanik and Malinin outlined necessary criteria for the design of better and more efficient power extracting technologies.

- The device must be capable of extracting energy from a wide range of amplitudes and frequencies.
- The device must be capable of operation along the entire wavefront, and height of the water layer.
- The device must be capable of exploiting both the kinetic and potential energies of the wave.
- The device must be protected or shut off during severe storm conditions.
- The device must be capable of adapting to changes in the water levels during ebb and flood due to seasonal variation in wave characteristics.

Depending on the method of conversion, the wave energy converters fall into three categories: point absorbers, terminators, and attenuators. **Point absorbers** are devices capable of absorbing energy from incoming waves in all directions; they are normally tethered buoy systems and, therefore, are most useful offshore in the intermediate depth of 50-150 meters. Oscillating Water Column (OWC) devices such as AquaBuoy and Archimedes Wave Swing (AWS) work based on this principle. **Terminators** are oriented perpendicular to the incident waves extracting power as they physically intercept the waves. They are called as such because they take advantage of all the energy contained in waves. Wave Dragon and Tapered Channel (TapChan) are two such devices. **Attenuators** are similar to terminator-type devices, except their principal axis is parallel to the wavefront (perpendicular to the wave direction). They work by extracting energy as waves pass overhead. Salter's Duck and Pelamis Sea Snake are two devices operating as attenuators. No large-scale commercial wave power plants of any type have been built yet, although major research is underway and several prototype systems have been built in Portugal, Norway, Japan, India, and Scotland.

We will discuss each of these devices briefly.

1. **Onshore and Nearshore Systems:**
   a. An *Oscillating Water Column* is the most common mechanism for extracting power from ocean waves. The oscillatory motion of the water will expand or compress a column of air trapped inside a chamber, causing its pressure to rise or fall. As the water rises and the air is compressed, the air is forced through a nozzle and runs a turbine. This can happen as water moves toward the shoreline, as waves pass over the crest line, or as the result of swells during a tide. As the water level falls, such as when the water recedes, when waves are at their troughs, or during the ebb tides, the air pressure decreases, and the direction of the flow is reversed (Figure 13-17a). Because of this bidirectional airflow, special turbines are designed that rotate in only one direction, no matter the direction of airflow. The first operational design of this device, called LIMPET (for Land-Installed Marine-Powered Energy Transformer), was installed on the Scottish island of Islay and generates 500 kW of electric power. A similar design, called Osprey, is installed in the UK and generates 1.5 MW. Most OWCs are still in the experimental stages.
   b. A *Tapered Channel* consists of a sloped funnel-shaped waterway and a reservoir constructed on top of a cliff or a structure a few meters above sea level. Because of the narrowing of the channel, waves force water to speed up, climb and pour into a reservoir providing the head. Water leaves through a hole at the bottom of the tank and turns a turbine, before being discharged back into the ocean or the sea. The scheme has low maintenance costs but works only when there is a deepwater shoreline and is most suitable when operated during peak demands.

2. **Offshore Systems:**
   a. The *Archimedes Wave Swing (AWS)* consists of a large air-filled chamber submerged below the sea surface, placed on floating platforms that move vertically (Figure 13-17b). As a wave crest passes overhead, the pressure over the top rises and applies a downward force and compresses the trapped air inside the chambers, and the float sinks. The process reverses as the wave trough passes overhead; air pressure drops and the float climbs back up.
   b. A *Wave Dragon* is a floating device that operates in a similar fashion to a tapered channel, except that the wave motion pushes ocean water into a reservoir above sea level, where water is let out through a number of turbines that run generators to produce electricity (Figure 13-17c). The Wave Dragon overtopping device consists of the main structure comprised of a reservoir and two or more wave reflectors that function by focusing the waves toward a ramp. The hydraulic head in the reservoir is used to operate a set of low-head Kaplan propeller turbines. The first prototype connected to a grid is currently deployed in Denmark.
   c. The *Salter's Duck* is a cam-shaped rocker that swings back and forth as a wave passes by. The shape of the rocker is such that the dynamic pressure caused by the wave motion efficiently forces the duck to rotate about an axis.
   d. The *Pelamis* (also called a sea snake) is a semi-submerged, attenuator-type, articulated structure composed of cylindrical sections linked by hinged joints. As the hinge bends and flexes, it pushes high-pressure fluid through a hydraulic device that drives a turbine and generator to produce electricity (Figure 13-17d).

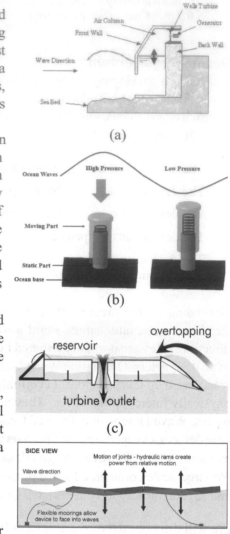

Figure 13-17
Wave Power Extracting Devices. a) Oscillating Water Column; b) Archemides Wave Swing; c) Wave Dragon; d) Pelamis Sea Snake.

Thermal Gradient

Incident solar energy is stored directly, as thermal energy in the top layer of ocean surfaces, and indirectly as the kinetic energy of wind, waves, and currents. Power generation through wind, waves, and currents was discussed above and in a previous chapter. Solar heating of oceans and ponds results in temperature gradients that can be exploited to generate electricity and/or heat using basic thermodynamic principles.

Ocean Thermal Energy Conversion (OTEC)

Oceans cover over 70% of the earth's surface area and are a huge source of thermal energy. Ocean Thermal Energy Conversion (OTEC) takes advantage of the temperature difference between the warm surface waters and cold deep waters of the oceans to drive steam turbines and produce electricity. Ocean waters between the Tropics of Cancer and Capricorn (latitudes between 23° N and 23° S) typically have the highest surface temperatures -- around 25°-30°C -- while the water below 900 meters is only 5°C. The temperature differences are very steady over time, between day and night, and from season to season. Figure 13-18 shows contours of the oceanic temperature difference between surface and deep waters.

French engineer Jacques D'Arsonval was the first to note the huge potential for using thermal gradients in the ocean to produce power. His proposed system was not implemented until 1930, when his student, George Claude, built the first OTEC plant at Matanzas Bay, off the coast of Cuba. Although the system functioned, the work needed to run the

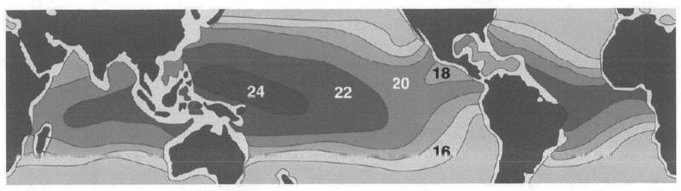

Figure 13-18
Contours of oceanic temperature difference between surface and 1000 m depth. The area around the equator has temperature gradients of around 24°C.
Image courtesy of Xenesys Inc.

pumps and other devices was more than the work output. Furthermore, difficulties in lubricating underwater pipes, salt corrosion, and growth of algae (biofouling) made the system inoperable and the project was abandoned. Many of the technical difficulties facing Claude have since been resolved and, now, there is a renewed interest in OTEC technology. In the United States, Hawaii is best suited to operate OTEC plants, but Florida and Puerto Rico also are good candidates.

OTEC plants can be constructed to operate in closed or open cycles. Closed-cycle systems use the ocean's warm surface water to vaporize a working fluid, such as ammonia, R-134a, or other refrigerants. In short, warm surface water causes the refrigerant to vaporize. The vapor then expands through a turbine that turns a generator to produce electricity. The vapor eventually is condensed by transferring its heat to the cold waters of the deep ocean, before being pumped back to the evaporator, completing the cycle. A schematic of a closed-cycle OTEC plant is shown in Figure 13-19a.

In open-cycle systems, water itself is the working fluid. Open-cycle systems work by boiling the surface water into a flash evaporator operating at a pressure so low (~ 2-4 kPa), that water boils at the temperature of the surface water (Figure 13-19b). The steam drives a low-pressure turbine to generate electricity. The steam is condensed back into liquid water in a condenser, which is then cooled by deep seawater before being discharged. The output of the condenser is desalinated water, one of the desirable by-products of the OTEC system.

In addition to open and closed cycles, an OTEC plant also can be designed as a hybrid, where steam is generated by flash evaporation of warm surface water and then used as a heat source for a closed cycle.

Example 13-2: What is the maximum theoretical efficiency of an OTEC plant operating in equatorial waters?
Solution: Assuming that an OTEC plant operates between a surface temperature of 25°C and a deepwater temperature of 5°C, the maximum efficiency is limited to its Carnot efficiency, which can be calculated as:

$$\text{OTEC maximum efficiency} = 1 - \frac{278}{298} = 6.7\%$$

Because of the power required for pumping cold water from the bottom of the ocean and other frictional losses, the efficiency of a practical OTEC device is lower than this value at around 2-3%; this is far below the 30-35% thermal efficiencies commonly found in conventional oil- or coal-fired steam plants. Unlike conventional plants, however, there are no fuel costs.

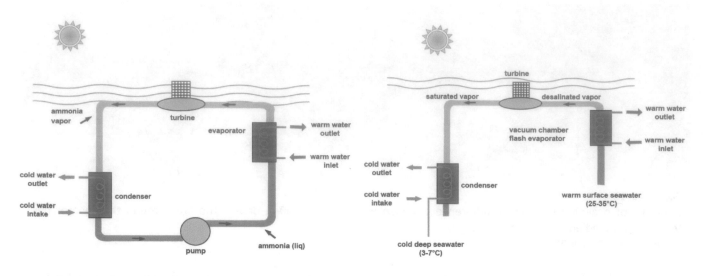

Figure 13-19
OTEC system: (a) Closed cycle, and (b) Open cycle

Benefits of OTEC System

Considering all the side benefits, OTEC could potentially fulfill an important role in the mix of energy alternatives we have at our disposal. Not only is OTEC a clean source of energy for offshore and nearshore applications, but it is also useful in many areas where conventional fuels are not. Examples are:

Aquaculture – Deepwater is not only clean but also has a significantly higher amount of nutrients that allow enhanced growth of marine algae and many marine organisms, such as salmon and lobster, that could not otherwise grow in a tropical environment. Deep seawater is also a huge sink for many industrial applications that require the dumping of waste heat.

Cooling – After the steam is expanded in the turbine, it is condensed in the condenser. The condensate is relatively free of impurities and can be used in many applications such as air conditioning, desalination, and chilled-soil agriculture.

Thermoclines

The temperature of the ocean decreases with depth. The decrease is not uniform. The rate of decrease is particularly high in the mid-latitudes, and in depths of between 200 and 1,000 meters. It has been suggested that the power output of conventional hydroelectric facilities can be significantly augmented when a distinct layer in a large body of water, such as an ocean or lake, where the temperature gradient is greater than that of the warmer layer above and the colder layer below (Figure 13-20). The layer of water is called **thermocline** and may form temporarily or permanently. Vast quantities of solar energy are stored in the form of freshwater thermoclines behind hydroelectric dams, far exceeding the energy stored in the gravitational potential. A typical 15°C thermocline can, in principle, increase the potential gravitational equivalent to 6.4 km of the additional head, far exceeding the energy stored in the gravitational potential.

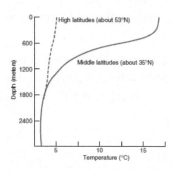

Figure 13-20
Thermoclines.

Salinity Gradient[††]

When a river runs into a sea, spontaneous mixing of fresh and saltwater occurs, without any work produced. When a semi-permeable membrane separates two bodies of water of different densities, water molecules move from the less salty (freshwater) to an area of more brackish (saltwater). The water rises until the pressure on both sides equalizes.[‡‡] This is called *osmosis*. The membrane is a synthetic material with microscopic-sized holes that filters out salt, bacteria, and viruses, but allows water molecules to go through. By applying a force on the salty side, the direction of flow can be reversed, squeezing out the freshwater in a process called *reverse osmosis desalination* (See Figure 13-21a).

The pressure difference between fresh river runoff and salty ocean and seawater also can be used to generate electricity (Figure 13-21b). This technique utilizes the difference in salinity between fresh river runoff and saline seas or oceans to produce electricity. It has been estimated that, globally, between 1.4 and 2.6 TW of power is available in the form of salinity gradients. The main barrier to this technology is the high cost of the membrane. Efforts are underway to develop less expensive membranes or come up with alternative designs that eliminate membranes, altogether. For a typical seawater concentration of 3.5% (35 grams of dissolved salt per liter of water),[§§] the osmotic pressure difference is about 2,700 kPa (~ 27 atmospheres), equivalent to a head of 270-m of water.·

Osmosis

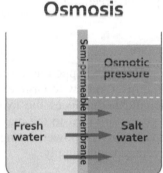

Water moves to the side with higher salt concentration. The pressure rise can be used to drive a turbogenerator to produce electricity.

(a)

Reverse osmosis

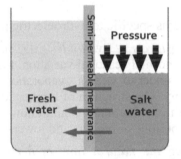

Pressure can be applied on the salty water. Fresh water will pass through the semi-permeable membrane (desalination).

(b)

Figure 13-21
(a) Electricity generation; (b) Desalination

Thermohaline Circulation

Outside of the earth's equatorial regions, weather patterns are driven mainly by ocean currents. Current in the upper 100 meters of the ocean's surface is principally driven by surface winds. Deep below the surface, currents are driven by density differences, which are themselves controlled by temperature and salinity gradients (i.e. thermohaline), earth's rotation, and tides. Factors resulting in reduced salinity are precipitation, water runoff, and heating by the sun. Water cooling, ice formation, and evaporation, on the other hand, result in an increase in salinity and thus density of water. The varying density of ocean water resulting from temperature and salt concentration results in the transport of a massive amount of water that directly affects our global weather pattern, and provides a means for carrying fresh water to the surface.

---

†† In Chapter 10, we discussed the "Solar Ponds" which exploits the thermal gradients in a body of water strongly affected by salinity gradients. It should be noted that this method does not harness osmotic power, only solar power.

‡‡ This is, by the way, why drinking a lot of salt water kills you. In an attempt to dilute the salty water in your stomach, water is sucked out of your body and the body dehydrates.

§§ Salinity has been traditionally expressed as parts per thousands (ppt for which the symbol o/oo is used), which is grams of salt per kilogram of solution Therefore the brackish water salinity of 35 ppt means 35 gram of salt per 1000 liters of seawater. The waters with the highest salinity are in the Red Sea and the Persian Gulf (40 o/oo); the lowest salinities occur in polar seas at around 5 o/oo).

Environmental Impact

Hydropower technologies have many of the same advantages as other renewable energy sources. It is considered to be clean and is one of the few sources of energy that do not contribute to global warming or produce any of the air pollutants that result from the combustion of fossil fuels. Besides, hydropower does not have the intermittency and unpredictability associated with solar and wind. In addition to generating electricity, hydropower has provided a variety of benefits that include water supply, flood control, navigation, and irrigation (Figure 13-22). It also has provided numerous opportunities for developing recreational activities such as water sports, fishing, boating, and public beaches.

This does not mean that hydropower is without any adverse environmental impact, however. These include erosion, sedimentation, and flooding as a result of changes to flow patterns upstream and downstream of facilities, and variation in water chemistry which, in turn, affects bacterial and algae growth, and impact on flora and fauna of the local and surrounding communities. Marshlands created during the construction and draining of a dam's reservoir may be also significant emitters of methane and other potent greenhouse gases.

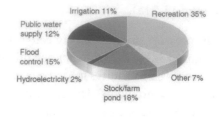

Figure 13-22
Many uses of hydro dams.
Source: U.S. Army Corps of Engineers, National Inventory of Dams

a. **Dams** - Concerns specific to hydroelectric projects are:

- *Fluctuating levels of available water supply* – This can happen as a result of severe drought, excess rainfall, or normal seasonal variation. Lakes and reservoirs with large exposed areas may undergo excess evaporation, which further reduces the available water supply. Construction of a pumped storage facility next to the main dam can smooth out fluctuations and allow a steady supply of power during peak hours and periods of higher- and lower-than-average water supply.

- *Interrupting the natural flow of a river* – Change in river conditions and adjacent lands may impact fish migration and aquatic populations, threaten the natural habitats of wildlife, affect vegetation, and degrade shorelines. One way to facilitate the natural upstream migration of fish is through the construction of a series of stepped pools called fish ladders. With the proper design, fish learn to bypass the dam, finding their way toward the ladder, and swim upstream (Figure 13-23). Building dams will require diverting ships and other marine transport, which may be difficult and cost-prohibitive.

Figure 13-23
Fish ladder.

- *Impeding the natural transport of sediments* – Restricting the amount of water flow results in a reduction in the river sedimentation downstream from the dam, and an accumulation of silt in lakes behind the dam. As the storage volume becomes filled with silt, the generation capacity of the plant is reduced, and the stored water may require periodic dredging and flushing of sediments at a considerable cost.

- *Affecting water quality* – Impounding water flow raises the surface water temperature which, in turn, affects the concentration of dissolved oxygen and other nutrients, and allows certain bacteria to grow in hydro rivers and reservoirs that potentially may pose a health hazard.

- *Causing floods* – Although dams can act as a flood control measure, there also are concerns for the flooding of lakes and rivers upstream from the plant. In addition, a dam structural failure -- in the event of an earthquake or other disasters -- could cause immediate flooding of the area below the dam, costing countless lives and enormous economic loss.

- *Displacing Population* – Large hydropower projects will have a huge impact on the surrounding population. Because of the potential dangers caused by a dam's failure and subsequent flooding, many people would have to be relocated, which, in turn, may have a considerable impact on the local economy. For example, it is estimated that up to 1.3 million villagers had to be relocated as a result of the construction of the Three Gorges plant in China.

b. **Run-of-the-River:** Hydroelectric stations using river currents have a marked impact on the river flow, both upstream and downstream of the installation, as they affect water availability, vegetation, and by inference, animal populations. Changes in the current velocity could have an important influence on the rate of sedimentation and may impact air quality along the river banks.

c. **Ocean Thermal Energy Conversion:** The environmental impact associated with OTEC operation is relatively minimal, and limited to some changes in local marine life and the release of CO_2, as cold water from the deep oceans is brought to the warm water surface. This release is, however, negligible compared to the amount of CO_2 release that would result from the use of fossil fuel to generate a comparable amount of energy. The major obstacle to OTEC development is the initial cost and limited suitable sites near shorelines. OTEC cold water pipes make up most of the costs, so OTEC sites cannot be more than a few kilometers away from the coastline. The best solution is likely to use the electricity generated by offshore OTEC platforms to produce alternative fuels, such as methanol and hydrogen, which then can be loaded onto tankers or flow through pipes.

d. **Waves and Tides:** The primary concerns raised against wave and tidal power are their vulnerability to freak and violent storms, noise, and the additional costs if electricity is brought to land. For many, the installation of large wave-energy devices, overhead transmission lines, and support facilities may not be aesthetically pleasing. Offshore or deepwater installations are advantageous because they are visually less intrusive, and can take advantage of higher wave energies; the cost is higher, however. Tidal power has the advantage that it is highly predictable; construction is not noticeable at a distance, so the visual impact is minimal. Furthermore, because the power-per-unit rotor area is higher for tidal turbines than wind turbines, for the same power capacity, sizes are smaller and the noise problem is less severe.

> **Solar Crock Pot**
>
> Indian workers have devised a cooking system that makes no demands on the critically short supply of wood, their traditional energy source. They dug a pond about 1-m deep and 8-m in diameter and lined it with impermeable plastic. The pond was filled with water and enough salt poured in to give a saline concentration of 20 percent at the bottom. The concentration of salt gradually decreased from the bottom to the top of the pond. The salt gradient prevents convection, as the saltwater is too heavy to rise. Thus the water at the bottom absorbs solar heat energy throughout the day and reaches a temperature over 80°C at the bottom. Food is placed in sealed pots and left in the pond for a whole day. This kind of cooking is equivalent to an electric "crockpot" which takes 75 W for 8 hours.

Economics of Hydro Energy

Power output from a hydroelectric station increases with the flow rate of the water and its available head. For a given power output, less water is required for the higher head, so the plant size would be smaller, and the cost of construction and equipment would be lower. Unfortunately, taller waterfalls tend to be in mountainous regions and areas with lower population density, so the transmission costs may be higher. Thus, before selecting the plant site, it is important to consider not only the total power but also the initial and operating costs, including the cost of transmission. Specific to different hydro energy technologies are:

Dams and other Impounds: The cost of producing electricity from water impounds is rather low, and competes favorably with electricity generated by burning fossil fuels - 3 to 10 cents per kilowatt-hour, depending on location, plant size, water flow rate, and head. The initial cost of construction varies widely depending on the topography, size of the water reservoir, and their immediate impact on populations living upstream or downstream from the plant. Run-of-water plants are not economical for developed countries but may make economic sense in developing countries with a vast network of waterways. Typically, the installed cost of hydro electrification projects is about $1,000-1,500 per kW for large, $2,500-3,000/kW for small (2.5-25 MW), and $10,000/kW for micro (below 500 kW) hydro projects.

Ocean Thermal Energy: Construction of OTEC plants is possible at only a few locations around the world, and therefore makes economic sense only under certain favorable conditions. Building an OTEC plant requires the movement of a substantial amount of hardware, piping, and floating platforms offshore. It is, therefore, considered a viable option, only in regions where electricity is needed far offshore from any land. The main attraction of OTEC technology is that it could be used not only to produce electricity, but also for desalination, space cooling, aquaculture, and agriculture. The technology can also be used to produce liquid fuels that then can be brought onshore by barges, and through underwater pipelines, rather than direct power transmission to shores.

Waves: The cost of deploying wave energy varies largely depending on several factors, including the technology, the geography, size of the plant, distance from the grid, and availability of resources at the site. One thing is clear that the cost is continuously dropping from the ¢7.5/kWh, today.

Salinity Gradients: Reverse osmosis has long been used in producing purified water in desalination plants. The forward osmosis – i.e., generating power by drawing freshwater into saltwater through a membrane – has been tried in limited applications, mainly in research institutions. The preliminary results suggest that the technology could be viable when an osmotic pressure potential of greater than 25 atmospheres is available. There are no commercial plants of this type available, as yet.

Summary

The ocean, alone, can fulfill all the energy needs of humans for a long time. Water is a clean source of energy, and environmental impact is relatively limited. The main advantage of this system is that, unlike wind energy, this system provides a constant and predictable source of power. Except for wave technologies, much of the hydropower potential in developed countries already has been exploited or is of limited significance. In contrast to wind, deep-water currents have relatively steady speeds and, therefore, no energy storage system is necessary. It appears that in the future, much of the hydropower development will be in developing countries, especially in Asia and Africa, where much of the world's small-scale and low-head hydro capacity exists. Tidal energy cannot satisfy a significant demand, as geographical locations limit its deployment. Ocean currents have vast amounts of energy, but because of their low speed, they have low energy densities. Salinity gradients, or the difference in salt concentrations with depth, may prove to be a major source of energy. Desalination plants are used routinely to remove salt from brackish water, but the technology is not yet well-developed enough to exploit salinity gradients for extracting energy.

Tides are clean, entirely predictable, and renewable sources of energy. The major drawbacks are the large distances of most suitable sites from population centers and the high capital cost of building barrages across estuaries. Also, tidal power can be used only a few hours a day when the tide is moving in or out of the barrage.

The number of locations where OTEC plants can be constructed is limited, but where possible, they can provide clean power with no recurring fuel costs. The thermal efficiency, however, is limited to that dictated by the Carnot efficiency. The temperature differential (and thus thermal efficiency) is considerably lower during the winter months; it is suggested that a minimum temperature difference of 5-15°C must exist at least for six months of the year if this approach makes any economic sense.

ⓐ *Digging Deeper: What is a Wave?*

Waves are seen in a variety of forms, all around us. They can be either of electromagnetic or mechanical types. **Electromagnetic waves** are produced by the vibration of charged particles and exist in an enormous range of frequencies, from very low radio to very high cosmic rays. We discussed the EM radiation in Chapter 4. **Mechanical waves** require a medium to transport their energy.

Although not all waves appear the same, they all have certain common characteristics. Unlike electromagnetic waves that can propagate through a vacuum, mechanical waves need a medium in which to travel. A sound wave is an example of a mechanical wave, so it is incapable of traveling through a vacuum. Waves are classified either as *transverse waves*, with vibrations perpendicular to the direction of propagation (violin strings, battle rope), or *longitudinal waves*, with vibrations parallel to the direction of the propagation (horn, radar, compressed spring, slinky, and human heartbeats). Ripples on the surface of the water are a combination of both transverse and longitudinal waves.

By far the most common representation of a wave is the sine wave, normally associated with a simple harmonic motion. The wave is symmetric about a line representing the equilibrium or rest position of the vibrating string if there were no disturbance moving through it. A wave is mathematically represented by its *wavelength*, (the length of one complete cycle of a wave, or the distance between two consecutive crests or troughs), *wave height*, (the vertical distance between crests and troughs). *Amplitude* is the maximum displacement from its rest position (Figure 13-24). In a sense, the amplitude is the distance from rest to crest, equal to one-half of the wave height. Other characteristics associated with the waves are *frequency* (the number of waves or cycles that pass a point in one second), or *period* (the time for one complete cycle of a wave oscillation). The water moves around circular orbits in deep water but becomes more and more elliptic as it approaches the beachfront and interacts with the seafloor (See Figure 13-15).

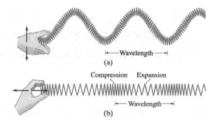

Figure 13-24
Traverse and longitudinal waves.

From these definitions, it appears that the period T is the reciprocal of the frequency f and vice versa.

$$T = \frac{1}{f} \qquad (13\text{-}2)$$

Another quantity of interest is the speed at which a disturbance is propagated on the wave or the *wave velocity*. Light has the highest speed of all. It moves at the incredible speed of 300,000 km/s, or about a million times faster than sound.[13] Sound propagates through the air at 343 m/s, while its speed increases to about 1,500 m/s in water. Small ripples in the pond travel at less than 1 m/s; ocean waves travel at around 1-10 m/s. Wave velocity is calculated by dividing the distance covered over one wavelength by the time it took to cover that distance.

$$u = \frac{\lambda}{T} = \lambda f \qquad (13\text{-}3)$$

Question: A battle rope trainer moves the rope in a periodic fashion. Will the wave reach the wall faster, if the athlete creates waves of larger wavelength or waves of larger amplitude?
Answer: Neither the wavelength nor amplitude of a wave affect the speed at which the wave travels. The speed of a wave is only altered by alterations in the properties of the medium through which it travels.

Question: What is the frequency of the second hand rotating around an analog clock?
Answer: The hand rotates one cycle every minute (60 s), frequency is f = (1/60) s^{-1} = (1/60) Hz.

Example 13-3: Ocean waves are observed to travel along the water surface during a developing storm. It is observed that waves splash every 6 seconds over the beach bed, what is the frequency and speed of the wave? Assume the waves are 5 meters in height and have wavelengths of 8 meters.
Solution: The frequency is the inverse of period, f = 1/6 = 0.167 Hz; the speed is u = λ.f = 8 m x 0.167 Hz = 1.33 m/s.

ⓐ Digging Deeper: Power Potential from Hydro Sources

A. From a Hydroelectric Plant

The theoretical water power potential is simply the potential energy of the water available in a reservoir. Potential energy increases with the height and amount of water that falls from a higher to a lower elevation.

$$P = \overset{\square}{m} gH \tag{13-4}$$

Where $\overset{u}{m} = \rho Q$ is the mass flow rate of water through turbines, Q is the volumetric discharge rate averaged over different seasons, ρ is water density (1,000 kg/m³), and g is the gravitational acceleration (9.81 m/s²). The actual power is somewhat smaller and must be modified by the efficiencies of the turbine and generator. Assuming combined generator-turbine efficiency η_o, the electrical power is calculated as:

$$P = \eta_o \rho g \overset{\square}{Q} H \tag{13-5}$$

Combined efficiencies on the order of 90% are common for large installations; the efficiency drops to 50% for smaller ones.

Total electrical energy

Assuming a power plant runs continuously for the entire year (one year is 8,760 hours), and substituting the mean discharge, Q_m, then total annual electricity generation is

$$E = 87,600 \, \eta_0 \, \overset{\square}{Q}_m H \quad \text{[kWh per annum]} \tag{13-6}$$

> **Example 13-4:** Estimate the power and total annual electricity generation capacity of the Three Gorges hydro-generation facilities in China. Assume an overall turbo-generator efficiency of 90%.
> **Solution:** Using data of Table 13-2, the theoretical power is
>
> $$P = 0.9 \times 1,000 \frac{\text{kg}}{\text{m}^3} \times 9.81 \frac{\text{m}}{\text{s}^2} \times 12,000 \frac{\text{m}^3}{\text{s}} \times 185 \text{ m} = 1.96 \times 10^{10} \text{ W} = 19,600 \text{ MW}$$
>
> in close agreement with the actual power. The maximum electricity production capacity is E= 8,760 P = 1.75x10⁸ MWh = 175 TWh. The reported generation capacity is 100 TWh or 57% of the maximum capacity. Two factors account for this: 1) the flow rate is not always at its maximum and must be adjusted for seasonal variation, and 2) some of the generators are off-line due to maintenance, and full generating capacity is not always possible.

B. From Pumped Storage

Pumped-storage hydropower involves pumping water to reservoirs at higher altitudes when electricity is not needed and reclaiming the electricity during times of peak demand by allowing water to drain to the lower reservoir. These reservoirs are of limited sizes, so heads are dropped as water is drawn down. The size of the reservoir is determined by the economics and the length of time the unit must operate to provide the additional power during the peak period. Mathematically, this can be calculated by integrating total energy as the head drops from z_2 to z_1.

$$P = \frac{\rho g A}{2t}\left(z_2^2 - z_1^2\right) \tag{13-7}$$

> **Example 13-5:** In a pumped storage facility, 500,000 cubic meters of water is pumped to a reservoir 50 meters higher. During the peak demand, the reservoir gate is opened and the water level is allowed to drop by 8 meters in 30 minutes. Assuming the reservoir is cylindrical with a diameter of 100 m, how much additional power is available, as water discharges?

Solution: Substituting into Eq. 13-7, the average power delivered during this period is:

$$P = \frac{1000 \frac{kg}{m^3} \times 9.81 \frac{m}{s^2} \times \frac{\pi}{4}(100 \text{ m})^2 \times (100^2 - 92^2) \text{ m}^2}{2 \times 30 \times 60 \text{ s}} = 3.29x10^7 \text{ W} = 32.9 \text{ MW}$$

C. *From Run-of-the-River*

Power can be extracted from river currents in a way similar to that from the wind. The total power contained in the water is found from a formula similar to the one developed for wind turbines (See Equation 12-1), except that the density of water must be used instead of the air:

$$P_{water} = \frac{1}{2}\rho A V^3 \qquad\qquad (13\text{-}8)$$

Like wind turbines, the maximum power available in water current is limited by the Betz limit. Assuming combined turbine-generator efficiency η_o, we have

$$P_e = \frac{1}{2}\rho C_p \eta_o A V^3 \qquad\qquad (13\text{-}9)$$

Where $C_p = 16/27$ is the power coefficient.

Example 13-6: A run-of-river hydroelectric power plant uses a river current at 5 m/s. Assuming there are five turbines each having a projected area of 4 square meters and overall turbine-generator efficiency of 90%, find:
   a. Power available upstream;
   b. Power available to run the turbine;
   c. How much electrical power is generated?
Solution:
   a. Total power available upstream is given by Equation 13-8.

$$P_{water} = \frac{1}{2}(1000 \ kg/m^3) \times 5 \times (4 \ m^2) \times (5 \ m/s)^3 = 1,250,000 W = 1.25 \ MW$$

   b. Total power available is limited by power coefficient, P = (16/27)x(1.25 MW) = 0.74 MW
   c. Not all the energy available in the water flow can be converted to electricity, and the result must be modified to account for turbine and generator efficiencies. Total electrical power is P = 0.74 **X** 0.90 = 0.67 MW.

Example 13-7: In the previous example, what is the electric energy generated by the plant in one year? Assume the plant has a capacity factor of CF – 72%.
Solution: The total amount of electrical energy that a plant produces in one year can be calculated by multiplying power by the number of hours, the plant is operating. Noting that there are 8,760 hours in a year, we get:

$$E_e = P_e \times CF \times 8,760 = 0.67 \times 0.72 \times 8,760 = 4.23 \text{ MWh}$$

D. *From Tides*

The power extracted from a tidal basin varies as the height of the water in the basin drops. The maximum power is produced at the point of highest potential energy when the reservoir is full. The minimum power is when the reservoir is nearly empty. The average power can, therefore, be estimated when the reservoir is half full, i.e., at its half range. Assuming the basin has a surface area of A, it will have a volume equal to $V = AR$. The total potential energy available is:

$$E = m \times g \times H = (\rho AR) \times g \times (R/2)$$

Assuming T is the tidal period, the average power that can be extracted from the tide is

$$P = \frac{E_p}{T} = \frac{\rho g A R^2}{2T} \qquad (13\text{-}10)$$

Question: Can we get more power per unit area of the ocean floor using bigger or smaller turbines?

Answer: It makes no difference! To get the most power, turbines must be spaced far enough from neighboring turbines so they don't disturb the flow. The power extracted from each turbine is proportional to the square of its diameter. At the same time, they must be spaced from each other several diameters apart. Incidentally, the same conclusion applies to the power potential from the wind.

Example 13-8: Estimate the average power generated by the La Rance tidal plant. The estuary has a basin area of A = 22.4 square kilometers, with a tidal range of R = 11.4 m. The bay experiences two tidal surges every 24 hours and 50 minutes.

Solution: Substituting in Equation (13-10) we have:

$$P = \frac{1000 \ \frac{\text{kg}}{\text{m}^3} \times 9.81 \frac{\text{m}}{\text{s}^2} \times 22.4 x 10^6 \text{m}^2 \times (11.3\text{m})^2}{(24 \times 3600 + 50 \times 60) \ \text{s}} = 3.14 x 10^8 \ \text{W} = 314 \ \text{MW}$$

The average power generated by the barrage is 240 MW, which gives an overall efficiency of 76%.

E. *From Tidal (Underwater) Currents*

Tidal current is the horizontal flow of water as a result of the tides. The power of an underwater current is equal to the rate of change of the kinetic energy of water as it crosses the turbine blades. Assuming that all the kinetic energy is exhausted to propel the turbine, power will be calculated as the product of the mass flow rate of the water and the kinetic energy of the incoming current:

$$P = \frac{1}{2} \rho A V^3 \eta_o = \frac{\pi}{8} \rho d^2 V^3 \eta_o \qquad (13\text{-}11)$$

where:

P = delivered power [W]

ρ = density of seawater [kg/m^3]

d = turbine diameter [m]

A = area swept by the water turbine [m^2]

V = current velocity [m/s]

η_o = the overall turbine-generator efficiency [-]

Example 13-9: Estimate the average power density that can be extracted from underwater tidal currents per square meter of the ocean floor? Tidal currents have a steady flow of between 1-2 m/s. To avoid wake interferences, turbines must be spaced between 5-10 diameters from each other.

Solution: Assuming a water density of 1,030 kg/m^3 and a separation distance of seven diameters, the power that tidal farms can generate per unit area of the ocean floor is:

$$\frac{P}{A_{Ocean\,Floor}} = \frac{\frac{\rho}{8}\pi d^2 v^3}{(7d)^2} \cong 8.25\ v^3\ \frac{W}{m^2}$$

At the average current velocity of 1.5 m/s, this yields to a power density of 27.1 W/m² of the ocean floor -- independent of the size of the turbines.

F. *From Waves*

The total energy of a wave is the sum of its kinetic and potential energies. For a sinusoidal wave, each component contributes to one-half of the total power. The power density (wave energy flux), defined as the power delivered by a wave per unit length of a wave crest, is obtained by dividing the total power transported per unit width along the wave crest in the direction of propagation.

For deep-water waves (d > λ/2), maximum power extracted per meter of a wavefront is given as:

$$\frac{P}{L} = \frac{\rho g^2 H^2 T}{32\pi} \tag{13-12a}$$

In these equations:

P = power of wave front [kW/m]

ρ = density of sea water [kg/m³]

a = wave amplitude [m]

L = wave width or crest length [m]

g = the local gravitational acceleration [m/s²]

$H - 2a$ = wave height [m]

T = period [s]

For a deep water wave, the period is related to the wavelength by:

$$T - \sqrt{\frac{2\pi\lambda}{g}} \tag{13-12b}$$

Substituting for values of g = 9.81 m/s², and ρ = 1,030 kg/m³ and if H is given in meters and T in seconds, equation 13-12a is approximated power for deep-water waves as:

$$P_0 / L = H^2 T \tag{13-12c}$$

In this equation, P_0 is surface wave power in kilowatts, H is wave height in meters, and T is the mean wave period in seconds.

Typical oceanic values of T are in the range 5-15 s; H varies from 0 for flat calm to around 15 m for severe storms, with median values of about 2 m in summer and 4 m in winter.

When waves travel into areas of **shallow water** (d < λ/20), they are slowed down by the ocean bottom. The free orbital motion of the water is disrupted, and the wave power becomes independent of period:

$$\frac{P_0}{L} = \frac{\rho g^{3/2} d^{1/2} H^2}{8} \tag{13-12d}$$

Except for regions very close to the shorelines, all water waves can be considered deep-water waves.

Wave power decreases rapidly as we go deeper, practically dying out at depths greater than $\lambda/2$.

$$P_d = P_0 \, e^{-2\pi d / \lambda} \tag{13-12e}$$

These results show that the power potential of waves increases as a square of the height is proportional to its period, and decreases exponentially with depth below the surface.

Example 13-10: The wave period and height of an ocean wave far from the shores are 5 s and 3 m. Find the maximum power that can be extracted from an ocean swell far from the coastline. Is the deep-water approximation valid? For a wave crest length of 100 m, what is the electrical power output if the overall efficiency of the wave energy converter device is 30 percent? Redo the problem when water is stormy with waves reaching a height of 10 meters. At what depth does the wave die down, so practically no power can be extracted?

Solution: Using Equation 13-12b, wavelength is calculated as

$$\lambda = gT^2 / 2\pi = 9.81 \, \text{m/s}^2 \times (5s)^2 / 2\pi = 39 \text{ m}$$

A deep-water approximation is valid for any d > 20 m (half the wavelength). Under these approximations, Eq. 13-12c applies. The deep-water energy flux is $P_0/L = (3)^2(5) = 45$ kW/m. The electrical output power is: $P_{elec} = (0.30)(100 \text{ m})(45 \text{ kW/m}) = 1,350 \text{ kW} = 1.35$ MW.

The power drops exponentially with depth according to Eqn. 13-12e. Substituting for d = 20 m, we have P/L ~ 1.8 kW/m diminishing by 96% from its surface value.

During stormy conditions, energy flux will increase significantly to $P/L = (10)^2(5) = 500$ kW/m, or 11 times the power when there are no storms. This result shows a major impediment in exploiting wave energy to generate electricity, as the structure must be able to tolerate many times the load it experiences during its normal operations. @

📚 Endnotes

1   Renewables, (2014). Global Status Report, Renewable Energy Policy Network for 21st Century, http://www.ren21.net

2   Smil, V., *World History and Energy,* Encyclopedia of Energy, *6*(2004), 549-561, Elsevier Inc.

3   IEA, (2016). International Energy Outlook, IEA, http://www.iea.org

4   Paish, O. (2002). Small hydro power: technology and current status. *Renewable And Sustainable Energy Reviews, 6*(6), 537-556, doi: 10.1016/s1364-0321(02)00006-0

5   International Journal on Hydropower and Dams, 1998 quoted in Emil F. Mosonyi, (2005), Hydropower, in Hydraulic Structures, Equipment and Water Data Acquisition Systems, [Eds. Jan Malan Jordaan, and Alexander Bell], in *Encyclopedia of Life Support Systems* (EOLSS), Developed under the Auspices of the UNESCO, Eolss Publishers, Oxford, U.K. 1998. Available at: http://www.eolss.net

6   U.S. DoE, (2004). Hydropower: Setting a Course for Our Energy Future," Publication No. DoE/Go-102004-1981, July.

7   Pumped Storage Hydropower- Summary Report on a Summit Meeting Convened by Oak Ridge National Laboratory, the National Hydropower Association, and the Hydropower Research Foundation, Washington, DC, September 20-21, 2010, Available at: http://www.esd.ornl.gov/WindWaterPower/PSHSummit.pdf

8   Hodges, H. & Hodges, H. (1971). *Technology in the ancient world.* Harmondsworth: Penguin.

9   Reynolds, J. (1975). *Windmills and watermills.* New York, NY: Praeger.

10 Gies, F. (1994). *Cathedral, Forge, and Waterwheel: Technology and Invention in the Middle Ages,* New York: Harper Perennial.

11 Frau, J. (1993). Tidal energy: promising projects: La Rance, a successful industrial-scale experiment. *IEEE Transactions On Energy Conversion, 8*(3), 552-558, doi: 10.1109/60.257073

12 Usachev, I. (2000). *Hydrotechnical Construction, 34*(8/9), 490-494, doi: 10.1023/a:1004191309697

13 Charlier, R. (2003). Sustainable co-generation from the tides:. *Renewable And Sustainable Energy Reviews, 7*(3), 187-213, <u>doi: 10.1016/s1364-0321(02)00011-4</u>

14 Bernstein, L. (1961). *Central Tidal-Power Stations in Contemporary Energy Production,* Moscow: State Publishing House.

15 See for example, B. D. T. , R. S. C. (1982). A two-basin tidal power scheme for the Severn estuary, In Conference on new approaches to tidal power.

16 Rodrigues, A. (2008). Wave power conversion systems for electrical energy production, Faculty of Science and Technology of Nova University of Lisbon, March. Available at: www.icrepq.com/icrepq-08/380-leao.pdf

17 Pielou, E. (2006). *The energy of nature.* Chicago, Ill.: University of Chicago Press.

18 Wilson, J. (1989). *Physics.* Saunders College.

19 Volshanik, V. & Malinin, N. (1998). Vol. II - Economics of Wave Power Production, *Encyclopedia of Life Support Systems* (EOLSS), Developed under the Auspices of the UNESCO, Eolss Publishers, Oxford, U.K.

20 Falcão, A. & Justino, P. (1999). OWC wave energy devices with air flow control. *Ocean Engineering, 26*(12), 1275-1295, <u>doi: 10.1016/s0029-8018(98)00075-4</u>

21 Islay LIMPET Wave Power Plant, http://www.wavegen.co.uk

22 Andrews, J. (2017). *Energy Science.* Oxford University Press.

23 Archimedes Wave Swing company website, http://www.waveswing.com

24 Thorpe, T. (1999). A Brief Review of Wave Energy, ETSU Report No. ETbSU-R-12.

25 Salter, S., Jeffrey, D., & Taylor, J. (1974). The Architecture of Nodding Duck Wave Power Generators, *The Naval Architect,* January, pp. 21-24.

26 Pelamis company website, http://www.pelamis.com

27 Takahashi, P. & Trenko, A. (1996). *Ocean Thermal Energy Conversion,* John Wiley and Sons.

28 Penney, T. & Daniel, T. (1989). *Energy From the Ocean: A Resource for the Future,* Encyclopædia Britannica, pp. 98–115.

29 Mcnichols, J. Ginell, W. & Cory, J. (1979). Thermoclines: A Solar Thermal Energy Resource for Enhanced Hydroelectric Power Production. S*cience, 203*(4376), 167-168, <u>doi: 10.1126/science.203.4376.167</u>

30 Loeb, S. & Norman, R. (1975). Osmotic Power Plants. *Science, 189*(4203), 654-655, <u>doi: 10.1126/science.189.4203.654</u>

31 Liu, C., Jae-Woo, P., Migita, R., & Gang, Q. (2002). Experiments of a prototype wind-driven reverse osmosis desalination system with feedback control. *Desalination, 150*(3), 277-287, <u>doi: 10.1016/s0011-9164(02)00984-0</u>

32 Zhong-Ai Hu, et al., (1999). Calculation of Osmotic Pressure Difference Across Membranes in Hyperfiltration,' *Desalination,* 121, 1999, pp. 31-137.

33 Rahmstorf, S. (2006). Thermohaline Ocean Circulation, In: *Encyclopedia of Quaternary Sciences,* Edited by S. A. Elias. Amsterdam: Elsevier.

34 Chen, H. et. al. (2009). Methane emissions from newly created marshes in the drawdown area of the Three Gorges Reservoir. *Journal Of Geophysical Research,* 114(D18) doi: 10.1029/2009jd012410

35 Sternberg, R. (2006). Damming the river: a changing perspective on altering nature. *Renewable And Sustainable Energy Reviews, 10*(3), 165-197, <u>doi: 10.1016/j.rser.2004.07.004</u>

36 Sharif, A. (2011). The potential of chemical-osmotic energy for renewable power generation, World Renewable Energy Congress, 8-13 May 2011, Linkoping, Sweden, 2011, pp. 2190-2197.

37 Ocean Energy Council (2020). https://www.oceanenergycouncil.com/ocean-energy/wave-energy/

38 See for example, Mayo, N. (1997) Ocean waves—Their energy and power. *The Physics Teacher, 35*(6), 352-356, <u>doi: 10.1119/1.2344718</u>

39 Izadparast, A. & Niedzwecki, J. (2011). Estimating the potential of ocean wave power resources. *Ocean Engineering, 38*(1), 177-185, <u>doi: 10.1016/j.oceaneng.2010.10.010</u>

40 Vining, J. (2006). Wave Energy Potential on the U.S. Outer Continental Shelf, Minerals Management Service Renewable Energy and Alternate Use Program, U.S. Department of the Interior.

🖐 Exercises

I. Discussion Questions

1. Describe how do the stadium fans move to produce a transverse wave? a longitudinal wave?
2. What is the difference between a light wave and a sound wave? Can you see the light or hear the sound of an explosion in a total vacuum?
3. Name the three common types of hydraulic turbines? What are the applications of each type? What is the difference between a reaction turbine and an impulse turbine?
4. What are the advantages and disadvantages of onshore, nearshore, and offshore installations?
5. What is the difference between a lunar day and a solar day? Why aren't they of the same duration? Explain why the interval between successive tides is 12 hours 50 min, instead of exactly 12 hours.

II. Numerical Problems

Impounds

1. Water flows over a section of Niagara Falls at the rate of 1.7×10^6 kg/s and falls 56 m. If all this energy could be converted to electrical energy by a power plant, at what rate would electrical energy be supplied? How many homes can this power accommodate? If the electrical energy were sold at 6 ¢/kWh, what would be the annual cost to the consumers? An average American home uses about 10,000 kWh each year.
2. Calculate power delivered by a hydroelectric generating station when water at a rate of 15 cubic meters per second drops on a turbine located at the bottom of a 70-m waterfall. Assume the water density of 1,000 kg/m^3.
3. A hydroelectric plant is supplied with water from a dam located 50 meters above the inlet to a turbine. As the water falls, its potential energy is converted into kinetic energy before it flows through the turbine at the rate of 10 cubic meters per second. Assume water has a density of 1,000 kg/m^3 and that both the turbine and generator efficiencies are $\eta_T = \eta_G = 100\%$. Estimate the electrical power in megawatts that this plant can produce.

Tidal Energy

4. Though negligible for small masses, gravitation proves to be an immense force when one considers the colossal masses of celestial bodies, such as the earth and the sun. Despite the tremendous distance between the earth and the sun, its gravitational force alone keeps the earth from straying off its orbit. To get an appreciation of the force exerted on the earth by the sun, estimate the thickness of a steel cable that could replace such a gravitational force. A steel cable with a cross-section of 1 m^2 can support the weight of roughly 10^5 tons.
5. The force of attraction between celestial bodies, the earth, the moon, and the sun were calculated in Example 13-1. Compare these with the force of attraction between nuclei and the electron of a hydrogen atom. (look up Appendix A, for the relevant data)
6. Find the force of attraction between a 70-kg car enthusiast Lisa Carr and a 1200-kg Ferrari located down the street in a showroom, 100 meters away from her?
7. A tidal barrage with a tidal range of 4 m and a period of 11 h 50 min, is used to extract electrical power. If the basin has a surface area of 400 acres and a turbine-generator efficiency of 22%. If the tidal barrage has five turbines, find the total electrical output.
8. Estimate the average power output available from the Severn Barrage tidal basin in the United Kingdom? The basin has a basin area of 520 km^2 and a tidal range of around 14 m -- the second-highest below the Bay of Fundy. Estimate the average power output from this estuary, once the plant is constructed. What is the annual electric energy production, assuming the turbine efficiency of 90%, and that the plant works only 80% of the time?

Ocean Thermal Energy

9. An OTEC plant utilizes the difference between the surface temperature of 30°C and the deep water temperature of 7°C. What is the maximum efficiency that can be expected?
10. In the example above, the OTEC system extracts 600 kJ of energy from warm surface water of 30°C and dumps 580 kJ of waste heat to the cold deep water of 7°C. What is the actual efficiency?

Run-of-the-River

11. Find the available power for a run-of-river hydro-

electric power plant if water velocity is 5 m/s and the turbine is 8 m in diameter.

12. How many turbines are needed to generate 4 MW of electric power, if each turbine has a projected area of 2 m² and the volumetric flow rate of water passed turbines is 25 m³/s? Assume combined turbine-generator efficiency of 96 percent.

Salinity Gradient

13. The osmotic pressure between ocean salt water (3.5% by weight) and fresh river water is 2,700 kPa. What is the equivalent head?

14. Calculate the theoretical maximum power that could be generated per cubic meters per second of a river flowing into the sea? Assume that the plant is operating using salinity gradients between fresh and saline water. *Hint:* Start from basic definitions to show that power is the product of pressure and volumetric flow rate.

Waves

15. Radar operates by emitting radio waves at 9.5 GHz. What is its wavelength?

16. Find the wavelength of a water wave of frequency 40 Hz traveling at 120 cm/s.

17. What is the maximum power that can be exploited from a deep-water wave with a wavelength of 15 m and a height of 5 m, traveling at a speed of 4 m/s? Assume combined turbine generator efficiency of 85%.

18. A wave energy converter is designed to produce 200 kW power when operating at the surface when waves with a wavelength of 50 meters pass by. How much would this device produce, if it is submerged at depths of 10 m? 50 m?

19. A deep-water wave produces 80 kW/m of crest length. Find the wave's amplitude and period, if the wave has a wavelength of 50 meters.

20. Under-water ocean currents with an average velocity of 2 m/s are used to extract power. For a turbine with a rotor diameter of 3 m, and overall efficiency of 45%, what is total energy (MWh) over ten- years? Assume ocean water has a density of 1,030 kg/m³.

III. Multiple Choice Questions

1. Wave motion in a medium is associated with the transport of

a. Mass only.
b. Energy only.
c. Both mass and energy.
d. Neither mass nor energy.
e. It depends on whether it is an EM or a mechanical wave.

2. To the nearest order of magnitude, how many times is the speed of light greater than the speed of sound?
a. 10^{10} times
b. 10^8 times
c. 10^6 times
d. 10^4 times
e. 10^2 times

3. What is an example of a longitudinal wave?
a. Light
b. Sound
c. Water
d. X-ray
e. Infrared

4. All electromagnetic waves travel through a vacuum at
a. The same speed.
b. Speeds that are proportional to their frequency.
c. Speeds that are inversely proportional to their frequency.
d. They cannot travel in a vacuum.
e. None of the above.

5. Electricity can be produced
a. By mixing the fresh runoff water with salty ocean water.
b. Through seperating ocean water to zones of hot and cold temperatures.
c. Through thermocline circulation.
d. Through the process of osmosis.
e. Through the process of reverse osmosis.

6. Energy can be extracted from water by
a. Exploiting its potential energy, as is done in hydroelectric and tidal plants.
b. Exploiting the temperature gradients in oceans, as is done in OTEC plants.
c. Exploiting its mechanical energy, as is done in ocean currents and surface waves.
d. Exploiting the energy in the nucleus of isotope deuterium, needed to power fusion reactors.
e. All of the above.

7. The best location for placing a water turbine is
a. Close to the top of a waterfall.
b. Halfway down the waterfall.
c. At the bottom of the waterfall.

d. Does not make any difference.

e. Depends on the topography of the area.

8. A pumped storage plant refers to

   a. The location where all pumps are stored.

   b. The feedwater pump used to deliver water downstream from the hydro plant in time of emergencies.

   c. The pump used during emergencies, when quick delivery of power is demanded.

   d. A means for storing electricity for later use.

   e. Both c and d.

9. A hydropower project that utilizes the river's natural flow for generating electricity during peak demand is called a

   a. Run-of-river project.

   b. Storage project.

   c. Waterfall project.

   d. Overflow project.

   e. None of the above.

10. The electric generation capacity from a hydropower plant will depend on

    a. The flow rate of water.

    b. The efficiency of the turbine.

    c. The head of the turbine.

    d. The generator's efficiency.

    e. All of the above.

11. Osmosis is best defined as the

    a. Random movement of water particles.

    b. Motion of water inside a container because of pressure gradients.

    c. Transport of water from an area of high salt concentration to an area of low salt concentration as a result of a pressure gradient.

    d. Transport of water molecules across a membrane from an area of high water concentration to an area of lower water concentration.

    e. None of the above.

12. Which of the following statements is not correct?

    a. Francis turbines are most suitable for pumped storage

    b. Kaplan turbines are best suited for low-power applications

    c. Kaplan turbines are best suited for high-head applications

    d. Pelton turbines are impulse-type.

    e. The flow direction in Kaplan turbines is radial.

13. High spring tides and low neap tides occur

    a. Twice a year, following the solar cycle.

    b. Twice a month, following the lunar cycle.

    c. Twice a day, roughly every 12 hours.

    d. Once a month.

    e. Once a day.

14. Spring tides occur

    a. During a full or a new moon.

    b. When the moon, the earth, and the sun are along a straight line.

    c. Mostly in spring.

    d. When the gravitational forces of the moon and the sun are perpendicular to one another.

    e. Both a and b.

15. Surface waves

    a. Travel at the same speed as electromagnetic waves.

    b. Do not require a medium to travel.

    c. Travel with speeds independent of the wavelength.

    d. Travel in circular patterns.

    e. Travel in a transverse direction.

16. The maximum power generated from tidal energy

    a. Increases with the area of the basin and the square of the average tidal range.

    b. Is independent of the average tidal range.

    c. Is independent of the basin surface area.

    d. Is independent of wave height during the high tides.

    e. Is independent of wave height during the low tides

17. The maximum power output of a dam with a head of 100 m and a volume flow rate of 1 m^3/s is about

    a. 1 kW

    b. 10 kW

    c. 100 kW

    d. 1 MW

    e. 10 MW

18. Which of the following statements is not true?

    a. As the tide rises, water moves toward the shore.

    b. Ebb current is the movement of water away from the shore.

    c. The vertical motion of the tides near the shore causes the water to move horizontally, creating currents.

    d. Tidal currents are the lateral movements of the tides.

    e. All of the statements are correct.

19. What percentage of U.S. electrical power comes from tidal plants?

    a. None of it

b. Roughly 1%
  c. About 2-3%
  d. About 5-7%
  e. More than 7%

20. The tidal interval is
  a. The time between two consecutive high tides or two consecutive low tides.
  b. The time between a high tide and the next low tide.
  c. The vertical difference between high and low tides.
  d. The vertical difference between the highest high and the lowest low tides.
  e. The period when strongest tides occur during the year.

21. Tidal electricity generation does not require
  a. Maintenance.
  b. A storage system.
  c. Waste disposal.
  d. High capital cost.
  e. Any of the above.

22. Which of the following statements is not correct?
  a. A major environmental concern regarding hydro and tidal plants is that the change in river conditions and surrounding beaches may impact fish and marine life.
  b. Dams act mostly to control floods, but also may be the cause for flooding the lakes and rivers upstream from the plant.
  c. To prevent the accumulation of silt, lakes behind dams occasionally must be cleaned at great costs.
  d. Unlike hydroelectric and tidal plants, wave plants have no environmental impact.
  e. Impounding water flow may cause certain bacteria growth in hydro rivers, which could potentially pose a health hazard.

23. Which of the following statements is not correct?
  a. The oceans rise relative to land at the point closest to the moon and fall relative to land at the point farthest away from the moon.
  b. Since gravitational force decreases with the square of the distance, the side of the earth facing the moon experiences the strongest pull.
  c. Tidal effects cause the Earth to stretch along the earth/moon line.
  d. The oceans rise relative to land on both sides of the earth-moon line.
  e. Although the sun exerts a higher gravitational

pull on the earth than the moon, its tidal effect is smaller than the moon.

24. Which of the following statements is correct?
  a. A tidal day is defined as the time of rotation of the moon about its axis.
  b. A tidal day is slightly longer than a lunar day.
  c. A tidal day is slightly longer than a solar day.
  d. A tidal day is another name for a lunar day.
  e. A tidal day is a period between a high and a low tide.

25. The highest high tides and lowest low tides occur
  a. When the moon and the sun are nearly at right angles to each other.
  b. When the moon and the sun are nearly in line with the earth.
  c. During summer, when the earth is closest to the sun.
  d. During winter, when the earth is closest to the sun.
  e. When the sky is clear and the moon is clearly visible.

26. The velocity of a wave is calculated by
  a. Multiplying the wavelength and period.
  b. Dividing the wavelength by period.
  c. Dividing period by the wavelength.
  d. Dividing the wavelength by amplitude.

27. What causes the tide?
  a. Gravity
  b. Wind
  c. Earthquakes
  d. Rotation of the earth
  e. All of the above

28. The substance in which a _____ is being dissolved is called a _____.
  a. Solvent, solute
  b. Solute, solvent
  c. Solute, mixture
  d. Solute, solution
  e. Solvent, solution

29. Deep water waves are
  a. Waves at bottom of wells.
  b. The wind blows for farther distances over the Waves at least 1 km deep
  c. Waves deeper than half wavelenth
  d. Waves deeper than 5 wavelenths
  e. Are the same as underwater tidal currents.

30. The maximum power that can be extracted from a tidal turbine is proportional to
  a. The area of the rotor and cube of current

speed.

    b. The diameter of the rotor and cube of current speed.

    c. The area of the rotor and square of current speed.

    d. The water temperature.

    e. None of the above.

31. Ocean Thermal Energy Conversion
    a. Is most efficient in temperate environments.
    b. Have efficiency in excess of Carnot limit.
    c. Have a maximum efficiency dictated by Carnot.
    d. Have higher efficiency during high tides.
    e. Not practical at this time.

32. Waves cause small particles floating on the surface to move in
    a. Vertical elliptical orbits.
    b. Vertical circular orbits.
    c. Horizontal elliptical orbits.
    d. Horizontal circular orbits.
    e. Depends on the speed wind blows.

33. Reaction turbines
    a. Have bucket-shaped blades bolted to the rim of a wheel.
    b. Are propeller-type Pelton turbines.
    c. Like wind turbines that use the pressure drop across the turbine to kinetic energy of the working fluid.
    d. Are used in mountainous regions with low heads and low flow rates.
    e. Are used at flat regions with high heads and high flow rates.

34. How many low tides are there in a day?
    a. 1
    b. 2
    c. 3
    d. 4
    e. It varies depending on geographical location.

35. Gravitational attraction is strongest
    a. Between a very large massive object like earth and a small object such as an apple.
    b. Between two very large bodies such as the sun and the earth.
    c. Between objects of different electrical charges.
    d. Between peoples of the opposite sex.
    e. All of the above.

IV. True or False?

1. The primary mover of surface waters is the wind.

2. The main application of a pumped storage plant is when demand is high and quick delivery of power (such as during emergencies) is needed.

3. Tidal energy exploits the available head between the flood and ebb tides.

4. Wave size is affected by wind velocity, wind duration, and distance from the shore.

5. The potential energy of tidal power increases with the basin area and the average range between the low and high tides.

6. Each day, high tides occur exactly at the same time as the day before.

7. The horizontal movement of the water accompanying tides is called a tidal current.

8. There exists a tremendous potential for constructing new hydroelectric power stations in the United States.

9. Tidal power plants are constructed to exploit the variation in the tides' potential energy in the same way that hydroelectric power stations use the potential energy from falling water.

10. Doubling the flow rate of water, doubles power extracted in a hydroelectric plant.

V. Fill in the Blanks

1. The best means of achieving the quick delivery of power during emergencies and power surges is through _____ plants.

2. The _____ are used to extract power from the natural flow of water in rivers and canals.

3. The power produced by underwater currents varies with the _____ of turbine diameter and cube of water _____.

4. Wave power is usually measured in the unit of _____ of a wavefront.

5. A desalination plant work through a process called _____.

6. An example of a floating wave energy converter is a _____.

7. We can extract power from moving water by installing _____ anchored to the bottom of ocean floors; power can be extracted from water in the same way that it is extracted from the wind.

8. Besides potential and kinetic energies contained in water waves, the temperature difference between the surface and deep ocean waters can be exploited to produce power in a process called _____.

CHAPTER 14

Economics of Energy

Wealth ~ Creative Commons by Petr Kratochvil

Not blind opposition to progress, but opposition to blind progress
~ Unknown (Sierra Club's slogan)

The view of the average human as builder conflicts with the view of the average human as destroyer, which underlies the thought of many doom sayers. ~ Julian Simon (1932-1998)

In Chapter 2, we defined energy as the capacity to do work. When it comes to the economics of energy, work is any economic activity that earns rent, produces goods and services, trades and barters, and as such follows the same laws of thermodynamics that govern physical systems. In the context of an entire economy, resources can be allocated by various means, such as market or planning. At any given moment, it is assumed that the economy has allocated the scarce resources in a way that maximizes profit while producing goods and services utilizing available technologies. The direction of change is toward higher productivity, better production methods, less material, and fewer environmental consequences. While economic activities are traditionally viewed as being motivated by profit, the ultimate motivation of economic activities is not to maximize profit or productivity, but rather to disperse energy. Economics organize themselves within systems to improve energy dispersal and to access new sources of energy. In other words, decision-making is ultimately about choosing the action that causes energy to flow in the shortest time. For example, when faced with two identical products where one is cheaper than the other, a consumer will likely choose the cheaper product.

As the economy continues to expand and industrial output grows, we are generating more and more hazardous wastes, which eventually, will end up in the air, in the water supply, and on land. Because society requires many services and products, it is understandable that a certain amount of pollution is tolerated. The dilemma is that, although sources are owned privately (either by state or private enterprises), the same entities have free access to the sink (atmosphere), which is owned by the public, as a whole.

The economic dilemma every human face is how to satisfy unlimited wants with limited resources. The resource limitations could be technological know-how, purchasing power, time, materials, and energy. This is why we choose (or are forced) to give up (or postpone) some desires to get other wants, which are seemingly more important to us. To meet these needs, so far, we have consumed fossil fuels, as if there is no end to them, and they are truly inexhaustible. As we learn that these resources are finite, and sooner or later, they deplete, we must make harsh economic and environmental choices to keep these resources lasting longer, or until we find economically suitable substitutes. The same is true with other resources at our disposal.

In this chapter, we will discuss the economic issues of energy and their impacts on our technological society, as well as various methodologies that are used by traditional and ecological economists to measure the cost of polluting the environment, in both monetary and non-monetary terms, and the role the government plays in regulating pollution. In particular, we will address pollution generated from fossil fuel combustion and the costs and benefits of environmental clean-up.

Competition

Perfect Competition: Market Efficiency

A perfect market is a competitive market in which economic forces operate unimpeded. For a market to be perfect, the following conditions must exist:

a. There are numerous buyers and sellers, and many other firms with products that are available and practically indistinguishable from the goods of interest. Buyers could easily substitute another product if there were shortages.
b. There are no legal, technical, or social barriers to the entry of new competitions.
c. A firm's only goal is to maximize its profits; in other words, firms have no interests (political, social, etc.) other than their economic interests.

In actuality, markets are not perfect and many technical (available to only certain industries), social (available only to certain groups), financial, property rights, and legal (patents and regulations) barriers can influence them. In a real market, there is only a limited number of buyers and sellers, so a few firms may collude to dominate the industry. Because the number of buyers is finite, there is a limit to how much product firms can sell, no matter how low the price. Monopolies (natural monopolies), cartels, and subsidized firms that provide specialized services that sell novelty items or offer products protected by patents and government regulations violate one or more of the conditions set above and are, therefore, not considered to be perfect markets. It should be noted that although most barriers to a perfect market (control of resources, predatory and retaliatory pricing, and excess capacity) are socially harmful, there are some advantages for a non-perfect market. For example, the economy of scale may reduce capital requirements and reduce costs to consumers. To a certain degree, patents and copyrights will foster entrepreneurship and promote innovation, which could lead to product differentiation, and brings a variety that spices up our daily lives.

Supply and Demand

To understand the many ramifications of economics, it is instructive to start with the concept of *supply and demand* and to explain how it determines a market price and quantity of a given good. The law of demand says that as the price falls, the quantity demanded increases, and the higher the price, the lower the quantity. At the same time, supply dictates the amount available at a specific price, or across a range of prices. All else remaining the same (*ceteris paribus*)it is reasonable to expect a demand curve to exhibit a downward slope, whereas a supply curve has an upward trend. [*] The point where these curves intersect is the **equilibrium point** (Figure 14-1). At equilibrium, there is no shortage or surplus. If there is a surplus, the producer will decrease production, a shortage will result, prompting the producer to increase the price, pushing the supply curve toward the same equilibrium.

Many factors besides price affect demand and supply. Factors that affect demand are changes in income, changes in the cost of living, consumer taste or trend, the expectation of future price or events, and the change in population. Factors that affect supply are changes in the costs of production (such as the cost of raw materials and labor), changes in technology, and changes in the amount of taxes and subsidies.[3]

It should be emphasized here that a change in the quantity demanded does not mean a change in demand. There are two ways that demand can change: a change in price or a change in overall demand. For a given market, a change in the price results in changes in quantity demanded (movement along the demand curve); the higher the price, the lower the demand, and vice versa.

For example, when the price of natural gas rises, buyers moveaway from natural gas and use substitutes, such as heating oil, kerosene, or wood. When the price drops, consumers switch back to natural gas again Even though the price didn't change, the demand curve could shift. Factors such as changes in income, (in case of aggregate demand) will determine the direction of the change. For example, when the price of natural gas rises, buyers move away from natural gas and use substitutes such as heating oil, kerosene, or wood. When the price drops, consumers switch back to natural gas again. In another scenario, when there is a shift in median income, people tend to buy a different quantity of a product. For example, in the

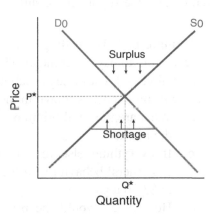
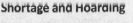

Figure 14-1
Supply and Demand. At equilibrium (P* and Q*) there is neither a shortage or a surplus.

Shortage and Hoarding

In 1973, following the Arab oil embargo, there was a gasoline shortage; long lines of cars formed at gas stations waiting hours to fill up their gas tanks. To prevent price gouging and black market profiteering, the government instituted a price control. Fearing increasing shortages, the average gas tank that was previously only one-quarter full was now being kept three-quarters full. With about 100 million cars on the American roads, and assuming the tanks had 20-gallon capacity, the hoarding resulted in a shortage of about one billion gallons in the first two weeks of the price control, causing a sudden increase in demand that actually exacerbated the shortage.

[*] It should be stressed here that, although the demand curve for the market, as a whole, has a downward slope, individual firms sell their products at given prices. The demand curve is a flat line for individual firms.

event of a cold winter, the demand for natural gas heaters increases for any given price, and there would be a shift in demand and supply curves move to a new equilibrium (Figure 14-2). At this equilibrium, people are willing to pay a higher price for natural gas. The opposite will be true when winters turn out to be milder than expected.

Supply curves also can shift, with factors such as number of sellers, expectations of future, or price of raw materials, technology, and inflation. For example, as technologies improve, the cost of production of solar cells decreases, so cell manufacturers are willing to supply more cells for a given price -- the supply curve shifts to the right (Figure 14-3).

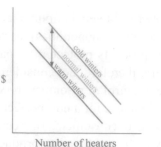

Number of heaters

Figure 14-2
Demand shift.

Number of cells

Figure 14-3
Supply shift.

Example 14-1: Depending on their incomes and needs, different customers are willing to pay different gasoline prices, as is shown in demand curve D_0 in Exhibit 14-1. Gasoline availability is also a function of the price customers are willing to pay, as shown in the supply curve denoted as S_0.

a. What are the equilibrium price of gasoline and the quantity supplied to the market?

b. If everything else remains the same (ceteris paribus), how would customers' behavior be affected if the price of gasoline drops 10 cents to $3.90 a gallon?

c. How much would the price of gasoline rise during the summer if demand rose by 20%? Assume that the government does not interfere in controlling supply and demand.

d. Now assume that the government mandates a price freeze setting a price ceiling of $4.00 per gallon. How would customers react to the change in demand during the summer?

e. How will the market react if it anticipates future shortages as a result of a 20% cutback in production by OPEC?

Solution:

a. The market equilibrium is at point A in graph a, where 100 million gallons of gasoline are supplied by the oil companies for $4.00 a gallon.

b. In this case, the demand curve is not affected. This does not mean the quantity demanded is the same. As gasoline prices drop, the quantity demanded will be greater (people tend to drive more or buy bigger cars), although the demand is still the same. The movement is along the demand curve to point B and 110 million gallons are sold.

c. As daily demand for gasoline climbs, the demand curve shifts to D_1 and customers are willing to buy 120 million gallons at the price of $4.00 (point C in graph b). In the short run, the market reacts and eliminates the initial shortage by driving prices up to point E, at which 120 million gallons are sold at $4.20 a gallon. In the long run, as prices rise, drivers will cut their driving (for example, by vacationing shorter distances or by carpooling), and equilibrium moves to point D. As a result, 110 million gallons are offered at the price of $4.10 a gallon.

d. With the price ceiling set at $4.00 a gallon, the oil companies are willing to sell only 100 million gallons of gasoline every day (equilibrium

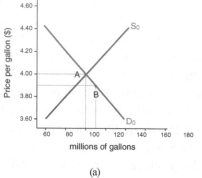

(a)

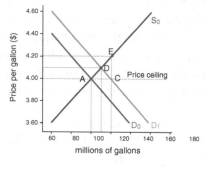

(b)

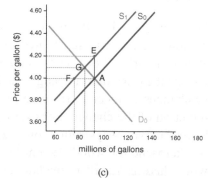

(c)

EX 14-1

point A in graph a). The daily gasoline demand, however, is 120 million gallons. To prevent a shortage, customers are willing to pay more, potentially causing a black market and driving up the prices to as much as $4.20 a gallon (point E). Because there is a price ceiling, drivers cannot legally pay more than $4.00 a gallon. In the absence of a black market, they have to pay in non-monetary terms, such as waiting in line. In a way, a new equilibrium is reached where 100 million gallons of gasoline are traded at $4.20, of which $4.00 is paid monetarily and $0.20 is paid in terms of waiting in line.

e. In this case, the supply curve shifts to S1 (graph c) while demand remains the same, and again we will face a daily shortage of 20 million gallons (AF), temporarily driving the price up to $4.20 a gallon (point E). In the long run, changes in consumers' driving habits and willingness to switch to alternative fuel vehicles and electric and hybrid cars reduce the gasoline demand. It eventually reaches a new equilibrium point G, where the price drops to $4.10 again.

It is clear from the previous example that the market has a built-in mechanism that reacts to shortages by raising prices and, ultimately, eliminating scarcity -- a force that brings back everything to equilibrium.

Externalities

When two people trade, the belief is that they mutually benefit from that trade. Unless they are required by law, buyers and sellers are unlikely to consider the effect of their trades on others. Many trades and agreements have some direct and indirect effects whose costs are not borne by the buyers and sellers and, therefore, prices do not reflect true costs. These costs are called **external costs** or **externalities** and include such things as the cost of healthcare associated with pollution and damage done to the environment, buildings, etc. Society-at-large must bear both the private cost of production, as well as the externalities distributed among various sectors. The sum of private and external costs is called the **social cost**. **Social benefit** is the total benefit (internal and external) to society from producing or consuming a good/service.

Depending on whether the externalities benefit or harm society as a whole, they can be positive or negative. Pollution is a *negative externality*, whereas cleaning the environment and research to eliminate an infectious disease are *positive externalities*. The true cost of energy is not limited to the price we pay for our utilities or at the gas station but also includes what we eventually pay in terms of degrading the quality of life by ruining the environment and our health. Additionally, the energy sector, petroleum. in particular, is highly subsidized by the government through tax incentives, low-cost access to leases, mapping, R&D on oil extraction, building pipelines, highways, and other infrastructure, and finally by military expenditures to protect the flow of oil. According to one estimate, in the last 30 years, the U.S. has spent a total of $230 trillion (1998 dollars) for oil imports. The government additionally spends somewhere between $100 billion and $300 billion on hidden costs like health care and lost productivity. According to a study by Rand Corporation, it is estimated that the US had spent $8 trillion on protecting oil cargoes in the Persian Gulf since 1976 when its military presence in the region was boosted following the first Arab oil embargo. This is all despite the fact that only 10% of the oil passing through the straits is actually destined for the US. Many other environmental costs such as the destruction of natural habitats and wildlife and the loss of species diversity (which are not commercially traded), cannot be accurately measured and are not included in these figures.

Question: What are the social costs associated with electricity generation using renewable energy sources?
Answer: With no energy conservation policies, social cost includes the cost of a rise in pollution, degrading health, social unrest, hunger, job loss, and a decline in the economy. Although photovoltaic cells emit no pollutants during operation, their manufacture requires large quantities of hazardous materials, and their ultimate disposal could release toxic elements, such as arsenic and cadmium, into the environment. Other renewable energy sources incur similar costs; the external costs associated with them are, however, a lot less than with non-renewable sources In a new study by the European Commission, the external costs associated with various energy technologies (fossil, nuclear, hydro, solar, and wind) for generating electricity were estimated. For non-market goods, such as

health care costs, noise, etc., an evaluation was made based on the willingness to pay for damages or willingness to accept the risks. The external cost of material was estimated from the emissions produced during its manufacture.

Damages to ecosystems (acid rain, ozone depletion, and global warming) as a result of fossil-fuel combustion were assessed by estimating the cost of avoidance. Because of different technologies used and material and labor costs, the cost is somewhat different from country to country and from one location to another. Table 14-1 shows the marginal external costs of electricity production in Germany. Data for other countries show similar trends.

Table 14-1 Marginal External Costs of Electricity In Germany (€ cent/kWh)						
	Coal	Natural Gas	Nuclear	Solar (PV)	Wind	Hydro
Damage Cost						
- Noise	0	0	0	0	0.005	0
- Health	0.73	0.34	0.17	0.45	0.072	0.051
- Material	0.015	0.007	0.002	0.012	0.002	0.001
- Crops	0	0	0.0008	0	0.0007	0.0002
Avoidance Cost						
- Ecosystem	0.20	0.04	0.05	0.04	0.04	0.03
- Global Warming	1.60	0.73	0.03	0.33	0.004	0.03

As these data suggest, electricity generated by wind energy has a very low external cost. The cost can be reduced even further by eliminating external costs associated with noise by installing wind farms some distance away from population centers. Nuclear energy has no externality with respect to classical pollution costs, such as health effects associated with pollutants like particulates and oxides of carbon, sulfur, and nitrogen. The cost of global warming is also minimal and limited to that associated with the construction of the nuclear plant. There are, however, other external costs associated with nuclear power. When uranium ore is mined, "tailings" are left behind; spent fuel also must be stored. In addition, there is an unaccounted risk from earthquakes, and accidental or deliberate sabotage or attack. The U.S. government has spent billions of dollars to find ways to store nuclear waste -- unsuccessfully. The cost of treatment and isolation of radioactive waste (for thousands of years) and damage from nuclear leaks is almost impossible to predict and, therefore, is not usually included in any external cost analysis. Because of the liability limits in the U.S., owners of nuclear plants cannot buy full liability insurance in case of major accidents or terrorist attacks. The lack of an insurance market – a market failure – should be a clue that there are unaccounted externalities.

The probability of a major nuclear accident is very low and, therefore, its externality (averaged over all nuclear plants) is relatively small. The same goes for the possibility of successful nuclear sabotage. In some countries, such as Switzerland, the government pays for hardening its reactors to protect against attack. That is one way to count the external cost -- the cost of avoiding the consequence of the attack. In the event of an accident, however, and for those directly affected by the accident, the external cost could be extremely high and greatly exceed that of all other forms of electricity generation.

Biomass has a relatively minimal impact on greenhouse gases, since carbon dioxide emission balances with that used up during plant growth. The impact could, however, become more pronounced as the price of biomass increases and rainforests are destroyed. Although biomass does not produce greenhouse gases, it is not clean. When burned, it still emits pollutants that are harmful to health and the environment. Air pollution impact varies greatly, depending on the type of biomass, the technology used, and the degree to which emission of pollutant gases into the atmosphere is controlled. Natural gas is relatively clean with respect to criteria pollutants. In terms of its impact on climate change, natural gas is a potent greenhouse gas. How great an impact it has, however, depends on which natural gas technologies are employed? Coal is probably the dirtiest of all fuels. Not only is coal a major producer of carbon dioxide, but it is also a major contributor to the particulates and sulfur dioxide emissions responsible for acid rain and other health effects.

Total and Marginal Costs and Revenues

The **total costs** of production can be divided into two types -- fixed and variable. **Fixed costs** are constant and exist whether or not any products are produced or services are delivered. Examples are rent, furniture, licenses, buildings, and the cost of purchasing equipment. Other costs -- called **variable costs** -- change as output changes. Examples are the costs of raw material and shipping expenses.

Although total costs are important, they are not the most important for a firm in deciding whether to expand or curtail production. What is critical, is the marginal cost and marginal revenue. **Marginal cost** (MC) is the additional or incremental cost of producing one extra unit of product or providing one unit of additional service. The marginal cost of oil production is the additional cost of producing one extra barrel of oil. Because higher production levels necessitate extraction from higher-cost fields, marginal cost increases as production rises. **Marginal revenue** (MR) can be defined as the additional or incremental revenue of selling one extra unit of product or providing one unit of additional service[†] As long as the marginal revenue is higher than marginal cost, i.e, marginal profit is bigger than zero, and the production of the additional unit is still profitable. Said another way, the total profit of the firm is maximum when the marginal cost of one additional unit produced is equal to the marginal revenue resulting from its sale (the price it gets for its goods). In the language of mathematics, the total profit is maximum when marginal profit, i.e. MP = MC - MR = 0.

Economic Efficiency

The term "efficiency" means different things to different people. Engineers talk about efficiency as the ratio of the desired output from a device to necessary input. An energy-efficient refrigerator uses less electricity for the same amount of cooling than a less-efficient refrigerator uses (See Chapter 4). An efficient worker performs the same work in the same time, and an efficient programmer writes the same program with fewer instructions.

Economists refer to efficiency in terms of the maximum profit that can be gained from a given transaction. The most widely accepted definition of economic efficiency is the **Pareto efficiency**. A market is most efficient when it makes the public, as a whole, "better off." As long as the market has not reached its most efficient point, the economic pie grows and, in principle, everyone can benefit by getting a bigger slice.[‡]

> **Question:** When does the market for car sales reach its peak economic efficiency?
> **Answer:** As long as there are buyers who are willing to pay for the cost of owning a car, and there are sellers who are willing to satisfy customers' demands, the market has room for additional cars. That is, the market is Pareto efficient when demand balances supply.

> **Question:** Is a "zero pollution" solution compatible with the concept of economical efficiency?
> **Answer:** The zero pollution option will not make the outcome economically efficient. Although the public is willing to pay for a certain amount of clean-up costs, at a certain point, the increase in the marginal cost of clean-up does not justify the marginal benefits; it brings enough economic hardship to a large enough number of people that the happiness of some would not make up for the unhappiness of the rest.

Taxes

One way to internalize the external costs is to impose Pigovian or pollution taxes. **Pigovian tax** refers to a tax applied to a market activity that is generating negative externalities and is intended to correct an inefficient market outcome. One example is waste disposal, which is taxed in the form of a lump sum fee per customer. For example, every American household is charged $10 a month for garbage collection. In some communities, these charges are included in property taxes or association fees. In either case, there are no incentives for customers to reduce waste.

[†] There are instances when no marginal cost or benefit exists. For example, there is no marginal cost for an extra plate in an all-you-can-eat dinner, and there is zero marginal benefit of an extra plate when you are no longer hungry.

[‡] By "better off" we only mean in terms of overall economical advantage. If the increase in a country's income comes with the destruction of cultural values, environmental degradation, and other adverse, non-quantifiable social implications, then an average person might actually be "worse off" as the result of the trade.

Unlike the U.S., European taxes are based on a scale starting from a low nominal value and increasing gradually as the volume of waste increases.

Energy is usually taxed indirectly in the form of gasoline and emission taxes. However, this may sometimes cause unwanted consequences. For example, taxing gasoline raises its price and so more people will switch to electric cars. To charge the batteries, electricity generated mostly from dirty coal-fired power plants is used, and the overall concentration of carbon dioxide may actually increase. It is, therefore, more reasonable to directly tax the pollution (for example, by taxing per kilogram of carbon produced) instead of placing indirect taxes on energy usage. Several states have begun imposing pollution taxes directly. Depending on what source of energy is being used, a surplus tax per kilowatt-hour of electricity produced is imposed.

The Facts: The Price of Gasoline in California

This is where the money we pay for each gallon of gasoline goes (January 11, 2010):

Cost of the crude (including profit)	$2.00	66%
Refining	$0.23	8%
Storage	$0.02	1%
Various taxes		
Federal excise tax	$0.18	
State excise tax (av)	$0.18	
State sales tax (av)	$0.25	
Total	$0.61	20%
Distribution and marketing	$0.18	6%
Total cost	**$3.04**	**100%***

* *Do not add up to 100% due to rounding*

Source: California Energy Commission, (http://energyalmanac.ca.gov/gasoline/margins/index.html

Question: How much tax should be imposed on a gallon of gasoline to cover its social cost? According to IPCC the average social cost of carbon emitted is $43 per ton of carbon ($12 per ton of carbon dioxide). Assume each gallon of gasoline, when burned, produces 100 kg of carbon dioxide.

Answer: Negative externalities is calculated as 0.1 tons of CO_2/gallon x $12/ton = $1.20 per gallon.

Imperfect Competition: Monopoly and Cartel

Monopoly

An efficient market is rarely possible. Buyers and sellers have fundamentally different interests. Sellers' interests are to limit supplies, increase demand, and raise prices. Buyers, on the other hand, like to push prices lower, limit demands, or even boycott. Also, the term is applied loosely to companies that have de facto control of a large share of a total market; Microsoft and AT&T (before its breakup) could, because of their sheer sizes, push their products to market at a price determined by the monopoly, thus preventing others from fair competition.[§] Also classified as monopolies are firms that control the entire market through many smaller, seemingly diverse companies; in the early twentieth century, Standard Oil controlled the exploration, extraction, and transportation of petroleum.

A **monopoly** is an industry with a single seller or a single provider of goods and services. In a monopoly, there is no competition and, therefore, the seller can control the market by creating temporary shortages and charge prices that are higher than they would be in a competitive market. Because the price being offered by the monopoly is usually high, the quantity demanded is smaller than in competitive enterprises. In monopolistic firms, prices are set at the point where total profit is maximized. They can sell more at lower prices, or they can sell less, but at higher prices. In either case, a monopoly can either control the output or fix the product price. Once the price is set, market demand will determine the quantity that can be sold at that price. Conversely, given the output, market demand determines the price at which that quantity can be sold.

Monopolies are characterized by a lack of viable substitute goods or the existence of high barriers to limit the entry of potential competitors into the market. The former could be because the monopoly controls a major resource, such as raw material, or a specific technology necessary to produce a product. The latter could include laws that forbid competition (exclusive control over a patent on a product or on the processes needed to produce the product), laws that effectively forbid competition (through heavy regulations and subsidy), state monopoly (such as printing money

---

§ Some argue that a monopoly can lead to higher quality -- Microsoft is working hard to maintain its monopoly, for example, by improving its product.

and issuing stamps), or natural monopoly in which production conditions and high initial costs make a sole provider more efficient (power and water distribution to private households).

Just like a monopoly that controls the market for its buyers, a *monopsony* is a market form in which a single buyer can substantially control the market as the major purchaser of goods and services, and thus dictate terms to its suppliers. A single-payer universal health care system, in which the government is the only "buyer" of health care services, is an example of a monopsony. Other examples are the defense and aerospace industries. Some may also consider "Walmart" as a monopsony entity.

Just like a competitive firm, monopolies and monopsonies maximize their profit when marginal revenue and marginal cost are equal; unlike a competitive firm, marginal revenue is not equal to the price. In fact, marginal revenue is below the price.

Example 14-2: Consider the market for heating oil in a large metropolitan area. Data of consumer behavior from previous seasons indicate that the total quantity of fuel oil sold decreases as price increases, as more and more customers switch to electricity to meet their energy needs. The cost is also a strong function of the quantity, as additional units must be imported from farther and farther distances. The total fixed cost for all firms is $4,000. The cost of production of each additional unit and the projected demand curve are given below. What is the total volume of heating oil and price offered to the market assuming that:
a. 100 firms are competing for the same market?
b. The biggest firm buys out the remaining 99 smaller firms and, thus, becomes the sole supplier of the heating oil?

Quantity	0	100	200	300	400	500	600	700	800	900	1000
Price ($)	42.00	40.00	38.00	36.00	34.00	32.00	30.00	28.00	26.00	24.00	22.00
Marginal Cost ($)	--	10.00	8.50	8.00	8.50	10.00	12.50	16.00	19.50	26.00	32.50

Solution: Whether a firm operates as a monopoly or competes in a competitive market, it is interested in maximizing its profit. As long as the revenue of producing one additional unit (marginal revenue) is higher than its marginal cost, the firm makes a profit. In a competitive market, there is a large number of competitors, so each firm can only charge a price equal to the marginal cost. Since, for a competitive firm, P = MR, its profit-maximizing output is where MC = MR = P. Attempting to charge any price above its marginal cost brings in additional profit and signals competitors to enter the market. In this example, marginal costs are reduced initially but increase as additional units are produced. At the same time, prices continue to decline with increasing output. The price becomes equal to marginal cost ($26) when 800 barrels of heating oil are sold cumulatively among the 100 retailers, bringing a total of $7,500 in profit.

Increasing production does not necessarily mean more profit. In a competitive market, each firm is only after its self-interest and tries to maximize its profit, even if it does not bring maximum profit for all firms, collectively. In a monopolistic firm, there is no competition, so a firm can set the price as it wishes and marginal revenue needs no longer be equal to the price. In this example, the monopoly's interest is in reducing the total quantity from 800 to 600, but to sell it at a higher price of $30 a barrel instead of $26, increasing total profit by $750 to $8,250. As could be expected, monopolistic enterprises lead to higher prices and lower outputs.

Qty	Price	Total Cost	Marginal Cost	Total Revenue	Marginal Revenue	Total Profit	
Q	P	TC	MC	TR	MR	TP	
0	42	4,000		0.00		-4,000	
			10.00		40.00		
100	40	5,000		4,000		-1,000	
			8.50		36.00		
200	38	5,850		7,600		1,750	
			8.00		32.00		
300	36	6,650		10,800		4,150	
			8.50		28.00		
400	34	7,500		13,600		6,100	
			10.00		24.00		
500	32	8,500		16,000		7,500	
			12.50		20.00		
600	30	9,750		18,000		8,250	Monopoly
			16.00		16.00		
700	28	11,350		19,600		8,250	
			19.50		12.00		
800	26	13,300		20,800		7,500	Competitive
			26.00		8.00		
900	24	15,900		21,600		5,700	
			32.50		4.00		
1000	22	19,150		22,000		2,850	

Cartel

When, instead of a single seller, a combination of a group of firms controls the flow of a good or service to a market, we have a **cartel** (or **trust**). In a cartel, a group of industries forms an alliance through which they can jointly decide on strategies that effectively control production and set prices. Like monopolistic enterprises, the cartels' main objective is to maximize profit, except that cartels strategize to maximize the collective profit of their members, even when different firms have conflicting interests. In practice, one or two larger firms control cartel policies and set quotas and prices. Smaller firms must exit or follow suit.

OPEC is one such entity formed in 1960 by six major oil-producing countries to control production and combat falling oil prices (See Chapter 3). In the years following the 1960s, OPEC had limited success, since the price per barrel[¶] of light crude was raised modestly from $1.80 to $2.59 in 1973. The most striking success was the Arab Oil Embargo and OPEC's cut back following the 1973 Arab-Israeli war. This resulted in a rapid rise in the price of oil to $11.65 by January 1974, which was gradually raised to $14 a barrel by 1978. The Iranian revolution in 1979 and the Iran-Iraq war of the 1980s gave OPEC another opportunity to push prices to as much as $40 a barrel in 1981. Adjusted for inflation to 2007 prices, this exceeded $100 a barrel (Figure 14-4). The rapid rise in the price of petroleum forced industrial nations to consume oil more efficiently and invest heavily in alternative sources of energy, such as wind and solar. Furthermore, high prices gave incentives to other nations to explore more of their own reserves and expand their production capacities. Because of these changes, along with the discovery of the North Sea and Norwegian oil deposits, and the flow of Russian oil, OPEC's role as an effective cartel was greatly reduced.

Within the next few years, Saudi Arabia lost its leadership role in controlling prices, and the price of oil continued to

¶ One barrel of oil is 42 gallons.

decline – falling to $15 a barrel by February 1986. OPEC tried many times to control prices by cutting production, but the strategy remained largely ineffective, and except for a short time during the 1991 Gulf War, prices stayed under $20. Various economic factors and the turmoil in Iraq resulting from the U.S. occupation caused oil prices rise to a record high above $142 a barrel in June 2008, the highest they have ever been in OPEC history. In the past few years, new techniques have lowered the cost of production of non-conventional petroleum to levels competitive with conventional liquids, and prices of oil are falling again.

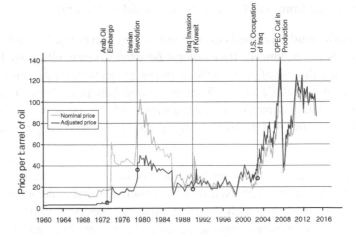

Figure 14-4
Oil prices from 1960 to 2008, adjusted to 2007 dollars.

It is important to point out that for a cartel to work efficiently, all members must agree to set aside economic differences and work in unison. In the case of OPEC, the internal economic factors, and external political pressures, along with rivalry among members and the emergence of non-member powerhouses, have effectively stopped OPEC from performing efficiently as a cartel.

Advantages and Disadvantages of a Monopoly

The major disadvantages of a monopoly are lower efficiency, higher prices, and somewhat poorer quality. Because they don't have to compete in the marketplace, monopolistic firms can set prices artificially high, are less efficient, and restrict innovation. As a result, the product quality, compared to quality in a competitive market, suffers. Some economists do not consider these actions as necessarily harmful if firms reinvest their profits in the industry to expand their internal R&D (research and development) efforts, building new plants, and upgrading existing equipment. According to the *Wall Street Journal*, Japan owes its impressive energy efficiency to big energy companies that tacitly agreed among themselves to increase the price of energy but reinvest the windfall back into energy research and development.

Goods and Bads

"**Goods**" are anything that people desire and, by extension, "**bads**" can be defined as all that they do not wish to have. Examples of goods are houses, cars, food, and energy. Examples of bads are pollution and noise. Garbage could be considered good or a bad, depending on whether we have to pay to get rid of our garbage, or if we are being paid by incinerator companies that burn it to produce electricity. Plastic bags can be considered goods when they are used to carry groceries, but bads when they no longer have any useful function and must be disposed of.

The goods that can be sold in a market or traded in a barter economy in exchange for other services and products are called **market goods**. **Non-market goods** are goods that are available to all without charge. Examples of market goods are televisions, hamburgers, oil, electricity and, in some instances, even pollution. Air and water are prime examples of non-market goods.[**]

Private and Public Goods

Private goods are goods whose consumption or use by one consumer precludes consumption or use by someone else. For example, a car sold to you is only for your own use (or your family and friends, if you wish). The gasoline that you put in your car cannot be used by any other car, except yours. Private goods *are usually exclusionary*. Watching a movie in a movie theater or riding a train requires buying tickets, so those who do not have tickets can be

---

[**] Except in the case of manufactured or bottled water.

excluded from watching the movie or riding the train.

Public goods are goods in common -- they can be used simultaneously by many individuals. Furthermore, once these goods are produced, they *cannot be exclusionary*, either by law or because of prohibitively high costs. Examples include the use of park services, police protection, roads, schools, and courts. The use of a public good by one person does not exclude others from using and benefiting from it, as well. One person enjoying park facilities does not prevent others from enjoying the same park. Unless it is overcrowded, the use of the university library by one student does not diminish its use by others, so there is no rivalry between students over library resources.

Without exclusion, private firms have little or no incentive to provide public goods. To make a profit, private firms require users to pay a fee for their products or services. For example, although TV broadcasting is a public good, cable companies can exclude non-subscribers and make a profit. For this reason, public goods are often provided by the government, which levies mandatory taxes on everyone. In certain instances, the government may hire private contractors to deliver public goods and pay them from general funds or by issuing bonds.

> **Question:** Is electricity a public or a private good?
> **Answer:** Strictly speaking, electricity is a private good since it is non-rival and exclusionary. Electricity is, however, an essential part of our daily lives and, as such, is consumed by the public at large. It is, therefore, argued by some that electricity should not be treated in the same fashion as other private goods. That's to say, as a matter of economic justice or fairness, electricity must be regulated or subsidized (offered at lower prices) to low-income customers.

In the United States and many capitalist countries, electricity has been subjected to the general laws of supply and demand and treated similarly to other conventional private goods. Because electricity generation is capital intensive, only a few firms control the electricity market. In economic terms, a production system that is controlled by limited producers is called an **oligopoly**. The problem with an oligopoly is that these firms can theoretically collude to fix prices, forcing smaller firms out of competition and, in effect, can become single, unregulated monopoly firms. When energy was deregulated in the United States, proponents cited "deregulation" as a measure intended to increase competition. In reality, deregulation of electricity resulted in major collusion among big energy firms that raised prices to unprecedented levels. Because the public required the service, it had no choice but to accept the highly inflated prices.

> **Example 14-3:** In the absence of any regulatory pressure, John is dumping his garbage (a private bad) in a vacant lot adjacent to his house. Two neighbors, Sue and Bob, are particularly upset and are even willing to pay for the cost of hauling John's garbage, which is $10 a month. Sue is willing to pay $7 toward the effort; Bob has volunteered to pay $5. Would enough money be collected to clean up John's garbage?
> **Solution:** Not necessarily! Knowing Bob's willingness to pay $5, Sue may conclude that $5 is all she needs to contribute toward the effort. By the same logic, Bob will volunteer to pay only $3, for a total of $8. As a result, each tries to free-ride off the desperation of the other and, as a result, not enough money is collected.

Environmental Economics

The environment is not only the source of raw materials but is also a sink for the wastes generated as a result of the exploitation of those same resources. As the economy continues to expand and industrial output grows, we are generating more and more hazardous wastes and toxic chemicals, which will eventually end up in the air, in the water supply, and on land. Because society requires many services and products, it is understandable that a certain amount of pollution must be tolerated. The question is where the balance lies and how much longer we can exploit our natural resources before the costs associated with environmental degradation outweigh the benefits of increasing production and material wealth. Economists differ in their approach to reducing environmental pollution but, at the same time, assure us that society, as a whole, benefits from proposed clean-up strategies. Most economists measure the cost/benefit ratio of environmental protection in monetary terms; there are some, however, who are not willing to put a figure on the natural capital and the ecological systems that support life. The dilemma is that, although sources are owned privately (either by state or private enterprises), the same entities have free access to the sink (atmosphere) which is owned by the public, as a whole.

Open Access and the Tragedy of the Commons

Two problems often associated with public goods are free riding and open access or the **tragedy of the commons**.

Free riding is a problem when each consumer of a public good is inclined to consume the good without sharing its cost of production – to free ride on the investment of others. *Open access* refers to the over-exploitation of natural resources to the benefit of each consumer at the expense of the community benefit. The major problem with environmental clean-up is that most natural capitals (ocean, forest, atmosphere, pastures) are not (and cannot be) privately owned. Because the interests of individuals do not match with those of the public, everybody ends up overexploiting the resources, something that in the long term cannot be in the interest of anyone. In economic terms, this is called the open access problem.

Let's consider a lake, commonly shared by the local population. Individual fishermen prefer open access to the lake, with little or no regulation on how much they can fish. They, therefore, opt for bigger boats, and larger fishing nets. Collectively, however, the entire population will suffer, as it inevitably leads to over-fishing, and polluting the lake. The same can be said of other public resources such as grazing lands and fossil fuels. Cattle herders or fishermen will rationally argue that if they do not exploit the land for more grazing, or use the lake for more fishing, somebody else will. It is, therefore, logical to exploit the land or to overfish the lake to its maximum limit and reap the benefits before somebody else does. Factory owners or coal companies have little incentive to bear the high cost of cleaning the air, even though their children and families living nearby may have to breathe the same polluted air. In a way, in the absence of environmental regulations, they reap the full benefit of avoiding the clean-up costs, although they have to pay only a fraction of the costs that air pollution will bring to the entire community. If contributions are totally voluntary, each person may not contribute his or her fair share, hoping to free ride on the contribution of others.

To prevent tragedy from happening, natural capitals must be protected. This can be done through individual action, raising social conscience, social pressure[††], by agreement between all interested parties, or through laws enacted by the government and other regulatory agencies.

Is There a Right Amount of Pollution?

Although having a clean environment is desirable to almost anyone, there is a limit to how clean it can get and how much it can cost. There are two schools of thought on what constitutes an efficient amount of pollution. Traditional economics treats pollution as a "good" that follows the same law of supply and demand that governs all other goods; it is most efficient at a level where the marginal cost of pollution reduction (supply) is equal to the marginal benefit to society, or what society is willing to pay (demand) to avoid it. Any measure that reduces or increases pollution beyond this level results in a reduction in total benefits to producers and consumers, alike.

The second group of economists (ecological economists), rejects this view as inherently unethical and unfair. They point out that personal safety is the innate right of every individual, and, independent of how much it costs, pollution must be brought below a certain level of risk to its victims. The former group advocates an **efficiency standard**, whereas the latter group believes a **safety standard** must be the basis of pollution control. Not surprisingly, efficiency advocates consider the safety standard as inefficient, whereas safety advocates consider efficiency standards to be inadequate in safeguarding the public and the environment.

[††] Even these have its own critics. As Hardin points out, it is not psychologically healthy to obligate people, on the basis of social conscience, or pressure to act against their own interests. It discriminates against people of good conscience, by denying them the opportunity to compete. After all, it will not work in the long run, as people of lesser conscience will become more successful, forcing their own values on the society.

Efficiency Standard

An efficient market is a market in which demand and supply are in balance. The market demand curve represents the amount people are willing to pay for one additional unit of output, at each price, i.e., what people pay for the pleasure of having one extra unit of the good (marginal benefit). Similarly, the market supply curve represents the cost incurred by the firm to produce each additional unit of good (marginal cost). If the price rises above this equilibrium point, the quantity demanded drops, but suppliers would be willing to increase their production, and new suppliers would be willing to enter the market. The imbalance between supply and demand pushes the price down and equilibrium is achieved again. The opposite will be true when the price drops, but the final result will be the same.

Applying this concept to pollution control, we note that the marginal costs of reduction (marginal damage function, or damage done by an additional unit of pollution) will be increasingly higher per unit reduction in pollution (easier clean-ups are done first)[‡‡] and marginal benefits of reduction are lessened as the air gets cleaner and cleaner. For example, it is costlier to reduce nitric oxide concentrations from 100 to 99 ppm than it would be to reduce them from 1,000 to 999 ppm. At the same time, the marginal benefit society receives drops -- in terms of lower health risks, for instance -- with a reduction in nitric oxide's concentration).

Figure 14-5 shows the estimated marginal costs of pollution abatement in Euros/ton, for 2010, for the former Soviet Union and member countries of the Organization for Economic Cooperation and Development (OECD). As the data show, the graph is highly nonlinear. With current technology, the cost of emissions reduction is fairly small for removal of up to 50% of the pollutants, rises rapidly up to 80%, and becomes prohibitively expensive if the last 20% of the emissions are to be cleaned up. That is, as the level of pollution in the atmosphere decreases, we reach a point where further clean-up efforts require costs too excessive for society to bear.

Safety Standard

Can one put a price tag on safety? Efficiency advocates, as we saw in the previous section, set the price at the point where the market is at its Pareto efficiency. *Safety advocates*, however, believe that people have a right to protect themselves against unsolicited harm to their immediate environment, and see safety as an essential human right that must be assured at an acceptable level, no matter the cost. Furthermore, they stress that polluters are the ones who must pay for the cost of cleaning the environment -- the public should not be victimized at the expense of profiteering by the polluting firms. In addition to being fair to the victim, the "polluter-pays" principle removes the incentive for polluters to pollute (free-ride). If polluters do not pay for the pollution, their production costs drop, which encourages, even more, polluters to enter the market, produce more

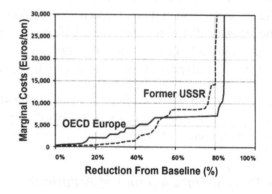

Figure 14-5
Cost of pollution abatement [Ref. 9].

goods, and create even more pollution. Furthermore, safety advocates refute the claims by efficiency advocates that suing the polluters can remedy the problem of environmental pollution by pointing out that victims often do not have the resources that large corporations have. Litigation is often quite costly and can take many years. Therefore, it is very likely that victims tolerate the pollution damage, giving polluters a free hand to pollute with little fear of retribution. Another concern raised with this option is that there are always those who try to free-ride on the outcome of the lawsuits filed by a few, without exposing themselves to excessive costs associated with the lawsuits. For example, a noisy tenant blasting his stereo in the middle of the night might inconvenience more than a few neighbors. Although one or more victims may be inclined to sue and evict this neighbor, others may refuse to contribute to the effort and hope others carry the burden.

Proponents of the efficiency standards, for their part, point to a number of drawbacks in safety standards. The first

---

[‡‡] It should be noted that unlike goods sold in a market, the marginal damage function slope normally gets steeper as emission increases. The curve may eventually level off, if no additional damage can be done (e.g. when all pond fish are dead).

criticism is that safety standards are, by definition, inefficient. Furthermore, the public will be best served if the money is spent on those environmental projects that save the largest number of lives. Because we have limited financial resources, accepting a small increase in a particular risk may release the money to carry out other safety measures. For example, allowing a slightly higher risk of cancer from pesticide use and diverting the money saved to reducing cancer from tobacco smoking, investing in accident-prevention measures, and educating the public about drug abuse, gun safety, and gang violence might, in fact, saves more lives, overall. Ultimately, how strict the safety standards should require a cost-benefit analysis.

> **Question:** Who should pay for hauling garbage and constructing new landfills, the government or private homeowners?
>
> **Answer:** When the government pays for the cost, individual households have little incentive to reduce waste, and landfills fill sooner. At any rate, in the long run, the cost will be distributed through all households by requiring them to pay higher taxes.

The Benefits of Environmental Protection

Depending on how one views the environment, different values can be placed on protecting it. The **utilitarian** considers the value of the environment only as long as it brings him happiness. Anything that does not affect him directly has little immediate value to him. Therefore, one cannot be easily persuaded to pay for expenses today, even though he might eventually be rewarded by cheaper products, better health, and a more pleasant environment. The **environmental ethicist**, on the other hand, sees protecting the environment as a moral issue; the environment belongs not only to us but also to all living organisms and all future generations. Society should seek to protect it, whether such action directly benefits today's humans or not.[§§] The EPA provides comprehensive reviews of the United States and the international experiences with economic incentives for protecting the environment.

Environmental protection has both market benefits and non-market benefits and maybe broken down into:

Use-value is the benefits people get from the direct use of a good. Use-value of a bicycle or a TV is the price we pay for the bicycle or TV, to exercise and use it for short commutes, and for watching the news and the entertainment. An example of the use-value of a lake is an increase in the number of water-sport enthusiasts, swimmers, and fishermen who use the lake.

Not all value is use-value, as some values do not benefit people directly, or in a short time. Examples of *non-use-value* are:

Option-value refers to a willingness to pay to preserve the option of experiencing a particular environmental amenity. Even if you won't go to the Grand Canyon this year, preserving it and its ecological systems may have value to you -- to preserve the option that you can visit it, sometime in the future.

Existence-value implies a willingness to pay for preserving the environment, even if it does not benefit us directly, such as protection of rain forests, and saving endangered species. The existence value of the lake is the value individuals place on simply saving the ecosystem because of their belief that other creatures -- animals and plants -- have the same inherent right to these resources as us, humans.

Cost-Benefit Analysis

The economic benefits of environmental protection can be divided into its market and non-market benefits:
Market benefits are measured in terms of increased efficiency and production, savings in the cost of energy expenditure, reduction in the cost of health care, and the creation of new jobs. For example, cleaning the water in a polluted lake can increase commercial fishing and tourism, reduce the rate of infectious disease, and appreciate

---

[§§] The differentiation between utilitarians and environmentalists only makes sense when basic human needs are satisfied. The poor have not seen any point in protecting the environment, as they do not receive much of the benefits. When poor countries are given sufficient incentives, their attitudes will necessarily change and they will see the value of environmental protection and conservation.

the price of the housing adjacent to the lake, all of which can be measured in dollars. One approach is to use a *hedonic regression* to estimate the utility or pleasure associated with an improved environment. For example, hedonic regression can be used to assess the value of a real estate in the absence of specific market transaction data. Because one building is different from another, it is often difficult to find an identical building that was sold recently. Instead, it is assumed that a house can be deconstructed into several characteristics, such as location, the number of bedrooms, the size of the lot, quality of neighborhood schools, etc. Hedonic regression treats these attributes separately and estimates prices for each of them. In essence, it assumes that there is a separate market for each characteristic. This information can be used to reconstruct a price index that can, in turn, be used to compare the price of housing in different cities or at different times.

Non-market benefits of cleaner lakes are the enhanced diversity of marine life, more enjoyable swimming, recreational fishing and boating, and improved air quality. Non-market benefits cannot be measured directly but can be estimated by polling people on their hypothetical *willingness to pay*, to avoid incurring specific damage and for the benefit of enjoying a cleaner environment, or, their *willingness to accept* compensation for a certain amount of pollution and its associated actual or perceived risks. Since different people value the benefits differently, the result is contingent upon the questions asked (**contingent valuation**).

The actual risk is often estimated as the probability that a certain pollutant causes a certain number of deaths every year, spread over the affected population. Usually, this is done by examining data from past cases of human exposure to the pollutant or by extrapolating laboratory data from animals exposed to various doses of pollutants. Many times, however, actual risks do not represent the perceived risks of exposure to pollution. For example, people may perceive that the risk of radiation from nuclear reactors is much higher than the risk from coal reactors, even though data show the actual health risks from exposure to radiation are far less than those of exposure to airborne toxins.

Once the benefits of environmental protection are evaluated, we need to assess the costs of noncompliance by determining losses to property and humans. Although placing a monetary value on human life seems highly insensitive, unfortunately, it is the only way the cost of environmental degradation and damage to humans can be measured. Perhaps a better way to view this approach is to look, instead, into the benefits of saving lives by investing in various pollution abatement strategies. Depending on the age, education, and income, the U.S. Environmental Protection Agency puts a number ranging from $475,000 to $8.3 million on the value of human lives. In contrast, the value of life in many poor countries has been estimated to be in the tens of thousands of dollars.

> **Question:** Some propose using the discounted future earnings of an individual to estimate the damage resulting from a loss of life. Others suggest the best way to measure the value of a life is the risk various people are willing to take to accept similar jobs. Comment!
>
> **Answer:** The first method is often used by the U.S. court system to determine monetary damage for a loss of life. The main objection to this method is that the lives of retired people or volunteers are greatly undervalued. The second method looks into how much people value their own lives when they participate in dangerous sports, volunteer for military service, or apply for risky jobs, such as law enforcement and firefighting. The main objection to this approach is that to support their families, many people have no choice but to accept high-risk jobs. Also, very few people are adequately informed of the actual risks they are taking when they accept new jobs or participate in dangerous activities, and may not reflect a full understanding of the actual risks they may face. Finally, this method does not take into account the preference of many participants who are inherently less risk-averse -- irrespective of -- the proceeds they may receive. One thing is certain; no matter which approach we use, we must face the ethical dilemma of valuing some lives more than others.

Economic Impacts

The economic impact of environmental protection can be studied in terms of the direct cost of clean-up, the potential loss of jobs, and the costs associated with monopolistic power. Engineering cost estimates of environmental protection in the United States have been steadily increasing from 1% of the GNP in the early 1970s to 2.8% of the GNP ($224 billion) in 2000, much of which is for improving water quality and clean-up of old, hazardous solid waste sites. The impact of environmental protection on employment has been minimal, at best. Despite what many "pro-business" activists claim, environmental regulations have not resulted in a large number of plant shutdowns and massive job losses. Labor statistics show that although some workers were forced to retrain and change jobs, environmental protection probably has led to a small net gain in U.S. employment. In fact, in the past quarter of a century, the majority of U.S. jobs lost have been due to increased competition from newly emerged industrial powerhouses like China, Korea, India, and Brazil, or due to the transfer of much of the U.S. manufacturing capability offshore, where labor is cheaper and taxes are lower. For the few cases in which there has been some loss of income due to environmental regulation, the utility derived from a cleaner environment compensated for the drop in utility from additional material goods.

Probably the most direct impact on environmental protection has been the consolidation of major environmental firms and an increase in the monopoly power that these firms exercise. The main reason for these mergers is that the cost of equipment required for clean-up is quite high and cannot be afforded by many small businesses. As we discussed in the previous section, monopolies may not be as efficient as a competitive market, and prices charged are somewhat higher.

Question: The costs for many of the new and clean energy technologies, such as photovoltaic and wind, have dropped below the social costs of older and more polluting technologies, such as coal and oil. Why haven't these technologies been promoted more aggressively or been adopted by the public in greater volume?

Answer: The renewable energy technologies are indeed the socially preferred option; however, their private costs are still above those of non-renewable energy sources. Unless they have a substantial profit advantage, no government promotion or subsidy can make clean technologies succeed. It should be noted that being competitive in the market is not enough for the public to transition to cleaner technologies. For example, in many instances, it can be shown that it makes economic sense to switch from electric and gas heating to solar heating and geothermal heat pumps. Nevertheless, many people are reluctant to invest in upfront costs to install new technologies because they lack knowledge about the advantages of clean technologies and have a strong perception that oil and coal are well-established, mature and proven technologies. Clean technologies have another major barrier to overcome. That is, they are offering consumers a service that they already have. Unless services are offered by financially secure, well-established firms, they often do not have the necessary resources to counteract advertising campaigns by existing firms. In the absence of such incentives it is reasonable to assume that, without government action (regulation and elimination of subsidies to conventional technologies), clean technologies will, for now, serve only the niche markets.

Environmental Legislation

Many economists consider the public ownership of resources (land, water, air) and free access to the environment as the main causes of environmental pollution; therefore, the only remedy to stop the abuse is through environmental regulations, pollution taxes, and fines. Three approaches -- command-and-control regulations, incentive-based regulations, and process-based regulations (or a combination of the three) -- often are used to address a variety of environmental problems.

Control-Based Legislation

Control-based legislation (also called **command-and-control legislation**) relies on directives (commands or standards) on how polluters should reduce their pollution, and by how much. These policies simply make excessive amounts of pollution illegal and are enforced by imposing fines, penalties, and taxes for non-compliance. Two types of standards are normally set:

Ambient Standards regulate the amount of pollutant that is allowable in the surrounding (ambient) environment.

Examples are ground-level ozone and sulfur dioxide in an airshed. The EPA has set National Ambient Air Quality Standards for six principal pollutants, called "criteria" air pollutants. (See Chapter 7: Air Pollution Standards)

Emission Standards regulate the level of emissions allowed by a specific source, that can be released into the environment. Examples are the sulfur dioxide emission per kilowatt-hour of electricity or sulfur content of coal per ton of output.

Under command-and-control (CAC) plans, firms are required to deploy the **Best Available Control Technology (BACT)** to control emissions. Although this approach dictates fair and balanced regulation to all players, regardless of their size, it is not necessarily an efficient one. For example, consider two firms, A and B, producing essentially the same product and residing in the same geographical area. Because of its size and the cleaner technology it employs, A has a lower cost-per-unit of pollution than B. From a fairness standpoint, A and B must reduce emissions-per-unit output by the same amount. From an efficiency standpoint, it is best if A reduces emissions by a greater amount than B, keeping the combined emissions the same. The combined cost of emission abatement by the two firms will be lower.

In the United States, environmental regulations are largely based on the CAC approach for most pollutants and are administered by the EPA, through such statutes as the 1990 U.S. Clean Air Act. The Act imposes penalties for those entities that violate federal and state guidelines on the type and amount of toxic substances, as well as their handling, use, and disposal. The rules are imposed uniformly for all polluters without considering costs and circumstances. The problem with this approach is that it is, by definition, "not cost-efficient" and can sometimes be outright ridiculous. For example, EPA regulations require that 30% of organic matter must be removed from inflows to sewage treatment plants. Although this regulation makes sense most of the time, it does not make sense in Alaska, which has some of the purest waters in the world. To comply with regulations, Alaska had to build a new $135-million treatment plant to remove 30% of almost nothing. Alaskan officials requested a waiver but were turned down. As a result, Alaskans had fish guts dumped into the water, just to be removed again, downstream, before it entered the treatment plant. Although the EPA mandate was satisfied, the water was more polluted than it would have been if nothing had been done at all.

The one exception to CAC legislation is the distinction it makes between new and old sources. Under this ruling, older sources (such as cars) do not have to meet the same stringent standards as newer ones. The reasoning behind this decision is both technical (higher costs are associated with cleaning the older sources) and political (it is much easier to pass regulations restricting firms that are not yet around or are in infancy). The problem with this approach is that it promotes the use of older and dirtier equipment for much longer, reduces the incentive for putting additional resources into research and development (R&D) work, and slows down investments in costlier, newer, and cleaner technologies. This is a serious objection that has been raised against any technology-based regulations for both new and old sources. The fear of developing better technologies is that, under BACT, firms are legally obligated to upgrade their pollution-control equipment at existing and newer facilities.

> **Question:** Examples of the CAC approach are the imposition of gasoline taxes and CAFE standards discussed in Chapter 6, both of which were designed to increase fuel efficiency. Comment on the viability of these approaches.
> **Answer:** The main problem with gasoline tax is that both clean and dirty cars are taxed at the same rate and taxes must be quite high to be effective. The main concern raised against CAFE standards is that higher gasoline efficiencies promote more driving and, as a result, total vehicle-miles traveled may increase.

Incentive-Based Legislation

To counteract many problems associated with control-based legislation, many economists propose developing incentive-based (IB) regulations in the form of emissions credits, allowable tax deductions, and other incentives. Likewise, those who are not complying will be penalized by paying higher taxes with fewer emissions credits. Two plans have been proposed: 1) to enact a **pollution tax** proportional to the amount of pollutants discharged into the air, and 2) to issue a **pollution permit** (emission credit) that can be auctioned off or freely traded in a pollution market.

Both systems are designed to put a price on pollution so that polluters carry the costs; this provides incentives to firms and others to seek less-polluting alternatives or better clean-up strategies. With taxing, the cost is direct – more pollution means more taxes. As an incentive, some tax breaks may be given to those industries that have met and exceeded the requirements set by law or have invested in research and development of cleaner technologies; tax credit for alternative fuels is another example. With pollution permits (also called *emissions trading* or the *cap and trade*), a regulatory body -- usually the government -- sets an overall cap on the total carbon emissions that drops annually: less pollution offers the opportunity to make permits available for sale, whereas more pollution requires additional permits to be bought from the government or less-polluting competitors. This encourages companies to invest in cleaner technologies or find efficient ways to cut emissions and sell the unused portions of their permits to others.

The principal motivation behind this strategy is that a uniform requirement placed on all emission sources would not be economically efficient, as some industries may not be able to effectively comply with the cleaning requirements. There are also, sharp differences in how pollution permits should be allocated. Some economists favor allocating a higher number of permits to industries that produce more pollution. The rationale is that as the overall cap tightens each year, the biggest polluters face the largest challenges in cutting emissions. Other economists propose allocating permits through an auction. Under this system, every company -- large or small -- would have to buy the rights to pollute. As a result, the biggest polluters would have to pay the most -- thereby providing them with the greatest incentive to cut emissions.[¶¶]

IB regulations applied to automotive emissions can take several forms that encourage both fuel efficiency and, at the same time, lower the vehicle-miles traveled. One possibility is an auto emissions tax that is adjusted, based on the total emissions the car has produced in one year since the last smog check. A congestion tax (higher toll charges for single-occupant cars or during rush hours) discourage traveling alone or during peak traffic. Another solution is to charge auto insurance on a *pay-by-the-mile* system; less would be charged to smaller cars and to people who drive less. Insurance rates will be higher for bigger cars and individuals who drive more. The final solution is the imposition of a revenue-neutral plan, referred to as the *feebate*; this system penalizes gas-guzzling cars by charging higher tax rates while rewarding highly fuel-efficient cars with rebates.

> **Example 14-4:** Suppose a city ordinance requires a reduction in total particulate emissions in an industrial area by 100 tons. There are only two polluting firms, A and B, each responsible for producing 150 tons of particulates or one-half of all of the particulate emissions in that area. What is the best strategy to achieve the required results in two scenarios in which firms can and cannot trade pollution permits? The cost of pollution abatement is $50 per ton for firm A and $200 per ton for firm B. What is the total cost of a reduction in each case?
> **Solution:** Firm B has a much higher clean-up cost than A. If emissions trading is permissible, it makes sense for firm B to buy 100 tons of emissions by paying firm A $50 per ton, for a total cost of $5,000. If emissions trading is not allowed or firms do not reach an agreement, then firms must cut emissions by 50 tons each. The cost of pollution abatement is $50 \times 50 = \$2,500$ for A, and $50 \times 200 = \$10,000$ for B, resulting in a total cost of $12,500.

The main objections raised against incentive-based regulations are hot spots. **Hot spots** refer to the elevated concentration of pollution near firms that find it economically advantageous to avoid or defer clean-up by paying a tax penalty or purchasing additional permits. This is particularly important for concentrated pollutants that are not uniformly mixed. Examples are nuclear wastes, toxic wastes, and sulfur dioxide or particulate emissions that

---

[¶¶] For example, conservatives want to limit the government's role as much as possible, accusing the government of being run by politicians and "special interests." Environmental pollution, they insist, will be resolved only when industries agree to reduce emissions voluntarily. The public, as a whole, will decide what steps to take to force polluters to cut their emissions by boycotting, suing, or switching to more environmentally friendly competitors. Progressives see the "good" government as necessary to serve the interest of the public by providing health care and assuring their welfare. They object, however, to the role of big businesses that – through their vast financial and intellectual assets – can influence the government and rally the public to support only those environmental measures that benefit them directly, no matter what the short- and long-term costs to consumers.

easily can build up in the vicinity of power plant smokestacks. The IB strategies on pollutants like carbon dioxide and chlorofluorocarbons are less important because their impact on overall air quality depends on the total volume of their emissions, not on the local concentration of those pollutants. To correct this problem, it often is suggested that penalties and permits are issued such that the maximum concentration of different pollutants within a given geographical area is not to exceed the state and federal ambient air and water quality standards.

Another problem raised by IB regulation is **monitoring and enforcement**. Unlike a CAC system, in which firms are required to install and maintain certain air quality abatement equipment, in incentive-based approaches, no such requirement exists, so constant monitoring and precise measurements of concentrations of pollutants in multiple monitoring locations are required to assure compliance. This can be quite complicated and cost-prohibitive.

Process-Based Legislation

Unlike control-based and incentive-based statutes that regulate the amount of pollutants that industry is allowed to release into the atmosphere, process-based legislation looks at the process or technology itself. Depending on the technology, different regulations can be enacted during different stages of development from R&D to prototyping, field testing, and commercialization. The process-based legislation is usually devised by various federal and state agencies that are charged with the administration of environmental policies.

> **Example 14-5:** Three utilities A, B, and C are emitting 1,000 tons of particulates each. The environmental regulations mandate the reduction of emissions by half. Three approaches are considered:
> a. Command and Control: Each firm reduces emissions by 500 tons. Because of the difference in ages of plants, the cost of reduction is $10/ton for firm A, $20/ton for firm B, and $30/ton for firm C.
> b. Cap and Trade: Firms are allowed to trade the right to pollute at $20/ton.
> c. Pollution Tax: Firms are required to pay fines at $20/ton of pollution they create.
>
> Determine the total cost of compliance under the three scenarios.
> **Solution:**
> - *Option a:* Under this scenario, each firm is required to reduce emissions by 500 tons.
>   Cost of compliance for Firm A is 500 tons x $10/ton = $ 5,000
>   Cost of compliance for Firm B is 500 tons x $20/ton = $ 10,000
>   Cost of compliance for Firm C is 500 tons x $30/ton = $ 15,000
>   Total reduction in pollution = 500 tons (Firm A) + 500 tons (Firm B) +500 tons (Firm C) = 1,500 tons
>   Total cost of compliance = 5,000 (Firm A) + $10,000 (Firm B) + $15,000 (Firm C) = $30,000
>
> - *Option b:* Under this scenario, firm A will likely choose to cut pollution by 1000 tons, and sell the credits for 500 tons to firm C at $20/ton.
>   Firm A cuts its entire pollution at a cost of 1,000 tons x $10/ton = $ 10,000, It sells its pollution credits to firm C for 500 tons x $20/ton = $10,000, for the net cost of $0.
>   Firm B cuts pollution by 500 tons, for a cost of 500 tons x $20/ton = $10,000
>   Firm C decides to buy pollution credit for 500 tons from Firm A for $10,000
>   Total reduction in pollution = 1,000 tons (Firm A) + 500 tons (Firm B) + 0 tons (Firm C) = 1,500 tons
>   Total cost of compliance = $0 (Firm A) + $10,000 (Firm B) + $10,000 (Firm C) = $20,000
>
> - *Option C*: It is cheaper for Firm A to cut all emissions. Firm B cuts pollution by 500 tons and pays a penalty for the other 500 tons. Firm C will opt to pay the penalty.
>   Cost to Firm A is 1,000 tons x $10/ton = $10,000
>   Cost to Firm B is sum of the cost of reduction (500 tons x $20/tons) + penalty (500 tons x $20/tons),

for a total of = $20,000
Cost to Firm C is 1,000 tons x $20/ton = $20,000
Total reduction in pollution = 1,000 tons (Firm A) + 500 tons (Firm B) + 0 tons (Firm C) = 1,500 tons
Total cost of compliance = $10,000 (Firm A) + $20,000 (Firm B) + $20,000 (Firm C) = $50,000

All three options will reduce the total emissions by the same amount. The command and control option has the least overall cost. Taxing the pollution is costliest to the firms, but also provides the government with a substantial revenue that can be used to invest in various pollution reduction efforts.

When Does Non-Compliance Pay Off?

Not all polluting industries choose to comply with regulations. From a purely economical standpoint, if polluters' marginal costs of compliance outweigh their marginal benefits, polluters are better off ignoring regulations. They may, instead, opt to pay fines and accept other punishments such as adverse public relations, potential losses in sales, and possibly even jail time. Costs of compliance are related to the cost of new pollution reduction equipment and the additional resources that ultimately are diverted to pollution control efforts. Benefits associated with compliance can be measured as the money saved due to reductions in the number of fines and other penalties, improved public relations, and a potential for higher sales volume. The marginal cost of compliance increases as a firm decides to comply more and more with the regulations. The marginal cost of compliance is highest when a firm does not comply with any regulations and, thus, is most vulnerable to being fined. As a firm complies more often, its chances of being caught, as well as its marginal benefit, fall (Figure 14-6). The point where MB and MC of the non-compliance cross, is where the firm can afford to stop compliance. For any additional incidence of non-compliance, the firm will have to pay fines that exceed its marginal benefit. From the previous discussion, it can be concluded that to reduce non-compliance, either the marginal cost of non-compliance must be increased (such as stiffer fines or longer jail time), or its marginal benefit is reduced.

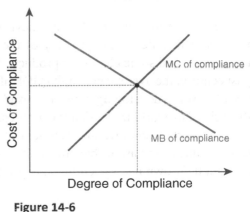
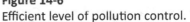

Figure 14-6
Efficient level of pollution control.

Globalization

Globalization, in the broadest terms, refers to the integration of world economies through increased trade and knowledge and the free movement of material, labor, and capital across international borders in search of new markets and investment opportunities. Although globalization is not new and existed at some level centuries ago, the technological advances of the past few decades have made it easier and quicker to complete transactions and the trend toward globalization has accelerated. Whether globalization benefits or harms a particular country has been the topic of much debate. Some consider globalization and a free market economy to be the keys to future world economic development. It fosters competition and improves efficiency by making the flow of technological innovations, skilled labor, and capital easier.

Critics contend that globalization encourages ever-more economic growth and production with no real concern about unequal and unsustainable patterns of consumption. International agreements, written primarily by large corporations and western governments, require such agencies as the **International Monetary Fund** (IMF), the **World Bank**, and the **World Trade Organization** (WTO) to oversee trade and investment agreements negotiated between member states. These organizations often impose regulations that put industrialized nations at an unfair advantage and, at the same time, increase their access to the natural resources of the developing countries. According to these rules, all resources, no matter where they lie, must be available for sale to the highest bidder, but the technologies used to discover, extract, and process these resources are regarded as proprietary, or "intellectual property" of the developers. According to these agreements, subsidies for many essential goods must be eliminated. This discriminates against smaller, less-developed countries, which cannot effectively compete with the well-developed, highly-automated agricultural and manufacturing practices of developing countries. As a result, many thousands of small farmers, artisans, and independent workers lose their livelihoods.

The role of energy is particularly important in shaping this debate. Certain types of energy, such as wind and solar, are inherently decentralized. Others, such as fossil and especially nuclear, are controlled by large corporations and governments; therefore the control over these resources and supply routes brings about economic, and political power. As we have seen by now, the world is divided into two groups: those that have vast fossil resources and those that have not. The countries that are endowed with these resources are mainly developing countries, mostly in the Middle East. Western and other industrialized countries are by far the greatest consumers of energy. The two most populous countries in the world, China, and India are growing rapidly to become the world's new economic powerhouses. This means that, not only will their demand for energy and fossil fuel accelerate, but also will their ecological footprints, the strain on natural resources, the release of carbon into the atmosphere, and higher levels of environmental pollution.

So far, the results of globalization have been mixed, at best. Rich countries have, in large part, benefited from international trade, although many of their citizens (especially those hired in low-tech industries such as textile, agriculture, and some electronic products) have suffered from losing jobs to lower-paid foreign workers. During the past century, the average per capita GDP of many industrial countries increased by as much as six-fold. In the last few decades, some developing countries, especially in Asia, have been able to benefit from globalization by increasing their share of world trade. Other countries, notably in Africa and in South America, have not been able to integrate with the world economy, and their per capita income has actually declined. What is clear is that globalization is here to stay and if they are to benefit, individual countries must embrace globalization on their own terms, taking into account their own history, culture, and traditions.

Globalization and the Environment

The impact of globalization on the environment has also its advocates and critics. Supporters of globalization see globalization as a vehicle that helps to develop and underdeveloped countries make progress toward democracy, reduces poverty, allows the transfer of cleaner technology, improves health, creates jobs, and provides environmental benefits in the form of greater investment in air and water quality.

The charge against globalization is that, since environmental laws are less strict and corruption is more rampant in some of the developing countries, many developed countries have moved their manufacturing sectors to those countries. Weaker environmental laws in developing countries have given governments and large corporations an effective argument to lower their own environmental laws, thus leveling the playing field to the detriment of the global environment.

Environmental Issues in Developed Countries

During the past few decades, our environment has undergone changes unseen by our predecessors. The global population has nearly doubled and the gap between rich and poor nations has widened. International conflicts have escalated, many of them because of competition for control of limited natural resources. We discovered that the sky over Antarctica (and, to a smaller degree, all over the world) has been losing ozone, resulting in a higher rate of skin cancer in many parts of the world. Acid rain has damaged millions of acres of land and has adversely affected marine life and other species. More than half of the tropical forests have been destroyed or greatly degraded. Many valuable species of plants and animals are now extinct or endangered. The continued dependence on petroleum has affected our health but also has resulted in global warming -- the full consequences of which are yet to be determined. The environmental issues associated with fossil fuel combustion were discussed in some detail in Chapter 7.

Until relatively recent times, most of our activities that affected the environment were local in scope. Clean-up required taking small steps over small geographical areas and short times. Today, the rapid rise in consumption of both materials and energy has made many environmental issues global in nature. Nuclear testing by one nation can have environmental repercussions thousands of miles away. The burning of fossil fuels, use of non-biodegradable products, and dumping of toxic wastes in rivers can impact the environment, globally.

One feature that separates global and local issues is their scale, both in magnitude and duration. Global issues are persistent; they cannot be solved overnight by one nation or one country, alone. Resolving these issues may require long-term planning; they are interconnected -- solving one, may, in fact, solve many other problems, or we may need to solve a multitude of other problems, simultaneously. Global warming, ozone depletion, and acid rain are among the most severe problems we are facing, worldwide.

Global warming has rightly received the most attention, as we may have to face consequences that last hundreds of years. The Kyoto Treaty was a positive step that required cooperation between industrial and poor countries. Under this plan, rich countries would reduce their emissions of greenhouse gases and, at the same time, provide incentives for poor countries to follow suit. Unfortunately, the United States, the most industrialized country and the largest contributor of greenhouse gases cited economic hardship and pulled out of the treaty, weakening the agreement and reducing its likelihood of success. Fortunately, that has been follow-up treaties that hopefully, if implemented will curb overall carbon emissions putting a cap on global warming.

Ozone depletion was recognized as a major environmental issue at the 1987 Montréal Protocol and later at the Rio Summit on biodiversity in 1992. Enforcement of the treaty required signatories to ban the import and export of products containing CFCs to and from non-member countries. This provision not only provided incentives for member countries to find ozone-friendly substitutes, but the reduced trade with non-members also provided the impetus for others to join the agreement. The two common substitutes for CFCs are hydrofluorocarbon (HFC) and hydrochlorofluorocarbon (HCFC). The former is not an ozone-depleting substance, but neither is it as efficient a coolant; the latter is a mildly ozone-depleting substance slated to be phased out by 2030.

Acid rain is formed when the sulfur and nitric oxides emitted from the stacks of coal and oil power plants react with the humid atmospheric air. The **UN Convention on Transboundary Air Pollution** drafted the "Protocol to Abate Acidification, Eutrophication, and Ground-level Ozone" sets ceilings for emissions of four pollutants -- sulfur dioxide (SO_2), nitrogen oxides (NOx), volatile organic compounds (VOCs), and ammonia (NH_3). The protocol also sets limits for specific emissions sources (power plants, refineries, farms, etc.), requiring the best available techniques to keep emissions down.

Environmental Issues in Developing Countries

Many of the environmental problems in developing countries are directly related to poverty. For people who lack safe drinking water, have inadequate sewage systems, and live in unsanitary conditions, conservation measures and environmental issues are some of the last things on their minds. Only when they achieve a simple means of subsistence and have sufficient resources to afford to address less immediate problems, do they become interested in long-term health issues and the consequences of environmental pollution. Most of these countries are heavily in debt and, therefore, any attempt at conservation and environmental protection must be linked to economic development and debt relief. Unless richer countries are willing to subsidize poorer countries to carry out environmental stewardship, the situation will deteriorate further and the environment will suffer even more. Debt relief does not have to come as a handout, however, and could require debtor countries to spend equivalent money on environmental programs such as family planning, water sanitation, land remediation, air quality improvements, etc. This is particularly important, as developing countries become more affluent and their environmental footprints become larger.

Another powerful tool to promote environmental protection is international marketable permits. Under this plan, once the target for reduction of a certain pollutant is set, a fixed number of permits is issued and distributed among developing and developed countries. Developing countries will have incentives to maintain their environments and, by doing so, will receive additional permits that they can exchange for clean-up equipment or use to upgrade their old and dirty technologies with new ones. Developed countries can buy the permits to avoid penalties and find new markets for shipping clean technologies. For example, a country can trade one million tons of carbon dioxide by switching from coal to natural gas, for a shipment of wind turbines, photovoltaic cells, or consulting expertise for increasing crop yields without the need for additional fertilizers.

The same goes for population control. In many poor countries, larger families provide a safety net that can help at times of sickness and old age. Children provide labor and bring in additional income. Because the infant mortality rate is higher, parents seek to have more children – especially males – to ensure that enough of them will survive to maintain minimal living standards and to carry on their genes. It might be argued by some that a reduction in infant mortality rate will increase population, which will, in turn, exacerbate the problem. This is what happened in the 1950s and 1960s, when improved health conditions, better nutrition, and vaccinations saved the lives of millions of babies, resulting in a population boom in many poor countries. The data also show that after the initial surge in population, the growth rate declined. This is attributed to better access to education, less pressure to have larger families, and an increasing allocation of family resources to improving the quality of life of fewer children. It now appears that proper family planning is an economically sensible way to address a wide range of global environmental problems in poorer countries.

Summary

Higher energy prices have direct and dramatic effects on the global economy. Because fossil fuels, especially petroleum, comprise the majority of our energy consumption, increases in oil prices have correlated closely with inflationary pressures. Though the U.S. has successfully reduced its dependence on imported oil in the last decade (measured as energy consumption per dollar of the GDP), other countries have not been able to follow suit. As the price of oil climbs, other commodity prices also will increase, likely affecting prices of non-energy-related exported and imported goods which, in turn, affect the global economy and may result in political instability in developing countries.

In the United States, government and businesses focus on short-term profit motives and quarterly earnings and not much on long-term interests. Banks and other sources of funding will seek to receive a return on their investments in as little as three to five years, rarely exceeding ten years. As a result, in many instances, lack of clear immediate revenues will stifle innovation or give it away easily to foreign competitors. For example, during the 1970s, when energy sufficiency and the environment became national security issues, the U.S. spent a tremendous amount of resources to support research and development of renewable energy technologies, such as solar photovoltaics, solar thermal, and wind. In the 1980s, soon after the energy crisis subsided and oil prices dropped, so did the support for alternative sources of energy and environmental protection. The Reagan administration reversed the energy independence policy of the former Carter administration by slashing federal research funds, and much of their tax credits and subsidies. At the time, the United States was the leading manufacturer of solar cells and wind turbines. Japan and much of Europe capitalized on these inventions by buying American companies and, at the same time, developing long-term energy policies that promoted energy efficiency, conservation, and the development of cleaner alternative sources of energy.

Today, Japan is the leading producer of fuel cells, and supplies over one-half of all hybrid and electric vehicles sold in the United States. Germany sells the highest number of solar cells. China is making the largest number of wind turbines. Unless the United States reverses its "cheap oil policy," not only will its reliance on foreign oil increase, but much of its engineering ingenuity and know-how will be relegated to foreign competitors.

The benefits of environmental protection and allowable amounts of pollution are difficult to measure. Economists are divided over the economic merit of pollution abatement, although they generally agree that some degree of environmental protection will benefit overall human wellbeing. Greenhouse gases, ozone, and acid rain are public goods because measures taken to reduce them by one country benefit all others. Poor countries are banking on receiving the benefits of environmental protection actions taken by more developed countries and, in that sense, they are getting a free ride. Within a country or municipality, the government can overcome the free-riding problem by imposing taxes and fines. At the international level, the imposition of environmental laws requires international cooperation, ratification of treaties, and the financial commitment of rich and industrial nations. Since the United Nations does not have the power or authority to force any member states to comply with the laws, the terms of enforcing the laws must be clearly spelled out in the treaty itself.

There is no clear strategy to ensure public health while, at the same time, maintaining optimal efficiency. When a command-and-control system is used, firms are required to install clean-up equipment. However, the government must ensure that the cost of abatement is not prohibitive and the economic welfare of the firm is also considered. Two incentive-based approaches were discussed. Permits can be issued by the government, auctioned off, or traded between firms to achieve an efficient level of pollution. Alternatively, fines and taxes can be imposed to reach the same results. Unfortunately, both approaches provide incentives for polluters to lie. In a tax system, firms are encouraged to underestimate pollution, since taxes will be imposed per unit volume or unit of weight of emissions. With permits, firms have an incentive to overestimate emissions, because they can get more permits. Process-based regulations are effective in assessing the total amount of waste in a given process, differentiating among various manufacturing technologies, and helping firms during their initial stages of development. What is clear is that neither safety nor efficiency alone can be used to set standards, and some risk/benefit analysis is needed to decide on the most effective approach.

As a final note, it is important to realize that various cleanup strategies discussed throughout this chapter assume that markets act freely without the influence of external forces. Unfortunately in many countries, environmental policies are often influenced by corrupt government officials and powerful interest groups.

In the United States, after a particular problem is identified, Congress acts to pass a bill that requires the government to study the problem and take necessary actions. The tasks of risk assessment and safety regulations are delegated to the EPA, which may then study the problem in-house or hire consultants. During this process, the EPA seeks input from the industry, the public, and environmental groups. The agency then drafts a regulation and sends it to the state governments for enforcement.

It is taken for granted that no matter how insignificant the ruling is, numerous lawsuits by various interest groups stalls the process. Many of the dirtiest industries, such as petroleum, chemical, and manufacturing firms, have huge financial and technical resources that they spend on advertising, promotion of candidates friendly to their position, and utilization of a large lobbying staff and legal firms, every step of the way. Even the EPA's top managers are influenced by high-ranking government officials who may hold the keys to their promotions and job security, and by industries that may, at some point in the future, hire them with very generous benefits packages. The best solution to reducing conflicts-of-interest is to eliminate or greatly reduce, the role of money in legislative and regulatory processes. This may require several approaches: banning or limiting political advertising, eliminating tax-deductible benefits for lobbying expenses; and disallowing government officials from accepting employment at firms that may have benefited from rulings during the tenure of those officials, for a certain number of years after they leave their government posts . The same can be said about top-level industry managers who may be appointed to sensitive government posts.

Finally, to implement political reform we must ensure that the principles of democratic government are taking hold. The collapse of the Soviet Union demonstrated that the centrally planned economy in socialist countries was even less effective in preventing an environmental disaster than market-based economies. The point is that democracy is a necessary ingredient to assure the free flow of information and to empower citizens and institutions to challenge the policies of the government when it is practicing detrimental environmental initiatives.

ⓐ *Digging Deeper: Money*

Before the invention of money, trades were conducted by bartering – the direct exchange of goods and services for other goods and services. A shoemaker could exchange his shoes with a teacher who could tutor his children or a tailor for a pair of pants. A housewife could borrow meat from a butcher, cook it and keep some for her family while delivering the rest to feed the butcher. In a small village with a handful of artisans, bartering was highly efficient.

Although bartering worked in feudal societies where only a limited number of products and services were available, it was largely ineffective in larger towns where a great variety of goods and services were needed. As societies grew and more goods and services were available, the number of exchanges became exceedingly large, and bartering became less attractive. With the invention of money, the need for direct exchange was eliminated, as individuals and businesses found a common unit of measure and value that could be exchanged for any number of products and services. Money also facilitated contracts for future activities and payments.

Wealth

In conventional capitalism, the quantity often cited as a measure of the economic health of a country is the **Gross Domestic Product (GDP)**, defined as the sum of the market value of all goods and services produced in a country during a year. Another closely related indicator is the **Gross National Product (GNP)**, which is calculated as the GDP plus what domestic companies earn from activities abroad, minus what foreign companies make from domestic activities in that country. In other words, GDP is the sum of all goods and services produced by labor and property located in a country, irrespective of who supplies them; GNP is the sum of all goods and services supplied to a country's citizens, irrespective of where they are physically produced.

Some economists object to the GDP and GNP as true indicators of wealth, because they limit wealth to only the portion of market activities in which income is generated. It neglects informal transactions between people that occur outside formal markets, and therefore, is not a particularly good indicator for countries with corrupt governments or big underground economies. Functions such as charity and housework are not accounted for, whereas the costs of cleaning the environment and health care are included. Furthermore, it does not distinguish between constructive and destructive activities. According to this definition, switching from a highly inefficient gas heater to an efficient one is "bad" for the economy, because it reduces the consumption of fossil fuels and the overall GDP. Waging a war, consuming more fast foods, and depleting of natural resources contribute to a higher GDP and therefore are "good" for the economy. By this criterion, a country can raise its GDP (although temporarily) by cutting all its trees, using up all its natural resources, and damaging its environment. In short, there is no distinction between desirable and undesirable outcomes, *what is important is only the money spent, not the value received*!

We will come back to the concept of wealth and its impact on human welfare in Chapter 15.

Future and Present Worth

In Chapter 1, we gave a few examples of how a quantity, such as savings in a bank, population, or energy consumption, grows exponentially. With no penalty for early withdrawal, a deposit of $100 in a 10-year CD (certificate of deposit) receiving 10% interest, grows to $100 \times (1.10) = \$110$ after a year, $100 \times (1.10)^2 = \$121$ after the end of the second year, and $100 \times (1.1)^{10} = \$259$ at the maturity date. Mathematically speaking, if the present value of a quantity is P and the rate of growth is r, then the future worth of a present value after n years have passed is (F/P) given by:

$$F = P(1+r)^n \qquad\qquad (14\text{-}1)$$

Rearranging this equation, we can find the present value of a quantity if we know its future worth, i.e., the present worth of a future value (P/F) is:

$$P = F(1+r)^{-n} \qquad\qquad (14\text{-}2)$$

For convenience, values of F/P and P/F are tabulated for various n and r values and are given in tables 14-2 and 14-3.

Table 14-2 Future Worth of a Present Value										
$F/P=(1+r)^n$										
r/n	1	2	3	4	5	10	15	20	25	30
0.01	1.01	1.02	1.03	1.04	1.05	1.10	1.16	1.22	1.28	1.35
0.02	1.02	1.04	1.06	1.08	1.10	1.32	1.35	1.49	1.64	1.81
0.03	1.03	1.06	1.09	1.13	1.16	1.44	1.56	1.81	2.09	2.43
0.04	1.04	1.08	1.12	1.17	1.22	1.48	1.80	2.19	2.67	3.24
0.05	1.05	1.10	1.16	1.22	1.28	1.63	2.08	2.65	3.39	4.32
0.06	1.06	1.12	1.19	1.26	1.34	1.79	2.40	3.21	4.29	5.74
0.07	1.07	1.14	1.23	1.31	1.40	1.97	2.76	3.87	5.43	7.61
0.08	1.08	1.17	1.26	1.36	1.47	2.16	3.17	4.66	6.85	10.06
0.09	1.09	1.19	1.30	1.41	1.54	2.37	3.64	5.60	8.62	13.27
0.10	1.10	1.21	1.33	1.46	1.61	2.59	4.18	6.73	1.083	17.45

Table 14-3 Present Worth of a Future Value										
$P/F=(1+r)^{-n}$										
r/n	1	2	3	4	5	10	15	20	25	30
0.01	0.99	0.98	0.97	0.96	0.95	0.91	0.86	0.82	0.78	0.74
0.02	0.98	0.96	0.94	0.92	0.91	0.82	0.74	0.67	0.61	0.55
0.03	0.97	0.94	0.92	0.89	0.86	0.74	0.64	0.55	0.48	0.41
0.04	0.96	0.92	0.89	0.85	0.82	0.68	0.56	0.46	0.38	0.31
0.05	0.95	0.91	0.86	0.82	0.78	0.61	0.48	0.38	0.30	0.23
0.06	0.94	0.89	0.84	0.79	0.75	0.56	0.42	0.31	0.23	0.17
0.07	0.93	0.87	0.82	0.76	0.71	0.51	0.36	0.26	0.18	0.13
0.08	0.93	0.86	0.79	0.74	0.68	0.46	0.32	0.21	0.15	0.10
0.09	0.92	0.84	0.77	0.71	0.65	0.42	0.27	0.18	0.12	0.08
0.10	0.91	0.83	0.75	0.68	0.62	0.39	0.24	0.15	0.09	0.06

Example 14-6: According to the U.S. DoE data, the world production of crude oil increased from 56 million barrels per day in 1980 to 68 million barrels per day in 2000. What is the average rate of increase of the world's crude over this period? What is the expected volume of crude in 2030 if the rate of production continues to increase at a similar rate?

Solution: We can think of the value in 2000 as the future worth of the value in 1980, i.e., $F/P = 68/56 = 1.21$. Consulting Table 14-2, we can see this corresponds to a rate of increase of about 1% per year, over the last 20 years of the past century. The same table can be used to extrapolate future production from 2001 to 2030. Interpolating for $n = 30$, we can find $F/P = 1.35$. The 2030 consumption of crude is estimated as $68 \times 1.35 = 92$ million barrels. It is left to the student to verify results by applying equation (14-1), instead of the tables.

Example 14-7: A new substitute to Middle Eastern oil is expected to be found in the next 20 years. The cost of production of energy equivalent to one barrel of oil is estimated at $100. What should be the price of a barrel of oil sold today in a competitive market? In a market with a substantial monopoly owner?

Solution: Assuming the market is efficient enough that no cost is associated with the extraction of oil from the Middle East, and that the cost of production remains the same, the oil should be priced at a value equal to its future price, discounted to the present time: $100 \times \{(P/F)\ n=20,\ r=0.05\ \} = 100 \times 0.38 = \$38$. It is very difficult to predict the cost of future technologies with certainty. Monopolies usually price their commodities at the cost of substitutes today, which could be substantially higher than \$38, at today's prices.

Example 14-8: U.S. domestic production of petroleum has been falling steadily since 1970, to 6.73 million barrels a day by 2008. This level of production constitutes a 1.75% drop from the previous year. Assuming that U.S. domestic production continues to fall at the same rate, how much petroleum would be left in U.S. reserves at the beginning of 2011? Total U.S. petroleum reserves were estimated to be 21 billion barrels at the start of 2009.

Solution: In 2009, we would be producing $6.73 \times 365 \times (1-0.0175)/1000 = 2.41$ billion barrels of oil (bbo). The remaining reserves would be $21 - 2.41 = 18.59$ bbo. The reserve drops by another 2.37 bbo to 16.22 bbo in 2010.

Doubling Time (Revisited)

Assuming a quantity grows exponentially at a rate of r per year, the quantity grows after n years as given by equation (14-1). Of interest is the time it takes for a present value to double, i.e., $F/P = 2$. Examining Table 14.2, for a rate of 7% per year, the doubling time is a bit longer than 10 years.

In general, it can be shown that doubling time is approximately calculated by dividing 72 by the percent interest rate (annual percentage growth rate). This approach is called the Rule of 72 and is expressed algebraically as:

$$T_2 = \frac{72}{R} \qquad\qquad (14\text{-}3)$$

Where T_2 is the doubling time in years, and R is the annual percentage growth $(R = 100 \times r)$. In example above, $T_2 = 72/7 = 10.3$ years.

Example 14-9: How long does it take for a deposit of \$5,000 in savings accounts to yield a total of \$20,000 in principal and interest? The bank pays 6% interest.
Solution: At the rate of 6% $(r = 0.06)$, it takes $72/6 = 12$ years to double the deposit. So the investment doubles to \$10,000 after 12 years and doubles, again, to \$20,000 after 24 years.

Cumulative Value of a Series of Future Payments

Also of interest is the cumulative value of a series of installments paid in equal intervals. For example, the total principal and interest paid on a home mortgage is the sum of all monthly payments over the course of a 30-year loan. Similarly, the cumulative value of energy consumption is the sum of energy used annually from the original reserves.

The analysis presented in the previous section can be used to forecast energy consumption from the present rate of consumption, assuming a certain growth rate. Of greater consequence is the amount of energy remaining at a future point in time. We calculated the remaining U.S. oil for the years prior to 2006. That procedure can be used until the oil reserves are depleted. A better way is to find a formal relationship for the cumulative consumption by adding all future consumption, by summing up the series:

$$C = P[1+(1+r)+(1+r)^2+(1+r)^3+....+(1+r)^{n-1}]$$

The mathematical series converges to give:

$$\frac{C}{P} = \frac{(1+r)^n - 1}{r} \qquad\qquad (14\text{-}4)$$

Equation (14-4) also can be interpreted as the future value of the stream of annual payments, accumulating interest compounded over time. The C/P factors are tabulated in Table 14-4.

Example 14-10: Given the data in Example 14-8, calculate how long U.S. petroleum reserves will last. Repeat the calculation for the total world petroleum reserves. The remaining world oil reserves are estimated at approximately 2,000 billion barrels; the current rate of consumption is 30 billion barrels annually and is expected to rise at a rate of 4% per year.

Solution: In this example, C is cumulative consumption equal to total U.S. oil reserves in 2009 ($C = 21$ bbo) and P is the total oil production in 2009 ($P = 6.73$ bbo), so $C/P = 21/6.73 = 3.12$. Assuming that the annual rate of consumption continues to increase at 1% a year, we can refer to Table 14-4 to find $3 < n < 4$ years. Interpolating, a better estimate will give a value of $n \sim 3.9$ years. Similarly, for the world, $C/P = 2,000/30 = 66.6$. For $r = 0.04$, we can estimate we will have petroleum for another 40 years.

Table 14- 4 Cumulative Value of a Series of Future Payments										
$C/P = [(1+r)^n - 1]/r$										
r/n	1	2	3	4	5	10	15	20	25	30
0.01	1.00	2.01	3.03	4.06	5.10	10	16	22	28	35
0.02	1.00	2.02	3.06	4.12	5.20	11	17	24	32	41
0.03	1.00	2.03	3.09	4.18	5.31	11	19	27	36	48
0.04	1.00	2.04	3.12	4.25	5.42	12	20	30	42	56
0.05	1.00	2.05	3.15	4.31	5.53	13	22	33	48	66
0.06	1.00	2.06	3.18	4.37	5.64	13	23	37	55	79
0.07	1.00	2.07	3.21	4.44	5.75	14	25	41	63	94
0.08	1.00	2.08	3.25	4.51	5.87	14	27	46	73	113
0.09	1.00	2.09	3.28	4.57	5.98	15	29	51	85	136
0.10	1.00	2.10	3.31	4.64	6.11	16	32	57	98	164
0.15	1.00	2.15	3.47	4.99	6.74	20	48	102	213	435
0.20	1.00	2.20	3.64	5.37	7.44	26	72	187	472	1,182
0.25	1.00	2.25	3.81	5.77	8.21	33	110	343	1,055	3,227
0.30	1.00	2.30	3.99	6.19	9.04	43	167	630	2,349	8,730

Annuities (Net Present Value)

Investors are interested in the return that their capital investment brings to them (ROI = Return on Investment). It also is understood that the greater the risk they take, the higher their expectations for returns will be. The minimum that any investors expect as their rate of return is the interest that they could collect if they had deposited their investment into a bank or other financial institution. Depending on the perceived risk that different projects have and the tolerance of the potential investor to the loss of capital, different investors may expect different rates of return.

Investors do not necessarily invest all the capital, upfront. Rather, it is common that they make a series of payments as the project proceeds. To make a wise decision on the profitability of the investment, all future revenues and costs must be discounted to the present. The **discount rate** is commonly chosen to be the expected rate of return.

The present value of a stream of annual payments or annuities, A, is calculated by summing equation (14-2) overall future payments:

$$P = A \left[1 + \frac{1}{(1+r)} + \frac{1}{(1+r)^2} + \ldots + \frac{1}{(1+r)^n} \right]$$

The series converges to give:

$$P/A = \frac{(1+r)^n - 1}{r(1+r)^n}$$
(14-5)

The *P/A* factors are calculated and summarized in Table 14-5.

Example 14-11: A $10,000,000 lottery win can be awarded either over 20 years, in installments of $500,000 each, or as $5,000,000 in cash, right away. Assuming the winner plans to deposit his money in a 20-year CD that pays 8% in interest, which option makes more sense?

Solution: The present value of the annual installments is $\{(P/A)_{n=20,\ r=0.08}\} = 10.59$. The present worth of all future installments is $500,000 × 10.59 = $5,295,000 and is somewhat better than the $5,000,000 in cash paid out today.

Example 14-12: The population of a large metropolitan area is expected to increase by 200,000 people within the next five years. To meet the future demand, a 200-MW wind farm is proposed for construction. The cost of construction is expected to be $5M in the first two years and an additional $2M for the following three years. The plant is expected to generate a net annual income (revenue minus maintenance costs) of $2M for 20 years after it is completed. Does this investment make economic sense? Assume an interest rate of 5%.

Solution: In the first five years $16M is spent while the plant is under construction. Starting in year six, the plant will generate revenues of $2M in annual income for the next 20 years after maintenance costs are deducted. A summary of the cost and income schedule is given below:

Year	1	2	3	4	5	6	7	...	25
Cost (M)	5	5	2	2	2	0	0	0	0
Income (M)	0	0	0	0	0	2	2	2	2

Note that *P/A* factors assume that all payments are equal and start from year one. As mentioned, there is no income for the first five years. To correct this, we subtract the net present value of income that would be generated for 25 years and subtract from it the lack of income opportunity for the first five years. Similarly, we can break down costs as an annual cost of $2M for five years, in addition to annual costs of $3M, for the first two years. This is best understood if the timeline table is rearranged as:

Year	1	2	3	4	5	6	7	...	25
Cost (M)	2	2	2	2	2				
Cost (M)	3	3							
Income (M)	2	2	2	2	2	2	2	2	2
Income (M)	-2	-2	-2	-2	-2				

The approach is to calculate the *P/A* factor for a series of annual payments starting in year 1. Consulting Table 14-5, the net present values of income and expenses are:

NPV(income) = [2(P/A, 0.05, 25) - 2(P/A,0.05,5)] = 2×14.09 – 2×4.33 = 19.52 M
NPV (cost) = [3(P/A,0.05,2) + 2(P/A,0.05,5)] = 3×1.86) + 2×4.33 = 14.24 M
NPV (income) / NPV (costs) = 19.52/14.24 = 1.37;
thus the investment makes sense.

Capital Recovery Factor

The capital recovery factor (annualized cost) represents the series of annual payments to pay off a loan. This is the reverse of the previous problem -- we know the present worth of all future payments (i.e., the loan principal). The result is:

$$A/P = \frac{r(1+r)^n}{(1+r)^n - 1}$$

(14-6)

A/P factors are tabulated in Table 14-6.

Example 14-13: What is the annual payment required to pay a $250,000 loan at 7% over 15 years?
Solution: Annual cost = loan amount $\times [(A/P)_{r=0.07,\, n=15}]$ = ($250,000) $\times$ 0.11 = $27,500.

Internal Rate of Return

A convenient way to evaluate the economic benefit of a project is to calculate the effective rate of return of all future transactions. Since payments and revenues take place at different times, a proper method of evaluation is to discount them to present value. The internal rate of return is computed simply by equating the NPVs for all future costs and incomes.

NPV (cost) = NPV (income)

Example 14-14: An investor is considering investing in the wind farm project described in Ex. 14-12. The investor also has an opportunity to purchase a government bond which is expected to earn a 10% return. Which option would be more advantageous?
Solution: To have a fair basis for comparison, the investor should compare the internal rate of return for the project and the rate of return from the bond. The internal rate of return can be calculated by equating the NPVs for income and cost.

NPV (income) = NPV (cost)
2 (P/A, r, 25) - 2 (P/A, r, 5) = 3 (P/A, r, 2) + 2 (P/A, r, 5); or
Δ (NPV) = 2 (P/A, r, 25) - 4 (P/A, r, 5) - 3 (P/A, r, 2) = 0

The problem must be solved by trial and error. Assume a rate of return and evaluate the equation above, until it converges. The effective rate of return for investing in the wind farm project is about 8%, which is less than the 10% that the bond would earn. Although the investment in the bond is a better choice financially, and an environmentally contentious investor may still consider the investment in the wind farm.

Cost of Living Adjustment (COLA)

We, along with economists, are well aware that money tends to lose its value over time -- a dollar today is worth considerably less than a dollar 10 years ago. This is partly caused by inflation, and partly by an increase in per capita income. The third reason that money is worthless today is that most people would prefer to buy (consume) sooner than later. How can we compare the cost of acquiring a good or service at two different times? Our salaries today are probably higher than they were 10 years ago, but does that mean that we are richer today? The answer depends on whether we can buy less or more with the money we earn today than with our income of 10 years ago. This means our salaries today must be discounted to account for inflation.

Purchasing Power Parity

A closely related indicator of the economic health of a country is the Purchasing Power Parity (PPP) defined as the cost of acquiring a "basket of goods and services" in terms of the number of hours needed to work to earn enough income to buy it in different countries. The PPP is a price index very similar in content and estimation to the consumer price index, or CPI. Whereas the CPI shows price changes over time, a PPP provides a measure of price level differences across countries. PPP is a convenient way to find the proper exchange rate between various currencies; different currencies needed to purchase the same basket of goods have equal values. It has been argued that since PPP considers the relative cost of living and the inflation rates, it is a better indicator than the GDP.①

Table 14-5 Net Present Value of a Series of Future Installments (Annuities)										
$P/A=[(1+r)^n-1]/[r(1+r)^n]$										
r/n	1	2	3	4	5	10	15	20	25	30
0.01	0.99	1.97	2.94	3.90	4.85	9.47	13.87	18.05	22.02	25.81
0.02	0.98	1.94	2.88	3.81	4.71	8.98	12.85	16.35	19.52	22.40
0.03	0.97	1.91	2.83	3.72	4.58	8.53	11.94	14.88	17.41	19.60
0.04	0.96	1.89	2.78	3.63	4.45	8.11	11.12	13.59	15.62	17.29
0.05	0.95	1.86	2.72	3.55	4.33	7.72	10.38	12.46	14.09	15.37
0.06	0.94	1.83	2.67	3.47	4.21	7.36	9.71	11.47	12.78	13.76
0.07	0.93	1.81	2.62	3.39	4.10	7.02	9.11	10.59	11.65	12.41
0.08	0.93	1.78	2.58	3.31	3.99	6.71	8.56	9.82	10.67	11.26
0.09	0.92	1.76	2.53	3.24	3.89	6.42	8.06	9.13	9.82	10.27
0.10	0.91	1.74	2.49	3.17	3.79	6.14	7.61	8.51	9.08	9.43
0.15	0.87	1.63	2.28	2.85	3.35	5.02	5.85	6.26	6.46	6.57
0.20	0.83	1.53	2.11	2.59	2.99	4.19	4.68	4.87	4.95	4.98
0.25	0.80	1.44	1.95	2.36	2.69	3.57	3.86	3.95	3.98	4.00

Table 14-6 Capital Recovery Factor										
$A/P=[r(1+r)^n]/[(1+r)^n-1]$										
r/n	1	2	3	4	5	10	15	20	25	30
0.01	1.01	0.508	0.340	0.256	0.206	0.106	0.072	0.055	0.045	0.039
0.02	1.02	0.515	0.347	0.262	0.212	0.111	0.078	0.061	0.051	0.045
0.03	1.03	0.524	0.353	0.269	0.218	0.117	0.084	0.067	0.990	0.051
0.04	1.04	0.529	0.360	0.275	0.225	0.123	0.090	0.074	0.064	0.058
0.05	1.05	0.538	0.368	0.282	0.231	0.130	0.096	0.080	0.071	0.065
0.06	1.06	0.546	0.375	0.288	0.238	0.136	0.103	0.087	0.078	0.073
0.07	1.08	0.552	0.382	0.295	0.244	0.142	0.110	0.094	0.086	0.081
0.08	1.08	0.562	0.388	0.302	0.251	0.149	0.117	0.102	0.094	0.089
0.09	1.09	0.568	0.395	0.309	0.257	0.156	0.124	0.110	0.102	0.097
0.10	1.10	0.575	0.402	0.315	0.264	0.163	0.131	0.118	0.110	0.106
0.15	1.15	0.613	0.439	0.351	0.299	0.199	0.171	0.160	0.155	0.152
0.20	1.20	0.654	0.474	0.386	0.334	0.239	0.214	0.205	0.202	0.201
0.25	1.25	0.694	0.513	0.424	0.372	0.280	0.259	0.253	0.251	0.250
0.30	1.30	0.735	0.549	0.461	0.410	0.324	0.306	0.301	0.300	0.300

The **Consumer Price Index** (CPI) was designed in 1983 to measure the average cost of living of average consumers. CPI calculated the cost for a basket of products and services (food, housing, transportation, clothing, health, etc.). Although CPI was a good indicator of inflationary pressure for a few years, its value became less and less indicative of the cost of living. The main reason is that CPI was based on a fixed set of commodities and ignored behavioral changes as technologies matured and peoples' tastes for goods and services changed. Furthermore, CPI ignored the impact of consumption on declines in the price of goods. In 1983, an average person traveled fewer miles and paid less for gasoline. The cost of a computer was much higher, however. As prices of some commodities rose sharply, consumers found other alternatives. As a result, consumer behavior today is widely different from that of 20 years ago, and the "basket" of goods and services used in 1983 does not give a true representation of the change in purchasing power of the average consumer.

The price of any item in dollar-values of year X can be calculated in terms of dollar-value of the price of any item in dollar-values of year Y from the equation below:

$$\$ value\ in\ year\ X = \frac{CF\ in\ year\ X}{CF\ in\ year\ Y}\ (\$value\ in\ year\ Y)$$

Example 14-15: Following the Iranian Revolution in 1979, the price of Middle Eastern oil reached an all-time high of $38 a barrel in early 1980. What was the price in 2016 dollars? Adjusting for inflation, are we paying more or less for gasoline today, compared to 1981 prices?

Solution: Using the CPI indicator (Table 14-7) to adjust for inflation gives us a conversion factor of CPI CPI(1980) / CPI(2016) = 0.383/1.115 = 0.343; every 2016 dollar was worth only 34.3 cents in 1980. The price of 1980 gasoline in 2016 dollars can be calculated by dividing the 1980 price by 0.343, ($38/0.343 = $110.68 in 2016 dollars). Compared to the $38 price of a barrel of crude today, we are buying oil at a much cheaper price than in 1980.

Table 14-7 The CPI Conversion Factor (Base Year 2008)									
Year	CF	Year	CF	Year	CF	Year	CF	Year	CF
1800	0.059	1920	0.093	1983	0.463	1999	0.774	2011	1.045
1810	0.057	1930	0.078	1984	0.483	2000	0.800	2012	1.066
1820	0.063	1940	0.067	1985	0.500	2001	0.823	2013	1.082
1830	0.05	1950	0.112	1990	0.607	2002	0.836	2014	1.100
1840	0.047	1955	0.124	1991	0.633	2003	0.855	2015	1.122
1850	0.042	1960	0.137	1992	0.652	2004	0.877	2016	1.145
1860	0.045	1965	0.146	1993	0.671	2005	0.907	2017	1.170
1870	0.07	1970	0.180	1994	0.688	2006	0.936	2018	1.198
1880	0.055	1975	0.250	1995	0.708	2007	0.963	2019	1.226
1890	0.049	1980	0.383	1996	0.729	2008	1.000*	2020	1.255
1900	0.046	1981	0.422	1997	0.745	2009	0.996	2021	
1910	0.051	1982	0.448	1998	0.757	2010	1.013	2022	

* To convert dollars of any year to 2008 dollars, divide the dollar value of that year by its conversion factor. For example, $1,000 in 1950 dollars is equivalent to 1,000/0.131=$7,634 in 2008 dollars.

Endnotes

1   Annila, A. & Salthe, S. (2009). Economies Evolve by Energy Dispersal. Entropy, 2009, 11, 606-633; doi:10.3390/e11040606

2   Heakal, R. (2014). What is Market Efficiency, http://www.investopedia.com.Adeyeye, A., et al. (2009). "Estimating U. S. Government Subsidies to Energy Sources," 2002-2008 Environmental Law Institute, September. Retrieved from http://www.elistore.org/reports_detail.asp?ID=11358

3   Adeyeye, A. et. al. (2009). Estimating U. S. Government Subsidies to Energy Sources, 2002-2008, *Environmental Law Institute*, September. Retrieved from http://www.elistore.org/reports_detail.asp?ID=11358

4   Stern, R. (2015). Oil Change- The World's Most Precious Commodity and the Future of U.S. Security, *Medill National Security Journalism Initiative*, http://nationalsecurityzone.medill.northwestern.edu/archives/oilchangeproject

5   Hu, P. (1996). Estimates of 1996 U.S. Military Expenditures on Defending Oil Supplies from the Middle East: A Literature

Review, Oak Ridge National Laboratory, Oak Ridge, TN, March.

6   Report EUR (2019). External Costs: Research Results on Socio-Environmental Damages due to Electricity and Transport, European Commission Directorate-General for Research Information and Communication Unit, B-1049 Brussels, Belgium, 2003. Executive Summary at http://europa.eu.int/comm/research/rtdinfo_en.html

7   WSJ (1990). "How Japan Became So Energy Efficient," *Wall Street Journal*, September 10, 1990.

8   The Tragedy of the Commons. (1968). *Science*, *162*(3859) 1243-1248. doi: 10.1126/science.162.3859.1243

9   Harmelen, T. (2002). An Analysis of the Costs and Benefits of Joint Policies to Mitigate Climate Change and Regional Air Pollution in Europe. Soil And Water Pollution, vol. 5, pp. 349-365.

10   National Center for Environmental Economics, EPA, (2001). The United States Experience with Economic Incentives for Protecting the Environment, EPA-240-R-01-001, January, http://yosemite.epa.gov/ee/epa/eerm.nsf/vwAN/EE-0216B-01.pdf/$file/EE-0216B-01.pdf

11   National Center for Environmental Economics, EPA. (2004) International Experiences with Economic Incentives for Protecting the Environment, EPA-236-R-04-001, November, http://yosemite.epa.gov/ee/epa/eerm.nsf/vwAN/EE-0487-01.pdf/$file/EE-0487-01.pdf

12   "Putting a Price Tag on Life," *Newsweek*, vol. 40. (1988).

13   Goodstein, E. (1999). The trade-off myth. Washington, D.C.: Island Press.

14   Dilorenzo, T. (1993). Unfunded Federal Mandates: Environmentalism's Achilles Heel? Center for the Study of American Business (St. Louis, MO).

15   King, S. Impact of Energy Taxes and Subsidies, in Theories and Practices for Energy Education, Training, Regulation and Standards, in *Encyclopedia of Life Support Systems* (EOLSS), Developed under the Auspices of the UNESCO, Eolss Publishers, Oxford , UK.

16   Dauvergne, P. (2005). Handbook of Global Environmental Politics, *Edward Elgar Publishing*.

17   Robert Reich's online blog, "Why McCain's 'Cap-and-Trade' Won't Work Nearly as Well as Obama's," May 27, 2008, http://robertreich.org/post/257309512

18   United Nation Economic Commission for Europe (2021). Retrieved from http://www.unece.org/fileadmin//DAM/env/lrtap/welcome.html

19   Stiglitz, J. (2002). Globalization and its Discontent, New York: *Norton Publishers*.

🙌 Exercises

I. Discussion Questions

1. Describe what economists mean by
   a. Existence value
   b. Safety standard
   c. Contingent evaluation
   d. Command-and-control legislation
   e. Economic efficiency

2. What are the differences between existence, use, and option values? Give examples for each.

3. According to one study, the maximum price elasticity for mpg is 0.21, meaning that a 1% increase in price leads to a 21% increase in fuel economy. How much should the price of gasoline be increased if we desire to achieve a 10% increase in automobile fuel efficiency?

4. Jill and Jack are sharing an office in a manufacturing firm. Jack is a smoker and claims he will be much more relaxed and productive if he smokes three cigarettes a day. Jill hates smoking and claims that she cannot handle the smell of even a single cigarette. Assuming that there is no regulation that bans smoking in the office, who is right? Is there a point where a compromise can be reached?

5. Should smoking be banned in public places? If yes, should imposing the ban be the responsibility of a government agency? Should it be decided through voting?

6. A new landfill in your neighborhood is expected to raise the cancer rate by 1 in 1,000 during your life time. To reduce the risk to 1 in 10,000, new monitoring and safety equipment has to be installed, which will cost $100 million. To pay for the cost, your property tax must be increased by $1 a month. Would you pay for it? What if higher costs necessitated an increase in property taxes of $10 a month? $50 a month? $100 a month?

7. A wireless telephone company needs to install its high-frequency, high-voltage transformers on the rooftop of your building. They offer you a flat fee of $10,000 for the right to install their equipment. Would you take it? Some research indicates a 1% increase in the rate of cancer for people living near these transformers. Would your neighbors have the right to sue you if you accepted the company's offer?

8. The same company wants to install a second unit in a poor neighborhood of the city. The company offers $2,000 for obtaining the right. Is this fair? What if the neighborhood voted to accept the offer?

9. Discuss three methods of encouraging automotive fuel efficiency. What are the advantages and disadvantages of each?

10. What is globalization and its effect on the environment? Is the overall trend positive or negative? How has globalization affected your community?

II. Problems

1. The worldwide consumption of petroleum was 150.8 quads in 2002. If consumption continues to increase at 2% per year, what will the world consumption of petroleum be in 2025?

2. A bacterial colony in a jar grows at the rate of 10% every hour. Find:
   a. The doubling time.
   b. If the jar were initially 1/8 full, how long would it take before the jar is completely full?
   c. Assume that a person is accidentally infected with only one bacterium. What is the bacterial population after one week?

3. Suppose the demand function for cigarettes is modeled by 200-.5x where x is the number of units and y is the price in dollars. Further, suppose the supply function is modeled by 2x-50. What is the equilibrium price and quantity provided? Suppose government regulation adds a $10 tax per unit of cigarettes. What is the new equilibrium quantity and price? Cigarettes are a good with an inelastic demand, what does this mean for the change in quantity demanded when the price increases?

4. If the government wants to limit the number of cigarettes smoked to 50 units, what should be the tax rate they set? Assume the original supply and demand functions for cigarettes in problem 3.

5. If an employer were to offer you: a) $10,000 a year in initial salary and a $2,000 raise every year, thereafter; or b) $1 a year in initial salary, but would double it every year for the next 20 years, which one would you choose? Why? Assume that the prevailing interest rate remains at around 5% for the 20-year period.

6. A start-up company in renewable energy has borrowed $5,000,000 from a bank at 6% interest, over 25 years. What is the annual repayment for this loan?

7. In the previous problem, assume that repayments

are to be made monthly. What are the monthly payments?

8. A loan agency has offered a customer the opportunity to pay off his $100,000 in existing loans using one of the following three options:
    a. By paying the balance immediately in cash.
    b. By paying 10 equal payments of $11,000 each, annually.
    c. By paying $50,000 now and a balloon payment of $60,000 in 10 years.

    Which option makes more sense to the customer? Assume an annual interest rate of 5%.

9. The national average price of regular gasoline in the United States is given by the DOE Energy Information Administration (all data are for August) as following:

Year	Price
1992	$1.03 per gallon
1994	$1.13 per gallon
1996	$1.17 per gallon
1998	$1.00 per gallon
2000	$1.45 per gallon
2002	$1.36 per gallon
2004	$1.85 per gallon
2006	$3.00 per gallon

    a. Adjusting the prices for inflation, which year offered the cheapest gasoline? Most expensive gasoline?
    b. What is the price of gasoline in today's dollars? In 2000 dollars? In 1950 dollars? In 1900's dollars?

10. The average price of gasoline in the U.S. was $2.60 a gallon at the gas pump in 2004. What was the price in 1950 dollars?

11. A utility company purchases two turbines, one in 2005 for the price of $2M and a second one in 2008 for $ 2.5M. What is the total cost of turbines in 2005 dollars? In 2008 dollars? In 2010 dollars?

12. Would it make sense economically if a person trades his gasoline engine car giving him a 20-mph gas mileage, with a hybrid vehicle with a fuel economy of 45 mph? To trade in his car, he must pay an additional $15,000 to the dealership. Assume he intends to keep the car for 10 years with a residual value of $3,000. He drives 15,000 miles annually and the price of gasoline remains constant at $3.80 a gallon. List all assumptions.

13. A bank is offering a flat interest rate of 5% a year in a retirement account. In 50 years when you plan to retire, which of these options will give you the most money?
    a. Lumped sum payment of $1 million at the end of the period.
    b. Investing $100,000 at the beginning of the period.
    c. Investing $5,000 each year for the entire period.

14. In the previous problem, suppose you went with option (b) and 25 years have passed. What is the present value of your retirement account should you need to sell it to pay off a debt?

15. The price per kilowatt-hour of offshore wind power is 24 cents. The price per kilowatt-hour of nuclear energy is 11 cents. Suppose there is a new regulation that will add a 10% tax on nuclear energy, which increases by 2% annually. How long will it take for offshore wind energy to be cheaper?

16. A tree can take on average 20 years to mature, longer for some species. In 2016, all the world's nations combined pumped nearly 38.2 billion tons of carbon dioxide into the air from the burning of fossil fuels. If the rate of release of carbon dioxide emission increases by 2% every year for the next 20 years how many trees should we plant right now to offset this future increase? A mature tree can remove 50 lb. of CO_2 each day.

III. Multiple Choice Questions

1. In an efficient market
    a. There are numerous buyers and sellers.
    b. There are no barriers to entry.
    c. There are numerous products that are essentially indistinguishable from the goods of interest.
    d. Firms' only goal is to maximize their profits.
    e. All of the above.

2. The supply curve is upward sloping because
    a. As prices increase, so do costs.
    b. As prices increase, demand for a product declines.
    c. As prices increase, demand for a product also rises.
    d. As prices increase, suppliers are willing to produce more.
    e. As prices increase, suppliers are willing to produce less.

3. In a perfectly efficient market, a firm's long-term profit will be maximized when
    a. Price equals fixed costs.
    b. Price equals total cost.

c. Fixed cost equals total revenue.

d. Total cost equals total revenue.

e. Marginal cost equals marginal revenue.

4. What is the economic term that describes situations in which multiple individuals, acting independently and in their self-interest, will ultimately deplete a shared limited resource?

a. Demographic transition

b. Tragedy of the Commons

c. Malthusian economics

d. Neo-Malthusianism

e. Heat death

5. Which of the following resources can be afflicted by "the Tragedy of the Commons"?

a. Public parks

b. A privately-owned amusement park

c. An open-source software

d. A neighborhood grocery store

e. None of the above

6. As a result of a rise in the cost of living, we expect

a. Both the price and quantity of goods to rise.

b. Price increases as the quantity of goods falls.

c. Price does not change as quantity of goods falls.

d. The quantity of goods does not change as price increases.

e. Both price and quantity of goods increase.

7. Firms often collude to form a cartel because

a. They can function aa monopolies.

b. It allows them to spend more money on innovation.

c. It furthers competition and increases their market shares.

d. Cartels are more efficient.

e. All of the above.

8. The Gross National Product (GNP) is defined as

a. The total value of all goods and services produced in a country in a given calendar year.

b. GDP plus what domestic companies earn from activities abroad, plus what foreign companies make from domestic activities in that country.

c. The sum of all market and non-market goods and services supplied by a country's residents.

d. The sum of all goods and services produced by labor and property located in a country, irrespective of who supplies them.

e. Another name for Gross Domestic Product.

9. The quantitative limitation placed by a government on an import is called a(n)

a. Quota.

b. Tariff.

c. Embargo.

d. Import tax.

e. Excise tax.

10. On the basis of the traditional economic theory

a. The cleaner the environment is, the more sustainable the economy will be.

b. The cost of environmental clean-up is a major drag on the economy.

c. Society must bear a certain amount of pollution.

d. Pollution is a good that follows the law of supply and demand.

e. Both c and d.

11. The regulations are in place that sets a limit on the amount of NOx emissions from passenger cars. This is an example of

a. Command and control regulation.

b. Incentive-based.

c. Cost-benefit analysis.

d. Ambient standard.

e. Pigovian taxation.

12. When it comes to environmental protection, efficiency standard advocates believe that

a. Personal safety is the innate right of every individual, and no matter the cost, must be guaranteed.

b. The marginal cost of reduction drops per unit of reduction in pollution.

c. The marginal benefit of reduction increases as the air gets cleaner and cleaner

d. An efficient market is a market in which demand and supply are in balance.

e. All of the above.

13. The unknown potential benefits of environmental protection are called

a. Use value.

b. Option value.

c. Existence value.

d. Hidden value.

e. Contingent value.

14. Picking up a plastic bottle off the street, and throwing it into the ocean is an example of

a. A positive externality.

b. A negative externality.

c. A positive, followed by a negative externality.

d. A negative, followed by a positive externality.

e. A neutral externality.

15. Which of the statements below is consistent with the operation of a profit-maximizing firm in a

competitive market that does not penalize polluters, no matter how much they pollute?

  a. Consumers pay the full social cost of production.

  b. Consumers pay only the external cost of production.

  c. Consumers pay only the external marginal cost of production.

  d. Consumers pay less than the socially efficient price since producers are subsidized by society.

  e. None of the above.

16. Which of the following is consistent with the command-and-control regulation?

  a. Taxing producers equal to the external cost created by their pollution.

  b. Requiring firms to lower their pollution levels according to best-available control technology.

  c. Requiring firms to reduce their pollution level to zero.

  d. Requiring firms to buy pollution permits to offset their pollution.

  e. Requiring firms to pay a penalty equal to the external cost of pollution.

17. Which of the following statements is <u>not</u> correct?

  a. The economical benefits of environmental protection can be measured only by its monetary benefits.

  b. Hedonic regression implies the pleasure one gets from an improved environment.

  c. Non-market benefits of environmental protection can be estimated by people's willingness to pay for those benefits.

  d. The willingness to accept compensation for some level of pollution is called contingent evaluation.

  e. None of the above.

18. Suppose two firms, A and B, each produce 10 tons of emissions every month. The local city council passes a bill that requires total monthly emissions to be reduced by eight tons. It costs firm A $5 and firm B $20 to cut emissions by one ton. The most efficient way to comply with the ordinance is for emissions trading that results in

  a. Firms A and B negotiating to trade emissions permits.

  b. Firm A cutting emissions by eight tons.

  c. Firm B cutting emissions by eight tons.

  d. Each of the firms A and B cutting emissions by four tons.

  e. Both a and b.

19. In the example above, assume that the law sets maximum particulate emissions at 12 tons per firm. What is the optimally efficient cost of pollution abatement?

  a. $ 60

  b. $ 90

  c. $ 130

  d. $ 240

  e. Not enough data is given

20. The main advantage of control-based regulations is that

  a. Because they exclude or relax fines on old sources, the clean-up costs are less.

  b. Because regulation is based on imposing the best available control technology, there is a great incentive for firms to spend money on R&D activities.

  c. They allow old industries to survive and, thus, hire new employees.

  d. They provide incentives to those who help improve air quality and reduce emissions.

  e. All of the above.

21. The main objection raised against incentive-based regulations is that

  a. Penalties cannot discourage firms from polluting.

  b. Localized hot spots may appear.

  c. It is always possible to buy permits at a lower cost than it takes to install new pollution-control equipment.

  d. It offers the opportunity to sell permits that are given out free.

  e. All of the above.

22. Which of the following statement(s) is/are correct?

  a. Proponents of safety standards believe that polluters must pay for the pollution.

  b. Safety standards remove incentives for polluters to free ride.

  c. Safety standards are inefficient.

  d. All of the above.

  e. a and b, but not c.

23. Non-market value of the yet-unknown potential benefits of a resource is called

  a. Use value.

  b. Option value.

  c. Existence value.

  d. Utility value.

  e. A charity.

24. _____ see protecting the environment as

a moral issue.

a. Hedonists

b. Utilitarians

c. Environmental ethicists

d. Existentialists

e. Environmentalists

25. On the basis of efficiency standards, which of the following can justify subsidizing the development of a hydrogen infrastructure?

a. The funding for hydrogen research has been increasing in the last few years.

b. The hydrogen sector has a strong lobbying presence in Washington, D.C.

c. Switching to hydrogen reduces our dependence on foreign oil and is, therefore, a positive externality.

d. Hydrogen is a necessary component for fuel cell operation.

e. All of the above.

26. Under the carbon trading scheme, which firms are most likely successful in cutting the highest percentages of their emissions?

a. Firms with the lowest emission reduction costs.

b. Firms with the highest emission reduction costs.

c. Firms with the lowest levels of emission.

d. Firms with the highest levels of emission.

e. Firms with the highest profit.

27. In the U.S., the doubling time of our exponentially growing electricity consumption rate was 10 years from 1900 to 1970. How did electricity consumption from 1960 to 1970 compare to all U.S. electricity consumption prior to 1960?

a. It was twice as much.

b. It was half as much.

c. It was an equal amount.

d. It was 1/6 as much.

e. It cannot be determined from the given information.

28. Since the 2000 census, the U.S. population has grown at a rate of 1.2% per year. In what year will the U.S. population double?

a. 2058

b. 2083

c. 2120

d. There is not enough information to predict the year.

e. None of the above

29. In 75 years, a small community of 10,000 people that enjoys a constant 2.8% annual growth rate will attain a population of about

a. 28,000.

b. 30,000.

c. 80,000.

d. 2,100,000.

e. None of the above.

30. An employer guarantees a salary increase of 7.2% a year for all employees. If a particular employee is hired at an initial annual salary of $30,000, how long would it take for his or her salary to reach $60,000?

a. About seven years

b. A bit sooner than 10 years

c. Ten years

d. A bit longer than 10 years

e. About 14 years

31. Statistics show that for the last few decades, the U.S. consumption of petroleum has doubled every decade. The corresponding annual percent growth rate is

a. 2%.

b. 7%.

c. 10%.

d. 13%.

e. None of the above.

32. $200 invested at 5% compound interest will grow to $800 in about

a. Four years.

b. Twenty-eight years.

c. Forty years.

d. Forty-two years.

e. Fifty-six years.

33. What is the present worth of $1,000 payable in five years, assuming an average discount rate of 4%?

a. $ 820

b. $ 850

c. $ 1,000

d. $ 1,170

e. $ 1,220

34. How much interest does $1,000 placed in a five-year CD paying 4% accumulate?

a. $ 2,220

b. $ 1,220

c. $ 820

d. $ 220

e. None of the above

35. Net National Welfare (NNW) is defined as

a. The total value of all goods and services produced in a country in a given calendar year.

b. The sum of all goods and services produced

by labor and property located in a country, irrespective of who supplies them.

c. The sum of all goods and services supplied by a country's residents, irrespective of where they are physically produced.

d. The total annual output of both market and non-market goods and services, and minus the cost of externalities and depreciation of natural and human-made capitals used up in production.

e. The total money spent on welfare agencies.

IV. True or False?

1. Along a standard demand curve, price and quantity are inversely related—when price rises, quantity demanded decreases and vice versa.

2. When the price of air travel rises, the price of travel by rail increases also. This is because the airline and rail travel are substitutes.

3. Externalities arise when private costs and social costs or benefits do not match.

4. Police protection is a prime example of a private good.

5. In the long run, no profit can be extracted in a perfectly competitive market.

6. When MB = MC, total net benefits are maximized.

7. A competitive market is Pareto efficient.

8. The main drawback of traditional command-and-control regulation is that it is not economically efficient.

9. The optimum level of pollution is not zero.

10. An environmental ethicist considers the environment valuable because it is the source of happiness to him and others.

V. Fill in the Blanks

1. In a competitive market, a surplus occurs if the price is set _____ the equilibrium price.

2. A monopoly is inherently _____ efficient than a competitive market.

3. According to the _____ theorem, it does not make any economic difference who pays for the pollution -- the polluters or the victims.

4. _____ advocates disagree with efficiency standard advocates and argue that polluters, not victims, should pay for the clean-up.

5. Polling people to find their willingness to pay for a product is called _____.

6. The environment is a _____ good and is therefore

subject to the same law of _____ _____ as other goods.

7. Cleaner beaches, greener parks, and water sports are examples of the _____ benefits of environmental clean-up.

8. In the United States, environmental regulations are usually mandated by _____.

9. The agency responsible for implementing U.S. laws on environmental protection is _____.

10. Under command-and-control strategy, to control emissions, firms are required to deploy the _____ technology.

PROJECT I - Power Plant Financing

1. It is estimated that a nuclear power plant will cost $3 billion to build. The utility needs to raise $2.4B for plant construction and equipment. The money is needed over a five-year period ($480M each year for five years) which is how long it takes for the plant to be built. There are three options available:

2. Borrow the total sum at the beginning of year one at a rate of 8%. The excess money will be invested in the stock market, where a historical average of 5% has been returned.

3. Borrow money from the bank as needed, i.e., $480 million at the beginning of years 1, 2, 3, 4, and 5. The bank charges 7% interest, per year.

4. Borrow the money monthly at the prime rate, i.e., borrow $8M for 60 months. The prime rate at the beginning of the year one is 4%, but is expected to rise by 1.5% every year, for the next five years.

At the end of year five, the plant is operational and the utility will be able to make a monthly payment of $5 million until the entire loan is paid off. Find:

a. What is the net present worth of the three options proposed above? Which option is economically more viable?

b. What is the effective interest rate of all future payments?

c. Redo the problem if a 3% cost-of-living adjustment is considered.

d. How many months does it take for all loans to be paid off?

e. What is the cumulative value of all payments for the option considered?

CHAPTER 15
Blueprint for a Sustainable Future

Tree Kahl Moon (Public Domain)~ Geralt

Simplicity, simplicity, simplicity ~ Henry David Thoreau (1817-1862)

We're not passengers on Spaceship Earth: We're the crew. We're not residents; we're citizens. The difference, in both cases, is responsibility.
~ Rusty Schweikart, Apollo astronaut (1935-)

W e started this book by defining energy and how it shaped our universe, our communities, and our modern way of living. Its many forms, uses, and political, economic, and environmental impacts were discussed. If humanity is to be sustained, we must continue to use energy, possibly at rates even faster than what we have been using in the past. The key question is not whether there is enough energy to make economic growth sustainable for a very long time into the future, but whether we will use energy intelligently and responsibly so as to assure the preservation of human life and improve its quality. We would like to conclude the book by suggesting an optimistic view of how the future could be if we take the necessary actions to preserve the environment and our natural resources.

We begin by discussing what sustainability is, and offer recommendations on how to achieve it on personal, national, and global levels. This does not necessarily have to be a painful process, but can be accomplished utilizing small steps that enrich our lives, as well as the lives of our children and grandchildren. All it takes, is an open mind, a little sacrifice, and a well-thought-out pathway.

Sustainability

The technological advances of the last few decades have provided unprecedented opportunities for greater material wealth, better health care, and more comfortable life for the great majority of people, but also have resulted in the accumulation of a tremendous amount of waste, depletion of a large fraction of our natural resources, and the acceleration of environmental degradation. This naturally leads to the question of how to continue with economic progress while keeping environmental damage to a minimum. It is important not to mistaken sustainability with environmentalism, as it is not a movement aimed only at saving the environment and the planet, but also address people welfare, fairness, justice, and equity. Two approaches to sustainability are proposed by economists:

Neoclassical economists consider a sustainable environment to be that which provides an average person a future with a living standard that is better than, or at least as good as, that of an average person today.[*] They maintain that our children will be collectively better off if the economy expands at a faster rate than that at which resources are depleted. Neoclassical economists are *technological optimists*; they believe that a free-market economy has the built-in mechanisms that would prevent ecological collapse, by promoting technologies, and by improving efficiency that will help overcome resource scarcity and environmental damage. They cite the increases in food production, discoveries of new energy reserves, and better and more efficient manufacturing technologies of the last century as proof that the overall standard of living around the globe has improved. They also claim that the trend will continue to improve in the future and conclude that we are living in a sustainable environment.

Ecological economists (or ecologists), on the other hand, consider an environment sustainable only if future generations can enjoy essentially the same resources and a similar environment as we do today.[†] Although technological advances can help prevent resource scarcity and environmental damages in the short term, they ultimately will be used to accelerate ecological abuses.

The broadest definition of sustainability accepted is one adopted by the UNESCO's World Commission on Environment and Development. Known as the Brundtland Report, sustainable development is defined as that which ***"meets the needs of the present without compromising the ability of future generations to meet their needs."*** Note that this definition is left intentionally ambiguous, as it does not define (and we don't know) what future generations will need, and how their needs are different from those of the current generation. The UNESCO report, however, declares "... *every generation should leave the water, air, and soil resources as pure and unpolluted as when it came on earth,*" and "... *each generation should leave undiminished all the species of animals it found existing on earth.*"

As Herman Daly, one of the early pioneers of ecological sustainability puts it, to be sustainable, three criteria must

---

[*] Neoclassical economics is a school of thought in which maximizing profit is the ultimate goal of any organization.

[†] Ecological economics is a branch of economists who see a direct link between the health of the ecosystem and that of human beings. Ecological economics is sometimes referred to as "Green Economics."

be met:

1. *For non-renewable resources*, the rate of use cannot be greater than the rate at which a renewable resource can be substituted, and to become available at comparable prices, once the non-renewable resources are exhausted.
2. *For renewable resources*, the rate of use can be no greater than the natural rate of regeneration. For example, geothermal hot water and steam resources are used at a rate that is being regenerated by nature.
3. *For environmental pollution*, the rate of emissions can be no greater than the rate at which pollution can be rendered harmless. For example, the volume of carbon dioxide emissions balances the removal of other substances, so that there is no net contribution of greenhouse gases into the environment.

Question: Can we continue to use fossil fuels at the current level and still maintain a sustainable environment?
Answer: Neoclassical economists do not see continued use of fossil fuels as necessarily bad, as increases in the rate of energy consumption increase economic output and help improve living standards; by allocating sufficient resources we can develop technologies that combat environmental damage and maintain a reasonable degree of sustainability. Ecological economists believe the damage caused to the environment, exceeds the benefits of fossil fuel consumption.

IPAT Equation

Among the first to quantify the impact of increasing consumption on the environment was the ecologist Barry Commoner who proposed a simple model commonly known as the IPAT equation. According to this model, total environmental impact *(ecological footprint)* is determined by three factors: the number of people, consumption per capita, and the state of technology (damage done per unit of consumption). This is represented as:

$$I = P \times A \times T \tag{15-1}$$

Impact = Population × Affluence × Technology

Where I is the impact (in terms of resource depletion or waste accumulation), P is the size of the population, A is affluence, and T is a technological factor that considers the state of the technology for obtaining resources and transforming them into products and wastes. According to this equation, the environmental impact on sustainability increases with both population and affluence. The product of population and affluence (P × A) represents an aggregate measure of total economic activity, such as total GDP. Poorer countries are often more populace and richer countries are bigger consumers, both tend to adversely impact the environment. Technology can have a positive or a negative impact. Furthermore, this equation points to two important conclusions: 1) Earth can support only a limited number of people in a sustainable manner; and 2) humanity has a clear choice -- between more people with poorer lifestyles and fewer people with a better quality of life. IPAT equation has been shown to be useful, to a limited extent, in assessing the contribution of different PAT factors to greenhouse gas (GHG) emissions. Although it describes the past fairly well, IPAT equation cannot predict the future as population, affluence, and technology all are interrelated, driven by a variety of social, political, and technical factors. For example, doubling population does not necessarily double the impact, as it also affects the consumer behavior. In other words, the impact depends not only on the size of the population but also on where the population rise is. The role of technology should be viewed in terms of its impact on consumption. A better way to quantify impact is

$$I = P \times C/P \times I/C \tag{15-2}$$

(Environmental) Impact = Population × Consumption per capita × Impact per consumption

To date, IPAT applications have been limited to evaluation of a single variable measure of environmental impact, such as air pollution, in a particular region. For example, the equation is helpful in assessing the contribution of different PAT factors to greenhouse gas emissions. The equation's usefulness is limited, however, when these factors are interdependent.

> **Example 15-1:** Using the IPAT model, estimate what impact automobiles have on global warming? In 2015, there were 7.2 billion people in the world.
>
> **Solution:** According to EPA estimates, given the current state of technology, every year an average passenger car emits 9,737 lb of carbon dioxide. The number for SUVs and pickup trucks is 13,573 lb.
>
> Taking the average carbon dioxide emission rate of (9,737 + 13,573) / 2 = 11,500 lb, and assuming that there is one car for every seven persons, we have:
>
> $$\text{Impact} = 7.2 \times 10^9 \text{ persons } \times \frac{1 \text{ car}}{7 \text{ persons}} \times \frac{11,500 \text{ lbs}}{\text{car}} = 11,829 \times 10^9 \text{ pounds} \cong 5.4 \text{ billion metric tons of } CO_2$$
>
> This accounts for roughly 15% of total carbon dioxide emissions (and thus global warming).[‡]

Population

The first factor in the IPAT equation is population. Neoclassical economists see population as an asset and believe its growth can be actually a positive factor for development. Their argument is that, with the right environment and proper training, people can be equipped with the skills to produce more than they consume. In addition, having more children lowers the median age and helps to remedy the shortage of manpower, which otherwise would be a major problem in sustaining economic and environmental health.

Contrary to the neoclassical view, ecologists consider population as the greatest drain on resources and the main cause of ecological degradation. That is no more evident than when we consider many of the most populous countries, are also among some of the poorest and have some of the highest birth rates. Contrasting those with sparsely populated countries with the highest per-capita income in the world shows that more population means less, not more, wealth, as more people means that already-scarce natural resources and social services had to be spread over a larger population.

This view originally was expressed by Thomas Malthus (1766-1834) who, in *An Essay on the Principle of Population*, warned that the exponential increase in population, along with the linear increase in availability (consumption) of resources, would lead, inevitably, to a massive number of poor dying from famine, disease, or war.[§] Based on that theory, famine and war were two necessary ingredients of any developmental process, a view attacked vigorously by Karl Marx.

> *The world suffers from excessive use of resources by the West as much as the excessive population in India and elsewhere.*~ Indira Gandhi, the Indian Prime Minister in her 1972 address to the United Nations.

In the last few years, social scientists, ecologists, and others have proposed new approaches to slowing the rate of population growth. Some, like ecologist Raymond Cowles, suggest economic motivations such as taxing large families and giving cash incentives to those who choose to have fewer children. Others, like Ken Boulding, take a more radical approach by proposing the introduction of a "child credit," similar to the concept of a "pollution credit" introduced in the previous chapter. According to this plan, every woman is allowed to have a set number of children. Those who opt for fewer children can sell their credits to those who wish to have more. Family planners can adjust the number of permits to assure that sustainability is maintained.

[‡] Vehicle information was taken from Motor Vehicle Statistics, and carbon dioxide emissions data were found from EIA Information Administration..

[§] Malthus was unable to take into consideration technological advancements such as the improvement in the quality of seeds, pesticides, and fertilizers or the effects of mechanized production and more effective irrigation methods. In addition, the recent development of biotechnology promises the possibility of genetically modified crops that will increase production and decrease infestations. He also could not be aware of advancements in education and the impact of women entering the workforce, two factors that reduce population growth. Furthermore, population growth in several industrialized countries has ceased and still, others have achieved negative growth. From the 1950s to 1980s, the Green Revolution era, food production increased more rapidly than population, however, it has become apparent that the use of land was excessive and the rate of crop yield has dropped significantly in the last 20 years, falling below the rate of population growth. A copy of the original paper published in 1798 can be found at http://www.esp.org/books/malthus/population/malthus.pdf.

Depending on how they see the population threat, different countries have opted for different coping strategies. Europeans, through education and by making birth control (including abortion) readily available, have succeeded in achieving near-zero population growth. Most African countries do not have the necessary resources for effective family planning. Americans are divided on the question of abortion and the woman's right to choose. China encourages late marriages and late childbearing by providing financial subsidies, longer maternity leaves, and better housing to couples with fewer children. Several developing countries have followed China's lead by providing public subsidies for housing, health care, and insurance to smaller families. During the last decade, Russia actually had a negative growth rate, mainly because of a large number of emigrants leaving for other countries after the Soviet Union was formally dissolved in 1991. No matter which approach is taken, there are always some, citing religious beliefs, who openly oppose abortion and any type of birth control.

As it stands, many developed countries have succeeded in stopping, or at least slowing, the growth rate of their populations. Unfortunately, the population continues to increase in many poorer less-developed countries and is likely to continue until it reaches equilibrium by mid-century (Figure 15-1). Table 15-1 shows the projected number of people living in different parts of the world in 2050.

Table 15-1 Projected Population in Various Countries by 2050					
Region	Population in 2015	Annual Growth %	Doubling time in years	Projected Population in 2050	% of total
Africa	1.16 billion	2.51	28	2.5 billion	26
Asia	4.38 billion	0.92	76	5.3 billion	54
North America	361 million	0.65	108	433 million	4
Latin America	630 million	0.94	74	784 million	8
Europe	743 million	0.12	583	1.2 billion	7
Oceania	39 million	1.37	51	57 million	<1
World	7.34 billion	1.38	51	9.7 billion	100

Source: UN Population Division, 2019. UN World Population Facts, https://www.un.org/en/ development/desa/population/index.asp

We cannot talk about population control without looking at immigration. It has been practiced throughout the centuries, sometimes by those in search of better economic opportunities, sometimes to escape political persecution, and at times as adventurers and to satisfy curiosity. In any instance, immigration has promoted diversity, has caused better mutual understanding among people, and has made the world a better place. In the twentieth century, faster and more convenient means of transportation, mainly airplanes, and ships, have accelerated this pattern. Oftentimes, when cheaper labor is sought, immigration has been promoted, whereas at other times economic problems at home have made foreign workers and expatriates unwelcome. What is clear is that, unless there is a more equitable distribution of wealth, a greater effort in educating the public, and better ecological policies in place, migration from developing to developed countries can become a problem sometimes in the future.

Affluence

The second factor appearing in the IPAT model is affluence. Classical economists see more consumption and higher gross domestic products (GDP) as an indication of a greater wealth, a healthier economy, and a higher standard of living. The ecological footprint as a result of higher consumption is largely ignored. Consequently, these economists object to reducing consumption on the grounds that it slows down economic expansion and results in the loss of jobs.

Ecologists, however, disagree with this assertion on several accounts. First, the material gain can bring happiness only up to a point, beyond which there is no correlation between the two. Second, the higher GDP per capita is not a sign of wealth, as it includes costs associated with pollution and other environmental damage. For example, a car accident contributes to the economy via the costs of repairing the car, providing medical treatment to potential victims, lawyers' fees, policing, tow trucks, etc. But, has the car accident improved overall human welfare? One million dollars spent on health care research will contribute as much to GDP and GNP as one million dollars used to build a refinery in a residential community. In fact, if GDP were a sign of wealth, a country could exhaust all its mineral resources, cut down all its trees, erode its soil, pollute its aquifers, and kill all its wildlife and fisheries, while its economy continued to grow (See Chapter 14).¶

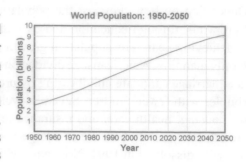

Figure 15-1

Past, present, and projected population. *Source: U.S. Census Bureau, International Data Base, April 2005.*

Another objection is that GDP does not account for non-market goods such as household activities and charitable and volunteering works where no money changes hand, although, they contribute to the economy as much as they would have if they had paid somebody to do it. Also, any activity done through bartering does not count. Imagine two people, let's call them Jack and Jane who barter their services. Jane is a math tutor; Jack is a plumber. Jack agrees to fix Jane's plumbing if Jane tutors his children. Neither one contribute to the GDP. However, if Jane was paying $50 to Jack for fixing her plumbing, and Jack was paying Jane $50 to tutor his children, their contributions to the GDP would be $100, even though the net effect would be exactly the same.

It should be noted that GDP was developed as an indicator of the economic growth during the Great Depression when the primary goal of the government was to stimulate industrial production. It worked well for the intended purpose. It was not, however, well suited to measure the health of an economy or well-being of its citizens. The data from the General Accounting Office (GAO) indicate that U.S.'s GDP has continuously grown by an average of 2.5% per year since 1973, reaching $21.4 trillion by December 2020. It, also, is estimated that up to a quarter of the GDP was wasted on nonproductive human activities such as lost productivity due to traffic congestion, absenteeism, and costs associated with highway accidents, property damage, environmental cleanup, and maintaining law and order, where no monetary value was generated. In addition, many of the social costs associated with climate change, distress, illnesses, and substance abuse have not been included, but may have to be borne out by future generations in terms of increases in crime rate, mental depression, unemployment, and other social ills (See Table 15-2). If we

Table 15-2 Nonproductive Expenses in the U.S.		
Activity	*How?*	*Billion $*
Highway accidents	Health care, repairs, loss of productivity, police, and judicial systems	250
Highway congestion	Loss of productivity	1,000
Driving (other)	Road repairs, pollution	400
Diet	Obesity, heart disease, substance abuse	450
Crime	Health, police, and prison	500
Clean-up of nuclear material	Extraction, processing, and disposal, nuclear weapons	300
Source: Hawken, P., Lovins, A., and Lovins, H., "Natural Capitalism: Creating the Next Industrial Revolution, Rocky Mountain Institute," 1999, pp. 57.		

¶ Even if monetary gains were the only indicator of affluence, higher income (GDP per capita) does not signify wealth because these values are calculated based on a single currency, usually $US, and cannot be translated to the real purchasing power of a citizen in his own country. In response to these problems, economists have devised an alternative measure known as Purchasing Power Parity (PPP), which tracks the cost of a basket of traded and non-traded goods and services across countries.

Measuring Happiness

What makes people happy? Being wealthy, healthy, spiritual, or having a loving family? Economists answer to this question is the higher consumption of goods, whether they are market goods (such as food, clothing, and cars) or nonmarket goods (such as clean water, ocean-view, or good friends). Others consider health, mobility, and long life of the primary importance. Still, many view philosophical teachings, whether by great thinkers of the time or religious doctrines, as the key to living a happier and more satisfying life.

The most common indicator of happiness is the Gross National Happiness (GNH) coined in 1972 by Bhutan's fourth Dragon King, and proposed to replace GDP as the sole measure of prosperity and considered such factors as sustainable development, preservation of cultural values, conservation of the natural environment, and the establishment of good governance in evaluating the nonmarket output contribution to economic health and well-being of its citizens. In 2011, the GNH concept was adopted, with some modifications, by the United Nations as a qualitative socio-economic development indicator of the overall life satisfaction of a country.

The criticisms raised against the GNH are that "happiness" is very difficult to define, as it means different things to different people. Even if such a definition were possible, it would be equally difficult to come up with a numerical scale for its quantification. Finally, even if such a scale could be defined, the answer would very much depend on the socio-economic status, upbringing, and historical and cultural values. Because of these difficulties in determining GNH, the method considered to be the most reliable is to devise a questionnaire asking about various aspects of individuals' lives, leaving the definition of "happiness" intentionally vague. Since 2012, the UN surveyed people in various countries and has collected data on real GDP per capita, social support, life expectancy, freedom to make life choices, and perceived corruption. Negative effects are included as the average of three indicators -- worry, sadness, and anger. The result is published in the World Happiness Report.* According to this ranking, Finland and Denmark have consistently been ranked number one and two. Other Nordic countries closely follow Denmark as having the happiest people. Among the 157 countries surveyed, the United States ranked 18 in the 2020 report; the least happy people resided in Afghanistan, Sudan, Rwanda, and other war-torn countries.

*For the latest report, see http://worldhappiness.report/.

---

subtract the cost of wasteful activities from the GDP, we might be surprised to find that the economy may not have grown at all (as Chinese found out, only a few years ago. See below)!

Green GDP

For environmentalists, well-being provided by nature is as important as well-being provided by market consumption. The fact that the informal economy is left out of consideration explains why GDP per capita for many countries can be extremely low, and so can easily be interpreted as the degree of unhappiness of its people. As a result, it has been suggested by many economists, that any measure of economic sustainability must include such externalities as noise, air, and water pollution, soil erosion, resource exhaustion, loss in biodiversity, radioactivity, and toxins. Several attempts have been made to develop alternative national income accounting systems that address these deficiencies. William Nordhaus and James Tobin proposed that GDP be replaced by the Index of Sustainable Economic Welfare (ISEW) monetizing the loss of biodiversity and costs caused by the climate change, clean-up of the environmental pollution, and poor public health due to exposure to chemical and nuclear materials. A more standardized method adopted by the United Nations is the Green GDP, calculated by factoring in the environmental consequence of the growth:

Green GDP = GDP + Leisure Value – Cleanup Cost – Social Cost

Leisure activities include such activities as volunteer work, gardening, and time spent with friends and family. Cleanup cost is calculated by such measure as the amount of carbon dioxide emitted, the volume of waste generated, the number of trees cut, and so on. Social costs are costs associated with the loss in productivity, resettlement due to the environmental damage, and repair to properties. In an effort to account for environmental damages.

In 2004, China experimented with using the Green GDP as the true indicator of economic health (See Box: China's Green GDP). The report was welcomed by environmental organizations who saw it as a call to environmental stewardship, but fiercely opposed by local officials whose bonuses were tied to maintain high growth figures, which ultimately led to the demise of accounting based on Green GDP.

Affluence and Waste

The affluent lifestyle enjoyed in many industrial countries, in particular, the United States, comes with a price: an ever-increasing volume of waste and a rapidly degrading environment. Waste is not only a result of inefficient material and energy use but also a consequence of our unquenchable appetite for over-consumption, by consuming products that are either unnecessary (disposable products, electric toothbrushes, motorized lawnmowers, etc.) or excessive (large cars, excess packaging, oversized air conditioners, super-sized food portions, etc.).

Waste problems in the United States became particularly severe following WWII when much of its technological capability was redirected towards manufacturing consumer goods, newer drugs, higher-quality cosmetics, and more potent pesticides, fertilizers, solvents, and lubricants. These products made life easier for most, but also resulted in numerous health problems and deterioration of the environment. As the economy became stronger and the average purchasing power of American families grew, so did the rate of consumption and the volume of waste. Today, according to EPA estimates, over 250 million tons (2 kg per person per day) of solid waste is produced each year -- spread over about 50,000 toxic waste sites in the United States.

> **China's Green GDP**
>
> The rapid economic expansion of the last couple of decades in China, produced unintended consequences in the form of great environmental degradation, and corruption (since local officials were rewarded for faster growth and not for environmental stewardship). In an attempt to reverse the damage, in 2004, China adopted the Green GDP as the official indicator of the Chinese economy. As a result of the new system of accounting, China's GDP fell by 3.05%, costing China 64 billion dollars in economic losses in 2004. The World Bank, citing large water shortages, air and water pollution, desertification and ecological losses, assessed a much greater loss of GDP -- between 8-12%. While some localities saw an opportunity to demand greater subsidies from the central government, others, pointing to the lack of widespread acceptance by other industrialized countries, saw the unilateral attempt to include the cost of environmental damage as a hindrance to modernization and progress, forcing China to abandon the Green GDP as the primary indicator of its economic health. Although China stopped measuring its Green GDP, many environmental economists continue to argue in favor of adopting the Green GDP, as the best indicator of the true health of one country's economy.

The cleanup and safe disposal of toxic waste has been debated between those who promote building bigger and bigger landfills and those who prefer incineration. Unfortunately, each method has certain drawbacks; landfills, even those lined with multiple layers of clay and nonporous plastics, are largely ineffective at keeping toxins out of the surrounding soil for long times; incineration is dirty and accompanies the production of significant amounts of air pollutants.

The best way to combat waste is to remove incentives for being wasteful and increase material and energy efficiency through better designs, more efficient utilization of materials, increasing product durability, and by recycling and reusing the scraps. Unfortunately, our economic system favors waste, while discouraging efficiency. For example, commission fees charged by building contractors, architects, and engineering firms often are based on the total cost of the project, and therefore the tendency is to oversize everything. The same can be said of the Original Equipment Manufacturers (OEMs) who furnish equipment and machinery. The sensitive alternative is to link prices and fees, to efficiency, rather than to a percentage of the total cost. In other words, designers and engineers should be rewarded for what they save, not what they spend.

Technology

The third factor impacting environmental damage is technology.** The impact of technology on our lives can be both positive and negative (technology can be a hero or a villain). On one hand, technology makes it possible to design machines that have better efficiencies and make elaborate tasks much easier to perform. On the other hand, technology promotes automation, usually resulting in faster resource depletion and additional waste. Consider, as an example, the impact of technology on automobile use. Automobiles have given us mobility by allowing us to move around faster, but also have resulted in higher levels of air pollution, and limited our physical activity, which affects

---

** Much of the material in this section has been adapted from two books written by Amory B. Lovins, published by Rocky Mountain Institute: a) Natural Capitalism: Creating the Next Industrial Revolution, 1999); and b) Reinventing Fire: Bold Business Solutions for the New Energy Era, 2011..

our health and general wellbeing. Increased efficiency, measured as miles traveled per gallon of fuel, has not helped either, as it has only caused people to buy larger, heavier cars and travel longer distances.

It should be noted here that, according to the Second Law of Thermodynamics, no matter what the technology, some of the available energy always turns into unavailable energy. As we are using up the most available forms of energy (primary energy resources, and raw materials), we are forced to resort to more advanced and more complex technologies that require higher expenditures of energy, more processed and synthetic materials, and greater environmental footprints. We are forced to drill deeper, switch to resources with lower energy density, and manufacture products made of synthetic materials, all in the direction of increasing entropy and adding disorder to the environment. As we become ever more technologically advanced, our dependence (and so our impact) on natural resources increases.

Fortunately, technological advances are on the horizon which, if used wisely, reverse some of the damage we have caused to the environment, and direct us toward a more sustainable path, affecting everything we build and consume, from microchips to potato chips. The most promising innovations are in the fields of manufacturing, transportation, agriculture, energy, and health.

Manufacturing

Manufacturing is undergoing major changes in reducing both material and energy consumption. For example, optical fibers have 40 times the carrying capacity of copper, which, potentially, can save an enormous amount of material and energy expended during extraction, manufacturing, and implementation of conventional copper cables. The same can be said of new composites that can replace heavy steel. Molded plastic parts produce far less waste than metals, potentially saving a great amount of material.

Factories of the future will use sensors embedded in the products that store information on the manufacturing process and relay data to the assembly line by connecting machines via the internet. The sensors continue to monitor the device even after they leave the factory floor and into the consumer's hands. Flaws in any step of manufacturing are detected and necessary steps to correct the problems are taken. More versatile design tools and better manufacturing techniques allow for the design of better and more efficient devices without sacrificing their functionality. The manufacturing practices prevalent in the past have been based mostly on the one-time use of materials, creating a large amount of waste that must be discarded. *Just-in-time* manufacturing and *made-to-order* manufacturing are two approaches being popularized in many manufacturing sectors; the exact amount of materials are being delivered at the exact time they are needed. This reduces the volume of scrap materials, eliminates the need for on-site storage, and minimizes the risk of spoilage and environmental damage.

New CAD/CAM (*computer-aided design* and *computer-aided manufacturing*) tools are available that help design products that weigh less and are stronger while consuming less energy and material. This is achieved primarily by making them less bulky while assuring that thermal and mechanical stresses in critical areas are kept below their safe limits. Rapid prototyping is a relatively new concept that uses CAD software to manufacture three-dimensional prototypes of a device at only a fraction of the cost, energy, and material. *Design for manufacturing* (DFM) is based on minimizing material and energy use during the entire chain of product development, from material extraction to processing, manufacturing, use, reuse, and disposal. Making products lighter and more durable is obviously the best choice. Proper reuse of material and recycling waste is the second-best option. For example, we can re-pulp paper products into cardboard, shred them and use as insulation, or incinerate them to generate heat. Clothing and furniture can be reused by more needy individuals, recycled into new products, or burned to generate energy. Glasses can be refilled over and over again or be crushed and made into new products. Metals can be re-melted and reused to manufacture new products.

Question: A beer canning company intends to reduce material waste by redesigning the shape of its beer cans.

What do you suggest?

Answer: For the same volume, cans that are fatter and shorter have the lowest total surface area and a smaller mass. It is left as an exercise to show that minimum surface area is achieved when a can's height is equal to its diameter.[††] It goes without saying that, another factor that can affect the choice is the practicality of the design.

Transportation

In the next two decades, transportation systems are expected to change radically, with major impact on world energy supplies. This is accomplished by:

Reduce demand -- by providing opportunities that reduce need for commuting. Faster Internet, wider bandwidth, and cheaper, more reliable, and more efficient computer networking, and offering flexible working hours will allow more people to work and shop from home. This has the synergistic effects of decreasing pollution and carbon footprint, and stress associated with traffic congestion.

Another step in reducing demand is better-designed neighborhoods that reduce our need for commuting. Unfortunately, Americans have opted for decentralization -- moving away from population centers to the suburbs. In the last three decades, 86% of the nation's growth was suburban. This resulted in heavier reliance on personal transportation and increased the number of miles traveled. European cities, on the other hand, have become more centralized. The larger population density is accommodated by better architectural planning, reducing the need for cars and transit. In Europe, 40-50% of trips are made via walking and biking, and about 10% are by transit. In contrast, in the United States, 87% of trips are by private cars and only 3% are by transit. What is required is developing a new architectural paradigm, the use of newer and more environmentally friendly construction materials, sustainable city planning, and behavioral changes by drivers.

Increase load factor -- This involves strategies that encourage changing from a more to a less energy-intensive transportation modes. The best modes are obviously walking and bicycling. Buses and trains are running mostly under capacity; current load factors for personal cars in the United States are 1.6 for passenger cars and 1.7 for light trucks. Offering free parking and flexible working hours, and taking steps to facilitate ride-sharing are also important steps to raise the occupancy rates.

Increasing the technical efficiency of energy use -- this involves designing more energy-efficient engines, improving the quality of roads, transitioning from freight trucks to freight rails and cargo ships, and electrifying the roadways can help in substantial energy savings. Other measures include minimizing driving during rush hour, and taking alternative routes with fewer stoplights, reducing the maximum highway speeds, closing windows while driving, and removing luggage racks when not in use, reducing load by turning off the air conditioner at low speed or going uphills. Piezoelectric crystals embedded in the asphalt can be used to harvest the kinetic energy of passing vehicles and produce electric currents to generate electricity. According to one estimate, the technology could produce as much as 44 megawatts of electricity from one single-lane, a one-kilometer stretch of roadway — enough to power 30,800 homes for a year. Other measures include the complete redesign of cars using more compact batteries, lighter and stronger materials, more efficient hybrid and fuel cell cars, and developing maglev and ultra-light rail. Solid-state batteries are being developed that will replace the liquid electrolyte with a thin layer of non-flammable ceramic material that can withstand much higher temperatures than current lithium-ion batteries. This allows increasing battery's energy density by at least two to three folds. Lighter vehicles need less power, and so, their powertrains would be smaller, which would further reduce weight.

Volkswagen has unveiled the world's most economical, compact two-seater car that uses less than one liter of fuel per 100 kilometers, equaling about 235 miles per gallon (Figure 15-2). The super-efficient plug-in hybrid uses a lithium-ion battery pack, an electric motor and a two-cylinder, 0.8-liter diesel engine for the powertrain, and weighs just 795 kg. It has a top speed of 99 mph, and emits just 38 grams of carbon dioxide per mile travelled. Compare

[††] For a fixed volume of a cylinder, $V = \pi d^2 L / 4$ (d is the diameter, and L is length), its total surface area $S = \pi dL + 2\pi d^2 / 4$ is minimized, when L = d. To prove, substitute for L in term of V, and put the derivative S with respect to d to zero.

this with the average sedan weighing twice as much, averaging 22.6 mpg, and emitting 395 grams of carbon dioxide per mile. According to company literature, the XL1 can be driven for up to 22 miles on electricity from the battery pack, which can be charged from a household electrical outlet. The major cost is that of carbon fiber, but expected to drop sharply as the industry matures, and prototype cars go into mass production.

Changes in behavior and overall systems effects -- Making cars more fuel-efficient does not necessarily save us a great deal of energy. For example, in the United States, as cars became more and more efficient, people chose to drive bigger and bigger cars, and the actual gallons–per-miles-driven increased. What we need is public awareness of environmental issues associated with overconsumption, and its willingness to help reduce impact by sacrificing some comfort and luxury when choosing among alternatives.

Figure 15-2
Super-efficient VW XL-1 Concept Car.
Image Courtesy of Volkswagen Corporation.

Agriculture

It is predicted that, by the end of this century, food shortages in many poor countries will be alleviated through better farming and irrigation systems, the development of hybrid seeds, and the production of food from municipal food waste. Planting proper trees and shrubs can help prevent the erosion of the soil, and slow rain runoff; new agricultural practices can be developed that rely on the efficient use of the soil, diversification of plants, and re-introduction of native animals that have been displaced by unsustainable agricultural practices.

Geographic Information Systems (GIS) are being developed that uses real-time digital satellite images, and information gathered from various sensing technologies that use electromagnetic radiation, gravitational force fields, acoustic data, lasers, cameras, radar, as well as real-time data on climate, prices, and availability of fertilizer to determine the best approaches to *precision farming* -- what, when, where, and how much to sow.

Genetic Engineering, also known as "recombinant DNA technology," allows manipulation of genetic material (DNA), and transfer of individual genes from one organism into another. By doing so, it is possible to develop crops that resist insects and diseases, offer better nutritional values and longer shelf lives. The proponents argue that genetically modified organisms (GMO) are good for the environment, as they enable no-till farming, which leaves soil undisturbed, releasing less carbon dioxide into the atmosphere. They also reduce pesticide use, increase yield thus reducing the size of agricultural land that must be set aside for growing food.

All genetically-modified crops available on the international market today have been designed using one of the three basic traits: resistance to insect damage; resistance to viral infections; and tolerance toward certain herbicides. The danger that some scientists foresee is that introducing foreign genes into food plants may have an unexpected and negative impact on human health. For example, they can spread through nature and cross-breed with natural organisms, contaminating native crops and future generations in an unforeseeable and uncontrollable way. It is theoretically possible to transfer antibiotic- or herbicide-resistant genes, used in creating GMOs, to humans and other animals, making them vulnerable to diseases.[‡‡] Another possibility is that these genes may create new allergens or cause an allergic reaction in susceptible individuals, or contaminate potentially non-target organisms (e.g., insects that are not pests). There is also a growing movement against major agribusinesses that patent the modified genes so they can be harvested only once, forcing farmers to purchase new seeds for each new harvest, and at the price dictated by these companies. The debate continues. Figure 15-3 depicts a Greenpeace poster implying the disaster that is bound eventually to happen if genetic engineering of crops continues without strict oversight. Some governments have

---

[‡‡] Today in the United States, food travels an average of 1300 miles from farm to plate; often the energy needed to produce it is many times the energy contained in the food itself.

proposed international regulations in a "Biosafety Protocol. " EU has banned the import of all foods containing genetically modified ingredients; the US imposes no such restriction. Many foods (at least in the United States) today have some GMO ingredients; corn syrups, soy, sugar, and milk are among the most common. By law, organic foods cannot contain any GMOs.

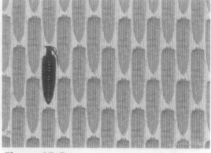

Figure 15-3
Corn grenade: the winning image from the Greenpeace Seeds of Trouble competition, 2002.
Image courtesy OF Greenpeace International (http://greenpeace.org).

Energy

As long as external costs are not internalized, fossil fuel and nuclear will be a cheaper and more convenient source of energy for some decades to come and, thus, remains a big part of our future energy portfolio. The true cost of fossil fuels includes the military expenditures associated with oil security, various subsidies to oil producers and customers in terms of tax breaks, and other exemptions and environmental and health damage resulting from burning fossil fuels. The true cost of nuclear energy includes the cost of storing nuclear waste, the cost of protecting nuclear reactor sites from potential threats by terrorists, and potential damage in event of a nuclear accident.

If the polluters are forced to pay for these damages and if the many subsidies are eliminated, prices will have to be raised, which may help to encourage lower consumption and better efficiency through the use of more environmentally friendly "green" products. The public, so far, has shown little interest in renewable resources because their cost of utilization is higher than that of fossil fuel and nuclear resources. Fortunately, every day, we are witnessing new innovations that continue to bring the cost down, making renewable energy competitive to non-renewable resources.

In the near future, we will witness fuel cells becoming ready for commercialization, providing premium electricity at efficiencies of 50-60% for stationary applications. The waste heat provided by high-temperature fuel cells can be recovered to produce steam that can be used directly in industrial applications or expanded in a gas turbine to produce more electricity. The waste heat from low-temperature fuel cells can be used for cooking and is ideal for hot water heating and space air conditioning. Further advances in solar, wind, wave, and ocean thermal technologies are expected to bring down prices, making renewable energy competitive with, or cheaper than, fossil fuels or nuclear fission, alleviating many of our concerns about energy and its effects on the environment. Fusion technology, although currently not available, may prove to be our ultimate source of clean and inexpensive energy for many centuries.

Advances in the field of **synthetic biology** will enable scientists to produce artificial genomes and re-engineer new organisms that cheaply and efficiently, turn plant fiber into ethanol and other biofuels. Scientists have discovered new strains of petroleum-degrading bacteria that thrive with no light or water, breathe carbon dioxide instead of oxygen, and break down toxic petroleum compounds to give off methane gas. These properties can pave the way for the development of a new and cheap class of biofuels, not to mention cleaning up oil and other hydrocarbon spills.

Figure 15-4
Efficient appliances are authorized by the DOE with special Energy (Green Star) labels. These models can save as much as 30% in energy.
Source: Federal Trade Commission.

More **energy-efficient devices** are expected to flood the market (Figure 15-4). These devices operate by automatically adjusting to consume the least amount of energy required for the task they are designed to perform. Washing machines will be equipped with fuzzy controllers that adjust the amount of detergents, water, heat, etc., depending on how dirty clothes are.§§ Dryers, microwave ovens, air conditioners, refrigerators, and vacuum

---

§§ Unlike traditional on/off controllers, fuzzy controllers work by assigning a weighting function that can vary by any number between zero and one..

cleaners are being designed that work on similar principles.

Lighting and illumination are making great progress toward energy efficiency. The old (and most common) incandescent lights have relatively short life and give off 95% of the electrical energy it consumes as heat, turning only 5% of it to light; an incandescent bulb contains a tungsten coil filament that turns red when electricity flows in a vacuum. A halogen lamp is a special type of incandescent lamp that places a capsule filled with a halogen gas around the heated filament that keeps the filament hot and improves its efficacy.

Instead of a glowing filament, compact fluorescent lamps (CFLs) work by passing electric current through a spiral tube containing a mixture of argon and a small amount of mercury vapor exciting the gas and produces ultraviolet light, which is absorbed by a fluorescent via the phosphorous coating painted on the inside of the tube and cause it to glow (Figure 15-5). Fluorescent lamps are about four times more efficient and last up to 10 times longer than incandescent lamps. *Lighting efficiency* is defined as the amount of light (lumens) to electrical power consumed. It is expressed as lumens per watt. For example, a 22 watt CFL has the same light output as a 100-watt incandescent.

Figure 15-5
Compact fluorescent lamps (CFL).
Source: National Renewable Energy Laboratory, U.S. Department of Energy.

A light-emitting diode (LED) works by passing a current through a p-n junction causing electrons to flow from the negatively charged pole to a positively-charged pole, in the process releasing photons of light. LEDs are about twice as efficient as CFLs and last 30-40 times longer than traditional bulbs. The price is still expensive, but as the prices drop, they are to become more widespread.

New architectural concepts allow construction of "green" or ecologically friendly **smart buildings** that incorporate many energy-saving measures at lower costs, without sacrificing convenience or safety -- for example, passive heating and cooling systems deploy newer phase-change materials, window overhangs, improved insulation, double-glazed air-tight glass, low-emissivity window coatings, windows with aerogel glazing, and better sensors are some of the technologies that are finding their way into average households. Roofs can be resurfaced with material that increases solar reflectance by at least 40%. According to one estimate retrofitting a 100 m² of roof offsets 10 tons of CO_2 emissions, and reduces summertime urban temperatures, leading to improved air quality. Photovoltaic cells eventually can be shaped to directly replace walls and windows or can be rolled out like a blanket, or layered like paint onto curved surfaces. Wind turbines can be designed as an integral part of future buildings, making these buildings a net exporter of energy.

Health

Factors directly affecting our health are the availability of clean water, clean soil, and clean air. Unfortunately, as the economy expands and more energy is consumed, we are finding the task of cleanup more and more difficult. According to a 2007 study conducted by the World Health Organization (WHO), over 2.4 billion or 40% of the world population lack access to clean water. In addition, WHO reported that, in 2012 alone, 7 million people died, one in eight total deaths, as a result of air pollution exposure. Landfills are the main cause of sources of soil and groundwater contamination as leachate migrate through refuse.

The biggest threat to our environment is, however, the release of vast amounts of carbon into the atmosphere, both from the widespread use of fossil fuels, and deforestation. We discussed issues of toxins in the atmosphere and global warming in Chapter 7. Below, we will address technologies that are being developed to mitigate greenhouse gases and other toxins in a more sustainable way.

Global Warming

Global warming is the gradual increase in the average temperature of the earth's atmosphere and its oceans, believed to be a result mainly from increased volumes of carbon dioxide and other greenhouse gases released by the burning of fossil fuels, land clearing, agriculture, and other human activities.

The scientific consensus is that, over the past 100 years, the average temperature of earth has risen between 0.4 and 0.8 °C, and unless steps are taken to combat global warming, the average global temperatures could rise an additional 1.4 to 5.8 °C by the year 2100. Temperature on the other hand is shown to be closely correlated to the concentration of carbon dioxide in the atmosphere, which remained below 280 ppm until 1858, but grown ever since to 417 ppm, in 2021 (Figure 7-.14). Worldwide, over 37 billion metric tons of carbon dioxide are emitted into the atmosphere every year, an average of five tons per every man, woman, and child -- about half of it from only three countries -- China, the US, and India (Table 15-3).

Table 15-3 Country's Share of CO_2 Emissions (Billion Metric Tons)			
	1990	*2019*	*% Increase*
China	2.4	10.9	454
United States	5.0	4.8	-0.04
Russia	2.4	1.7	-29
India	0.7	2.5	257
EU	5.7	2.9	97
World	**22.5**	**37.0**	**64**

To slow down warming trend, the concentration of greenhouse gases, carbon dioxide in particular, must be lowered substantially. The best way to control emissions, is to reduce the fossil-fuel combustion through energy efficiency, and switch to fuels with higher hydrogen to carbon ratio, or non-carbon renewable energy fuel (decarbonization). In the absence of adequate support for cleaner alternative sources of energy, the remaining options are stopping carbon dioxide's release into the atmospheric air by storing it in other mediums (sequestration), and by modifying atmospheric processes through geoengineering (Table 15-4). No matter which option is selected, we must assure that it is safe, effective and environmentally benign, cost competitive, and viable at commercial scales.

It should be noted that although improved combustion is useful in removing such pollutants as particulates and hydrocarbon, it does not help in reducing carbon dioxide, which is the product of complete combustion of fossil fuels.

Table 15-4 Carbon Dioxide Mitigation and Adaptation		
Mechanism	*Implementation*	*Risks*
Reduction in Carbon Emissions	• Behavioral modification • Energy efficiency	• None
Decarbonization (Removing carbon before it is produced)	• Switch to nuclear and renewable sources • Clean coal (steam reforming)	• Security concerns (for nuclear option) • Costly
Carbon Capture and Storage (Removing carbon after it is produced)	• Increase re-forestation • Use biodiesel and ethanol • Injecting it into the ground • Sequestering in deep ocean	• Reduce land available to grow food • Limited reservoirs • Expensive to retrofit
Geoengineering (Changing the environment to offset emissions)	• Seeding clouds with barium oxide to increase planetary albedo and cloud cover • Injecting sulfuric acid droplets and sulfate particles	• Costly and risky • Ocean acidification • Ozone destruction • Potential for international conflict • May favor some countries at the expense of others

Decarbonization

Decarbonization can be accomplished by switching to alternative fuels with higher H/C ratios. Coal has no hydrogen and is, therefore, considered to be the dirtiest of all fossil fuels. Natural gas has four hydrogen atoms for each carbon atom and is considered relatively cleaner. The best option, is of course, to remove carbon altogether and use pure hydrogen. Hydrogen is, however, highly explosive and has a low density, and must be kept at high pressure, which makes it even more dangerous. A good way of utilizing hydrogen is through fuel cells. Fuel cells are devices that combine hydrogen and oxygen in the air to produce electricity (See Chapter 6). The only product is water vapor, which is not a pollutant.

One possible approach to decarbonization is by converting natural gas to hydrogen by steam reforming. The process is similar to coal gasification described in Chapter 5. In this method, natural gas reacts with steam at high temperatures to produce carbon monoxide and hydrogen, followed by carbon monoxide reaction with water vapor, which yields to the formation of carbon dioxide.

$$CO + H_2O \rightarrow CO_2 + H_2$$

The final process involves separation of hydrogen and carbon dioxide. Hydrogen is stored and used as fuel, while carbon dioxide is captured and deposited in underground storages.

Carbon Capture and Storage

Atmospheric carbon dioxide can be reabsorbed in rock, recycled through photosynthesis by planting new trees, or by ocean fertilization.

Reforestation

Trees play important roles in removing carbon dioxide and cooling the environment. Photosynthesis helps by removing carbon dioxide and converting it into carbohydrates and food (Chapter 11). Furthermore, plants give back some of the water, drawn up through the roots, and exit the plant through its pores or stomata — in its leaves. As this "sweat" evaporates, heat is removed from the air, cooling themselves and the surrounding air. Unfortunately, trends point in the opposite direction. In the last few decades, much of the existing rainforests have been lost to logging and used as wood fuel or cut down to pave the way for urbanization.

Enhanced Weathering of Rocks

When fresh silicate rocks are exposed to carbon dioxide, they form metal oxides that, when released into the ocean or spread over lands, combine to form carbonate -- a major sink for carbon dioxide. Major benefit of CO_2 sequestration by mineral carbonation is the environmentally benign and virtually permanent trapping of CO_2 in the form of carbonated minerals. The idea is to crush rock and spread it over a wide area of the ocean surface. The rocks would absorb the carbon dioxide and turn into carbonates that would then wash into the ocean.

In a similar fashion, large absorbent filters, coated with certain chemicals can be constructed that absorb carbon dioxide as air blows past them. Another approach is to introduce fine mist of calcium hydroxide droplets, which reacts with atmospheric carbon dioxide and rains down as a solid calcium carbonate. The problem with this approach is that it is slow and requires large areas.

Ocean Nourishment

Ocean nourishment is the concept of providing additional nutrients to the ocean surface for increasing the fish population catch. The approach is to add a nitrogen-rich fertilizer, such as urea, into areas where fish populations are decreasing. Not only will this help in providing additional nutrients, but also will help in sequestering up to 800 million tons of carbon (corresponding to 2.9 billion tons of carbon dioxide) per year. If phosphorous is added to the fertilizer, the potential is much larger. Also, seeding the ocean with nitrogen or iron accelerates the growth of carbon-dioxide-eating plankton. Because ocean fertilization has not been practiced on a large scale, some are afraid of unwanted or unexpected consequences. More research is underway.

Geoengineering

Geoengineering refers to the deliberate large-scale manipulation of the environment, in order to affect the earth's climate so as to reduce the effect of global warming. Geoengineering is the most controversial and, at this time, is discussed only in academic circles. The most obvious approach is to offset the effects of increased greenhouse gases by reflecting a small percentage of the sun's light back into space. Among methods being considered are:

a. Solar Radiation Management (SRM)
b. Carbon Capture and Storage (CCS)

Solar Radiation Management

This can be done by either reducing the incoming solar radiation, or increasing the outgoing terrestrial radiation. The goal of such proposals is to balance reduced-insolation cooling with the increased heating from greenhouse-gas emissions Solar radiation entering the atmosphere is reduced by deploying sunshades or deflectors in space in earth's orbit, by increasing the ocean and land reflectivities, and by increasing the albedo of stratocumulus clouds. In one approach a cloud of small space crafts (space mirrors) are placed 1.5 million kilometers from the earth that block part of the sun's radiation that impacts the earth. Input radiation also can be controlled by increasing the surface albedo (land and ocean) through extensive use of white paint on building structures, covering deserts with reflective material, enhanced upwelling, iron fertilization, and phosphorus/nitrogen fertilization. Increasing cloud reflectivity by doping it with particles tiny enough that scatter the sunlight, but not large enough to block the infrared light reflected by terrestrial radiation. Some examples include deploying fleets of aircraft that crisscross the skies releasing dust into the low atmosphere; and, by reflecting sunlight back into space via hydrogen-filled, aluminized balloons into orbit.

Another approach is to mimic the effects of volcanic eruptions[*] by injecting sulfate aerosols into the upper stratosphere, thus directly cooling the planet;[¶¶]

The major criticism against these approaches is the high degree of uncertainty in their effectiveness, and the potential unwanted consequences that damage the environment. For example, it is not clear what impact massive amounts of sulfur in the atmosphere will have on ocean acidification, without a credible exit strategy. While sulfates would likely offset warming, they do nothing to reduce the acidification of oceans caused by raising levels of carbon dioxide in the atmosphere; also, effect on the precipitation patterns. is not clear. Furthermore, these aerosols will remain in the atmosphere for hundreds of years, even after the carbon dioxide emission is halted.

Sequestration

This approach aims at massive efforts to remove carbon dioxide from the atmosphere, compressing it before transporting it to a suitable storage site where it's injected into the ground. This can be done in two ways: (a) by capturing and cleaning emissions at the source, and (b) capture after it is released into the atmosphere and mixed with the ambient air. The first approach or Direct Air Capture (DAC) relies on installing scrubbers that have been fitted to chimneys and catalytic converters on trucks and buses are of this type. Because of the huge number of point sources, this procedure is largely ineffective.

The ***air-capture method*** aims at removing carbon that is already released into the atmospheric air. The process involves pumping air through corrugated sheets of material soaked with solutions that absorb carbon dioxide to form carbonate. As the carbonate settles down through the stack, it is collected and sequestered, or combined with hydrogen to produce hydrocarbon fuel.

The second method focuses on sucking ambient air, and remove carbon dioxide befoore depositing it in abandoned oil or gas fields (Figure 15-6). An example of this type of strategy is to engineer "artificial trees." Instead of turning into fruit or roots or tree trunks, it simply gets collected by resin in a reversible chemical process (Figure 15-7).

¶¶ The eruption of Mt. Pinatubo in the Philippines in 1991 resulted in a decrease of the world's average temperature by 0.5°C for a couple of years.

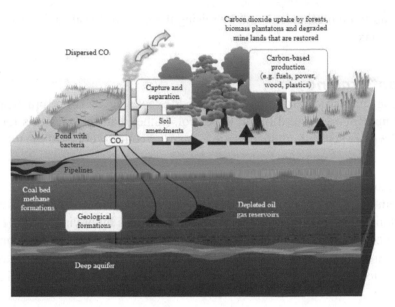

Figure 15-6
Carbon Sequestration
Source: Wikipedia, Creative Commons

Carbon Abatement Strategies

Different approaches have been suggested to internalize environmental costs (Chapter 14). Some economists propose the passage of additional "nuisance laws" that allow the public to sue for damages caused by the reckless release of noxious emissions and toxic pollutants into the atmosphere. Two examples that they often cite and which have had some success within the last few years are: 1) the costs incurred by tobacco companies to pay for health damages caused by cigarette smoking, and 2) the clean-up of the Exxon Valdez oil spill in Alaska and BP oil spill in the Gulf of Mexico. Environmental activists, on the other hand, are pushing for a "carbon tax" to account for future costs of climate change and to cover other health costs and damage to the environment. How much those costs will be and how much tax should be levied is difficult to estimate. No matter which approach is adopted, polluting companies are far from being supportive of these measures; they fight every lawsuit and regulation that limits their activities. Even in those rare instances that they lose, they pass the costs back to customers, making the fight less appealing to an average consumer. Educating the public in supporting environmentally-friendly legislatures, fostering conservation measures, as well as switch to less-polluting, more efficient-energy alternatives seems to be our best option.

Figure 15-7
Artificial Tree
Source: ASME Digital Collection

It should be noted that even renewable energy technologies are not entirely "clean." We still need some fossil fuels for manufacturing solar photovoltaics, fuel cells, and batteries that use large quantities of highly toxic materials (arsenic, cadmium, selenium, boron, etc.). Many of our activities and the products we use routinely are petroleum-based; unless there is a great push to reduce our fossil-fuel addiction, develop greener manufacturing technologies, reduce consumption, promote efficiency, and replace current materials with more environment-benign alternatives, we cannot make a true dent in our environmental issues.

To curb emissions of greenhouse gases, generally, two approaches are considered: by limiting the quantity of a pollutant through a cap-and-trade mechanism, and by raising the price of fossil fuels based on their carbon content through imposing a carbon tax.

Emission or "Carbon" Trading

Setting a unique set of standards to control emission from different sources is not practical; certain pollutants and emissions from older equipment are more difficult to control. Rather than set standards for an individual pollutant, it may economically make more sense if companies are allowed to collectively hold the total emissions at some pre-determined value.

Emission trading (also known as the cap and trade) refers to the establishment of an emissions market in which emission credits are traded. The Kyoto Protocol set up a mechanism that allowed companies and countries to continue producing pollutants as long as they could offset their higher emissions by buying credits from those that opted for cleaner technologies, and/or deployed effective emission-control strategies. Under this plan, every country is given a certain number of "pollution credits." The more carbon dioxide (or other greenhouse gases) produced, the more credits are used. Since the total number of permits is limited, the permits have a certain financial value that can be traded on the open market.

The countries that invest in cleaner technologies (solar, wind, and other renewables), or make policies that promote efficiency, will not use all their credits, and therefore can sell them in the emission market. The money they make can be then reinvested in developing even cleaner technologies. Credits also will be given if a country invests in energy efficiency or invest in pollution reduction technologies in developing countries. The rationale for this option is that as long as the total emission is reduced on a global scale, it does not matter where these reductions are made.

Opponents of the cap and trade programs argue that most of the emissions come from developing countries and, therefore, emission caps should be imposed on those countries, as well. Unless there are caps on their emissions, no significant overall reduction of greenhouse gases is possible. At the current time, there is no cap on emissions by the developing countries. Another objection is that this approach may actually encourage certain practices that could potentially increase (rather than decrease) overall greenhouse gas emissions. For example, companies may be inclined to buy emission credits rather than put efforts in cleaning the environment.

The most successful cap-and-trade system to date is the Acid Rain Program created under the 1990 Clean Air Act Amendments. It set a permanent cap on the total amount of sulfur and nitrogen oxides the primary precursors of acid rain. By 2014 the program succeeded to reduce annual sulfur dioxide emissions by 85% below the amount emitted in 1980.

Carbon Tax

Taxes are based on the amount of carbon emissions per unit of energy production (kg per kWh of electrical, or kg per MJ of thermal energy). This scheme is popular in most European countries, in which electrical suppliers are obligated to acquire a certain fraction of their energy from the renewable sources. The main objection to a carbon tax is that industry passes costs on to consumers; since poor spent more of their income on energy-intensive goods and fuel, they are being affected unproportionately more by this additional tax.

There is no nationwide carbon tax levied in the United States, although some states have imposed some carbon tax added to their utility bills.

> **Worth Remembering** – Carbon is naturally sequestered in our atmosphere, air, water, and soil. The greatest amount of carbon, about 50 trillion tons, is dissolved in ocean waters; another 800 billion tons is in air, and an additional 2.5 trillion tons are tied up in organic matter such as trees and soil.

A Blueprint for a Sustainable Future

Throughout the ages civilizations have risen and crumbled, many times as a result of their own mistakes and those of their forefathers. Many of these mistakes were, of course, inevitable, because they lacked the necessary technological know-how, and their immediate survival depended on the unsustainable exploitation of their natural resources. In addition, the population was relatively small and natural resources were abundant, so they moved to more fertile lands and friendlier environments and set up new centers of civilization. Because of the availability of a vast amount of resources and the relatively small populations, the ecology remained, to a great extent, sustainable. It has been only in the last century that accelerated growth in technological innovation, along with exponential growth in population, the rapid pace of economic expansion, and a lack of respect for the environment, have brought about conditions that could put us at risk for ecological disaster. As Diamond asserts, the main problem is not the world population itself -- although it has been named most often -- but the total population impact. If all people living in the Third World were to raise their standard of living and adopt the lifestyles of inhabitants in the First World, we would need 12 times the resources we are consuming and inflict 12 times the environmental damage we are causing today -- something the Earth certainly cannot sustain.

In a book titled *Natural Capitalism,* published by the Rocky Mountain Institute, Hawken and Lovins propose a new system in which resource productivity, rather than human productivity, drives the new economy. By increasing resource productivity, the same output is achieved, but less material and energy are consumed. The authors question the widely accepted assumption that what is good for us, must also be good for the world -- proposing instead, a radically new and contrasting paradigm, which proclaims that what is good for the world, also will be good for us. To make *our lives better*, we must strive to make the world better, and to make the *world better* we must first *understand it* better. The new economy will contrast modern capitalism in that economic prosperity will be measured *not by* gains in material well-being, but by natural capital that includes all the familiar resources used by humans -- water, minerals, oil, trees, fish, air, soil, etc. Natural capital also will encompass all living organisms -- humans, animals, plants... as well as wetlands, oceans, and marshlands. Furthermore, unlike "industrial capitalism" that considers only human financial and manufactured capital as important in the creation of wealth, "natural capitalism" also keeps stock of **natural capital**, and includes them in determining wealth. Whether we follow a sustainable or a non-sustainable future depends largely on how we preserve our biological diversity, how much we increase resource productivity, how much of the natural resources we exploit, and how much we leave for our children. According to many environmentalists and ecological economists, we have been, and unfortunately still are, continuing many practices that are unsustainable.

To assure sustainability, policy makers, economists, and educators have much work to do. Today's economy is driven by maximizing profit with little regard to natural capital. Many policies are in place that tax innovation and resource productivity but encourage waste and inefficiency. For example, we continue to support fishing fleets, even though existing fishing capacity far exceeds the sustainable yield of oceanic fisheries. Subsidizing forest industries by building roads for transporting wood has increased logging. Similarly, subsidizing agricultural farms to cover irrigation and pesticide costs has resulted in large-scale land abuse and salinization.

As we discussed earlier, sustainability cannot be achieved unless poverty is eliminated. Many developing countries have been borrowing heavily to subsidize basic necessities and much of their economic development needs. The total external debt of these countries has grown tenfold during the past three decades, from $245 billion in 1970 to more than $2.4 trillion in 2005. The poverty of these countries cannot be eliminated unless there are sincere efforts and a substantial commitment from richer countries in the form of debt relief, transfer of clean technology, international development aids, and reduction of trade barriers on goods imported from poorer countries.

Educators also have a great degree of responsibility for introducing their students and the public to issues related to energy and the environment, and for advising them on policies and practices that discourage waste and promote sustainability. Unfortunately, even many consumers who claim to favor environmentalism are not willing to pay more, accept the loss of some comfort, or forfeit minor customary features to buy more environmentally friendly products. The prospect is getting brighter, however, with gradually increasing sales of consumer products that carry labels identifying them as environmentally friendly, by such internationally recognized organizations as the *Forest Stewardship Council* (FSC), *Marine Stewardship Council* (MSC), and *Leadership in Energy and Environmental Design* (LEED). We believe consumer attitudes will significantly change as health effects associated with increasing pollution, global warming, and depletion of natural resources become more apparent.

Below are some guidelines for what we can do as small steps to move toward a sustainable future or at least reduce the environmental footprint and slow down the damage we already are causing to the environment.

On the Personal Level

Simplify your life – Use simpler machines. Use tools that require more of your muscle power, like bicycles, manual hacksaws, etc., which are also good for your health.

Find a hobby – Participate in leisure activities like music, sports, arts and crafts. They tend to enrich your life and are relatively non-consuming and non-polluting.

Drive less – Find alternative commuting, use public transport, rideshare, or carpool. Use Zipcars or other car-share programs (U.S. vehicles are idle 96% of the times).[***] Walk, or use bikes, more often, especially for distances less than two miles. Work at home instead of going to work, as much as possible. Move into a neighborhood closer to your work, school, and shopping area.

Minimize your energy losses – Repair leaky faucets and water pipes. Replace incandescent lights with fluorescent lights, insulate walls and roofs, and replace old appliances with energy-saving appliances.

Use ecologically friendly (green) materials – Consider using natural or recycled materials when buying new homes or remodeling your existing house. Buy only materials that meet environmental and safety standards.

Change your diet – Eat more vegetables and less meat. Consume organic instead of processed foods.

Reduce, reuse, and recycle – Reduce material consumption by extending products' useful lives. Don't buy new products unless you absolutely need them; share or repair whenever possible. When it is necessary, purchase only

---

[***]. According to company brochure, each of its vehicles takes 15-20 personal cars off the road.

durable and energy-efficient devices. Replace disposable with reusable products. Manufacturers do not pay your energy bills. In fact, to reduce costs and expand their market base, they have every incentive to make their devices less efficient and less durable. Reuse items (for other applications) instead of buying new ones; upgrade to a newer model and give the old one to a needier owner. Recycle only if the options for repair, reuse, and upgrading are no longer available.

Educate yourself – Learn about people and their cultures, travel to foreign countries, and explore the beauty of their lands, language, religion, and cultural heritage. Take a course in environmental stewardship.

On the Community and National Levels

Promote sustainability – Restore the environment to the condition of equilibrium by planting new trees, cropping native species, protecting wildlife, and enhancing fisheries. Reward efficiency and penalize waste by cutting subsidies to polluting industries, and giving rebates to manufacturers, builders, and those who save material and energy.

Be proactive – Don't wait until the environment is so stressed that the damage done has become irreversible; look for signs of stress, and act to resolve the problem in a timely fashion.

Empower individuals – Encourage individuals to practice conservation. For example, city planners can build convenient bike routes and transit authorities can subsidize bike costs. Companies can institute flex-time, allow employees to work from home, build shower facilities for bikers, and partially subsidize rent for employees who live nearby.

Deploy empowering technologies – This helps increase productivity while preserving natural resources. Examples are those that improve irrigation, reduce pest damage, and encourage soil conservation and enrichment. They also accelerate research and development of renewable energy sources.

Revamp manufacturing practices – This can minimize energy and material use during the entire life of the product. Design for durability, reusability, recyclability, and for manufacturing practices that promote energy efficiency and allow for easy repair, dismantling, reuse of scrap materials, and disposal of waste.

Eliminate subsidies – Subsidies to industries that promote the inefficient and unproductive use of materials and energy, and to agricultural companies that produce products that degrade soil fertility, pollute the environment, or waste a large amount of water should be eliminated. Internalize the externalities so that the price of a product reflects the full cost, including health costs and costs of cleaning the environment. The only exception is to subsidize those industries and products that are beneficial to society but need help to overcome initial market barriers.

Reform tax laws – Reduce or eliminate the income tax and substitute it with environmental and carbon auctions and carbon taxes. Carbon taxes are levied against individuals and corporations in proportion to the amount of fossil fuel they consume. In carbon auctions, companies bid for the right to pollute. This makes sense because labor earns income from productive work, whereas polluting corporations and energy-inefficient industries profit by being wasteful and non-sustainable. Industries should be taxed on the amount of raw material and energy they use and the toxic pollutants they release into the atmosphere, in order to cover health costs, environmental clean-up, and restoration of the environment to pre-release conditions. Higher taxes will increase the cost to polluting companies and result in a loss in sales. This forces companies to make their products safer, more efficient, and produce less waste.[†††] Proceeds should be reinvested in projects that promote sustainability – for example, use carbon auctions and carbon taxes to build a hydrogen infrastructure. The proceeds from pollution tax can be redirected as subsidies to clean and make industries efficient, or used to spur research and development in resource productivity. Income from parking rentals and toll roads can be used to pay for efficient public transportation, and savings from dematerialization can

---

[†††] This point has been refuted by some economists who argue that, for a purely efficient market, a shift from income tax to pollution tax will have a net negative impact on the economy. Others argue that the conclusions are made based on false assumptions and that the net effect is, indeed, positive. [See, for example, Economics and the Environment, 3rd Ed. by E. S. Goodstein, John Wiley & Sons, Inc., 2002, pp.170-173.

foster more efficient manufacturing. The interest on car loans can be increased while decreasing mortgage interest for community housing. Those with too many children can be penalized; the proceeds can help improve education, provide better health care, and build playgrounds for children.

Participate in local and national politics – Support politicians who advocate and promote realistic, sustainable environmental policies and short-term goals that are consistent with long-term objectives.

Educate – Teach the public environmental and energy literacy, the need for proactive practices and social activism. Universities should integrate energy and environmental courses in the liberal arts and engineering disciplines. This book is intended as a small step in that direction.

On the Global and International Levels

Support democratic governments – When these governments work to reduce poverty, support human rights, provide education, protect the environment, and promote sustainable economic development, they should be given support.

Empower grass root activists and microenterprises – Give loans and technical assistance to millions of tiny family-owned businesses or microenterprises with only a few employees. These small businesses are more flexible, lack bureaucracy, have strong ties to their local communities, can bring social benefits at only a fraction of the cost, and help more effectively protect their immediate environment and, thus, global ecology.

Oppose war and military intervention – Securing the flow of oil and other natural resources by force is neither the answer to our short-term energy needs nor is it in our long-term interest. Military interventions will undoubtedly antagonize people, encourage extremism, and cause political instability that eventually reverberates throughout the world.

Support the elimination of economic inequality – Forgive debts to poorer nations, transfer sustainable technologies to developing nations, and support globalization efforts, but only as much as it reduces the gap between industrial and poor nations, helps maintain peace and encourages disarmament. Help to eliminate poverty by providing free education, jobs, and basic health care.

Summary

In this text, we covered different aspects of energy and problems associated with the uncontrolled consumption of raw materials and non-renewable energy resources. Thus far, we have been abusing the environment and exploiting our natural resources in an unsustainable way. In fact, the latest studies by the leading conservation organization, World Wildlife Fund, suggest that the world biodiversity (renewable resources and land) has plummeted in the last forty years and that humans use natural resources faster than what earth can provide by 1.5 times.

The choice to continue on this path or take steps to modify our living habits toward a sustainable path is up to us. If we use history as evidence, unless we make a deliberate effort in reaching sustainability, we will have to fight many more wars over the control of natural resources -- land, water, minerals and, especially, oil. What is clear is that the longer we wait to introduce meaningful changes in the way we are currently using our natural resources and treating our environment, the more difficult it will be to achieve a sustainable future. Technological advances can help sustainability for as long as society, as a whole, makes a concerted effort to direct them toward that goal. Short of that commitment, technology will serve only to promote its implicit goal of unhindered material growth, while increasing stress on the environment and, potentially, causing its eventual collapse. The major challenge of our times is how to improve the standard of living of the average person without putting undue pressure on the resources at our disposal.

The highly industrialized countries, the United States, in particular, have the largest economies, the most access to technology, and vast intellectual and financial resources. They are also the biggest polluters and producers of wastes and have the moral responsibility to lead the world toward practices that enable our children to enjoy a sustainable future and a healthy environment, for many generations to come.

> *For in the end, we will conserve only what we love. We will love only what we understand. We will understand only what we are taught.* ~ Baba Dioum (1937-)

Endnotes

1 Brundstat Commission (1987) Report of the World Commission on Environment and Development: Our Common Future, http://www.un-documents.net/wced-ocf.htm)

2 Daly, H. (2005) Economics In A Full World. *Scientific American,* vol. 293, no. 3, pp. 100-107. doi: 10.1038/scientificamerican0905-100

3 Daly, H. (1990) Toward some operational principles of sustainable development. *Ecological Economics,* vol. 2, no. 1, pp. 1-6. doi: 10.1016/0921-8009(90)90010-r

4 Meadows, D. (2004) *Limit to Growth: 30-Year Update.* Chelsea Green Publishing.

5 Commoner, B. (1972) The Environmental Cost of Economic Growth. in Population, Resources and the Environment. Washington, DC: Government Printing Office, pp. 339-63.

6 Ehrlich, P., & Holdren, J. (1971) Impact of Population Growth. *Science,* vol. 171, no. 3977, pp. 1212-1217. doi: 10.1126/science.171.3977.1212

7 Chertow, M. R. (2001) The IPAT Equation and Its Variants; Changing Views of Technology and Environmental Impact, *Journal of Industrial Ecology,* vol. 4, no. 4, pp. 13-29. Available at: http://mitpress.mit.edu/journals/pdf/jiec_4_4_13_0.pdf

8 MIT (2008) *IPAT Equation,* http://web.mit.edu/2.813/www/Class%20Slides%202008/IPAT%20Eq.pdf

9 IPCC (2001) Special Report on Emissions Scenarios: a special report of Working Group III of the Intergovernmental Panel on Climate Change. Cambridge, UK: Cambridge University Press, http://www.grida.no/climate/ipcc/emission/050.htm

10 Simon, J. (1980) Resources, population, environment: An oversupply of false bad news, *Science,* vol. 208, pp. 1431-1437.

11 Diamond, J. (2014) *Collapse.* New York: Penguin Books.

12 Marx, K., Engels, F., MEEK, D., Meek, R., & Malthus, T. (1953) *Marx and Engels on Malthus. Selections from the writings of Marx and Engels dealing with the theories of Thomas Robert Malthus. Edited with an introductory essay and notes by Ronald L. Meek. Translations ... by Dorothea L. Meek and R.L. Meek.* London: Lawrence & Wishart.

13 Hardin, G. (1993) 'Living Without Limits,' *Ecology, Economics, and Population Taboos,* Oxford University Press.

14 Boulding, K. (1971) Collected Papers, Vol II, Foreword by T. R. Malthus, Population First Essay, *Colorado Associated University Press.*

15 Carnell, B. (1977) China's One-Child Policy, http://www.overpopulation.com/one_child.html

16 Global Trends 2015: A Dialogue About the Future with Non-government Experts, *Central Intelligence Agency,* Report GT-2015, 2000, http://www.cia.gov/cia/reports/globaltrends2015

17 Bureau of Economic Accounting, U.S. Department of Commerce, http://www.bea.gov

18 See for example, W. Nordhaus, and J. Tobin, "Is Growth Obsolete?", *National Bureau of Economic Research,* 1972.

19 Xiaohua, S. (2007) Call for a return to green accounting, *China Daily,* 19 April 2007.

20 U.S. Environmental Protection Agency, http://www.epa.gov/epawaste/nonhaz/municipal/index.htm

21 Owen, A. (2004) *Energy Policy, in Energy Policy,* [Ed. Anthony David Owen], in Encyclopedia of Life Support Systems (EOLSS), Developed under the Auspices of the UNESCO, Oxford, UK: Eolss Publishers, http://www.eolss.net

22 Gellings, C. & Parmenter, K. (2004) *Energy Efficiency in Passenger Cars and Trucks, in Efficient Use and Conservation of Energy,* [Eds. Clark W. Gellings and Kornelis Blok], in Encyclopedia of Life Support Systems (EOLSS), Developed under the Auspices of the UNESCO, Oxford, UK: Eolss Publishers, http://www.eolss.net

23 Piezoelectric Energy-Generating Roads Proposed for California, http://inhabitat.com/piezoelectric-energy-generating-roads-proposed-for-california.

24 Researchers find ultra-thin solution to primary obstacle in solid-state battery development (2016), *Phys.Org,* December 19, https://phys.org/news/2016-12-ultra-thin-solution-primary-obstacle-solid-state.html

25 U.S. EPA. (2012) *Light-Duty Automotive Technology, Carbon Dioxide Emissions, and Fuel Economy Trends: 1975 Through 2011,* http://www.epa.gov/otaq/cert/mpg/fetrends/2012/420r12001a.pdf

26 Kahn, H., Brown, W., & Martel, L. (1983) *The next 200 years.* New York: Quill.

27 Greenpeace International, http://www.greenpeace.org/international/campaigns/genetic-engineering

28 Cartagena Protocol on Biosafety to the Convention on Biological Diversity. (2000) Published by the Secretariat of the Convention on Biological Diversity, http://bch.cbd.int/protocol

29 Kim, J., & Crowley, D. (2007) Microbial Diversity in Natural Asphalts of the Rancho La Brea Tar Pits. *Applied And Environmental Microbiology,* vol. 73, no. 14, pp. 4579-4591. doi: 10.1128/aem.01372-06

30 Schuman, J., et al. (1992) 'Technology Reviews: Lighting Systems', LBL-33200.

31 Akbari, H. & Rosenfeld, A. (2008) 'White Roofs Cool the World, Directly Offset CO_2 and Delay Global Warming', Research Highlights, LBNL Heat Island Group, http://www.energy.ca.gov/2008publications/CEC-999-2008-031/CEC-999-2008-031.pdf

32 Akbari, H., Menon, S., & Rosenfeld, A. (2008) 'Global cooling: increasing world-wide urban albedos to offset CO2', *Climatic Change,* vol. 94, no. 3-4, pp. 275-286. doi: 10.1007/s10584-008-9515-9

33 WHO (2007) Combating Waterborne Diseases at the Household Level. Part 1, World Health Organization.

34 WHO (2014) News Release 25 March, 2014, World Health Organization, http://www.who.int/mediacentre/news/releases/2014/air-pollution

35 U.S. DOE, http://www.fossil.energy.gov/programs/sequestration/overview.html.

36 Azar, C. (2004) '*Carbon Dioxide Mitigation and Adaptation Options*', in Climate Change, Human Systems and Policy, [Ed. Antoaneta Yotova], in Encyclopedia of Life Support Systems (EOLSS), Developed under the Auspices of the UNESCO, Oxford, UK: Eolss Publishers, http://www.eolss.net

37 U.S. EPA, *Acid Rain Program Basic Information,* https://www.epa.gov/airmarkets

38 Rosenfeld, A., Kaarsberg, T., & Romm, J. (2000) 'Technologies to Reduce Carbon Dioxide Emissions in the Next Decade'. *Physics Today,* vol. 53, no. 11, pp. 29-34. doi: 10.1063/1.1333283

39 Cortez, L. & Cerqueira Leite, R. (2008) 'Relation Between Biofuel Versus Fossil Fuels', in *Petroleum Engineering* - Downstream, [Ed. Pedro de Alcantara Pessoa Filho], in Encyclopedia of Life Support Systems (EOLSS), Developed under the Auspices of the UNESCO, Oxford, UK: Eolss Publishers, http://www.eolss.net

40 Herzog, H., Eliasson, B., & Kaarstad, O. (2000) 'Capturing Greenhouse Gases'. *Scientific American,* vol. 282, no. 2, pp. 72-79. doi: 10.1038/scientificamerican0200-72

41 Shepherd, J. (2009) *Geoengineering the climate.* London: The Royal Society.

42 Savage, N. (2001) 'Greenhouse Effects, R.I.P'. *Discover,* August.

43 Rotman, D. (2013) 'A Cheap and Easy Plan to Stop Global Warming'. *MIT Technology Review, 116*(2), 53-56.

44 Diamond, J., (1999) *Guns, Germs, and Steel,* W. W. Norton.

45 Hawken, P. (2006) *Natural capitalism.* Boston: Back Bay Books.

46 Swamy, M. & Kumara, R. (2004) 'Does Non--Inclusion of Intangible Asset Values Lead to Distortion of Financial Statements and Mislead Judicious Financial Decision Making?', *Journal Of Financial Management & Analysis,* vol. 17, no. 1.

47 United Nation Environmental Program; State of the Environment and Policy Retrospective; 1972-2002, http://www.unep.org/geo/geo3/english/pdfs/chapter2-2_land.pdf

48 *The CIA Fact Book,* http://www.cia.gov.

49 Human demand outstrips nature's supply, *World Wildlife Fund,* http://wwf.panda.org/about_our_earth/all_publications/living_planet_report/demands_on_our_planet

Exercises

I. Discussion Questions

1. How do neoclassical and ecological economists differ on what sustainability means? On what points do they agree?

2. What are the various factors that limit the world population?

3. Do the different views expressed by ecologists and economists represent their widely different value systems?

4. Why is GDP a bad measure of sustainability? List at least two problems. Does a better index of sustainability exist?

5. Compare the GDP and NNW data for your country and conclude whether consumption is on a sustainable path.

6. What does the word "development" mean to you? What do you mean by land development? Human development? Economic development? Are these concepts compatible with ecologically sustainable development? What is a viable global development?

7. What is the significance of the IPAT Equation? Define terms and give examples of how this equation is used.

8. Define "Sustainable Energy" and give some examples of sustainable and non-sustainable energy use.

9. What strategies could governments and individuals use to adapt to global climate change?

10. Visit the websites for the non-government organizations (NGO) listed above, and make a summary of the mission and activities carried out by each organization:

    a. What are the missions, goals, and objectives of each organization?

    b. Where do their budgets come from?

    c. What have their major accomplishments been, and how have they impacted world sustainability? Explain.

    d. Do any of these organizations appeal to you and your philosophy? Are you willing to perform some volunteer work or contribute financially?

    e. Do you know of any other international organization that has had significant success in helping stop environmental degradation?

II. Multiple Choice Questions

1. Based on UN assessment, what is the medium predicted population of the world at the end of the 21st century?
   a. Around 6 billion
   b. Around 8 billion
   c. Around 10 billion
   d. Around 16 billion
   e. More than 16 billion

2. The part of the earth's crust, waters, and atmosphere, that supports life is called
   a. Biosphere
   b. Hydrosphere
   c. Lithosphere
   d. Mesosphere
   e. Thermosphere

3. The rigid outer part of the earth consisting of the crust and upper mantle is called the
   a. Atmosphere
   b. Lithosphere
   c. Hydrosphere
   d. Stratosphere
   e. Troposphere

4. Which of the following factors limit(s) the ultimate population of the world?
   a. The size of the earth
   b. The area of the arable land
   c. The amount of available food
   d. Environmental factors such as global warming and pollution
   e. All of the above

5. Sustainability implies
   a. Using natural resources as slowly as possible.
   b. Using only as much as is replaced by natural processes.
   c. Not introducing new technology too quickly.
   d. Discovering new resources to allow maximum economic growth.
   e. All of the above.

6. To make the earth sustainable, we need to devise strategies that
   a. Keep human birth and death rates in balance.
   b. Assure soil erosion does not exceed the natural rate of new soil formation.
   c. Assure enough trees are planted to offset deforestation.
   d. Use renewable energy at a rate that is slower than its sources are regenerated.
   e. All of the above.

7. Which type of light bulb has the highest efficiency?
   a. Halogen
   b. Incandescent
   c. Fluorescent
   d. LED
   e. All are equally efficient
8. The higher the efficiency of an electrical appliance,
   a. The faster it uses energy.
   b. The more energy it uses.
   c. The cheaper it is.
   d. The shorter the payback period.
   e. All of the above.
9. According to Oxfam (Oxford Committee for Famine Relief) report,
   a. The eight richest people earn as much as the lower half of the total population of the world.
   b. The eight richest people earn as much as the bottom half of the world combined.
   c. The richest 20% has as much wealth as the rest of the population of the world.
   d. The richest 10% has as much wealth as the rest of the population of the world.
   e. The richest 5% has as much wealth as the rest of the population of the world.
10. Which of the following light sources gives the highest light output for a given input of electricity?
   a. Incandescent bulb
   b. Halogenated bulb
   c. Light-emitting diode
   d. Fluorescent bulb
   e. High-intensity discharge
11. The best philosophy for dealing with the increasing volume of garbage is to
   a. Reduce material consumption as much as possible.
   b. Recycle.
   c. Reuse.
   d. Increase the number of landfills.
   e. Incinerate.
12. Which of the following statements is/are true?
   a. Populations increase in the United States at a faster rate than in Europe.
   b. Population growth is higher in poorer countries.
   c. People with less education are likely to have more children.
   d. Africa has the largest percentage of population growth.
   e. All of the above.
13. The main reason that many U.S. manufacturing firms relocate their plants to developing countries is
   a. Immigration policies have practically shut off the flow of immigrant workers to the United States.
   b. Environmental regulations are less stringent in developing countries.
   c. Labor costs are lower in developing countries.
   d. a, b, and c.
   e. b and c, but not a.
14. Carbon footprint is a measure of
   a. The total amount of greenhouse gases emitted.
   b. The total of the ecosystem services needed to prevent climate change.
   c. The total land area needed to absorb the carbon.
   d. The total land area needed to produce carbon.
   e. The difference between the total land areas needed to produce and to absorb the carbon.
15. Dematerialization implies:
   a. The reduction in material consumption.
   b. The reduction in human's appetite to accumulate material wealth.
   c. The elimination of poverty in the developing countries.
   d. The reduction in wealth in the developed countries.
   e. The reduction in cost of end-of-life disposition.
16. "Food mile" is a measure of
   a. The distance food travels between the point it is produced and the point it is consumed.
   b. The area of ecosystem services required to produce food.
   c. The ecological footprint of food.
   d. The carbon footprint of food.
   e. None of the above.
17. Over the last decade, food production has
   a. Remained about the same
   b. Increased globally
   c. Increased, decreased, and remained the same, depending on the country
   d. Decreased globally
   e. Fluctuated from year to year
18. Among options to reduce material and energy waste is to
   a. Increase energy efficiency.
   b. Minimize material use.
   c. Better design.
   d. Recycle and reuse scraps.
   e. All of the above.
19. Which of the following adjustments would be made

to any increase in GDP in order to derive an Index of Sustainable Economic Welfare (ISEW)?

    a. Subtract the monetary value of personal consumption.

    b. Subtract the costs of environmental degradation.

    c. Subtract the costs of protection of oil fields in the Middle East.

    d. Subtract the cost of charitable and voluntary works.

    e. All of the above.

20. The most effective strategy to carbon abatement is

    a. Geoengineering.

    b. Carbon storage.

    c. Enhanced weathering of rocks.

    d. Decarbonization of fuels.

    e. Reforestation.

III. True or False?

1. Roughly one-quarter of the US GDP is wasted on nonproductive human activities.

2. Just-in-time manufacturing is the process by which a manufacturer can deliver their product without delay.

3. Design for manufacturing is the process by which material and energy consumed through the product life-cycle are minimized.

4. "Natural Capitalism" is the doctrine practiced in all capitalist countries.

5. Sustainable development requires new resources to be found as fast as they are consumed.

6. The neoclassical economists see the population as an asset.

7. According to Lovins, human productivity, rather than resource productivity, will fuel the future economy.

8. The best approach for minimizing waste is recycling.

9. The IPAT equation states that the impact of technology on the environment will increase proportionally to the rate at which the technology grows.

10. Geoengineering is the study of geological formations, in an attempt, to find new sources of fossil fuels, yet to be discovered.

11. The greenhouse effect is one reason that allowed life to flourish on the earth. Without the greenhouse effects, the temperature on earth would be too cold to support life.

12. Decarbonization is the process of trapping carbon dioxide in the form of carbonated minerals.

13. The best way to reduce the impact of consumption on environmental degradation in to apply newer and newer technologies.

14. Natural capital refers to a rise in the capital when money is deposited in a saving account.

15. Ocean enrichment refers to adding nutrients to the ocean surface to increase the fish population.

IV. Fill in the Blanks

1. The largest number of humans that the Earth can sustain indefinitely at the current rate of per capita consumption of natural resources is known as the Earth's holding _____.

2. According to the World Resource Institute, by 2050, roughly one of every two persons will live in ____.

3. The U.S. produces roughly _____ million tons of toxic wastes every year.

4. Unlike _____ who consider population the main cause of environmental degradation, _____ economists see population as an asset and a necessary component for a sustainable economy.

5. An effective method of _____ is the steam reforming of methane to hydrogen.

6. _____ can have either positive or negative impact on the environment.

7. Using CAD software to manufacture a three-dimensional prototype of a device is called _____.

8. Large-scale injection of sulfur dioxide into the upper atmosphere to cool the atmosphere proposed to combat global warming is coined as _____.

9. Cultivating the right plant, at the right time, and in the right place is called _____ agriculture.

10. According to the EPA estimates, every American produces roughly _____ of wastes each day.

PROJECT I -- Energy and Affluence

From the discussion given in this chapter it appears that industrialized countries consume considerably more energy than developing and under-developed countries. In fact, many economists see a strong correlation between a country's wealth as measured by Gross Domestic Product (GDP), or Gross National Product (GNP) and per capita energy consumption. In this project, you are asked to prepare a spreadsheet tabulating the latest published data for several developed and developing countries. Search the Internet to find the latest population and economic data. Good sources for this information are the

World Bank and the Energy Information Administration. CIA's World Fact Book (https://www.cia.gov/library/publications/the-world-factbook) also may be consulted.

a. Plot the per capita energy consumptions of these countries, versus their GDP and GNP on a log-log scale.
b. Calculate the ratio of the total energy consumption and GDP for the United States, China, India, and the country of your birth. Which country uses energy more efficiently?
c. Discuss the pattern and whether such a correlation exists, or not. If not, explain the discrepancy.

PROJECT II - World Outlook in 2100

According to some scenarios, within the next few decades, the world population will increase to nine to ten billion, renewable resources will significantly diminish, and as a result of global warming, many areas of the world will be adversely affected. It is expected, also, that many parts of the world will experience major political upheaval that requires substantial redistribution of wealth and natural resources. You are asked to envision possible scenarios on where the world is heading and how the world will look like at the end of the current century. In your opinion, is it going to be a better and more equitable world? What would be the potential challenges, and how will the world deal with them? In short, do you see our children live a happier, safer, and a more comfortable lifestyle than we do now?

PROJECT III - Life Cycle Analysis: Electric versus Conventional Bikes

In this project, you are asked to carry out a simple qualitative life-cycle (cradle-to-grave) comparison of the energy expenditure between electric and conventional bicycles.

a. What are your assumptions in making this comparison?
b. Which one consumes more energy per kilometer of travel? What form of energy is used by an electric bike? By an ordinary bike?
c. What are the differences if individuals pedal faster than an electric bike? If the rider travels twice as fast on an electric bike than a conventional bike?
d. Which one takes more energy to manufacture? Describe what each component does and what forms of energy it requires to operate.

e. What are the total energy costs to manufacture different batteries? Compare four types of batteries -- Li-Ion, NiCad, NiMH, and lead-acid. [You can consult the paper by Rydh, C., "Life Cycle Inventory of Recycling Portable NiCad Batteries," *Resource Conservation, and Recycling*, March 2002, Vol 34, 289-309, to find energy costs for manufacturing and shipping various types of batteries]. Which battery is the most energy-efficient?
f. What is the energy cost associated with the production of food necessary for the delivery of muscle power to operate the conventional vehicle?
g. Does it make economic sense to buy an electric bicycle? In terms of energy efficiency? In terms of convenience, health benefits, etc.

PROJECT IV -- Biosphere II

In 1991, to simulate ecological processes on Earth and assess the possibility of life within a closed system, eight scientists, four men, and four women entered a tightly sealed glass and steel greenhouse structure named Biosphere II (Biosphere I refers to the Earth, itself). The structure, located near Oracle, Arizona, was 3.5 acres – the size of three football fields – and became home to the scientists for two years. The experiment originally was designed to last 100 years, with scientists rotating every few months or years. All air, water, and nutrients were recycled within the system, which was almost entirely isolated. Sunlight and electrical power were allowed into the dome, and every two weeks, samples of soil, air, and other species were sent outside, through an airlock, for further tests and analysis.

The building housed a diversity of ecosystems or biomes, including a desert, a tropical rainforest, a savannah, a marsh, a field for farming, and an ocean with the coral reef. The scientists were accompanied by insects, pollinators, fish, reptiles, and mammals that were supposed to replicate the Earth and its ecosystem.

Research the results of these studies, and the follow-up experiments and answer the following questions:

a. Why was the project called Biosphere II?
b. How much did the project cost?
c. What were the primary goals of the project? Did the project achieve its goals?
d. How did scientists maintain their diets? Where did food and water come from?

e. What were the chief complaints of the inhabitants during the two-year confinement?

f. What species survived the experiments and which perished? Why?

g. How different was the atmosphere of Biosphere II from Earth's atmosphere? Could the environment be maintained? How high did the level of carbon dioxide rise?

h. How did the quality of water, air, and soil change? Was the ecosystem capable of repairing and maintaining itself? How did plant and animal lives flourish under these conditions? Did any of its species become extinct?

i. Do you consider the experiment a success? Was it worth the amount of time and money spent?

j. What were the lessons learned?

k. What is the status of Biosphere II today?

l. Do you have suggestions for further experiments or better utilization of the resources and facility?

PROJECT V -- Sustainable Village (Group Project)

A group of 10,000 families is planning to design a completely self-sufficient and sustainable community for its members and their children. As a consultant, you are asked to develop a blueprint of how such a community would be built. You are going to advise the villagers on:

a. What source of energy they should use. Where they should find the resources, and what advantages and disadvantages of various energy options will have.

b. What kind of food should be produced and how the villagers should produce it.

c. The kind of tax structure you would recommend, assuming that the villagers have the option to devise their tax laws and enact their environmental regulations.

d. How the community should pay for public goods, such as health-care costs, cleanup costs, and salaries of police, teachers, etc.

e. What schools would look like, and who would pay for education.

f. What sports facilities and entertainment facilities you would recommend.

g. Any restrictions on activities they can engage in, or the number of children they can have. The kind of incentives they should offer for family planning or for keeping the environment clean. How should they handle waste?

h. How would they use resources, assuming the villagers have access to limited amounts of oil and other fossil resources at reasonably low prices?

i. What would the villagers use for transportation between their homes and work, and for taking long trips and vacations?

PROJECT VI -- Sustainability and the Social Responsibility

In this project, you are asked to analyze the pattern of energy use in your household and investigate ways of reducing fossil fuel consumption and helping the environment. First, you are asked to estimate the annual energy consumption in your household by adding up the energy 1) spent to produce your food, 2) needed for lighting, 3) required to run your electrical and gas appliances, and 4) used to meet your transportation needs. Then you are asked to estimate the potential savings in fossil fuel consumption if you make slight modifications in your lifestyle.

Start by answering the following questions:

1. How many people live in your household? What are their ages and genders?

2. Is any member of your household a vegetarian?

3. List all electrical and gaseous appliances in your house. How many hours is each appliance used on a typical day?

4. How many lights are usually on? What kind are they?

5. How many cars do you have in your home? How many miles is each car driven? What are their fuel efficiencies?

Now calculate the following:

a. Total food calories consumed in your household each day.

b. Gallons of fossil fuel needed to grow the food you need. (It takes roughly ten fossil fuel calories to produce each food calorie in the average American diet. This number may vary widely in different countries.)

c. Energy used for lighting.

d. Total electrical energy used to operate the appliances and for lighting. Compare this to the actual energy used as indicated in your electricity bill.

e. Total thermal (natural gas) energy used in your household (cooking, heating, etc.). Compare this to actual energy used as indicated in your gas bill.

f. Total energy needed for transportation.

g. Add items a-f to find the total annual energy consumption in MJ. How many barrels of petroleum do you use to meet your annual energy needs? (1 bbl = 6.1×10^9 J)

h. Explain sensible approaches to cut your total energy use without significantly changing your lifestyle. You may consider some changes in diet, buying more energy-efficient appliances, switching to alternative sources of energy, turning off the air conditioner, lights, and other appliances when not needed, carpooling, taking public transportation, replacing your cars with more fuel efficient vehicles, etc. Be careful to create adjustments that you can actually make with little effort and cause no discomfort and require no or only minor sacrifices in your standard of living.

i. How much fossil fuel can you save by making these changes? How much money can you save?

j. How much can the U.S. save in fossil fuel imports if all Americans were to make similar adjustments? What would the impact be on the environment? On the U.S. economy?

PROJECT VII -- Ecological Footprint

How many planets does it take to support your lifestyle? Take this quiz designed by the Global Footprint Network, an umbrella network of 70 international organizations committed to educating the public in living sustainably. (*http://www.footprintnetwork.org/en/index.php/GFN/page/calculators*).

a. What are your biggest areas of resource consumption?

b. How many Planet Earth did we need if everyone lived as you would?

c. How many global acres of land would you need to support your lifestyle?

d. Can you reduce your footprint without dramatically affecting your lifestyle? How?

e. Recalculate your footprint, if you made these adjustments.

Remedial Math

Fractions

Presentation: The proper way of representing a fraction is a form that has a numerator smaller than a denominator. Examples are 2/3, and 3 5/13. When the numerator is larger than a denominator (improper fraction), extract the largest whole number that is possible.

$$26/7 = (7 + 7 + 7 + 5)/7 = 7/7 + 7/7 + 7/7 + 5/7 = 3 + 5/7 = 3\ 5/7.$$

Comparison: To find out which of the many fractions is the largest or smallest, rewrite the numbers to all have the same denominator (common denominator). The numerators define smallest and largest numbers.

Example: Arrange the following numbers from smallest to the largest: 2/3, 3/8, and 5/6.
Solution: The common denominator among the three numbers is 24. 2/3 = 16/24, 3/8 = 9/24, 5/6 = 20/24. The smallest number is 3/8, and the largest is 2/3.

Operations:

$$2/3 + 4/7 = 14/21 + 12/21 = 26/21 = 1\ 5/21$$
$$2/3 - 4/7 = 14/21 - 12/21 = 2/21$$
$$2/3 \times 4/7 = 8/21$$
$$2/3 : 4/7 = 2/3 \times 7/4 = 14/12 = 1\ 2/12 = 1\ 1/6$$

Exponential

Presentation: Exponential are convenient way of expressing the repeated multiplication of a number by itself. For example, 10 multiplied 5 times by itself is $10\times10\times10\times10\times10 = 10^5$.

Operations:

$$3^3 + 2^2 = (3\times3\times3) + (2\times2) = 27 + 4 = 31$$
$$3^3 - 2^3 = (3\times3\times3) - (2\times2\times2) = 27 - 8 = 19$$
$$3^3 \times 3^2 = (3\times3\times3) \times (3\times3) = 3^{(3+2)} = 3^5$$
$$3^3 : 3^2 = (3\times3\times3) : (3\times3) = 3^{(3-2)} = 3^1 = 3$$

Power of Ten

Addition and Subtraction: $2\times10^2 + 10^{-1} - 0.3\times10^1 = (2\times100) + (1\times0.1) - (0.3\times10) = 200 + 0.1 - 3 = 197.1$

Multiplication: $\quad 10^a\times10^b = 10^{a+b}$; $10^2\times10^3 = 10^5$; $(2\times10^{-3}) \times (4\times10^2) = 8\times10^{-3+2} = 8\times10^{-1} = 0.8$

Division: $\quad 10^a/10^b = 10^{a-b}$; $10^2/10^3 = 10^{2-3} = 10^{-1}$; $(2\times10^{-2})/(10^{-3}) = 2\times10^{-2+3} = 2\times10^1 = 20$

Power: $\quad (10^a)^b = 10^{a\times b}$; $(10^2)^3 = 10^{2\times3} = 10^6$; $(2\times10^2)^{-1.5} = 2\times 10^{-2\times1.5} = 2\times10^{-3} = 0.002$

Inversion: $\quad 1/10^a = 10^{-a}$; $1/10 = 10^{-1}$

Power	Value	Name	Prefix
10^{-12}	0.000000000001	Trillionth	pico
10^{-9}	0.000000001	Billionth	nano
10^{-6}	0.000001	Millionth	micro
10^{-3}	0.001	Thousands	milli
10^{0}	1	One	---
10^{3}	1,000	Thousand	kilo
10^{6}	1,000,000	Million	Mega
10^{9}	1,000,000,000	Billion	Giga
10^{12}	1,000,000,000,000	Trillion	Tera
10^{15}	1,000,000,000,000,000	Quadrillion	Peta
10^{18}	1,000,000,000,000,000,000	Quintillion	Exa

Logarithms

Definition: $N = a^x$; $x = \log_a N$

for $a = e = 2.71828$; $N = e^x$; $x = \ln N$ (natural logarithm)

for $a = 10$; $N = 10^x$; $x = \log_{10} N = \log N$ (logarithm base 10)

Operations:

$\log (a \times b) = \log (a) + \log (b)$: $\log 6 = \log (3 \times 2) = \log 2 + \log 3 = 0.301 + 0.477 = 0.778$

$\log (a/b) = \log (a) - \log (b)$: $\log 3.5 = \log (7/2) = \log 7 - \log 2 = 0.845 - 0.301 = 0.544$

$\log (a^b) = b. \log (a)$: $\log 81 = \log (3^4) = 4 \log (3) = 4 (0.477) = 1.908$

$\log (1/a) = - \log (a)$; $\log 0.2 = \log (1/5) = -\log 5 = -0.699$

Geometry:

Circle of radius r: Circumference = $2\pi r$; Area = πr^2

Square of side a: Circumference = $4a$; Area = a^2

Sphere of radius r: Surface Area = $4 \pi r^2$; Volume = $4/3 \pi r^3$

Cylinder of radius r and length L: Surface Area = $2 \pi r L$; Volume = $\pi r^2 L$

Cube of side a: Surface Area = $6 a^2$; Volume = a^3

Abbreviations & Acronyms

Organizations

AQMD	Air Quality Management District
DNA	Defense Nuclear Agency
DOD	Department of Defense
DOE	Department of Energy
DOT	Department of Transportation
EIA	Energy Information Administration
EU	European Union
EPA	Environmental Protection Agency
FERC	Federal Energy Regulatory Commission
GAO	Government Accountability Office (Formerly General Accounting Office)
IAEA	International Atomic Energy Commission
IMF	International Monetary Fund
INPO	Institute of Nuclear Power Operation
NASA	National Aeronautics and Space Administration
NATO	North Atlantic Treaty Organization
NHTSA	National Highway Traffic Safety Administration
NIST	National Institute of Standards and Technology
NOAA	National Oceanic and Atmospheric Administration
NRC	Nuclear Regulatory Commission
OPEC	Organization of Petroleum Exporting Countries
UN	United Nations
UNESCO	United Nation Educational, Scientific and Cultural Organization
USGS	United States Geological Survey
USSR	Union of Soviet Socialist Republics
WANO	World Association of Nuclear Operators
WHO	World Health Organization
WTO	World Trade Organization

Acronyms

CAD	Computer Aided Design
CAFE	Corporate Average Fuel Economy
CAFTA	Central America Free Trade Agreement
CAM	Computer Aided Manufacturing
COLA	Cost of Living Adjustment
LEED	Leadership in Energy and Environmental Design
NAFTA	North Atlantic Free Trade Agreement
OTEC	Ocean Thermal Energy Conversion
SALT	Strategic Arms Limitation Treaty
START	STrategic Arms Reduction Treaty

Abbreviations

ABM	Anti Ballistic Missile
ANWR	Arctic National Wildlife Refuge
BEV	Battery-operated Electric Vehicle
BMI	Body Mass Index
BMR	Basal Metabolic Rate
CAA	Clean Air Act
CHP	Combined Heat and Power
CNG	Compressed Natural Gas
COP	Coefficient of Performance
CPI	Consumer Price Index
CWA	Clean Water Act
DNA	Deoxyribo Nucleic Acid
DU	Depleted Uranium
EER	Energy Efficiency Ratio
FER	Fossil Energy Replacement Ratio
FFV	Flexible Fuel Vehicle
GDP	Gross Domestic Products
GNP	Gross National Products
ICE	Internal Combustion Engine
IGCC	Integrated Gasification Combined Cycle
IPCC	Intergovernmental Panel on Climate Change
IPP	Independent Power Producers
ISO	Independent System Operators
ITER	International Thermonuclear Experimental Reactor
LEV	Low Emission Vehicle
LMFBR	Liquid Metal Fast Breeder Reactor
LNG	Liquefied Natural Gas
LPG	Liquefied Petroleum Gas
MHD	Magneto Hydro Dynamics
MRI	Magnetic Resonance Imaging
MTBE	Methyl Tertiary Butyl Ether
NAAQS	National Ambient Air Quality Standards
OEM	Original Equipment Manufacturer
PMM	Perpetual Motion Machines
PNGV	Partnership for New Generation of Vehicles
PX	California Power Exchange Corporation
RNA	Ribonucleic Acid
SDI	Strategic Defense Initiative
SI	International System (of units)
SOC	State of Charge
STP	Standard Temperature and Pressure
TNT	Trinitrotoluene
ULEV	Ultra Low Emission Vehicle
USCS	United States Customary System
VOC	Volatile Organic Compounds
ZEV	Zero Emission Vehicle

Additional Resources

		Government Agencies
1		***Energy Information Administration, U.S. Department of Energy, (http://www.eia.doe.gov).*** Operated under the U.S.-DOE, the EIA provides policy-neutral data, forecasts, and analyses to promote sound policy making, and public understanding regarding energy and its interaction with the economy and the environment.
2		***Energy Star, (http://www.energystar.gov).*** Energy Star is a joint program of the U.S. Environmental Protection Agency and the U.S. Department of Energy. Its mission is to protect the environment through energy-efficient products and practices.
3		***Environmental Protection Agency, (http://www.epa.gov).*** The mission of the EPA is to protect human health and to safeguard the natural environment -- air, water and land -- upon which life depends.
4		***National Energy Technology Laboratory, (http://www.netl.doe.gov).*** NETL implements a broad spectrum of energy research and development (R&D) programs including energy analysis, education, and conducts research in fossil energy technologies for industry and the Government.
5		***National Institute of Standards and Technology, (http://www.nist.gov).*** The NIST Laboratories conduct research that advances the nation's technology infrastructure and is needed by U.S. industry to continually improve products and services.
6		***National Renewable Energy Laboratory, (http://www.nrel.gov).*** The NREL is the only federal laboratory dedicated to the research, development, commercialization, and deployment of renewable energy and energy efficiency technologies.
7		***U.S. Geological Survey, (http://www.usgs.gov).*** USGS is a multi-disciplinary science organization that focuses on biology, geography, geology, geospatial information, and water.
8		***United States Global Change Research Program, (http://www.globalchange.gov).*** The U.S. Global Change Research Program (USGCRP) coordinates and integrates federal research on changes in the global environment and their implications for society by 13 federal agencies.
9		***U. S. Nuclear Regulatory Commission, (http://www.nrc.gov).*** The NRC regulates commercial nuclear power plants and other uses of nuclear materials, such as in nuclear medicine, through licensing, inspection, and enforcement of its requirements.

Non-Government Organizations

10		***American Petroleum Institute, (http://www.api.org).*** Collects data and covers the latest industry news on issues related to gasoline, natural gas, diesel and heating oil, and oil sands and shale.
11		***British Petroleum, (http://www.bp.com).*** British Petroleum compiles statistical data on various energy resources. Their Statistical Review of World Energy is an annual report with a rich set of data on reserves, production, and consumption of energy sources
12		***Club of Rome, (http://www.clubofrome.org).*** The Club of Rome is an independent, not-for-profit organization with membership from different fields of science and public policy, from academia, civil society, and business. The club engages in independent analysis of critical issues in world affairs by provoking debate, by briefing top leaders in government, business, and civil society and by disseminating publications.
13		***Electric Power Research Institute, (http://www.epri.com).*** The Electric Power Research Institute (EPRI) is an independent, non-profit company performing research, development, and demonstration in the electricity sector for the benefit of the public.
14		***Electricity Storage Association, (http://www.electricitystorage.org).*** The trade association established to foster development of energy-storage technologies.
15		***International Atomic Energy Agency, (http://www.iaea.org).*** The IAEA is the world´s center of cooperation in the nuclear field. It was set up as the world's "Atoms for Peace" organization in 1957, within the United Nations family. As an independent international organization related to the United Nations, the Agency works with its Member States to promote safe, secure, and peaceful nuclear technologies. Three main pillars -- or areas of work -- underpin the IAEA´s mission: Safety and Security; Science and Technology; and Safeguards and Verification.
16		***International Energy Agency, (http://www.iea.org).*** The International Energy Agency (IEA) is an intergovernmental organization that acts as energy policy advisor to 28 member countries in their efforts to ensure reliable, affordable, and clean energy for their citizens. Founded during the oil crisis of 1973-74, the IEA's initial role was to coordinate measures in times of oil-supply emergencies. As energy markets have changed, so has the IEA. Its mandate has broadened to incorporate the "Three E's" of balanced energy policy making: energy security; economic development; and environmental protection.
17		***Intergovernmental Panel on Climate Change, (http://www.ipcc.ch).*** The Intergovernmental Panel on Climate Change (IPCC) is the leading scientific body for the assessment of climate change, established by the United Nations Environment Programme (UNEP) to provide the world with a clear scientific view on the current state of climate change and its potential environmental and socioeconomic consequences. It reviews and assesses the most recent scientific, technical, and socioeconomic information produced worldwide, relevant to the understanding of climate change. It does not conduct any research nor does it monitor climate-related data or parameters.

18	NEI	*Nuclear Energy Institute, (http://www.nei.org).* The Nuclear Energy Institute (NEI) is the policy organization of the nuclear energy and technologies industry and participates in both the national and global policy-making process.
19		*Organization of Petroleum Exporting Countries, (http://www.opec.org).* The Organization of the Petroleum Exporting Countries (OPEC) is a permanent, intergovernmental organization, created in 1960 by Iran, Iraq, Kuwait, Saudi Arabia and Venezuela. The aim was to develop strategies, issue policies, and analyze the status of petroleum reserves among member states. The five Founding Members were later joined by eight other members, Algeria, Angola, Ecuador, Gabon, Libya, Nigeria, Qatar, and United Arab Emirates. OPEC maintains its headquarters in Vienna, Austria.
20		*Sierra Club, (http://www.sierraclub.org).* Founded by the influential naturalist and conservationist, John Muir (1838-1914), the Sierra Club aims to promote the responsible use of the Earth's ecosystems and resources; and to educate and enlist humanity to protect and restore the quality of the natural and human environment; and to use all lawful means to carry out those objectives.
21		*Union of Concerned Scientists, (http://www.ucsusa.org).* The Union of Concerned Scientists is the leading science-based nonprofit, working for a healthy environment and a safer world. The UCS combines independent scientific research and citizen action to develop innovative, practical solutions and to secure responsible changes in government policy, corporate practices, and consumer choices.
22		*United Nations Environment Programme, (http://www.unep.org).* Established by the United Nation, the UNEP is designed to provide leadership and encourage partnership in caring for the environment by inspiring, informing, and enabling nations and peoples to improve their quality of life without compromising that of future generations.
23	World Bank	*World Bank, (http://www.worldbank.org).* The World Bank provides financial and technical assistance to developing countries around the world. The mission is to fight poverty by providing resources, sharing knowledge, building capacity and forging partnerships in the public and private sectors.
24		*World Energy Council, (http://www.worldenergy.org).* The WEC is a UK-based, international organization operating in nearly 100 countries, including most of the largest energy-producing and energy-consuming countries. Established in 1923, the organization undertakes research, collects data, facilitates education, and promotes use of renewable sources of energy.
25		*Word Nuclear Association, (http://www.world-nuclear.org).* Disseminates information on various aspects of nuclear technology, including news, updated databases, outlook, and research briefs.

A

absolute zero: the lowest possible temperature at which all internal energy disappears (-273.15° C).

acidic: a substance with pH lower than 7; the opposite of *basic.*

acid rain: a rain with a pH less than 5.6.

activity: the rate at which a radioactive material disintegrates. Activity is measured in *becquerel* or curie.

aerobic: occurring in the presence of oxygen or air. Also, see *anaerobic.*

albedo: the fraction of sunlight that is reflected by earth, ice, and cloud back into space.

algae: plants which grow in moist or aquatic environments.

alkaline: basic, the opposite of *acidic.*

alpha particle: a particle consisting of two neutrons and two protons. The nucleus of a helium atom. Also, see *beta particle* and *gamma ray.*

alternating current (AC): the flow of charge constantly changing direction. Almost all power produced by electric utilities in the United States is AC, which shifts direction at a rate of 60 times per second. Also, see *direct current (DC).*

alternative fuel vehicle (AFV): motor vehicles that run on fuels other than petroleum.

altitude: the distance above sea-level; the angle between the sun and the horizon. When the sun is on the horizon (sunrise and sunset), this angle is zero. Solar altitude is maximum at solar noon. The complement of solar altitude angle or the angle of the sun from a vertical line directly overhead is called zenith angle.

amperes (amp): the unit designating the amount of electricity flow through a conductor.

anaerobic: occurring in the absence of oxygen or air. Also, see *aerobic.*

anemometer: a mechanical instrument used to measure wind speed and direction.

angle of incidence: the angle at which the sun's rays or insolation strike the Earth's surface.

Antarctic Circle: latitude of 66.5° South. The northern limit of the area of the Earth which experiences 24 hours of darkness or 24 hours of daylight at least once during the year. Also, see *Arctic Circle.*

anthracite: hard coal found deep in the Earth containing a high percentage of carbon and little volatile matter. It burns very hot, with little flame.

anthropocentric: human-centered.

anthropogenic: human-made; usually used in the context of emissions that are produced as the result of human activities.

aquaculture: aquatic organism farming.

aquifer: a permeable rock layer that stores a significant amount of water or fluid.

Arctic Circle: an imaginary line drawn parallel to the equator, at 23°28 prime; S of the North Pole. The southern limit of the area of the Earth which experiences 24 hours of darkness or 24 hours of daylight at least once during the year. Also, see *Antarctic Circle.*

ash: fine particles of solid or molten rock material ejected during a volcanic eruption or the non-organic, non-flammable substance left over after combustion.

associated gas: natural gas found in contact with oil in naturally occurring underground formations. The gas may be present in a free state or dissolved in the petroleum. Also, see *non-associated gas* and *dissolved gas.*

atmosphere: the layer of gases that surrounds the Earth.

atom: the smallest unit of an element that still maintains its chemical characteristics.

atomic mass number: the total number of an atom's protons and neutrons.

atomic number: the number of protons in the nucleus of an atom.

atomic mass: the combined weight of an atom's electrons, protons, and neutrons.

autotroph: an organism that produces its own food – it does not require outside sources of organic food energy for survival. Also, see *heterotroph, chemical autotroph,* and *photosynthetic autotroph.*

azimuth: the angle between a north-south line on the Earth's surface and the horizontal projection of the sun's rays, measured from true south. By convention, solar azimuth is negative before noon and positive after noon.

B

backscattering: the fraction of solar radiation that is directed back into space as a result of particles scattering in the atmosphere.

bads: opposite of "goods." Bads usually refer to anything we have to pay money to discard. Examples of bads are air pollutants, garbage, and toxic wastes.

baghouses: a series of fabric bags that act as filters to remove particulate matter from the polluted air.

barometer: an instrument for measuring atmospheric pressure.

barrel: 42 U.S. gallons. One barrel of oil has an energy content of 6 million Btu.

base load: the minimum power production needed during a year.

basal metabolic rate (BMR): the number of calories a body burns at rest to maintain normal body functions. BMR changes with age, weight, height, gender, diet, and exercise habits.

basic: a substance with a pH greater than 7. Also, see acidic.

battery: a device that stores chemical energy and produces electric current. Batteries are typically built for specific purposes and they differ in construction, accordingly. Broadly speaking, there are two applications that manufacturers build their batteries for starting and deep cycle.

Starter batteries have many thin lead plates which allow them to discharge a lot of energy very quickly for a short amount of time. Most starter batteries only will tolerate being completely discharged a few times before being irreversibly damaged.

Deep-cycle batteries have thicker lead plates that make them tolerate deep discharges better. They cannot dispense charges as quickly as starter batteries. Some "marine" batteries are sold as dual-purpose batteries for starter and deep-cycle applications.

becquerel (Bq): a unit of radiation activity equal to one disintegration per second.

beta particle: an electron emitted from the nucleus of a radioactive isotope. Also, see alpha particle and gamma ray.

binding energy: the energy required to decompose a nucleus into its constituent, elementary particles (see *mass defect*).

biochemistry: the chemistry of life.

biodegradable: matter that can be degraded, decomposed, or broken down by microorganisms into simple compounds, such as water and carbon dioxide.

biodiesel: a fuel derived from vegetables and other organic matter having essentially identical composition to diesel fuel refined from petroleum.

biodiversity: refers to the diversity of different species (species diversity), genetic diversity among individuals within each species (genetic diversity), and the diversity of ecosystems (ecosystem diversity).

bioenergy: energy from biomass

biofuel: a fuel made from plants and other biomass.

biomass: living tissue accumulated over an area in a particular time interval.

biome: a large assemblage of animals and plants that include many communities of a similar nature.

biosphere: the layer adjacent to the Earth's surface in which all life exists. The biosphere consists of all living things, plant and animal. Also, called ecosphere.

biotic: referring to life, or influenced by living organisms.

bituminous coal: soft coal of medium quality containing relatively large amounts of carbonaceous matter. Bituminous coal has a heating value somewhat lower than anthracite and is used primarily for the generation of electricity, production of coke, and space heating. Also, see anthracite and lignite.

blackbody: a body that emits electromagnetic radiation, at any temperature, at the maximum possible rate. It also absorbs all electromagnetic radiation that is falling on it.

body mass index (BMI): a widely used measurement for obesity calculated as the person's mass divided by the square of the height.

bottled gas: the liquefied petroleum gas stored in cylinders under pressure – mainly propane and butane.

breeder reactor: a nuclear reactor that produces more fuel than it consumes. It is specially designed to actively convert non-fissionable isotopes of U-238 into fissionable isotopes of Pu-239, which then can be used as fuel.

British thermal unit (Btu): a unit of measurement of heat defined as the amount of energy required to raise the temperature of one pound of water one degree Fahrenheit. One Btu is equal to 252 calories or 1055 joules.

brown coal: See lignite.

brownout: when the capacity of a power plant exceeds demand and the voltage to consumers drops by a few percent, such that lights often dim.

buffer: a protective barrier. A substance capable of neutralizing acids and bases and thereby maintaining the original pH of the solution.

bushel: unit of mass measurement usually reserved for grains and other agricultural products. 1 bushel = 25.45 kg.

butane: a paraffin with a chemical composition of C_4H_{10}. It is used primarily for blending into high-octane gasoline, residential and commercial heating, and manufacturing of chemicals and synthetic rubber.

C

CAFTA: See *Central American Free Trade Agreement.*

calorie: a unit of heat energy. The amount of heat required to raise the temperature of 1 gram of water 1 degree Celsius, at standard atmospheric pressure. One heat calorie is equivalent to 4.2 joules. It is common to differentiate heat calories from food calories by using a lowercase "c." Also, see *Calorie.*

Calorie: food calorie equivalent to 1,000 calories. It is common to differentiate food calories from heat calories by capitalizing the "C." Also, see *calorie.*

capacity factor: the fraction of a power plant's capacity that is utilized, on average, over time.

cap-and-trade system: in this system companies are allowed to continue polluting but must buy the right to pollute from companies that implement strategies that reduce their pollution.

carbohydrate: an organic compound composed of carbon, oxygen, and hydrogen atoms, such as sugars, starch, and cellulose.

carbon capture and storage (CCS): The process of capturing and storing CO_2 emissions at the power plant, instead of releasing them into the atmosphere.

carbon dating: the process of determining the age of certain archeological artifacts of a biological origin, such as bone, cloth, wood, and plant fibers.

carbon dioxide: molecules of a gas composed of one carbon and two oxygen atoms (chemical formula of CO_2).

carbon monoxide: a colorless, odorless, tasteless, and highly poisonous gas made up of one carbon and one oxygen atom, formed by the incomplete combustion of carbon or carbonaceous material, including gasoline. The chemical formula for carbon monoxide is CO.

carbon tax: tax levied on fossil fuels (or any fuels) in proportion to the amount of carbon emitted during combustion.

carnivore: an organism that consumes other living animals. Also, see *herbivore, omnivore, secondary consumer,* and *tertiary consumer.*

Carnot efficiency: the highest theoretical efficiency of any thermal device (such as a heat engine, a refrigerator, or an heat pump) can have when operating between the two thermal energy reservoirs at temperatures, T_L and T_H.

carrying capacity: the maximum population of a species that a certain habitat can support.

cartel: an association of manufacturers or suppliers with the purpose of maintaining prices at a high level and restricting competition. See, also *oligopoly.*

cash crops: an agricultural crop grown for sale for profit. The term is used to differentiate marketed crops from subsistence crops, which is necessary to feed the producer's family and livestock.

cast iron: is made after removing of impurities from pig iron.

catalytic converter: a device that takes the pollutants emitted by automobile exhausts and smokestacks (CO, NOx, and hydrocarbon) and converts them into less harmful substances (CO_2 and N_2).

cell: the smallest self-functioning unit of living organisms. Some organisms, such as bacteria, consist of only one cell, but most of the organisms found on Earth are made up of many cells.

cellulose: the fibrous, woody material composed of lignin, making up three-quarters of plant material. Also, called lingo-cellulose.

Celsius scale: a temperature scale in which water boils at 100° and freezes at 0°.

Central American Free Trade Agreement (CAFTA): a trade agreement signed between the United States, Costa Rica, Honduras, Guatemala, and Nicaragua in 2005, under which these countries will remove all trade barriers, tariffs, and quotas between them. Also, see *North American Free Trade Agreement (NAFTA)*.

chain reaction: in nuclear reactions, when the fissioning of one atom releases neutrons that induce the fissioning of other atoms, and so forth. Similarly, in chemical reactions, the release of heat and radicals results in a release of additional heat and radicals that make the reaction self-sustaining.

charcoal: is made from wood by heating without air at a high temperature. The wood will not burn, but instead turn into charcoal. The by-product of making charcoal is tar.

chemical autotroph: an organism that uses the external energy found in chemical compounds to produce food molecules. The process used to produce food by these organisms is known as chemosynthesis.

chemical energy: energy stored in molecular bonds. The energy generated when a compound undergoes chemical combustion decomposes or transforms to produce new compounds.

chemosynthesis: a process in which organisms extract inorganic compounds from their environment and convert them into organic nutrient compounds, without the use of sunlight. Also, see *photosynthesis*.

chlorofluorocarbons (CFC): artificially produced compounds composed primarily of carbon, fluorine, and chlorine that were introduced in the mid-1930s, used in refrigerants, solvents, and insulating foam material. These chemicals eventually were implicated in the deterioration of the ozone layer and subsequently banned.

chlorophyll: the green pigment in plants and certain bacteria used to capture the energy in light through photosynthesis.

Clean Air Act: a federal statute enacted in 1963 that was the first of a series of acts and amendments that exerted increasing federal pressure on air polluters to clean up their emissions.

Clean Water Act: a federal statute enacted in 1972 that has been very successful in improving the water quality of lakes and rivers.

climate: the general pattern of weather conditions for a region over a long time period.

coal: the black or brown rock formed under pressure from organic fossils in prehistoric times, that is mined and burned to produce heat energy. Depending on its carbon content, coal is classified as *anthracite*, *bituminous*, or *lignite*.

coal gas: gaseous product of heating coal in the absence of oxygen, which consists of mainly carbon dioxide, methane, and unburned hydrocarbon (Also, called town gas or illumination gas).

coefficient of performance (COP): a non-dimensional measure of the ratio of the useful heating (or cooling) load delivered to the corresponding energy input. Also, see *thermal efficiency*.

cogeneration: a power plant that produces several types of energy simultaneously – such as electricity and heat – that can be used locally, such as in an electric generating station that uses waste heat from its gas turbines to produce steam for conventional steam turbines.

coke: is coal after all volatile matters the purest form of carbon. Unlike coal, it burns with no smoke; It burns at higher temperature of coal is an important industrial product, used mainly in iron ore smelting, but also as a fuel in stoves and forges when air pollution is a concern.

combined cycle plant: See *cogeneration*.

compressed natural gas (CNG): natural gas that has been compressed under high pressure, typically between 2,000-3,600 psi, and is held in a container.

condenser: a heat exchanger in which the refrigerant is heated to a high pressure and temperature and then condensed to liquid by rejecting heat.

conduction: the transfer of heat through a material by the motion of adjacent atoms and molecules without gross displacement of the particles. Also, see *convection* and *radiation*.

conductivity: the ability of a material of a given thickness to transfer heat or electricity.

constant dollar: the dollar value in which the effect of changes in its purchasing power has been removed.

consumer: an organism that gets its organic nutrients from the consumption of the tissue of producers and other consumers because it cannot synthesize the organic nutrients it requires. Different consumers are *carnivores, herbivores,* and *detritivores.*

consumer price index (CPI): an index designed to measure the changes in the prices of goods and services as a ratio of the cost of a bundle of products and services at current prices, to its cost at a base year.

control rod: a rod made of substances such as cadmium or boron with the ability to absorb neutrons used in a nuclear reactor to control or even halt the nuclear chain reaction.

convection: the transfer of energy by means of mass motion through a medium as a result of a temperature or density gradient. Also, see *conduction* and *radiation*.

cooling load: the rate at which heat must be extracted from a space in order to maintain the desired temperature within the space.

cooling tower: a device for cooling water through direct contact with air.

core: a layer rich in iron and nickel found in the interior of the Earth. It is composed of two sub-layers: the inner core and outer core. The core is about 7,000 kilometers in diameter.

Coriolis force: an apparent force that, as a result of the Earth's rotation, deflects objects to their right in the Northern Hemisphere and

corporate average fuel economy (CAFE): average fuel consumption in miles per gallon, based on city and highway fuel economy measurements performed as part of federal emissions test procedures.

criteria pollutants: pollutants that are mandated by Congress for regulation, including particulate matter, sulfur dioxide, nitrogen dioxide, ozone, lead, and carbon monoxide.

critical mass: the minimum amount of fissile material required for maintaining a chain reaction.

crude oil: simply called crude, it is the petroleum found in the earth before it is refined into oil products.

cumulative production: the total amount of energy that has been produced so far.

curb weight: the weight of a vehicle without passengers or cargo. It includes all standard equipment, tires, spare tire and wheels, all fluids and lubricants to capacity, a full tank of fuel, and the weight of major optional accessories normally found on the vehicle.

D

degree day: a convenient way to measure the energy need for a given day, calculated by taking the average of the day's high and low temperatures. The difference between this temperature and the design temperature (taken as 65°F) summed up over all days that require heating (colder than 65°F) is the number of heating degree-days. Similarly, the temperature difference summed up over all days that require cooling (warmer than 65°F) is the number of cooling degree-days.

demand: the rate at which energy is delivered.

demand-side management: in economics, the methods used to manage energy demand including energy efficiency, load management, fuel substitution, and load leveling. See Also, *supply-side management*.

density: a measure of how tightly the atoms of a substance are packed; mass per unit volume. For gases, density is the number of atoms and molecules per unit volume. Also, see *specific gravity*.

deoxyribonucleic acid (DNA): the basic hereditary molecule of life on Earth and the material of which genes are composed. A form of nucleic acid that is organized into a double-helix molecule. DNA is used by most organisms to chemically code their genetics and to direct the development and functioning of cells.

depleted uranium (DU): mostly U-238, a toxic and radioactive waste product of the enriching of uranium in nuclear reactors. Because of its high density, DU has been used in manufacturing armored vehicles, missile warheads, and various types of ammunition.

depth of discharge (DOD): a measure of how deeply a battery is discharged. When a battery is 100% full, the DOD is 0%.

Conversely, when a battery is 100% empty, the DOD is 100%.

deregulation: elimination of regulation from a previously regulated industry or sector of an industry.

detritivores: organisms that recycle detritus (decomposing organic matter), returning it into the food chain.

deuterium: an isotope of hydrogen with a nucleus containing one proton and one neutron and an atomic mass number of 2.

diffused solar radiation: solar radiation received by the Earth's atmosphere or surface that has been modified by atmospheric scattering.

direct current: electricity flowing continuously in the same direction. See Also, *alternating current.*

direct energy conversion: direct production of electricity from an energy source without transferring the energy to a working fluid or steam. For example, photovoltaic direct solar electricity conversion.

dissolved gas: natural gas dissolved in oil within a reservoir.

distillation: the desalination of salt water by evaporation, so as to remove the dissolved salts.

dose: the amount of ionizing radiation absorbed per unit mass of irradiated material.

double glazing: windows made of two sheets of glass with an airspace between.

doubling time: the time it takes a population of a given size, growing at a fixed rate, to double in size.

E

ecological footprint: total burden that various human activities put on the Earth.

ecology: the study of interrelationships of animals and plants to one another and to their environments.

economic efficiency: a term that refers to the optimal production and consumption of goods and services; occurs when prices of products and services reflect their marginal costs.

economics: the study of the production, distribution, and consumption of goods and services.

ecosystem: the interacting system of the biological community and its nonliving environment.

efficacy (lighting): the ratio of light from a lamp to the electrical power consumed, expressed as lumens per watt and including ballast losses.

efficiency: the ratio of what we get, to what we put in. Applied to energy, it is the useful energy delivered by a device to the energy supplied to it, over the same period or cycle of operation. The first law efficiency is the ratio of useful output to input. The second law efficiency is the ratio of actual output to output under ideal conditions for the same input.

electric vehicle: a vehicle powered by electricity, which usually is provided by batteries but Also, may be provided by photovoltaic (solar) cells or fuel cells.

electrical generator: a device that converts thermal, chemical, or mechanical energy into electricity.

electric resistance heater: a device that converts electric energy into heat, which can be transferred to space by fans.

electrical energy: energy resulting from electric current created by a flow of charged particles (electrons).

electrolysis: the process of breaking a chemical compound down into its elements by passing a direct current through it. Electrolysis of water, for example, produces hydrogen and oxygen.

electron: an elementary particle consisting of a charge of negative electricity equal to about 1.602×10^{-19} coulombs and having a mass of about 9.109534×10^{-28} grams, when at rest.

electrostatic: related to, or caused by electron charges, not in motion (static electricity).

electrostatic precipitator: a device to remove charged particulates from smoke coming out of a smokestack.

El Niño: the occasional development of warm, ocean surface waters along the coast of Ecuador and Peru. El Niño normally occurs around Christmas and usually lasts for a few weeks to a few months. See Also, *La Niña.*

emigration: the process of leaving one country to take up permanent or semi-permanent residence in another; the opposite of *immigration.*

emission standard: the maximum amount of a pollutant legally permitted to be discharged from a single source.

emissivity: the ratio of total radiative flux from a body to that of a black body, under the same environmental conditions.

emittance: the energy radiated by the surface of a body per second, per unit area. Emittance values range from 0.05 for brightly polished metals to 0.96 for flat black paint.

energy capacity: the energy delivered in kilowatt hours by a battery or an electrical generating station.

energy density: the energy contained in a given volume of a material (J/m^3).

energy efficiency ratio (EER): the ratio of cooling capacity of an air conditioning unit in Btu per hour to the total electrical input in watts under specified test conditions.

energy intensity: in transportation, the ratio of energy input to a process, to the useful output from that process; expressed in gallons of fuel per passenger mile.

entropy: the measure of the disorder or randomness of energy and matter in a system.

enzyme: protein used to facilitate and regulate chemical reactions within living cells.

equator: the great circle of the celestial sphere whose plane is perpendicular to the axis of the Earth. Location on the Earth with a latitude of 0°.

equilibrium: a condition in which one or more attributes of a system does not change with time.

equinox: either of the two times each year when the sun crosses the equator and day and night are of equal length everywhere. The autumnal equinox occurs on the first day of fall (around September 22). The vernal equinox occurs on the first day of spring (around March 21).

estuaries: transitional ecosystems between ocean and freshwater biomes; a partially enclosed coastal area at the mouth of a river where nutrient-rich, fresh water meets with salty ocean water.

EV: See *electric vehicle.*

evaporative cooling: cooling by exchange of latent heat from water sprays, jets of water, or wetted material.

external combustion engine: a heat engine where working fluid is heated by combustion in an external source, through the engine wall or a heat exchanger. Examples are steam power plants and Stirling engine. Also, see *internal combustion engine.*

externality: cost borne by people who are not party to the transaction that is imposed upon them.

F

Ferrel cell: three-dimensional atmospheric circulation cell located at roughly 30 to 60° north and south of the equator.

fertile: in the nuclear industry, this refers to nuclides that do not directly undergo induced fission but from which *fissile* material is generated. For example, uranium-238 is not fissionable itself but can be fissionable by absorbing a fast neutron and converting into plutonium-239.

fissile: in the nuclear industry, this refers to nuclides capable of sustained chain reactions and fission. The three most important fissile materials are uranium-233, uranium-235, and plutonium-239.

fission: the release of energy from the splitting of an atom's nucleus. This is the energy process used in conventional nuclear power plants to make the heat needed to run steam electric turbines. Also, see *fusion.*

fissionable material: any material with atoms that can undergo nuclear fission. Uranium-238 is a fissionable material, but not fissile.

flare gas: natural gas that is burned as it is released from an oil field. No energy is collected from this process.

flat plate collector: a device used to collect solar energy; made of a piece of metal painted black on the side facing the sun, to absorb the sun's heat. The heat can be transferred to a liquid and then used as desired (for instance, to heat a building).

flexible fuel vehicle (FFV): a vehicle that can operate on either alcohol fuels (methanol or ethanol) or regular unleaded gasoline, or any combination of the two, from the same tank.

flue gas: gas that is left over after fuel is burned and which is disposed of through a pipe or stack to the outer air.

fluidized bed combustion: a process where coal is pulverized (turned into powder) and then carried by a stream of air and burned. The process reduces sulfur dioxide emissions from coal combustion.

fog: droplets composed of water, ice crystals, or smoke particles.

food chain: the movement of energy through the trophic levels of organisms. In most ecosystems, this process begins with photosynthetic autotrophs (plants) and ends with carnivores and herbivores.

food web: the complex patterns of energy flow in an ecosystem that describe the interrelationships by which organisms consume other organisms.

fossil: the remains of living organisms, such as hard and soft parts of plants and animals, tracks and burrows, whole organisms preserved intact in amber or tar, and fossilized dung.

fossil fuels: carbon-based remains of organic matter that have been geologically transformed into *coal*, *oil* and *natural gas*.

Freon: See *chlorofluorocarbons*.

fuel: a substance that can be burned to produce heat.

fuel cell: a device that converts the chemical energy of a fuel directly into electricity. The principal components of a fuel cell are catalytically activated electrodes for the fuel (anode) and the oxidant (cathode) and an electrolyte to conduct ions between the two electrodes. Electrons are bypassed through an external wire which constitutes an electric current.

fuel rod (nuclear): a long, slender tube that holds fissionable fuel. Fuel rods are assembled into bundles called fuel elements or assemblies, which are loaded, individually, into the reactor core.

fumarole: a vent or opening in a volcanic region from which hot gases and vapors escape.

fusion: the combining of isotopes of light elements to form a heavier element, the process of which releases heat and electromagnetic radiation energy. Also, see *fission*.

fusion energy: a technology, presently under development, in which atoms are combined under the most extreme heat and pressure. It is the energy process of the sun and the stars.

G

gamma radiation: ionizing radiation with a wavelength less than 0.03 nanometers that readily penetrates the body tissues of organisms.

gasohol: gasoline that contains 10% ethanol by volume.

GDP: See *gross domestic product*.

gene: organic material responsible for passing along inheritance or traits. In most organisms, these adaptations are coded through the organic molecule DNA.

genetic code: The sequence of rules by which DNA constructs the genes.

geostrophic wind: the wind in the upper atmosphere that moves parallel to isobars.

geothermal energy: energy with its origin in the internal heat of the Earth.

glacier: the accumulation of snow and ice developed over a long time period.

glazing: a covering of transparent or translucent material (typically glass or plastic) used for admitting light.

global warming: the warming of the Earth's average global temperature because of an increase in the concentration of *greenhouse gases*.

glucose: the simple, six-carbon sugar with the chemical formula $C_6H_{12}O_6$.

gluon: the massless, subatomic particle that binds (glues) quarks together.

GNP: See *gross national product*.

greenhouse effect: the characteristic tendency of some transparent materials (such as glass) to transmit short-wavelength, solar radiation and block radiation of longer wavelengths (such as heat). This tendency leads to a heat build-up within the space enclosed by such a material. In the atmosphere, greenhouse effect refers to the warming of the lower atmosphere due to the accumulation of greenhouse gases that trap heat near the surface of the Earth. See *global warming*.

greenhouse gases: gases responsible for the greenhouse effect.

grid: a network of interconnected power lines and generators that is managed so that the generators are dispatched, as needed, to meet the requirements of the customers connected to the grid at various points.

The electric utility companies' transmission and distribution system that links power plants to customers through high-power transmission line service (110-765 kilovolts [kV]); high-voltage primary service for industrial applications and street rail and bus systems (23-138 kV); medium-voltage primary service for commercial and industrial applications (4-35 kV); and secondary service for commercial and residential customers (120-480 V).

gross domestic product (GDP): the total market value of all goods and services produced in a country, in a given calendar year.

gross national product (GNP): the total market value of the goods and services produced by a nation before deduction or depreciation charges and other allowances for capital consumption, which is widely used as a measure of economic activity. In the United States, GNP is calculated quarterly by the Department of Commerce.

Gulf stream: the warm ocean current that originates in and around the Caribbean and flows across the North Atlantic to northwest Europe.

H

half-life: the time required for one-half of the nuclei in a radioisotope to disintegrate. Half-lives for radioisotopes range from a few millionths of a second to several billion years. Also, see the *doubling-time.*

halon: chemical compound containing fluorine, bromine, chlorine, or iodine used in fire fighting. Halons, like chlorofluorocarbons, are considered destructive to the Earth's ozone shield.

hazardous waste: wastes that are particularly dangerous or destructive in one or more of the following ways: ignitable, corrosive, reactive, or toxic.

heat capacity: the amount of energy necessary to raise the temperature of a given mass by one degree. Heat capacity may be calculated by multiplying the mass by the *specific heat.*

heat engine: an engine that converts heat to mechanical energy. Examples are automobile engines, jet engines, and power plants.

heat pump: a device for transferring heat from a low-temperature medium (outside air in the winter) to a high-temperature medium (air inside the house).

heat transfer: energy transferred from one object to another because of the temperature difference between them. Heat is commonly transferred by *conduction, convection,* and *radiation.*

heating load: the rate at which heat must be added to space in order to maintain the desired temperature within the space.

heating value: the amount of heat given off by the complete combustion of a unit mass of fuel.

herbicide: a chemical substance used to kill weeds.

herbivore: an animal that consumes plants. Also, known as a primary consumer. Also, see *omnivore* and *carnivore.*

hertz: a unit of electromagnetic wave frequency equal to one cycle per second.

heterotroph: an organism that cannot produce its own food. Also, see *autotroph.*

horsepower: a unit of power equal to 746 watts.

hot dry rock: an impermeable subsurface rock 5,000 meters or more below the Earth's surface, heated by geothermal energy.

hot spot: an area of exceptionally high species richness or concentration (e.g., near a power plant or smoke stack).

hybrid vehicle: a vehicle with two or more power sources, normally an internal combustion engine, together with an electric propulsion system.

hydroelectric power: (or hydropower); electricity produced by falling water that turns a turbine generator.

hydrosphere: oceans and other waters of the Earth.

hydrothermal reservoir: an underground zone of porous rock containing hot water and dry steam.

I

immigration: the process of entering one country from another to take up permanent residence. The opposite of *emigration.*

incineration: the burning of trash and garbage at high temperatures in a large furnace for disposal and to generate electricity.

independent system operator (ISO): a neutral operator responsible for maintaining instantaneous balance of the grid system. The ISO performs its function by controlling the dispatch of flexible plants to ensure that loads match resources available to the system.

indigenous energy resources: power and heat derived from sources native to a region. These include geothermal, hydro, biomass, solar, and wind energy. The term usually is understood to include cogeneration facilities.

industrial smog: air pollution resulting from various industrial activities, consisting of a combination of sulfur dioxide, suspended droplets of sulfuric acid, and a variety of suspended solid particles. Also, see *photochemical smog.*

infiltration: the uncontrolled leakage of air through cracks and gaps in a building's windows, doors and duct systems.

inner core: the inner region of the Earth's core made of solid iron and nickel. The inner core has a diameter of about 1,200 kilometers.

insolation: the total amount of solar radiation (direct, diffuse, and reflected) that is received by the Earth's surface.

instability: atmospheric condition where a parcel of air is warmer than that of the surrounding air, causing it to rise in the atmosphere.

installed capacity: Also, called the nameplate capacity -- the total manufacturer-rated capacities of equipment such as turbines, generators, condensers, transformers, and other system components.

Intergovernmental Panel on Climate Change (IPCC): a large, international group of officials, scientists, and other researchers who, under the auspices of the United Nations, have been investigating the issue of global climate change, particularly potential, future global warming.

internal combustion engine: an engine in which fuel is burned inside. Examples are cars' gasoline or rotary engines. Also, see *external combustion engine.*

ion: an atom or group of atoms that carry either positive (*cation*) or negative (*anion*) electrical charges.

ionization: the process of stripping an atom of its electrons. Also, see *plasma.*

ionizing radiation: the emission of alpha or beta particles or gamma rays from radioisotopes that can dislodge one or more electrons from atoms they strike. The free electrons can form charged ions in living tissue that can react with, and damage, cells, or cause cancer.

ionosphere: a region in the atmosphere above 50 kilometers from the Earth's surface where relatively large concentrations of ions and free electrons exist. The ionosphere is important in communications because it redirects AM radio transmissions and, thus, extends the range that radio transmissions can travel.

isotope: a form of an element in which the number of neutrons in its atomic nucleus is different than the number of protons.

isotopic dating: dating technique used to determine the age of rocks and minerals through the decay of radioactive elements. Also, see *carbon dating.*

J

joule: a unit of work or energy equal to the amount of work done when the point of application of force of 1 newton is displaced 1 meter in the direction of the force. It takes 1,055 joules to equal a British thermal unit (Btu). It takes about 1 million joules to make a pot of coffee.

K

Kelvin scale: a scale for measuring temperature. In this scale, absolute zero is 0 kelvins, water boils at 373.15 kelvins and freezes at 273.15 kelvins.

kerogen: the bituminous material in shale that yields oil, when heated.

kerosene: a petroleum distillate suitable for use as an illuminant when burned in wick lamps.

kilowatt-hour (kWh): the most commonly used unit of electricity consumed over time, i.e., one kilowatt of electricity supplied for one hour.

L

La Niña: very strong, tropical Pacific trade winds in the central and eastern Pacific Ocean. Also, see *El Niño.*

land breeze: surface winds blown from land to water during the night. Also, see *sea breeze.*

landfill gas: gas generated by the natural decomposition of municipal solid waste by anaerobic microorganisms in sanitary landfills. The gases produced, carbon dioxide and methane can be collected by a series of low-level pressure wells and can be processed into a medium-Btu gas that can be burned to generate steam or electricity.

last mile delivery: the delivery (communication fiber, electrical wiring, or gas pipeline) from the public network to private homes and firms.

latent heat: the energy required or released when a substance changes phase without changing its temperature. Latent heat of fusion is the amount of energy absorbed during melting or released during freezing. Latent heat of vaporization is the amount of energy absorbed during vaporization or released during condensation.

latitude: a north-south measurement of position on the Earth, measured in degrees, minutes, and seconds. A line connecting all places of the same latitude is termed a parallel. Latitude ranges from (0°) at the equator to 90° north and 90° south at the North and South Poles.

lava: the molten magma released from a volcanic vent or fissure.

leeward: the side facing away from the wind. The opposite of windward.

lever: a bar that can move freely around a fixed position. There are three kinds of levers. In the first class lever, the fulcrum is between the force and the weight (shovel, seesaw, and scissors). When the weight is between the fulcrum and the force, the lever is called a second class lever (tweezers, wheelbarrow). In third class levers, the force is located between the fulcrum and the weight (baseball bat).

life expectancy: the average number of years that a typical person at a certain age can expect to live.

light duty vehicles: combined automobiles and light trucks.

light-year: the distance that light travels in a vacuum, in one year -- approximately 9.7 trillion kilometers.

lignin: amorphous polymer making up about a quarter of plant material that provides rigidity and, together with cellulose, forms the woody cell walls of plants and the cementing material between them.

lignite: Also, called brown coal, is the coal with carbon content somewhere between that of bituminous coal and peat. The texture of the original wood is often visible in lignite.

limestone: the sedimentary rock composed of carbonate minerals.

liquefaction: the process of making synthetic liquid fuel from coal. The term also is used to refer to a method for making gasoline and heating oil from petroleum.

liquefied natural gas (LNG): a mixture of gaseous hydrocarbons, mainly propane and butane, that change into liquid form under moderate pressure.

liquefied petroleum gas (LPG): the same as propane. LPG is commonly used as a fuel in rural homes for space and water heating, as a fuel for barbecues and recreational vehicles, and as a transportation fuel.

lithosphere: the rigid crust of the Earth.

LNG: See *liquefied natural gas.*

load: the amount of electric power supplied to meet one or more of end users' needs.

load shedding: refers to temporarily cut off of electricity to certain consumers during times of extreme demands.

longitude: a west-east measurement of position on the Earth measured in degrees, minutes, and seconds. A line connecting all places of the same longitude is termed a meridian. Measurements of longitude range from the Prime Meridian (0°) to 180° west and 180° east from this point.

LPG: See *liquefied petroleum gas.*

M

magma: the molten rock beneath the Earth's crust. To extract energy from magma resources requires drilling near, or directly into, a magma chamber and circulating water down the well in a convection-type system.

magnetohydrodynamics (MHD): a means of producing electricity directly by moving liquids or gases through a magnetic field.

mantle: the zone of the Earth below the crust and above the core.

marginal cost: in economics, the cost to the utility of providing the next increment of product or service.

mass defect: difference in the atomic mass and mass of its constituent particles.

mass number: the total number of neutrons and protons in the nucleus of an atom. An approximate measure of the mass of an atom.

Also, see *atomic number*.

mean solar day: the time it takes to complete one Earth rotation, relative to the sun (for example, from midnight to midnight). This measurement takes 24 hours and is longer than a sidereal day because it includes the effect of the Earth's revolution around the sun.

mechanical work: the work associated with a force acting in the direction of motion.

meridian: a circular arc passing through the poles. All points on the same meridian have the same longitude.

metabolism: enzymatic reactions performed by the cells of a living organism.

methanol: Also, known as methyl or wood alcohol, a colorless, highly toxic liquid with essentially no odor and very little taste. Methanol is formed by steam reforming natural gas, by the distillation of wood, or the catalytic reaction of carbon monoxide (CO) with hydrogen (H_2), under high temperature and pressure. Methanol is the simplest alcohol and has the chemical formula of CH_3OH. In transportation, methanol is used as a vehicle fuel by itself (M100) or blended with gasoline (M85).

methyl tertiary butyl ether (MTBE): a clean-burning oxygenate with high octane and low volatility added to unleaded gasoline to reduce carbon monoxide emissions. It is one of the primary ingredients in reformulated gasoline.

microwave: electromagnetic radiation with a wavelength between 0.1 to 100 centimeters. It falls between infrared and radio wavelengths on the electromagnetic spectrum.

moderator: a substance like water, graphite, or beryllium used in a nuclear reactor to slow down fast neutrons.

monopoly: a situation where one firm controls market sales. A monopoly can produce a given level of output at a lower total cost than can any combination of multiple firms.

mountain breeze: the local, thermal circulation pattern in mountainous areas, where surface winds blow from areas of higher elevation to valley bottoms during the night. The reverse happens during the day.

municipal solid waste: locally collected garbage, which can be processed and burned to produce energy.

muon: negatively charged elementary particle which, during a collision with a nucleus, neutralizes the charge of a proton.

mutation: the change in the structure of a gene or chromosome.

N

NAFTA: See *North American Free Trade Agreement*.

natural gas: gas commonly found in the pores of sedimentary rocks of marine origin, composed mainly of methane, but Also, containing ethane, butane, propane, and other gases.

neap tide: a tide that occurs every 14 to 15 days and coincides with the first and last quarter of the moon. This tide has a small tidal range because the gravitational forces of the moon and sun are perpendicular to each other. Contrasts with *spring tide*.

negative feedback: the change in the state of a system that counteracts the effect of the initial alteration.

neutron: an atomic sub-particle found in the nucleus of an atom. This particle is similar in mass to a proton but does not have a charge.

nitrogen fixation: the biological or chemical process where gaseous nitrogen is converted into solid forms of nitrogen. Biological fixation is done by specialized microorganisms like bacteria. Chemical fixation occurs at high temperatures. One natural process that can produce enough heat to fix atmospheric nitrogen is lightning.

non-associated gas: natural gas that is not trapped with petroleum in the same reservoir. Also, see *associated gas*.

non-ionizing radiation: a form of electromagnetic radiation that does not have enough energy to cause ionization of atoms in living tissue. Examples of this type of radiation include radio waves, microwaves, infrared light, and ordinary light. See Also, *ionizing radiation*.

non-renewable resource: a resource that is finite in quantity and is being used faster than its ability to regenerate itself. Fossil fuels are a prime example of non-renewable energy sources.

North Atlantic Free Trade Agreement (NAFTA): trade agreement signed between the United States, Mexico, and Canada in 1992, in which the three countries agreed to remove all trade barriers, tariffs, and quotas between them. Also, See *Central American Free Trade Agreement (CAFTA)*.

nuclear energy: energy stored in the nucleus of atoms. Power obtained by splitting heavy atoms (fission) or fusing light atoms (fusion). A nuclear energy plant uses a controlled atomic chain reaction to produce heat. The heat is used to produce steam which runs conventional turbine generators.

Nuclear Regulatory Commission (NRC): an independent federal agency that ensures strict standards of public health and safety, environmental quality and national security are adhered to by individuals and organizations possessing and using radioactive materials. The NRC is the agency that is mandated with licensing and regulating nuclear power plants in the United States. It was formally established in 1975 after its predecessor, the Atomic Energy Commission, was abolished.

nucleic acid: an organic compound composed primarily of carbon, hydrogen, nitrogen, oxygen, and phosphorus. DNA or deoxyribonucleic acid, the genetic blueprint of life, is an example of a nucleic acid.

nucleus: the dense central portion of an atom that is composed of neutrons and protons.

O

octane: a rating scale used to grade gasoline according to its antiknock properties. A measure of gasoline's resistance to self-ignition too early in the engine cycle, which causes knocking. The higher the octane rating, the lower the chance of premature ignition.

OECD: acronym for the *Organization for Economic Cooperation and Development.* The OECD is an international organization established in 1948 to stimulate growth among the member states in Europe, the United States, Canada, Mexico, and Japan.

OEM: acronym for *original equipment manufacturer.*

oil shale: a type of rock containing organic matter, kerogen, that produces oil when heated to high temperatures.

oligopoly: a market situation in which only a few producers control the market. Also, see *cartel.*

OPEC: See *Organization of Petroleum Exporting Countries.*

organic matter: matter that contains living organisms or non-living material derived from organisms.

organic molecule: Any molecule containing carbon and involved in forming life. Carbon dioxide and carbonate minerals are not considered to be organic.

organism: any form of life.

Organization of Petroleum Exporting Countries (OPEC): founded in 1960 to unify and coordinate petroleum polices of its members. OPEC's headquarters is in Vienna, Austria. OPEC currently has 13 members which include Saudi Arabia, Iran, Venezuela, Libya, Indonesia, United Arab Emirates, Algeria, Nigeria, Ecuador, Gabon, Iraq, Kuwait, and Qatar.

original equipment manufacturer (OEM): An entity that manufactures complex systems from components usually bought from other manufacturers.

outer core: the outer region of the Earth's core that is 2,300 kilometers thick and composed of liquid molten metals, mostly iron, but Also, some nickel. The temperature of the outer core is relatively uniform and varies from 5,000°C to about 4,000°C at the edges of the outer core.

oxygenation: a method for blending oxygen-rich liquids into gasoline in order to convert carbon monoxide to carbon dioxide and to better oxidize volatile organic compounds. The increased oxygen content given by oxygenates promotes more complete combustion, thereby reducing tailpipe emissions. Also, see *reformulated gasoline.*

ozone: a tri-atomic form of oxygen. It is formed naturally in the atmosphere by photochemical processes. Ozone is a poisonous gas and, in the lower atmosphere, an air pollutant. In the upper atmosphere, ozone acts as a shield protecting life on Earth from deadly ultraviolet radiation from space.

ozone layer: a layer in the stratosphere containing ozone, most concentrated at an altitude between about 12 and 16 miles (20-25 km). This layer is important to the presence of life on the Earth since it absorbs harmful ultraviolet radiation.

P

particulate matter (PM): small particles of either a solid or a liquid that form smoke or soot.

pascal: the unit of pressure defined as newtons per square meter (N/m^2). One atmosphere is approximately 100 kilopascals.

passive solar system: a solar heating or cooling system that uses no external mechanical power to move the collected solar heat. Examples of passive solar systems are common glass, solar roofs, and solar chimneys.

PCB: (or *polychlorinated biphenyls*) -- a group of organic compounds used in the manufacture of plastics and formerly used as a coolant in electric transformers. In the environment, PCBs are highly toxic to aquatic life.

peak load: the amount of electricity needed at the time of highest demand. Daily electric peaks on weekdays occur in the late afternoon and early evening. Annual peaks occur on hot summer days.

peaking capacity: the capacity of generating equipment intended for operation during the hours of highest loads.

peat: partially decomposed remains of organic matter that have accumulated in a water-saturated environment over a very long period of time. Geologically, peat is considered a very young form of coal.

permafrost: the zone of permanently frozen water found in high-latitude soils and sediments.

permeability: a measure of the ability of soil, sediments, and rock to transport water. Permeability is dependent on the porosity of the medium the water is flowing through. Some rocks, like granite, have very poor permeability. Sand is the most pervious while clay has the lowest permeability; silt is somewhere in the middle.

Persian Gulf: the waterway bordered by the countries of Iran, Iraq, Bahrain, Kuwait, Qatar, Saudi Arabia, and the United Arab Emirates.

petrochemicals: chemicals made from oil.

petroleum: a generic term applied to oil and oil products.

phases of matter: matter can exist in three different forms: gas, liquid, and solid. Some consider plasma as the fourth phase of matter.

phlogiston: hypothetical material substance that fire is made of *(Greek)*.

pH scale: a scale that is used to measure acidity; a pH of 7.0 is neutral, lower numbers are acidic, higher numbers are basic (alkaline).

photocell: See *photovoltaic.*

photochemical smog: a condition that develops when primary pollutants (oxides of nitrogen and volatile organic compounds created from fossil fuel combustion) interact under the influence of sunlight to produce a mixture of hundreds of different and hazardous chemicals known as secondary pollutants. Also, see *industrial smog.*

photon: a discrete packet of electromagnetic energy.

photosynthesis: the chemical process whereby green plants and some bacteria can capture the energy of the sun and synthesize organic compounds from water and carbon dioxide.

photovoltaic: a semiconductor device that converts light directly into electricity.

pig iron: also known as crude iron, is obtained by smelting iron ore in a blast furnace and is cast in molds. Pig iron has a very high carbon content which makes it very brittle and not useful directly as a material except for limited applications and making steal.

plankton: a collective term for a variety of marine and freshwater organisms that drift on or near the surface of the water.

plasma: a hot, ionized material consisting of nuclei and electrons. It is sometimes regarded as the fourth state of matter.

plate tectonics: the theory that the Earth's lithosphere is divided into numerous plates that are in motion, relative to each other; the continents ride on the backs of the plates and, thus, move ("drift") over geologic time.

plutonium: a heavy element containing 94 protons. Fissionable isotopes of this element can be used as fuel in nuclear reactors and Also, can be manufactured into bombs.

pollutant standards index (PSI): an index defined as a measure of air quality. An index of 100 is assigned to moderate air quality. Higher numbers indicate poorer air quality.

population density: the number of individuals of a particular species per unit found in a specified area.

positive feedback: the process in which a system responds to change in a way that magnifies the initial change.

power (electrical): the product of voltage and current, measured in watts. Power over time is usually defined in watt-hours (Wh), the product of the average number of watts and time. Your energy utility usually bills you per kilowatt-hour (kWh), one of which is 1,000 watt-hours.

power (mechanical): the product of force and velocity. Alternatively, it can be calculated by dividing work by the time it takes to perform that work.

power (thermal): a measure of the amount of heat flow in unit time. It often is expressed in kJ/hour, kW, or Btu/hr.

power density: power per unit volume (W/m^3) or per unit area (W/m^2); in engines, it usually implies power per unit volume of an engine or a gas turbine. In the wind power industry, it refers to power per unit rotor area. When we discuss biomass resource, we often refer to the power generated per unit area of the land mass.

power plant: a central station generating facility that converts some form of energy into electrical energy.

ppm (parts per million): a common unit of concentration of gases or vapor in air. For example, 1 ppm of a gas means that 1 unit of the gas is present for every 1 million units of air.

predator: a consumer organism that feeds on prey.

primary carnivore: See *secondary consumer.*

primary consumer: an organism that subsists on the producers (plants) for nourishment, usually herbivores.

primary pollutant: air pollutants that enter the atmosphere directly from the source, such as tailpipes and smokestacks. Also, see *secondary pollutant.*

primary producer: an organism that occupies the first trophic level in the grazing food chain. These organisms are photosynthetic autotrophs.

producer: any of the various organisms (like green plants) that produce their own food by photosynthesis and may become food sources for other organisms.

protein: an organic substance primarily composed of carbon, hydrogen, nitrogen, and some other minor elements that are arranged in about 20 different compounds known as amino acids. The various amino acids found in a protein are linked together by peptide bonds.

proton: a positively charged elementary particle identical to the nucleolus of a hydrogen atom.

pumped hydroelectric storage: a system in which excess power is used to pump water to a reservoir during off-peak periods. During peak periods, the reservoir is used to operate auxiliary hydroelectric generators.

pyrolysis: the process of heating and partial oxidation of biomass under controlled conditions.

Q

quad: one quadrillion (10^{15} Btu), an amount of energy equal to 170 million barrels of oil.

quarks: elementary particles that combine to make neutrons and protons.

R

rad (radiation adsorbed dose): a unit for measuring absorbed radiation. One rad equals 100 ergs of radiation energy per gram of absorbing material.

radiant energy: energy transferred by the exchange of electromagnetic waves from a hot or warm object to one that is cold or cooler. In some cases, it refers to the radiation emitted from the sun.

radiation: the flow of energy via electromagnetic waves such as light.

radioactive decay: the natural decay of the nucleus of an atom.

radioactivity: a property of isotopes of atoms from a nucleus as it disintegrates. In the process, some elementary particles (such as alpha and beta particles) and energy (such as gamma rays) are emitted.

radioisotope (radioactive isotope): an unstable isotope of an element.

radiometer: an instrument used to measure radiation over a range of wavelengths.

Rankine cycle: the steam-cycle consists of a boiler, a steam turbine, a condenser, and a pump.

reformer: a device for on-board production of hydrogen.

reformulated gasoline: a cleaner-burning gasoline with the oxygenate additive MTBE.

refuse: refers to both trash and garbage.

remediation: efforts to reduce effects of pollution after it has been released into the environment.

reserves: a retainer or holder of a resource for use at a future time. Natural resources that have been discovered and can be exploited for profit. Proved reserves are reserves that are expected to be recovered from future explorations, and which can be produced economically through application of improved recovery techniques. Inferred reserves (or indicated reserves) are estimates of the amount of reserve growth.

respiration: the process of the "burning" of food molecules in an organism to release the energy required for all metabolic processes. Also, see *photosynthesis*.

retail market: a market in which electricity and other energy services are sold directly to the end-use customer.

ribonucleic acid (RNA): a form of nucleic acid used by most organisms to read the genetic information found in DNA and to produce specific organic molecules used in the development and functioning of cells. Also, see *DNA*.

S

salinity: concentration of dissolved salts in water.

scattering: the atmospheric process where small particles and gas molecules diffuse rays of incoming solar radiation in random directions without changing their wavelengths.

sea breeze: surface winds blown from water to land during the daytime. Also, see *land breeze*.

Second Law of Thermodynamics: See *thermodynamics (laws of)*.

secondary consumer: an animal that feeds on *primary consumers*.

secondary pollutants: pollutants not emitted directly from the source but formed after primary pollutants and other components of the air react, mainly with ozone. Also, see *primary pollutants*.

secondary standard: an air-quality standard designed to protect property, vegetation, etc., as opposed to health.

sedimentary rock: a rock formed on or near the Earth's surface by the settling or precipitation of materials.

shale oil: See *oil shale*.

shrub: a woody plant species that is smaller than a tree. Shrubs usually do not have trunks.

sidereal day: the time it takes the Earth to make one complete rotation relative to the position of a fixed star. This measurement takes 23 hours and 56 minutes. Also, see *solar day*.

smog: a mixture of smoke and fog, mostly a brown haze of photochemical pollutants. Also, see *photochemical smog*.

sin tax: euphemism for a tax levied on certain activities that are subjects of widespread disapproval -- usually alcohol and tobacco.

SOC: See *state of charge*.

soil permeability: the rate at which a fluid moves vertically through the soil.

soil porosity: the ratio of the volume of voids to the total volume of the soil.

solar cell: a photovoltaic cell that can convert light directly into electricity. A typical solar cell uses semiconductors made from silicon.

solar collector: a device that absorbs solar energy to heat a fluid. The heated fluid can be used directly or used to heat water or space.

solar concentrator: the process of concentrating sunlight on a relatively small area.

solar day: the time it takes the Earth to complete one rotation about its axis (24 hours). Also, see *sidereal day*.

solar energy: thermal and light energy radiated from the sun.

solar noon: the time of the day when the sun is aligned with true north and true south. Half-way between sunrise and sunset.

solar power satellite: a proposed process of using satellites in geosynchronous orbit above the Earth to capture solar energy with photovoltaic cells, convert it to microwave energy, beam the microwaves to Earth where they would be received by large antennae, and changed from microwaves into usable electricity.

solar radiation: electromagnetic radiation that originates from the sun. Also, see *insolation*, *direct solar radiation*, and *diffused solar radiation*.

solid waste: garbage, trash, refuse, and rubbish that result from mining, agricultural, commercial, and industrial activities.

specific energy: energy per unit mass (J/kg). In batteries, it is defined as the rated energy capacity of a battery divided by the total battery system weight; measured in watt-hours per kilogram.

specific gravity: the ratio of the mass of a body to the mass of an identical volume of water at a specific temperature. Also, see *density.*

specific heat: the amount of heat needed to raise the temperature of one gram of a substance one degree Celsius. In U.S. customary units, the quantity of heat, in Btu, needed to raise the temperature of one pound of material one degree Fahrenheit.

speed of light: the velocity of light in a vacuum (3×10^8 meters per second).

spring tide: a tide that occurs every 14 to 15 days and coincides with the new and full moons. During this time, tides have the largest range because the gravitational forces of the moon and the sun are complementary to each other. Also, see *neap tide.*

state of charge: describes how full a battery is charged. The exact voltage-to-battery charge correlation is dependent on the temperature of the battery. Cold batteries will show a lower voltage, when full, than hot batteries.

stoichiometric: substances with exact proportions, such that, when they react, produce only carbon dioxide, water vapor, and nitrogen.

strategic petroleum reserve: stockpiles of government-owned crude oil stored at various reserves that can be drawn upon during emergencies and severe oil-supply disruptions. A reserve of 750 million barrels of oil is available that can be released only by the order of the President of the United States.

stratosphere: the thermal layer of the atmosphere above the troposphere (11 to 50 kilometers above the Earth's surface) in which temperature increases with altitude. The ozone layer exists within the stratosphere. Also, see *troposphere.*

strip-mining: the surface mining of minerals and resources such as coal.

subatomic particles: extremely small particles that make up the internal structure of atoms.

sublimation: the change in phase of matter directly from solid to vapor without passing through the liquid state. Examples of substances undergoing sublimation at standard temperatures and pressures are dry ice and iodine.

subsidence: the sinking of the Earth's surface.

substation: an intermediary facility that steps up or steps down the voltage in utility power lines. Voltage is stepped up where power is sent through long-distance transmission lines. It is stepped down where the power is to enter local distribution lines.

superconductor: a synthetic material that has very low or no electrical resistance. A major research effort is underway to find materials that behave as superconductors near room temperature. Once found, electrical transmission lines may be built that offer little or no resistance, thus conserving the energy usually lost in transmission.

supply-side management: in economics, refers to all efforts required to find new resources and processes that improve supply of a natural resource. See Also, *demand-side management.*

surface waves: a special type of seismic wave that travels across the Earth's surface, causing the Earth's surface to roll or sway like waves on the ocean.

sustainability: a method of harvesting or using a resource so that the resource is not depleted or permanently damaged. Neoclassical economists equate it with economic progress, while ecologists define sustainability as meeting the needs of today's generation, without reducing the quality of life for future generations.

sustainable growth: development that focuses on making social, economic, and political progress to satisfy global human needs, desires, aspirations, and potential without damaging the environment; Also, known as sustainable development.

syncrude: synthetic crude oil made from coal or from oil shale. Also, see *synfuel.*

synfuel: synthetic gas or synthetic oil. Fuel made by artificial means (in contrast to that which is found directly in nature). Also, see *syncrude.*

T

tailing: leftover from processing natural resources, such as tar sands, uranium, etc.

therm: a unit of energy equal to 100,000 Btu, mostly used to express amounts of gas consumption.

thermal conductivity: See *conductivity.*

thermal efficiency: the ratio of work output to energy input.

thermal energy: See *heat.*

thermal power plant: any electrical generating facility that use heat to boil water, or another working fluid, to turn it into vapor or steam used to run a generator. Examples of thermal power plants are oil, coal, gas, nuclear, and geothermal. The wind, hydroelectric, or solar photovoltaic electrical generating facilities are not considered thermal plants.

thermal storage: a material with high specific heat capable of storing energy. Typical thermal mass materials include concrete, rock, brick, and water.

thermocline: the transition layer of water between the mixed warm layer at the surface and the cold, deep water.

thermohaline: thermohaline circulation is a part of the large-scale ocean circulation that is driven by global density gradients created by surface heat and freshwater fluxes.

thermodynamic equilibrium: a condition where all non-uniformities (temperature, pressure, density, electric potential, etc.) have smoothed out.

thermodynamics: the study of the conversion of energy into other forms and of their practical applications.

tidal current: an ocean current created by the tidal rise and fall of the ocean surface.

tidal period: the time it takes for one tidal cycle (between two high tides).

tide: the cyclical rise and fall of the surface of the oceans caused by the gravitational attraction of the sun and moon on the Earth.

ton of refrigeration: the cooling effect equal to 12,000 Btu/hour.

town gas: See *coal gas*.

transformer: an electronic device used to raise or lower one electric potential to another.

trophic level: a group of organisms that occupy the same position in a food chain.

tsunami: a large ocean wave formed as a result of underwater seismic activity or volcanic eruption. Its height is rather small, about 1 meter in open oceans, but reaches over 15 meters in height when it enters shallow coastal waters.

U

ultraviolet radiation: electromagnetic radiation with a wavelength between visible and x-ray (0.1-0.4 micrometers).

upper mantle: the layer of the Earth's interior between *lower mantle* and *crust*.

uranium: a radioactive element, commonly used as fuel in fission reactors.

utility: an entity that owns or operates facilities for generation, transmission, distribution, or sale of electricity; a regulated, vertically integrated electric company.

V

valley breeze: the wind pattern that develops as a result of non-uniform heating between the valley to areas of higher elevation.

vapor: the state of a compound at temperatures above its boiling point.

vapor pressure: the pressure exerted by vapor molecules at a given temperature.

vernal equinox: the time at which the sun crosses the equator, when day and night are of equal length, everywhere, indicating the start of spring. It occurs around March 21 or 22.

viscosity: a measure of resistance to flow in a fluid due to intermolecular friction.

visibility: the distance that a large object can be seen with the naked eye.

visible radiation: the electromagnetic radiation visible to the naked eye.

volatile organic compounds (VOCs): organic molecules mainly composed of carbon and hydrogen atoms.

volt: the unit of electromotive force. It is the amount of force required to drive a steady current of one ampere through a resistance of one ohm. The power delivered to homes and offices is 120 volts in the U.S. and 220 volts in Europe.

voltage: the potential to perform work through electricity.

W

watt: a unit of power in SI units, named after James Watt. 1W =1 J/s.

wedge: a moving inclined plane.

wind: motion of air relative to the Earth as a result of a pressure or temperature difference.

wind chill factor: the temperature that still air would have to be, to result in the same sensation as a combination of wind and temperature on exposed human flesh.

windward: the side facing the direction from which wind is blowing. See Also, *leeward.*

winter solstice: the shortest day of the year or first day of winter (around December 21 or 22).

work: the energy required to displace a force by a distance along the direction of force.

X

x-ray: electromagnetic radiation with a wavelength between gamma rays and ultraviolet radiation.

Y

Yucca Mountain: the now-abandoned site in Nevada where a permanent repository for nuclear waste is being built. It was scheduled to open for operation in 2011.

Z

zenith: the highest point reached in the heavens by a celestial body. The complement of solar altitude angle or the angle of the sun from a vertical line directly overhead is called zenith angle. Also, see *altitude.*

A man travels the world in search of what he needs and returns home to find it.
~ George Augustus Moore (1852-1933)

By definition...

$1\ N \equiv 1\ kg.m/s^2$ $1\ A \equiv 1\ C/s$

$1\ lbf \equiv 32.2\ lbm.ft/s^2$ $1\ V \equiv 1\ J/C$

$1\ Pa \equiv 1\ N/m^2$ $1\ \Omega \equiv 1\ V/A$

$1\ J \equiv 1\ N.m$

$1\ W \equiv 1\ J/s$

Constants

Avogadro's number $= 6.023 \times 10^{23}\ mol^{-1}$

Charge of the electron $= 1.6 \times 10^{-19}\ C$

Density of air @ STP $= 1.2\ kg/m^3$

Density of water @ 4°C $= 10^3\ kg/m^3 = 1\ g/cm^3 = 62.4\ lb/ft^3$

Heat capacity of water $= 4.18\ kJ/kg.K = 1\ cal/g.°C = 1\ Btu/lb.°F = 1.163\ kWh/kg.K$

Standard atmosphere @ 15°C and 101.325 kPa

Mass of an electron $= 9.1 \times 10^{-31}\ kg = 0.000549\ amu$

Mass of a neutron $= 1.675 \times 10^{-27}\ kg = 1.008665\ amu$

Mass of a proton $= 1.672 \times 10^{-27}\ kg = 1.007276\ amu$

Mass of the moon $= 7.4 \times 10^{22}\ kg$

Mass of the earth $= 6 \times 10^{24}\ kg$

Mass of the sun $= 2 \times 10^{30}\ kg$

Radius of hydrogen atom (Bohr radius) $= 5.29 \times 10^{-11}\ m$

Radius of the moon $= 1.738 \times 10^3\ km$

Radius of the earth (at equator) $= 6.4 \times 10^3\ km$

Radius of the sun $= 7 \times 10^5\ km$

Average distance between the earth and the sun $= 1.495 \times 10^8\ km$

Average distance between the earth and the moon $= 3.84 \times 10^5\ km$

Solar constant $= 1.34 \times 10^3\ W/m^2$

One sun $= 10^3\ W/m^2$

Speed of light (in vacuum) $= 2.998 \times 10^8\ m/s$

Speed of sound in air (at STP) $= 331\ m/s$

One light year $= 9.46 \times 10^{12}\ km$

Stefan-Boltzmann's constant $= 5.67 \times 10^{-8}\ W/m^2.K^4$

Planck constant $= 1.054 \times 10^{-34}\ J.s$

Avogadro number $= 6.02 \times 10^{23}\ mole^{-1}$

Universal acceleration of gravity on earth's surface $= g = 9.81\ m/s^2 = 32.174\ ft/s^2$

Universal gravitational constant $= G = 6.67 \times 10^{-11}\ m^3/kg\text{-}s^2 = 6.67 \times 10^{-11}\ N\text{-}m^2/kg^2$

Universal gas constant $= R_u = 8.314\ kJ/kmol.K = 1.545 \times 10^3\ ft.lbf/lb\text{-}mol.R = 1.986\ Btu/lb\text{-}mol.R$